Stress Management for Chronic Disease
(PGPS-152)

Pergamon Titles of Related Interest

Agras EATING DISORDERS: Management of Obesity, Bulimia and Anorexia Nervosa
Blanchard/Andrasik MANAGEMENT OF CHRONIC HEADACHES:
A Psychological Approach
Blechman/Brownell HANDBOOK OF BEHAVIORAL MEDICINE FOR WOMEN
Farber STRESS AND BURNOUT IN THE HUMAN SERVICE PROFESSIONS
Holzman/Turk PAIN MANAGEMENT: A Handbook of Psychological Treatment Approaches
Meichenbaum STRESS INOCULATION TRAINING
Van Hasselt/Strain/Hersen HANDBOOK OF DEVELOPMENTAL AND PHYSICAL
DISABILITIES
Weiss/Katzman/Wolchik TREATING BULIMIA: A Psychoeducational Approach

Related Journals

*Free sample copies available upon request

CLINICAL PSYCHOLOGY REVIEW
SOCIAL SCIENCE & MEDICINE
ARCHIVES OF CLINICAL NEUROPSYCHOLOGY

PERGAMON GENERAL PSYCHOLOGY SERIES

EDITORS

Arnold P. Goldstein, Syracuse University
Leonard Krasner, Stanford University & SUNY at Stony Brook

Stress Management for Chronic Disease

Edited by

Michael L. Russell
Baylor College of Medicine

Published in cooperation with the
Houston Behavior Therapy Association

PERGAMON PRESS
New York • Oxford • Beijing • Frankfurt
São Paulo • Sydney • Tokyo • Toronto

U.S.A.	Pergamon Press, Maxwell House, Fairview Park, Elmsford, New York 10523, U.S.A.
U.K.	Pergamon Press, Headington Hill Hall, Oxford OX3 0BW, England
PEOPLE'S REPUBLIC OF CHINA	Pergamon Press, Room 4037, Qianmen Hotel, Beijing, People's Republic of China
FEDERAL REPUBLIC OF GERMANY	Pergamon Press, Hammerweg 6, D-6242 Kronberg, Federal Republic of Germany
BRAZIL	Pergamon Editora, Rua Eca de Queiros, 346, CEP 04011, Paraiso, São Paulo, Brazil
AUSTRALIA	Pergamon Press Australia, P.O. Box 544, Potts Point, N.S.W. 2011, Australia
JAPAN	Pergamon Press, 8th Floor, Matsuoka Central Building, 1-7-1 Nishishinjuku, Shinjuku-ku, Tokyo 160, Japan
CANADA	Pergamon Press Canada, Suite No. 271, 253 College Street, Toronto, Ontario, Canada M5T 1R5

First edition 1988

Library of Congress Cataloguing-in-Publication Data
Stress management for chronic disease.
(Pergamon general psychology series; 152)
"Published in cooperation with the Houston
Behavior Therapy Association."
Includes index.
1. Chronic diseases. 2. Stress (Psychology) –
Prevention. I. Russell, Michael L. II. Houston
Behavior Therapy Association. III. Series.
[DNLM: 1. Chronic Disease. 2. Stress, Psychological –
Therapy. WM 172 S91538]
RC108.S77 1988   616   87-18985

British Library Cataloguing in Publication Data
Stress management for chronic disease. –
(Pergamon general psychology series: 152).
1. Chronically ill – Care and treatment
2. Stress (psychology)
I. Russell, Michael L. II. Houston
Behavior Therapy Association
616'.001'9   RC108

ISBN 0-08-032807-5

Printed in Great Britain by A. Wheaton & Co. Ltd., Exeter

To Michael L. Russell, PhD (1947–1986)
In Memoriam

Table of Contents

Foreword

The goal of this volume is to present to clinicians in the health field an introduction to the current concepts and methods of managing stress with medical patients. The topics chosen for each chapter represent the most active, emerging areas in this field. The emphasis in each chapter is on clinical application as supported by an appropriate synthesis of the literature, to aid the reader in understanding the theoretical constructs involved.

The authors recognize that stress has a threefold effect on the patient. Stress affects the patient psychologically by altering his outer mood and functioning. It can disrupt the patient's life-style and interactions with friends, family, and co-workers. This can compromise the patient's ability to follow the medical treatment regimens prescribed by a physician. Stress can also have direct, profound, physiological effects that compromise the patient's medical care. Writing for other clinicians, the authors describe each of these effects on specific medical conditions and diseases.

The book contains three major sections. "General Topics" discusses issues of broad interest that are not disease specific. The second section, "Common Procedures," reviews interventions frequently used to manage stress. "Applications with Medical Patients" focuses on the management of stress with specific medical patient populations.

The authors were invited to contribute to this volume because they are actively involved in the management of stress with medical patients in the clinical setting. In addition, they share a similar behaviorally based approach to their clinical work.

This volume will be of primary interest to practicing clinicians who are directly involved in patient care, including internists, family physicians, psychologists, nurses, physicians' assistants, dietitians, physical therapists, occupational therapists, and social workers. In addition, it would be an excellent text for clinical training of students in these fields.

The impetus for this volume grew out of a conference sponsored by the Houston Behavior Therapy Association (HBTA) under the leadership of its president, Michael L. Russell. While editing this book, Mike passed away. All of his friends and colleagues in HBTA mourn his passing. We miss him very much and dedicate this book to his memory.

John P. Foreyt
Department of Medicine
Baylor College of Medicine
Houston, Texas
January 14, 1988

Part I
General Topics

Chapter 1

Stress Management for Chronic Disease: An Overview

Merrill P. Anderson

INTRODUCTION

Chronic diseases represent one of the major health problems in the industrialized world. With the recent exception of AIDS, most infectious illnesses are either preventable or highly treatable in these countries. Thus, chronic diseases remain the primary causes of premature death and disability. They account for a major portion of health care expenditures by individuals, businesses, and government, and they contribute to suffering and reduced quality of life in their victims and their families. The most widespread chronic health conditions are cardiovascular disorders including hypertension, musculoskeletal and pain syndromes, diabetes, cancer, and pulmonary disorders. Management of these diseases can be divided into three stages: prevention, treatment of acute episodes, and long-term management and rehabilitation. In varying degree, broadly defined psychological factors (behavioral, cognitive, emotional) are involved at all three stages. Recognition of the role of psychological and behavioral factors in the genesis, treatment, and long-term management of these conditions has contributed to the rapid development of behavioral medicine as an emerging health care specialty and perspective.

Stress is perhaps the most fascinating, controversial, and pervasive concept in the behavioral medicine field. Stress–health connections are fascinating because the idea of a linkage between mental and emotional factors and physical health touches on age-old philosophical questions about how the mind and body relate, about how humankind's subjective and objective natures can be reconciled. To accept the idea of stress as an important aspect of health care is to embrace a holistic, rather than a dualistic, concept of health care, in which disease, health and treatment are a function of persons rather than of mechanistic forces and interventions visited on people by nature and by their physicians. Not that such a perspective makes health care any easier; in fact, it complicates the picture immensely.

Controversy about stress is related to problems of defining the terms and to the unfortunate simplifications that pervade the field. *Stress* is a loosely used term that describes emotional distress, the situational conditions that appear to provoke such distress, or both. Generally, stress refers to degrees of emotional and behavioral disturbance that do not qualify as psychopathological, and stress management refers to efforts aimed at reducing the frequency and intensity of such emotional disturbance. More thorough discussions of the definitional issues are found in the other chapters of this volume and will not be belabored here.

Simplifications and exaggerated claims abound in the stress–health field. Much is blamed on stress, and much is promised as a result of its remedy or cure. Of course, there is some hucksterism in these claims, but the propensity to simplify is also a reflection of the state of knowledge in the area. The scientific basis has grown tremendously in the past decade. Much of what is known is highly suggestive, but much more remains unknown. The frustrating reality is that stress–health connections are complicated and subtle. In the face of the knowledge base, the urgency and fascination of the questions, and, let us not forget, the economic interests of some health care professionals, the temptation to simplify is almost irresistible. Simplification helps us cope with the complex subtlety of the interactions by providing the illusion of understanding and control. The readers of this book will learn that simple, straightforward answers about stress–health interactions are simply not available.

STRESS–ILLNESS CONNECTIONS

The pervasiveness of stress concepts in behavioral medicine is illustrated by three commonsense propositions about stress–illness connections: (a) stress causes illness, (b) illness causes stress, (c) reducing stress reduces risk for exacerbation of existing illness. These propositions are discussed throughout this volume in the context of specific diseases and treatment procedures they are discussed here in a general way.

Stress as a Cause of Illness

The proposition that stress factors are causally related to the development of illness involves three general pathways. The first is through the direct effects of psychological stress on the functioning of bodily systems, specifically hormonal systems. The second is through the effects of stress-influenced behaviors, which contribute to health-relevant physical changes. And third, and somewhat different from the other two, is the idea of *illness* as a behavioral response to stressful conditions.

Physiological arousal associated with psychological stress involves activation of various hormonal systems, the most cited being hypothalamic–adrenal medullary arousal and pituity–adrenal cortical arousal. Hormones implicated are catecholamines, cortisol, and insulin, as well as other neurotransmitters. In the area of cancer, much interest is focused on the effect of stress on the functioning of the immune system. The basic hypothesis is that chronic levels of psychological stress lead to overactivation of these systems and that, over time, the body becomes more vulnerable, until some organ system begins to function maladaptively. Examples of diseases hypothesized to be influenced in this way are coronary artery disease, hypertension, diabetes, some pulmonary disorders, cancer, some chronic pain syndromes (temporomandibular joint dysfunction (TMJ), headaches), and menstrual problems.

A less direct pathway between stress and illness is through the health consequences of various behaviors that are presumed to be influenced by the degree of stress being experienced. Most of these behaviors are consummatory, and examples include cigarette smoking, poor dietary habits such as overeating and use of alcohol, and other forms of drug abuse. For some people these behaviors come to play a role in their coping repertoire, generally as a way of either reducing tension or increasing arousal. In the face of chronic stressors and the absence of more adaptive coping behavior, these people engage in such behaviors excessively. Over time, this places them at risk for health problems. Examples of illnesses known to be influenced by behavioral excesses include coronary artery disease (cigarette smoking), cancer (cigarette smoking), diabetes (obesity), and hypertension (obesity).

Some illnesses or medical conditions are thought to be best conceptualized as behavioral responses to stressful circumstances. In these cases, the condition of "having a physical problem" comes to play a role in how the person manages her or his environment and emotions, such as by avoiding unwanted responsibility, expressing anger, and asserting control. In the pure sense, these conditions involve an absence of organic findings to support the report of physical symptoms. More commonly, there is an exaggerated reaction to a physical anomaly. These disorders are typified by hypochondriacal reactions, somatization disorders, psychogenic pain disorders, and some eating disorders (anorexia and bulimia).

Clear evidence to support the proposition that stress causes illness is hard to come by. In the case of organ damage due to excessive stress-mediated physiological arousal, the interaction between genetics and physiological, psychological, and situational characteristics is so complex and subtle that clear, unequivocal answers come slowly. In addition, the time spans over which these effects are presumed to contribute to disease end points are so long that controlled study is very difficult. This is clearly an area in which controversy abounds and simplification is rampant. In this volume, the reader is referred to discussions of this proposition in the chapters on hypertension, pulmonary disorders, diabetes, headaches, temporomandibular joint disorders, and gynecological conditions. To the extent that these connections are established, treatment implications are largely preventive. In other words stress-management interventions are focused on reducing arousal so that the disorder does not develop or is not exacerbated. There is less controversy about the influence of behavioral excesses on health outcomes but more controversy about the link between the behavioral excesses and stress. For example, do people smoke or overeat because of stress? The answer is yes, for some of the people some of the time. These behavior patterns are multiply determined and reinforced, and it is a simplification to attribute them entirely to stress. Treatment implications focus on developing alternative ways of coping with stressful situations or emotional states and providing psychological support during the potentially stressful process of eliminating or gaining control over the behavioral excess.

Evidence for ''illness behavior'' as a way of coping with stressful conditions is even more difficult to identify. These conditions are more clearly in the realm of psychological disorders than of physical disorders. They tend to be defined by an absence of positive physical findings or by a judgment that physical findings are not sufficient to account for the behavioral manifestation (reported symptoms).

Issues related to the stress-causes-illness proposition are discussed in various chapters in this book, but this is not their primary focus. Rather, this volume is more concerned with the second and third commonsense propositions about stress and health, namely that illness causes stress and that reduced stress reduces risk of recurrent illness; in short, the role of stress management once illness is already manifest.

Illness as a Stressor

The stress of illness is a result of the multiple demands for adjustment precipitated by the illness. There are differences between the stresses of acute and chronic illnesses. Acute illnesses typically involve an emergency reaction in which normal routines are suspended and all energies and resources are mobilized to cope with the trauma for a defined period of time. The potential for stress is high, but the duration of the episode is relatively short. In contrast, chronic illnesses can involve adjustment of broad aspects of life-style over an extended, even indeterminate, period. These adjustments might occur in behavioral, cognitive, emotional, interpersonal and social, and physical spheres of functioning. Insofar as stress is an outcome when subjectively perceived demands exceed perceived resources for responding to the demands, difficulties with these adjustments to chronic illnesses are the basis for potentially chronic elevations of stress, which can then contribute to a host of problems.

Behavioral adjustments are related to both restrictive and prescriptive aspects of illness and treatment. Restrictive aspects include limitations in physical capacity (endurance and stamina, strength) that can disrupt vocational, avocational, family, and sexual functioning. These limitations can compromise the economic position of the victim, as well as his or her ability to obtain satisfaction in other areas of achievement and relationship. Prescriptive behavioral adjustments refer to the behavioral aspects of treatment. These include introducing new behaviors (taking medications; monitoring bodily function, as in diabetes), eliminating some behaviors (smoking and using alcohol and other drugs), and modifying others (dietary and exercise habits). Both restrictive and prescriptive behavioral adjustments contribute to the cognitive, emotional, and social adjustments associated with chronic illnesses.

Cognitive adjustments associated with chronic illness include learning new information relevant to the disease and its treatment, making changes in important belief systems, and learning specific cognitive coping skills. Information can be an important resource for coping. Appropriate information can reduce the threat of illness and improve compliance with treatment. Effort might be required to learn the information. Some patients resist the new learning, and others seek more information than they can reasonably use. Both extremes represent styles of coping with the threat of illness.

Chronic illness can precipitate changes in beliefs about the self, about what is of value, and about what can and cannot be controlled in life. With respect to beliefs about oneself, behavioral limitations can cause changes in one's economic or family roles, with the result that important sources of self-worth and identity are undermined. Victims of chronic illnesses frequently report a questioning of previously held values and priorities. Sometimes this is a by-product of behavioral limitation. Some of it is in reaction to the life-threatening aspects of illness that can stimulate evaluation of the quality and meaningfulness of one's commitments. Changes in priorities and values are often critical components of stress management. Illness forces people to confront the fact that they are not in control of all aspects of their lives. Before the onset of illness, people lived with a set of beliefs about the extent of control they had over their lives. Illness threatens those beliefs and raises the specter of mortality, the ultimate sense in which personal control is limited. In a more everyday sense, illness forces people to reconsider their ideas about how much control over themselves and their circumstances is necessary for their emotional well-being. Adjustments to chronic illness can involve letting go of excessive control in some areas and learning to exert more effective control in others.

Cognitive skills for improved coping are useful in adjusting to several chronic conditions. Examples of specific cognitive coping skills include cognitive relaxation methods in the management of pain syndromes and hypertension, self-talk strategies for urge control in eating disorders and other substance abuse areas, and various applications of imagery and visualization skills as a means of achieving distraction, of altering mood or arousal, and of covert behavioral rehearsal.

Emotional adjustments to chronic illnesses are, by and large, normal reactions to major life stressors. The emotional distress is a reflection of the threats, losses, and frustrations inherent in the illness or imagined to be associated with it. Threat to life, self-esteem, vocational and financial status, and relationships lead to anxiety and fear; perceived losses in any of these areas contribute to depression; and, frustrations in these areas fuel anger. Some degree of these reactions is to be expected. Indeed, the absence of emotional response might be more pathognomic than its presence. The issue for treatment is to facilitate movement through the reactions, so that the reaction does not become complicated and chronic, in which case it can threaten health and treatment compliance.

Interpersonal adjustment associated with illness frequently involves changes in roles within family relationships and the emotional reactions of one's interpersonal environment to illness. Role changes within families can impinge on delicate balances of

independence and dependence, power and control, and strength and weakness. Victims, as well as family members, can be threatened in their security and self-esteem as a result. Often the needs of the family members go unmet for extended periods of time because of an understandable inclination to defer to the patient's needs. In the extreme, this can lead to family members feeling disfranchised from their normal needs within their relationship with the patient, whether those be needs of dependency, emotional expression, or sexuality. Because of the new circumstances, special demands are placed on communication skills to bridge the gap between the old, familiar pattern of expectations and the new situation. Ultimately a new balance must be achieved that accommodates as much as possible the needs of all members of the interpersonal network. If these adjustments are not made, the potential for emotional distress is higher and the potential for treatment compliance is reduced.

A final sphere in which illness causes stress is the physical domain. Most chronic conditions involve some degree of physical discomfort, pain, or unpleasantness. Cardiac patients might experience shortness of breath, chest pains, or fatigability. Many patients endure various pains (low back, head, TMJ, gynecological). Pulmonary patients grapple with episodes of respiratory distress. Insulin-dependent diabetics self-administer injections. Physical discomfort and pain are psychological stressors in their own right. They are experienced as threatening, frustrating, and noxious. Patients must devote energy to avoiding, moderating, or eliminating these discomforts, whereas before illness was manifest, these concerns were not a feature of their lives.

As understandable and as normal as the stress of illness might be, such stress also represents a potential complication of illness that can threaten optimal recovery, adjustment, or rehabilitation. Stress reactions potentially involve large amounts of negative affect and stimulate a variety of coping behaviors. Some of these behaviors are constructive in terms of long-term adjustment, and some are focused on short-term relief from distress (palliation) and are not helpful in long-term adjustment.

The negative affects associated with stress reactions include anxiety and fear states, depression, and anger. These emotional states have their physiological components, which can adversely affect symptoms and disease itself (see previous discussion of direct effects of stress on illness). Even more likely, however, are the effects of stress on treatment compliance and on quality of life. Negative affect associated with disease can undermine compliance with treatment regimens through several pathways. Depressed patients might not have the interest or motivation to undertake a difficult treatment. Avoidant behavior associated with anxiety can interfere with adjustment. Denial of the significance of illness can undermine the urgency of complying with treatment. Frustration and anger can be discharged onto the interpersonal environment, thus threatening support from families, friends, and professionals and treatment compliance. Quality of life, which is always a relative term, can be further impaired by the chronic negative affect and by the reduced number of satisfactions available from daily life compared with what might be available from a more satisfactory accommodation to illness.

The goal of stress management with respect to the stress of illness is to reduce, as much as possible, the frequency, intensity, and chronicity of negative emotional reactions through the promotion of constructive coping, both problem oriented and emotion oriented, in order to prevent complications, to improve treatment compliance, and to enhance quality of life. The chapters in this volume provide ample illustrations of how these goals are accomplished with various chronic illnesses.

Stress and the Reduction of Morbidity

The final commonsense proposition about· stress–illness connections is that reduced stress contributes to reduced risk for exacerbation or recurrence of chronic illness. There are two pathways through which stress levels can be assumed to be a factor in risk for recurrence. *First,* lower levels of stress are assumed to be associated with lower levels of emotional and behavioral arousal and thus with lower levels of physiological mobilization. This is essentially the stress-causes-illness proposition revisited, with the exception that this third proposition refers to the effect of stress on illness once organ systems have already been compromised. As a result of the illness, tolerance for stress (in either intensity or duration), with recurrent physical symptoms, could be lower than before. *Second,* lower levels of stress are assumed to be associated with optimal treatment compliance, compared with higher levels of stress. Obviously, improved compliance with treatment is assumed to

lead to lower risk of recurrence of symptoms or disease, The ways in which stress might effect compliance were briefly discussed under the discussion of illness as a cause of stress.

Stress in the context of this third proposition refers to more than stress due to demands for adjustment imposed by illness. It also applies more generally to stress associated with perceived demands in other areas of daily life (of vocation, family, daily hassles). The concerns overlap with those in the illness-causes-stress proposition, because most people cope with the demands of illness much as they cope with other life demands. The focus of stress-management interventions under the third proposition, however, tends to be on reduction of a stressful life-style, and on coping with the unique demands of illness.

A recent illustration of the third proposition is the recently completed Recurrent Coronary Prevention Project (Friedman et al., 1984). This was a 5-year controlled study that examined the effects on cardiac recurrence of an elaborate stress-management intervention focused on reducing the strength of the coronary-prone (Type-A) behavior pattern. The stress-management intervention was compared with two other treatments, one of which involved an equal number of group meetings, but without the stress-management component, and the other of which approximated usual cardiologic care (checkups at specified intervals). At 4½ years, the recurrence rate for nonfatal infarcts in the Type-A treatment group was approximately half of that in the other groups. And, among those in the treatment groups, recurrence was the lowest among those with the greatest reductions in coronary-prone behavior. This study illustrates the potential contribution of stress management to management of chronic illness. The same dramatic benefits might not apply to other illnesses in which stress has not been as directly implicated as a contributing factor as it has been in coronary heart disease. In other illnesses the long-term benefits of stress-management interventions, in terms of risk for recurrence, are probably in the area of improved treatment compliance (see discussion on diabetes in chapter 16).

GENERAL COMMENTARY

This section offers commentary on four broad issues relevant to the field of stress management and chronic illness: (a) the need to acknowledge the psychological significance and depth of emotional distress in response to illness, (b) the recent shift in emphasis in the field from stressors to coping processes, (c) the emergence of the biopsychosocial model and treatment implications that it raises, and (d) the role of the psychologist and mental health professional on the treatment team. All of these issues are discussed or illustrated more thoroughly in other chapters of this book. The comments here are designed to underscore the issues so that the reader will be sensitized to them.

Significance of Emotional Distress

In all of the enthusiasm for stress management with medical patients, it is always important to remember that emotional distress in reaction to chronic illness has its roots in very real problems that touch on fundamental psychological issues. It is all too easy to slip into thinking of overt distress or other less constructive responses to illness as indications of "deficient coping" for which the patient is, in a sense, blamed. Lazarus has discussed these issues elsewhere under the title *The Trivialization of Distress* (Lazarus, 1985).

Psychological reactions to illness, from denial and noncompliance to incapacitating anxiety and depression, are based in the most central conflicts of human life. Illness, especially life-threatening and chronic illness, forces people to confront existential issues that remain relatively obscure in the course of normal living. The principal issue raised is that of mortality and limitation. Some chronic illnesses (cardiac, cancer, pulmonary, diabetic) carry the threat of death, and all chronic illnesses involve a more indirect representation of death: limitation by one's body. Confrontation with issues of mortality and limitation raises questions of priorities and values and can threaten important defensive structures in the personality. All of this can be deeply upsetting, and it is often evidenced by increased emotional distress and disrupted behavior.

The point of these comments is not to overly dramatize the emotional reactions of medical patients but to emphasize that the distress is grounded in fundamental concerns. These are not simply issues of deficient coping (though that could be involved) or of uncooperative patients. The issues are trivialized on the intervention side by treating them as problems that can be "cured" or "managed" by defined procedures such as relaxation, biofeedback, or cognitive restructuring.

Lazarus (1985) recommended that the antidote to trivialization tendencies is to give more recognition to the significance of emotional reactions to illness and to the importance of helping people through these reactions. More specifically, he urged health care providers to be sensitive to the individual meanings that illness can have and to the individual differences in coping style that people bring to illness. Both of these structure the patient's response, and both must be acknowledged, for empathy to be established and for a proper appreciation of the patient's perspective on the demands of treatment.

Lazarus also cautioned health care professionals to respect and encourage emotion-focused coping for its own contribution to well-being and not to rush headlong into problem-focused interventions (e.g., exercise, smoking cessation) at the expense of adequate attention to the emotional issues. On several occasions, in working with cardiac patients, this author has found that a patient could be more fully and productively engaged in a problem-focused intervention such as smoking cessation or exercise only after adequate time had been devoted to his or her emotional state. In many cases it was important to respect some aspects of the patient's defense against emotional trauma (emotion-focused coping methods) and to individualize the problem-focused treatment around the defensive needs.

Life Events Versus Coping Processes

The early history of the stress–illness field involved emphasis on the role of stressful life events and environments in creating medical risk. Research focused on the relationship of illness to life changes (divorce, death of spouse, job changes, birth, and so on) to stressful job environments (air traffic control), or to stressful living conditions (urban environments). Although interesting relationships were found, this approach has been plagued by the observation that only a minority of the people exposed to the events and environments in question developed illness. Something else was clearly involved.

As Blair Justice discusses in chapter 2, the current emphasis in the stress–illness field is on the quality of coping as a major determinant of health outcomes. Coping is defined as the efforts people make to adapt to environmental and emotional demands. Coping can be behavioral or cognitive and usually is both problem focused and emotion focused. Effective coping (with *effective* defined as reduced health risk) is thought to involve psychological flexibility, use of multiple coping strategies (emotion focused and problem focused), and adequate access to coping resources. Effective copers are possibly at less risk to disease in the first place and should recoup from and adapt to disease more easily than less effective copers.

Three elements of coping that are especially important for victims of chronic illnesses are information, sense of control, and extent of social support. Information is often underestimated as a therapeutic intervention. Much anxiety, hopelessness, depression, and frustration is based on exaggerated fears or incomplete understanding about the illness or the treatment. Appropriate and adequate information can serve as a marvelous anxiolytic or antidepressant. In many cases, threat is reduced, hope is renewed, and barriers are removed as a result of timely and appropriate information. There is always a judgment to be made about how much information is enough and how much is too much. The information must be presented in terms the patient can understand, and, to the frustration of many health professionals, the information must usually be repeated over and over before it is internalized. Finally, time taken to provide information, to patiently answer questions, to insure understanding, constitutes one of the most reassuring human actions that can be offered to frightened and depressed individuals.

Patients' sense of control over self and circumstance is critical to their emotional and behavioral well-being. All victims of illness have their sense of control disrupted. Regaining a sense of control that is in keeping with the realities of the situation is an essential element of effective coping. As with information, control is a double-edged issue. Attempts to have more control than is possible over self and circumstances breed as much distress as does insufficient control. Many stress-management interventions have a common therapeutic effect in that they encourage a realistic sense of control. For example, providing information is a straightforward way of improving a patient's sense of control over her or his circumstances. Relaxation, biofeedback, and hypnotic methods can enhance a patient's sense of control over body and emotions. Interventions focused on moderating coronary-prone behavior attempt to reduce a hypertrophied, almost desperate need for control, so that the harried Type A can make better distinctions between that which can and should be controlled, that which can but need not be controlled, and that which cannot be controlled.

Social support is the final element of coping that is important for the chronically ill. Social support is generally considered a coping resource. That is, social support can be used to help adapt to the demands of illness so that the burden is not entirely on the patient. Lack of support is well known as a factor in poor compliance with treatment regimens in such areas as smoking cessation, weight loss, and exercise rehabilitation. An understanding social environment can provide an opportunity to share the emotional distress and can provide reassurance of the victim's continuing worth and value. In contrast, an unsupportive or absent social network can greatly complicate coping efforts. Issues of family support and family stress are thoroughly discussed in Copeland's contribution to this volume (chapter 3). All too often, family members are not involved in treatment as much as they could be or need to be. There are major potential benefits to patients from recruiting the patient's proximal social environment into the treatment as much as can be done. This is especially important when significant emotional distress or noncompliance is present.

The Biopsychosocial Model and Interdisciplinary Communication

The chapters in this book and, indeed, the field of behavioral medicine all illustrate the emergence of the biopsychosocial model of health, illness, and treatment. This conglomerate of a word could be a more scientific-sounding way of talking about a holistic approach to these issues. Whichever term is used, the model stipulates that health, illness, and treatment, broadly conceived, are a function of persons. To view illness as only a biological state is to miss the impact of illness on psyche, of psyche on illness, and of illness on the interpersonal environment or the reverse. Much the same could be said of limited views of health and treatment. The health care community has a long way to go before all of the interaction among these various aspects of a person's life are understood. Presently, we have enough knowledge to know that they do interact and that treatments that acknowledge such interaction are more complete, satisfying, and potentially effective than those that do not.

For this model to be effectively implemented, all disciplines on the health care team must subscribe to the model and recognize each other's value. Cooperation and open communication among team members is an absolute necessity if effective treatment is to occur. Throughout this book the authors of the various chapters emphasize the need for communication and cooperation among physicians, mental-health professionals, and other members of the team (e.g., nurses, family members, and exercise specialists). Especially in the area of stress management with chronic illness, physicians and mental-health professionals must present a common rationale for the stress-management interventions. Many patients are thoroughly indoctrinated in the illness-as-biology theory and resist referral to a psychologically oriented treatment with the objection that the problem is not "all in my head". The answer, of course, is that the problem is in both biology and head, rather than in one or the other. The various members of the treatment team need to work cooperatively with each other to see that their treatments complement, rather than compete with, each other. However, health care remains a human endeavour with very significant economic aspects, so issues of cooperation and open communication are likely to continue to plague the most idealized realization of the biopsychosocial model. Within the constraints of the health care network, such cooperation should be the goal toward which all providers strive.

Psychology and the Health Care Team

The psychologist or other qualified mental health professional has a central role to play on the health care team in the treatment of victims of chronic illnesses. Issues of behavior change, stress management, and social support are important influences on treatment outcome. Indeed, once acute medical issues are handled, much of the treatment for these conditions is behavioral. A common fallacy is to underestimate the complexity of the psychological and behavioral component of illness and treatment and to trivialize it by suggesting it can be handled with glossily printed self-help materials or briefly reviewed with the patient by nursing, technical, or lay personnel. The previous discussions in this chapter and the presentations in the remainder of this book demonstrate that the problems are significant and that the treatments for them are complex and time consuming. They are not reducible to simple formulas and packaged programs. They are individualized treatments based on thorough assessments of all levels of the problem, and they challenge the clinical skills of their providers. Of all the mental-health disciplines, psychology is perhaps the best prepared to offer the range of services needed to address the emotional and behavioral

aspects of chronic illnesses. Psychologists are trained in assessment and treatment. They are more thoroughly versed in the theory and practice of behavior change than those in any other discipline. The majority of the stress-management issues in chronic illnesses are within the range of "normal" functioning, and this is more the province of psychology than of psychiatry. Psychopathological levels of disturbance are involved in a minority of cases, and psychiatry becomes involved in these cases because of psychiatry's expertise with psychotropic medications.

OVERVIEW OF THIS VOLUME

All of the propositions and comments about the stress field presented in previous sections of this chapter are discussed in greater detail and with more specific illustrations in the remainder of this book. These chapters offer excellent discussions of the theoretical, empirical, and clinical work being done with stress management and chronic illness.

Most of the current theoretical issues about stress, coping, and stress and coping and health outcomes are concisely reviewed by Justice in chapter 2. He introduces the stress–coping model of Richard Lazarus, which is the dominant paradigm in the field. He presents the arguments for coping as the psychological variable most relevant to health outcomes. In addition, Justice briefly reviews the work that has been done under other theoretical models such as Type A, hardiness, social support, and the giving-up and given-up syndrome. He concludes with brief discussions of efforts to train coping skills and of applications of stress management to specific disorders.

The family is often the forgotten victim and the forgotten resource in chronic illnesses. Families are critical to treatment compliance and to patient morale. In chapter 3 Copeland presents a thorough review and discussion of stress, illness, and the family. She covers such topics as the positive and negative contributions families can make to treatment, family characteristics associated with "good copers," dimensions of family response important for long-term adjustment, the range of clinical interventions with the family, and the importance of good communication between the family and the treatment team. Copeland's chapter is rich in clinical insight and sensitivity. Most of her examples are from work with cancer patients, the patient group with which she works clinically. Her chapter provides a much needed corrective to the individually oriented interventions dominating the behavioral medicine field. All behavioral medicine practitioners should remember that *social* is an equally important element of the biopsychosocial model.

The elderly are another group frequently forgotten and misunderstood when it comes to stress, stress management, and chronic illness. In chapter 4 Woods and Rusin discuss *gerontophobia* and associated myths about the elderly, reasons for underutilization of mental health services by the elderly, characteristics of the elderly as they pertain to stress-related disorders, and assessment issues with the elderly. They emphasize the value of a coordinated, team approach to the stress–illness problems of the elderly. The chapter helps to overcome stereotypic thinking about the elderly among health care providers.

Relaxation procedures, in one form or another, are the most frequently used interventions in behavioral medicine. As Charlesworth and Nathan note in chapter 5, relaxation procedures are the "aspirin" of behavioral medicine. Charlesworth and Nathan briefly describe the major categories of relaxation interventions, discuss the advantages and disadvantages of taped rather than "live," relaxation-training programs, and review a variety of psychological and psychosomatic disorders for which relaxation training could be a useful component of a comprehensive treatment plan. Especially useful is their caution about the need for nonphysician health care providers to ensure that a thorough medical examination is conducted on patients presenting with psychosomatic disorders prior to undertaking relaxation treatments.

Few areas are plagued by as many myths, fads, and exaggerated claims as nutrition and stress. In chapter 6 Becky Reeves provides a succinct overview and summation of the literature on such topics as the effects of stress on nutrition; the effects of nutrition on behavior, mood, and cognition; and stress management through nutrition therapy. Devotees of fad diets and various nutrition ideologies will find little support for their beliefs or claims here. With some exceptions, an important conclusion of Reeves's chapter is that little is known about the complex area of stress–nutrition interactions. Perhaps that helps explain why there are so many players in this portion of the health care marketplace.

Hypnosis has enjoyed a resurgence of respectability in clinical and research spheres over the past couple of years. Hypnosis remains primarily a clinical art that resists the most persuasive kinds of empirical study. This could be one reason it has been the object of so much sensationalism. Certainly hypnosis has a long tradition as a treatment for various medical problems, especially in the pain area but also for other psychophysiologic disorders. Stubits surveys the general topics in the field (theories and misconceptions, client suitability, trance depth, inductions and deepening techniques, Ericksonian contributions) and discusses the clinical application of hypnotic techniques to various medical and habit disorders. Her chapter illustrates how hypnosis can be one element of a multifaceted therapeutic strategy.

Perhaps nowhere in medicine do psychological and somatic problems become so complexly intertwined as in pain symptoms. Reflecting the attention provided this area in behavioral medicine, three chapters of this volume are devoted to pain disorders. All of them discuss general issues in the conceptualization of pain, the contribution of stress and coping to pain disorders, and the central role of psychological and behavioral interventions in the treatment of pain. Each chapter is oriented to a specific category of pain disorders. Chapter 8 focuses on low back pain, chapter 9 covers temporomandibular joint disorders, and chapter 10 reviews headaches. Tarbox and Conners provide a thorough overview of chronic pain as a syndrome from both a theoretical and a clinical perspective (assessment and treatment issues). Their chapter orients the psychologist to medical aspects of pain treatment and provides a reasoned discussion of the place of biofeedback in treatment. Diddel's contribution is rich in sensitivity to clinical issues in working not only with TMJ and pain patients but also with all victims of chronic illnesses. Especially useful are discussions of the distinction between psychologically well-adjusted people with stress-related problems and those whose problems are rooted in psychopathology, of how well-adjusted people with stress-related symptoms resist accommodating to the bodily limitations signaled by their somatic symptoms, and of how pain can subtly become part of an avoidance pattern in response to an otherwise stressful life-style. Bourianoff and Stubits discuss headaches as a psychophysiological disorder and the role of stress-management intervention in their treatment. They provide a useful review of the diagnostic process with headaches (medical, environmental, psychological) and of the major psychological and medical approaches to treatment.

Stainbrook's presentation of stress management and hypertension (chapter 11) introduces hypertension as a disorder, the complexities of the assessment of hypertension, and the place of psychological and psychophysiological factors and treatment in the etiology and management of the disorder. His section on the diagnosis of hypertension is an excellent orientation for nonphysician providers to the many factors that can influence blood pressure and to the necessity of understanding the procedures used to arrive at a diagnosis. Stainbrook discusses the potential of 24-hour blood pressure profiling and of worksite measurements for more accurate diagnosis of the disorder. With respect to stress-management interventions for hypertension, Stainbrook emphasizes the potential of various relaxation procedures on the grounds that these are more specific treatments for hypertension than more broadly based stress-management program.

Stress management with postmyocardial infarction patients is discussed in chapter 12 by Revel, Baer, and Cleveland. Most of the focus of their discussion of problems and treatments is on the acute stage after a heart attack, while the patient is recovering in the hospital. Their general review covers the common psychological complications of heart attacks, including denial, anxiety, and depression, as well as assessment and treatment considerations. They describe a stress-management program for hospitalized myocardial infarction (MI) patients and present data on its effectiveness. The intervention emphasizes techniques to increase participants' awareness of daily stress reactions and to foster their application of relaxation skills to these daily situations. One strength of the program is its emphasis on generalizability of stress-management skills to daily life.

As Bradshaw observes in her introduction to chapter 13, obstetrics and gynecology is an area that has not been the focus of much stress-management research or clinical attention. Her chapter underscores the many stress-related issues and, thus, the opportunities for useful intervention. Bradshaw reviews the psychological and emotional complications of common obstetrical and gynecological conditions (pregnancy, birth, postpartum states, various menstrual disorders). Clinically, she emphasizes the importance of early identification of patients at risk for psychological complications and the therapeutic value of information and education, social support, and enhancement of the patient's sense of control over her body. She discusses how standard stress-

management assessment and treatment alternatives can be applied to these disorders.

Foreyt and McGavin's discussion (chapter 14) of stress management and eating disorders (obesity and weight loss, anorexia, bulimia) is an excellent application of the Lazarus stress-coping paradigm to a specific disorder. Their discussion ties together theory and clinical application, empirical research and clinical application, and depth psychology and practical intervention. The complexities of the disorders and of effective treatment for them are given their full measure of respect. Their discussion of stress-management interventions emphasizes the central importance of cognitive factors (beliefs, attitudes) in the disorders and in treatment.

Pulmonary disorders are another area with which many in the stress-management field are not familiar. Alpher and Tobin (chapter 15) rectify that problem with their view of psychological factors and breathing disorders and of the place of psychological intervention in the treatment and management of these disorders. They conclude that, at the present stage of knowledge, stress-management interventions (largely varieties of relaxation training) have their greatest utility in management of disorders once they are manifest, rather than as curative treatments. Through careful practice and instruction, patients can learn to predict episodes of respiratory distress, perhaps to inhibit them through the use of distraction techniques, and to decrease emotionality, which could be a precipitating and aggravating factor. The chapter provides an introduction to the physiology of breathing disorders that will enlighten many nonphysician health care personnel.

Czyzewski, in chapter 16, surveys the major stress issues in the treatment of diabetes. Two major hypotheses about stress–diabetes interactions, metabolic and adherence are presented, and the evidence for each is reviewed. The author concludes that stress is clearly potentially disruptive to treatment compliance, but the evidence is sparse for clinically significant (for diabetes) metabolic consequences of stress-related psychophysiological mobilization. Accordingly, the principal treatment implications for stress management are to focus directly on ways of enhancing compliance. Insofar as life-stress episodes threaten compliance behavior general stress-management interventions are useful. Czyzewski cautions that widespread recommendations for relaxation treatments with diabetic patients are not warranted by the data. Rather, such treatments should be helpful for a selected group of diabetic patients who exhibit marked levels of anxious tension.

As was observed at the beginning of this introductory chapter, stress is one of the most fascinating, controversial, and pervasive concepts in behavioral medicine today. As a survey of the stress–illness field, this volume does little to dispel the fascination. These remain remarkably intriguing topics that touch our deepest sense of ourselves as whole beings. Controversy about stress–illness connections is, I think, reduced by the balanced, reasoned, practical discussions contained in these chapters. The book documents the pervasiveness of the stress concept in behavioral medicine, yet does so in a way that realistically views contributions of stress to illness etiology and of stress management to treatment of chronic illnesses. I am confident that the kinds of interventions described in these chapters will continue to grow in sophistication and effectiveness. The population of victims of chronic illnesses will be the ultimate beneficiaries of that growth.

REFERENCES

Friedman, M., Thoresen, C., Gill, J., Powell, L., Ulmer, D., Thompson, L., Price, V., Rabin, D., Breall, W., Dixon, T., Levy, R. & Bourg, E. (1984). Alteration of Type A behavior and reduction in cardiac recurrences in post-myocardial infraction patients. *American Heart Journal, 108,* 237–248,

Lazarus, (1985). The Trivialization of Distress. In J. Rosen & L. Solomon (Eds.) *Prevention in Health Psychology.* Hanover, N H: University Press of New England.

Chapter 2

Stress, Coping, and Health Outcomes

Blair Justice

Although stress and coping are "two faces of the same coin" (Roskies & Lazarus, 1980, p. 45), only recently has the focus shifted to how people respond to stress — how they cope — as a central mediator of health outcomes. Stress management has become more a matter of adopting cognitive and behavioral coping patterns that reduce the risk of pain and illness than of trying to avoid the pressures of life. Before exploring ways that coping patterns affect health and disease, and the key role cognitions play in the process, we need to consider why the shift away from stress has occurred.

In 1982 when the Institute of Medicine of the National Academy of Sciences assembled a panel of experts to review the present status of stress in health and disease, no agreement on the definition could be reached (Elliott & Eisdorfer, 1982). The panel did agree that people encounter *activators* that arouse them at point *X*, that they have *reactions* at *Y*, and that they experience consequences at *Z*. But neither the *stressors* at *X* nor the *stress* at *Y* causes illness at *Z*. What largely explains the outcome are mediators in between, with coping a primary factor.

Despite continued efforts to use the word *stress* to link psychological influences with illness (Mikhail, 1981, Singer, 1980); definitional problems have historically plagued the term. Its elusiveness has led frustrated researchers to describe the concept as "inaccurate and unnecessary" (Hinkle, 1974),

"awkward and poorly expressive" (Wolf & Goodell, 1976), and a useless impediment (Cassel, 1974).

The chorus of complaints has been so persistent that Mason (1975) finally asked what was keeping the term alive and in use. He suggested that the word "strikes some deep, responsive chord within us" and thus assures its survival "in spite of all the confusion it creates" (p. 35). Its very lack of precision has let it be used to explain "a wide variety of outcomes, mostly negative, that otherwise seem to defy explanation" (Baum, Singer, & Baum, 1981).

Appealing as the term seems to be, dissatisfaction with the word *stress* grows. Ader (1980), in his presidential address to the American Psychosomatic Society, said " 'stress' contributes little to an analysis of the mechanisms that may underlie or determine the organism's response. In fact, such labeling, which is descriptive rather than explanatory, may actually impede conceptual and empirical advances" (p. 312). Kasl (1983) has urged that "the more specific questions we can propose and answer, the less we have a need for the troublesome and recalcitrant concept of stress" (p. 81).

Stress has been described as a stimulus (Hinkle, 1974), a response (Selye, 1976), an interaction between the two (Kasl, 1983), a state (Mikhail, 1981), an environmental condition (Baum, Singer, & Baum, 1981), and anxiety or frustration (Appley & Trumbull, 1967). Stress is a process (Baum, Deckel,

& Gatchel, 1982), a relationship (Lazarus, 1980) or experience (Wolf, 1968) that refers to an imbalance (McGrath, 1970), or a lack of it, between people and their environment (French, 1974).

Because the concept is so versatile and the term is so ubiquitous (Antonovsky, 1979; Kobasa, Hiker, & Maddi, 1979; Roskies & Lazarus, 1980), the word lacks the precision and power to integrate and explain. Coping responses, both the overt and covert behaviors people use in attempts to deal with problems, seem to offer greater promise of understanding why people get sick and what can be done to prevent and manage illness.

A PERSPECTIVE ON COPING

Historically, coping and adaptive efforts have long been closely linked to health and disease. Nineteenth-century medicine was influenced by Bernard's view of disease as "the outcome of attempts at homeostasis in which adaptive responses to noxious forces, although appropriate in kind, were faulty in amount" (H. G. Wolff, 1953, p. vi). Sechenov, Bernard's Russian student, emphasized the organism's capacity to adapt, as mediated by the nervous system, to changes in the "milieu exterieur" (Wolf & Goodell, 1976).

In this century, Harold Wolff extended Bernard's concept of disease to emphasize that "man, confronted by threats, especially as they involve values and goals, initiates responses inappropriate in kind as well as in magnitude" (1953, p. vii). Wolff was particularly impressed by the influence of thoughts and attitudes on bodily changes. Dubos (1965) had a similar position, noting that "the characters of a disease are determined more by the response of the organism" (p. 327) and that the response involves adrenal and other hormones, which in turn are "affected by psychological factors and by the symbolic interpretation the mind attaches to environmental agents and stimuli" (p. 328). Stewart Wolf (Wolf & Goodell, 1976) concluded that bodily changes "derive from the individual's evaluation of his experience" (p.110) and that "the adaptive behavior of the viscera, like that of skeletal muscles, becomes ultimately a matter of the needs, goals and purposes of the individual" (p. 119). Hinkle and Wolff (1957) linked adaptation and health to reactions that are "in proportion to the meaning" an individual attaches to events and situations and his or her perceptions of them.

These authors integrated the psychological and physiological into theories of health and disease

without invoking *stress* as a unifying concept. It is true that they also did not use the word *coping*, but what they referred to as adaptive efforts and patterns of reaction became incorporated into the concept of coping. And what they were saying was consistent with the observations of current investigators who have stated that "there is mounting belief among research and clinical workers that how people cope with stress is even more important to overall morale, social functioning and somatic health than the frequency and severity of the stress episodes themselves" (Roskies & Lazarus, 1980 p.38).

SELYE'S EMPHASIS ON COPING

Even Selye himself (1978a), whose search for a "unified theory" of disease was based on the concept of nonspecific stress, repeatedly emphasized coping as the primary determinant of outcome. Although he did not use the term *coping*, he made a point of saying that "how you take it" determines consequences. For instance, in *The Stress of Life* (1978a) he repeated this idea no fewer than six times, almost in the same language: "it is 'how you take it' that determines, ultimately, whether one can adapt successfully" (p. 74), and "this brings us back to our key phrase, namely, that what matters is not so much what happens to us, but the way we take it" (p. 178), and "here again, we meet the basic principle that what matters is not really what happens to you but the way you take it" (p. 394).

One of Selye's favorite illustrations, in both his writings (1978a) and his lectures (1978b), linked physiological outcome to maladaptive perception and coping behavior. The story concerns what an individual does "if you happen to be a coronary candidate" and "you meet a helpless drunk who showers you with insults but is obviously quite unable to do any harm" (p. 450). Nothing will happen, Selye said, if you choose to ignore the drunk and pass on by. However, if you become insulted and react with hostility, "the result may be a fatal heart accident." What "caused" the fatal coronary, he noted, was not the drunk or his words but "choosing the wrong reaction" (p. 450).

In explaining differential expressions of the stress response and General Adaptation Syndrome, Selye relied on "conditioning factors," particularly internal ones, which included past experience and hereditary predisposition. Conditioning factors, he suggested, strongly influence an individual's efforts to adapt to stresses. Selye was also a tireless promoter of "altruistic egoism" (Cherry, 1978), which he identified as not only a philosophy of life but also an important method to manage stress, in other words, a coping strategy. He defined altruistic egoism as "looking out for oneself by being necessary to others and thus earning their goodwill" (p. 70). People with stress-linked diseases, Selye said, are those who have "emphasized either too much selfishness or too much self-sacrifice" (p. 70).

COPING IN RECENT YEARS

Coping, as a term applied to efforts to manage stress or troublesome demands, difficulties, and challenges, has grown in usage only in recent years. In fact, attention was focused on stress so long that Ilfeld was led to observe that "except for a few pioneers, the issue of how people manage stress is only recently being pursued" (1980, p. 2). The little coping research that was done more than two or three decades ago concentrated on adaptation under extreme conditions. For instance, in 1953 David Hamburg and colleagues reported on the "adaptive problems and mechanisms" of patients with severe burns (Hamburg, Hamburg, & de Goza, 1953). As in early stress research, life-threatening conditions or severe disturbances were studied most, and defense mechanisms were seen as the primary attempts at adaptation (Menninger, 1954).

Gradually it became clear that, even when faced with severe illness or pain, people use more than intrapsychic defenses to deal with the problem. Coping, including active attempts at problem solving or mastery, began to be used to conceptualize adaptive efforts. Some authors (e.g., Haan, 1977) made a distinction between coping and defenses; others, between defenses and mastery. Murphy (1974) defined coping as any attempt to master a new situation that is potentially threatening, challenging, or gratifying. Lazarus, who did much to shift the focus from stress to coping, and Launier (Lazarus & Launier, 1978) defined it as an effort to manage environmental and internal demands that tax or exceed a person's resources. They included intrapsychic defenses and attempts at mastery and problem solving within the concept of coping. White preferred to make "adaptation" the central concept and define coping as "adaptation under relatively difficult conditions" (White, 1974, p. 49).

If we conceive of coping as a cycle, we can see that people go through a number of steps and stages as they attempt to handle a problem. As seen in Figure 2.1, coping starts at *A* with an appraisal as to whether something is positive, negative, or neutral. At *B* there is a belief about what needs might be in jeopardy and how severe the possible consequences could be. At *C* there is a perception of how much, if any, control the person has over the situation and what influence the situation's context might exert. Activation of defense mechanisms occurs at *D.* After some initial affective, behavioral, or physiological effect is experienced at *E,* follow-up coping efforts are made at *F.* These might be focused on reducing the problem or relieving feelings. Depending on what effects such coping efforts have, the initial problem at *A* is then reappraised. Coping cycles are completed rapidly, and many can be experienced before a problem is resolved or relieved or a person accepts the situation or gives up. If there is no satisfactory resolution or relief, health consequences are likely to be one outcome.

CONCEPTUAL ADVANTAGES TO COPING

The shift in attention from stress to coping has been advanced by the recognition that people everywhere are faced daily with difficulties that threaten or challenge them, and they make all sorts of attempts to adapt. What kinds of efforts they make or fail to make now seems to be more important to their health and well-being than is the nature, frequency, or magnitude of the demands.

Demands in life are ubiquitous and part of the "average expectable environment" (Roskies & Lazarus, 1980). As Roskies and Lazarus suggested, "If all of us are stressed," then the question becomes why is it that "not all of us are troubled or sick?" (p. 40). Coping, rather than stress, would seem the more promising concept to explore. It has several advantages as an integrating concept.

1. It can be defined with some degree of precision and agreement. It is the process by which individuals attempt to (a) modify or eliminate whatever problem they are facing; (b) reduce its intensity by changing their views of it; (c) relieve its effects by diverting themselves or employing various other means such as taking tranquilizers, drinking, or doing something physical; (d) or all of these steps (Justice, 1987, Lazarus & Launier, 1978).

2. It has correlates that are cognitive, emotional, physiological, behavioral, and social that lend themselves to quantitative measurement in both the laboratory and naturalistic settings.

Coping cycle

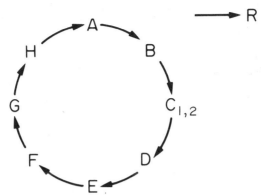

Fig. 2.1. Coping cycle.

A: Appraisal of situation or event as to valence: negative, positive, or neutral.
B: Belief as to how negative (harmful), based on priority "needs" in jeopardy and meaning of possible consequences.
C_1: Context of situation or event: physical setting (work, home, alone, in a crowd), social, temporal (night, day); environmental dimensions (relationship, growth, order); reminder of previous experience; other stressors already existing.
C_2: Control contingency or capacity as based on perceived coping resources, deficits, or both.
D: Defense mechanisms (unconscious) activated.
E: Effect experienced (affective, physiological), or both exhibited (affective, physiological, behavioral, performance).
F: Follow-up coping: problem-focused (cognitive, environmental), feeling-focused (affective, somatic).
G: Gauging of results (subjective and objective effect).
H: How much adjustment to make in A, based on how much better or worse situation or event is and person feels.
R: Repetition (with intensification or reduction) of cycle or resolution.

3. It has a multidimensional complexity that discourages reductionistic cause-and-effect formulations and encompasses a host of mediating variables, each of which can be tested. Social support, social context, information, beliefs, skills, humor, health status, genetic influences, all constitute resources or deficits that help determine the nature and outcome of coping efforts.

4. It is process oriented and dynamic rather than structural and static (Lazarus, 1980). It addresses the action and inaction, steps and missteps people actually take in dealing with life's difficulties and the reactions and consequences they experience.

5. By using a coping matrix (Table 2.1), attention can be directed toward studying coping modes or strategies, coping functions, and coping resources, all of which profoundly affect whether people get sick and, if they do, what courses their illnesses will take.

COPING MODES AND LEVELS

Under the rubric presented in Table 2.1, which is adapted from Folkman and Lazarus (1980) and Pines and Aronson (1980), coping can be problem focused, feeling focused, or both. Problem-focused coping includes efforts to change the external problem or the internal source of its intensity (how the problem is appraised). Feeling-focused coping is action that relieves the painful or distressing effects of the problem, as opposed to its causes.

The coping modes or strategies employed can be direct action, indirect action, or inhibition of action. Problem-focused action can be taken on the levels of external or internal environment. An example of action on the external environment would be using assertiveness or negotiation in an attempt to resolve a conflict with another person. Problem-focused coping directed at the internal environment would be cognitive restructuring, disputing irrational beliefs, and changing internal dialogue, all of which could serve to reduce the intensity of the problem. Direct action and inhibition of action differ from indirect action in that they imply conscious or deliberate efforts to change a problem, keep it from getting worse, or relieve its effects.

On the feeling-focused side, action can be on the somatic level, the emotional level, or both. Taking a hot bath or a tranquilizer would be direct action on the somatic level. Finding something to laugh about

Modes and Strategies

Table 2.1. Coping Matrix

	Problem Focused	Feeling Focused
Direct Action	*On external environment:* Problem-solving techniques Assertiveness; type A behavior Negotiation; persuasion; attack Seeking and applying information Enlisting help of others *On internal environment:* Cognitive restructuring, relabeling Correcting cognitive distortions Changing internal dialogue	*On somatic level:* Physical exercising Relaxation exercises Taking hot bath Taking a drink or tranquilizer *On emotional level:* Talking about source of stress Going to party Watching TV Taking vacation
Indirect Action	*Toward external environment:* Avoiding Ignoring Leaving *Toward internal environment:* Keeping optimistic outlook	*On somatic level:* Drinking Eating Smoking *On emotional level:* Defense mechanisms Talking Pursuing hobby Getting ill; collapsing Giving up
Inhibition of Action	Vigilant watching and waiting Doing nothing as a strategy "Freeze" response	Lying back and hoping
Resources	Social Support Information Beliefs, attitudes Skills Humor Sense of challenge, novelty, commitment Health Material resources	

or going to a party or movie would be more on the emotional level. Additional examples are given in Table 2.1.

Undergirding the modes and strategies are coping resources, whose presence or absence serves to facilitate or impede successful adaptation. These correspond to Antonovsky's (1979) "generalized resistance resources," which he sees as central to the question of who gets sick under stress and who does not.

Among the coping resources, social support has received the most attention although a number of other studies have examined the influence of information on effective coping (Hamburg & Adams, 1967; Wallace, 1984). Folkman and her colleagues (Folkman, Schaefer, & Lazarus, 1979) have noted the importance of distinguishing between coping processes and coping resources. The processes

encompass direct action, indirect action, and inhibition of action on both problem and palliative levels, and the resources "are usually not constant over time, that is, they are likely to expand and contract . . . as a function of experience, degree of stress, times of life and the requirements of adaptation associated with different styles of life or periods in the life course" (p. 383). Resources might be available to a person at one time but not at another. It is also useful to recognize that, when they are available, they serve the function of facilitating whatever coping mode or strategy is being attempted.

The coping matrix reflects the levels on which efforts at adaptation take place: the psychological, the emotional, the physiological, and the behavioral and social. Adaptation might be successful at one level but not at another. Type-A behavior (direct-action, problem-focused) might bring social rewards but physiological risks. Drinking (direct-action, feeling-focused) might lift morale and mood but be maladaptive somatically and behaviorally. Denial (indirect-action, feeling-focused) might be adaptive in terms of inhibiting psychological or physiological arousal but maladaptive if it keeps a person from seeking necessary medical treatment such as for pain in the chest or a lump in the breast (Hackett & Cassem, 1975; Katz, Weiner, Gallagher, & Hellman, 1970).

Whether a given mode is effective or ineffective is also dependent on time and situation. Denial, for instance, can be useful in the acute phase of a heart attack or a severe burn if it prevents the patient from being overwhelmed while being treated, but it can be dysfunctional later, when realistic appraisal of limitations must be made for rehabilitation to proceed (Cassem & Hackett, 1971; Krantz, 1980).

Cognitive restructuring (direct-action, internal, problem-focused) could be effective in reducing the intensity of the stressor, but, if it is carried to the point of completely discounting a problem, it can be maladaptive socially and in performance. Similarly, preoccupation with a hobby (indirect-action, feeling-focused) can divert attention from a problem and relieve discomfort, but on the social level it could lead to isolation.

PSYCHOPHYSIOLOGICAL OUTCOMES OF COPING

A number of outcome studies have been identified with the various strategies, processes, and resources reflected in the multidimensional matrix and three-part definition of coping. There are many examples of coping efforts that reduce the intensity of a problem through cognitive means. For instance, Meichenbaum and his coworkers (Meichenbaum & Turk, 1976) have associated cognitive, problem-solving techniques emphasizing self-instruction and positive self-statements with reduction of pain and anxiety. Rational-emotive therapists (Ellis, 1973) have reported relief of a variety of emotional disturbances from a disputing of irrational beliefs. Beck (1972) has used cognitive therapy for depression, with the focus on elimination of cognitive distortions.

Katz, Weiner, Gallagher, & Hellman 1970) studied women undergoing breast biopsies and found that various adaptive efforts, including cognitive restructuring, were associated with lower levels of hydrocortisone. Kobasa and her colleagues (Kobasa,

Maddie, & Courington, 1981) reported that managers under high stress, as measured by life changes, were at reduced risk of illness if they were high in sense of control, challenge, and commitment. Dimsdale (1974) listed "differential focus on the good" as a leading coping strategy associated with survival and maintenance of health among concentration camp victims. Bourne, Rose, and Mason (1967) found that among a group of helicopter medics in the Vietnam War, individual perception and interpretation of the environment were more important than any "objective" measure of the danger involved. Although risk increased for the medics on flying days, their levels of corticosteroids did not rise significantly. The medics looked upon their jobs as life-saving missions for which they could expect recognition and awards.

The important role of general beliefs and attitudes as coping resources has also been examined. Hinkle and cohorts (Hinkle et al., 1958; Hinkle, Kane, Christenson, & Wolff, 1959) did studies in which they found that the health status of Chinese immigrants and Hungarian refugees, all of whom had undergone multiple changes and threatening experiences, was a function of how the subjects looked at their lives. Those who regarded their lives as interesting and change as something to be expected, or those who looked at problems with benign attitudes, had fewer illness episodes. Beliefs and attitudes brought to bear on a particular change or move have also been correlated with health outcomes. A study of a group of elderly patients relocated from one nursing home to another in Chicago (Aldrich & Mendkoff, 1963) showed that the mortality rate in the following months was lowest for those who accepted the move philosophically and next lowest for those who got angry. Highest mortality was among those who tried to deny the reality of the relocation.

The effects of behavioral coping strategies have also been studied. In the Korean War, a comparison was made between an attacking company actively initiating a battle and a defending company, which was on the fighting line but not engaged in the offensive (Davis, 1956). It took the men in the attacking company about 6 days to return physiologically to baseline, in terms of corticosteroid levels, salt balance, and white blood-cell count, but the defending company required 13 days. The major difference between the two groups was apparently in the degree of control perceived by the attacking company, compared with the passive role of the defending company.

Rodin (1979) demonstrated a reduction in cortisol levels among residents taught problem-solving skills in a nursing home. Problem-solving techniques, designed to modify conditions giving rise to problems, were taught to one group, which was compared with a group that received only attention, a group that received no intervention, and a group in which responsibility was induced. On follow-up 1 year later, only the group that was taught coping skills continued to show reduced cortisol levels. A greater sense of perceived control and the value of having control were significantly higher in the group receiving the instruction.

The enhancement of control also seems to have resulted from explanations given a group of heart attack patients on the causes, effects, and treatment of myocardial infarction and from an opportunity to "participate" in their treatment (Cromwell, Butterfield, Brayfield, & Curry, 1977). They had access to cardiac monitors so they could obtain an electrocardiogram (EKG) tracing whenever they felt symptoms, and they were taught mild isometric and foot-pedaling exercises to do under supervision. In effect, they were given skills to help modify the problem of being sick and in a hospital. These patients had short hospital stays compared with a similar group of patients who were given minimum, routine information and no chance to participate in their recovery.

The importance of information in increasing a sense of control and facilitating a patient's recovery was also demonstrated recently in a study in England (Wallace, 1984). Sixty-three patients undergoing a gynecological operation (laparoscopy) were studied to determine the effects of giving 20 of them an informative booklet on the surgery telling them how to deal with preoperative fear and postoperative symptoms and how best to promote their recovery. These women were compared with 26 others in the total group who received routine care only and 17 who got a booklet that gave global, reassuring statements but little information on the surgery. Results demonstrated that women in the first group had less fear and anxiety, lower heart rate and blood pressure, and reduced pain after surgery. They also recovered faster in the hospital and at home, returning to normal activities sooner than did patients in the other to groups.

PALLIATION EFFORTS

As for coping that relieves the emotional or somatic effects of stress, a number of studies have focused on defense mechanisms (Vaillant, 1977; C. T. Wolff, Friedman, Hofer, & Mason, 1964). Recently, physical exercise has been examined as a coping mode (Sinyor, Schwart, Peronnet, Brisson, & Seraganian, 1983). The *relaxation response* has also received considerable attention (Benson, Kotch & Crassweller, 1977). Tranquilizers and alcohol probably remain the most widely used attempts at palliation.

Activity as a diversionary device was considered by Gal and Lazarus (1975), who reported that sailors got relief from symptoms of seasickness by forcing themselves to carry on with their assigned tasks. Bourne, Rose, & Mason (1968) found that, in Vietnam, a special forces unit expecting an enemy attack showed no significant elevation in levels of 17-hydroxycorticosteroid. The men coped with the threat of impending battle by engaging in a "furor of activity," building defenses and maintaining equipment.

Some studies illustrate how a set of cognitive coping modes can qualify as both a problem-focused technique and a feeling-focused, palliative strategy. For instance, Langer, Janis, and Wolfer (1975) reported on a group of patients who were taught cognitive-reappraisal techniques, calming self-talk, and cognitive control through selective attention. The reinterpretation of events served as direct problem-solving action on the internal level, and the calming self-talk and selective attention helped relieve the pain and discomfort of surgery. As compared with a control group, the patients who were taught the coping skills had significantly less anxiety, and the percentage of those requesting pain relievers and sedatives was significantly smaller.

In a study by Folkman and Lazarus (1980) of the ways 100 middle-aged people coped in a community setting, both problem-focused and feeling-focused coping were used in nearly every stressful episode. Of the 1,332 coping episodes analyzed, only 2% involved a single coping function.

BIOLOGICAL MECHANISMS INVOLVED

Just as a classification of coping functions, strategies, and resources lends itself to testing empirically for their effects across a wide range of demands, difficulties, and challenges, and on different levels of adaptation, so can biological mechanisms associated with some of the modes be identified or hypothesized. Sympathetic–adrenal activation of the fight–flight response described by

Cannon (1929) appears to be associated with problem-solving modes applied to situations with some potential for controllability. Frankenhaeuser (Frankenhaeuser 1979; Frankenhaeuser, Nordheden, Myrsten, & Post, 1971) has noted an increase in epinephrine and norepinephrine, but not cortisol, in tasks and situations where subjects are challenged or threatened and must exert effort but perceive some control. In fact, actual suppression of pituitary–adrenal activity was observed. On the other hand, where control was not perceived, both cortisol and epinephrine increased.

These findings were consistent with a model proposed by Henry and Stephens (1977) that emphasized an association between sympathetic–adrenal activation and dominant, aggressive behavior and between pituitary–adrenal stimulation and subordinate, passive behaviors. In Corley, Mauck, and Shiel's (1975) experiments with squirrel monkeys confined to chairs while subjected to electric shock, the animals that had no control fared worse than did their partners who had the responsibility of turning off a light once a minute to avoid the shock for both. Five of the 6 helpless monkeys collapsed with bradycardia and four died in asystole. The animals with the responsibility for the light and avoiding the shock developed hypertension, suggesting excessive sympathetic arousal, and eventually myocardial fibroses and degeneration.

Buell and Eliot (1979) have designated the pituitary–adrenal response as the "playing dead reaction," which would qualify it as a palliative or feeling-focused strategy. Engel and Schmale (1972) have identified a similar response as "conservation withdrawal," which can accompany a giving-up reaction, triggered by an appraisal of no solution being available.

In contrast, Jarvik and Russell (1979) have conceptualized the playing dead reaction, or conservation–withdrawal, as a "freeze" response intended to be a problem-solving strategy. They proposed that the freeze response is "a period of relative inactivity representing the optimal response to a given threat. It does not imply . . . hopelessness. On the contrary, 'freeze' is seen to result from conscious or unconscious appraisal which suggested it as the response most likely to enhance chances for survival" (p. 198). It remains to be established, the authors said, how frequently freeze is associated with "vigilant watchfulness and autonomic hyper-arousal and how often with autonomic hypo-arousal, as in fainting or swooning" (p. 198).

Schmale (1972) hypothesized that conservation–withdrawal involves "a predominance of parasympathetic activation and a relative sympathetic inactivity" (p. 29). Wolf (1967) suggested that the mechanism is "not simply a vagal discharge but a more complex patterned reaction that includes vagal inhibition of the heart" (p. 1022). It is characterized, he said, by circulatory adjustments that include bradycardia, decreased blood flow to the skin and viscera, and increased arterial pressure and by metabolic adjustments in which there is a fall in blood pH, an increase in lactic and other organic acids, and a rise in blood carbon dioxide and potassium. This oxygen-conserving process is similar to the dive reflex and might be invoked "in response to emotionally charged or threatening events" (p. 1022).

McClelland (McClelland, Floor Davidson, & Saron, 1980) has linked power needs, often associated with Type-A behavior, to chronic sympathetic overactivity, particularly where there is inhibition of action in the face of "power stress." Both sympathetic overactivity and excessive adrenocortical levels have been identified with suppression of the immune system. In fact, studies (e.g., Ahlqvist, 1981) suggest that all hormones and neurotransmitters are potentially capable of influencing immune responses.

Physiological mechanisms have also been hypothesized for coping strategies designed to relieve excessive activation. For instance, Benson's "relaxation response" is characterized by "change consistent with decreased sympathetic tone" (Benson et al., 1977, p. 929).

INCREASED RISK OF DISEASE

An increase in both general and specific risks of illness or disease has been posited for various coping responses. The giving up–given up reaction, associated with helplessness–hopelessness and conservation–withdrawal, was viewed by Schmale and Engel (1967) as preceding the development of illnesses of all types in people with somatic predisposition. The same kind of defeatist response has been specifically predictive of cervical cancer (Schmale, Iker, 1971).

Depression, hopelessness, giving up, each has been associated with both the onset and the course of cancer. A 17-year prospective study (Shekelle et al., 1981) of 2,020 employees of Western Electric in Chicago found that those with higher scores on depression, (as measured by the Minnesota

Multiphasic Personality Inventory MMPI) proved to have a significantly greater risk of developing cancer. The association between depression and cancer still remained after controlling for smoking, alcohol consumption, family history of cancer, and occupational status.

The giving-up reaction associated with bereavement has been linked to a significantly greater death rate for the widowed (Helsing, Szklo, & Comstock, 1981). The mechanism by which such a response can damage health was suggested in a prospective study by Schleifer, Keller, Camerino, Thornton, & Stein (1983), who found that surviving spouses of women who died of breast cancer had suppressed lymphocyte activity for 2 months after their wives' deaths.

Less serious illness has also been associated with giving up and depression. Among two groups of entering nursing students, a significant association was found between giving up and subsequent rate of illness (mostly respiratory ailments, gastrointestinal GI disorders, chronic headaches) and between depression and illness (Parens, McConville, & Kaplan, 1966).

Coping modes that are not likely to resolve problems and might even make them worse have been identified with a sense of helplessness and an increased susceptibility to disease. Jacobs, Spilken, and Norman (1969), in studying coping patterns of college students, found that those who would rebel, attack, or become defiant in the face of external problems would end up feeling helpless and with a significantly higher risk of upper respiratory infections.

Hostility is another response that is increasingly being identified as a health risk. The Western Electric Health Study (Shekelle, Gayle, Ostfeld, & Paul, 1983) found that higher hostility scores on the MMPI predicted higher rates of death from coronary disease, as well as all causes, for 1,877 men over a 20-year period. The association between hostility and heart disease held up after controlling for age, blood pressure, serum cholesterol level, and cigarette smoking.

In a 25-year study of 255 physicians who took a battery of tests while students at the University of North Carolina Medical School, those with above-the-median hostility scores on the MMPI had a four times greater incidence of heart disease (Barefoot, Dahlstrom, & Williams, 1983). Of those with higher hostility, 13.4% died during the 25 years, compared with 2.2% of those with below-median scores. An Association has also been found between high hostility scores and degrees of occlusion from atherosclerosis (Williams et al., 1980). Of 424 patients undergoing coronary arteriography for suspected coronary heart disease, 70% of those with higher hostility scores had significant occlusion, whereas only 48% with lower scores did.

Several large-scale epidemiological studies have established a relationship between hostility and risk of heart disease. A factor analysis of interview variables for a subset sample of the Western Collaborative Group Study found that a high "potential for hostility" and increased "irritation at waiting in lines" were the characteristics that most strongly differentiated those who developed coronary heart disease from those who did not (Chadwick, & Rosenman, Matthews, Glass, Rosenman, & Bortner, 1977; Chesney, & Black, 1981). Another large-scale survey, the Framingham Heart Study, showed on factor analysis that those who developed coronary heart disease (CHD) scored significantly higher on suppressed hostility and on Type-A behavior (Haynes, Feinleib, & Kannel, 1980).

Although at least three recent investigations have failed to find relationships between Type-A behavior and risk of heart disease (Case, Heller, Case, Moss, & the Multicenter Post-Infarction Research Group; Shekelle, Gale, & Norusis, 1985; Shekelle et al., 1985), both the Western Collaborative Group Study and the Framingham Heart Study found that Type As have a coronary rate that is twice as high as that for Type Bs.

REDUCED RISK OF DISEASE

Other cognitive and behavioral coping patterns have been identified as decreasing a person's risk of illness, promoting recovery from disease, or prolonging life. People who are optimistic about their own health have been shown to be at reduced risk of dying. This is true even if objective measures of health status such as laboratory tests and doctors' examinations show them to be in poor health. In contrast, people who believe they are in poor health but are objectively in good or excellent health have an increased mortality risk.

Among 6,928 American adults whose health was monitored for 9 years, the mortality risk for health optimists among the men was more than two times less and among the women five times less (Kaplan & Camacho, 1983). In Canada, among 3,128 people 65 years and older who were studied over 6 years, those who believed their health was excellent had nearly three times less risk of death than did those who perceived their health as poor (Mossey & Shapiro, 1982).

Kobasa (1979) and Kobasa et al. (1979, 1981) have demonstrated that optimistic appraisal and a sense of control, challenge, and commitment protect a person under stress from risk of illness. They did prospective studies of more than 200 executives, 157 attorneys, 100 gynecology outpatients, and a group of military men. When subjects under equally high stress were compared for illness, those high in "psychological hardiness" (control, challenge, commitment) had half the average illness scores of those low in hardiness, as confirmed by medical records.

Although social support has been identified as a *protective resource* in a number of studies (e.g., Berkman & Syme, 1979; Medalie & Goldbourt, 1976), Kobasa and her coworkers found optimistic appraisal and psychological hardiness to be even more powerful in reducing the risk of illness (Maddi & Kobasa, 1984). In fact, for the person low in hardiness who has high family support, more illness is reported.

A fighting spirit has emerged as a powerful coping response for prolonging life among cancer patients. In a group of 69 women in London who underwent mastectomies for malignant tumors, those who were cancer-free 5 years later had a fighting spirit or, surprisingly, used strong denial to deal with their disease (Greer, Morris, & Pettingale, 1979). In the United States, 35 women with metastatic breast cancer also were followed to determine if psychological reactions were associated with length of survival (Derogatis, Abeloff, & Melisaratos, 1979). Those living more than 1 year were more vocal in their feelings and were fighters. Levy (1983) found that, among 22 women with recurrent breast cancer, that those who showed spirit and anger in coping with their illness lived longer. They also had less suppression of natural killer-cell activity, indicating that their immune systems were less impaired.

TEACHING COPING SKILLS AND RISK CONTROL

If some coping patterns increase the risk of illness and others decrease it, then can effective coping skills be taught to people to improve their chances for health? There is evidence to suggest that training in cognitive and behavioral coping skills can be useful in

the treatment and prevention of a variety of chronic disorders.

The Recurrent Coronary Prevention Project in San Francisco has demonstrated that coronary-prone Type As can significantly reduce their risk of a second heart attack by modifying their cognitions and behavior (Friedman et al., 1984). A total of 592 myocardial infarct patients who received group counseling on changing their beliefs and behavior were compared with 270 who were given only advice on diet, exercise, and medication and 151 who simply got annual checkups. Those in the first group had almost half the coronary recurrence rate (7.2%) of those who did not get instruction on changing coping patterns (the second group's recurrence rate was 13%; the third's, 14%). It was found that participants who made the biggest changes in Type-A beliefs and behaviors had a recurrence rate over 3 years that was only one-fourth that of people who failed to show any change.

Participants were taught to control AIAI (aggravation, irritation, anger, and impatience) and to identify early signs of being extremely aroused. Changes in their beliefs and behavior were confirmed by four different measures; questionnaires given to participants themselves, to their spouses, to someone else who knew them well, and a videotaped structured interview. The interview emphasized the detection and measurement of hostile attitudes and a sense of urgency (Friedman et al., 1984).

Whether coronary-prone people can modify their toxic beliefs and behavior before they experience myocardial infarction has been a question of debate. Tentative evidence now suggests that both Type-A behavior and hostility can be changed among healthy men who could be at risk of coronary heart disease but have no symptoms.

The Montreal Type A Intervention Project (Roskies, 1985) compared three different methods of modifying behavior: jogging, cognitive–behavioral techniques, and weight training. Thirty-three Type As were enrolled in the jogging program; 37 were in stress management, emphasizing cognitive changes, and 37 lifted weights. Each program lasted 10 weeks.

The biggest changes occurred among those in the cognitive modification program. They had significant changes both in their Type-A scores and hostility. No significant changes were made by those in the other groups.

Jenni and Wollersheim (1979) succeeded in making significant reductions in Type-A behavior by using cognitive restructuring. A comparable group of Type

As were given stress-management training, consisting primarily of relaxation exercises, but the reduction in Type-A scores (as measured by the Bortner scale) was not as great. A third group, made up of people put on a waiting list, was also tested but given no treatment. No improvement in Type-A behavior occurred in this group over the 6 weeks during which the programs were conducted.

For the group taught cognitive restructuring, emphasis was placed on making each participant aware of how irrational thoughts produce excessive physiological reactions and distress. The A-B-C model of human disturbance, developed by Albert Ellis (1973), was used to demonstrate that stressful events do not cause distress. When something bad happens at *A,* and the person feels anxious, depressed, or hostile at *C,* that person's thoughts and attitudes at *B* must be changed to eliminate or reduce the distress. In particular, for coronary-prone Type As, it is necessary to change cognitions based on such maladaptive beliefs as "people and things must be as I want or it's awful." Although type behavior and anxiety levels were both reduced in the Jenni study, no significant changes occurred in cholesterol or blood pressure, which are risk factors for coronary heart disease.

Roskies and her colleagues, in an earlier study (Roskies, Sperack, Surkis, Cohe, & Gilman, 1978), did succeed in lowering cholesterol and blood pressure in Type As. In their pilot project, they randomly assigned 27 healthy professionals and executives to two groups. Those in the first group received brief psychotherapy, and the other men got behavior therapy. Each group met for 14 weekly sessions. At the end, both groups had made improvements in terms of serum cholesterol, trilgycerides, and blood pressure levels and on measures of psychological well-being (less anxiety, more satisfaction with work, family, and so on).

In a second study (Roskies et al., 1979), the investigators focused on 6 Type-A men who had evidence of clinical CHD but had not suffered a heart attack or experienced other symptoms. After receiving behavior therapy for 14 weeks, they also showed reductions in cholesterol, triglycerides, and blood pressure. Psychological well-being also increased. Six months after the end of treatment, the general finding was that the improvements had continued for measures of cholesterol, blood pressure, psychological symptoms, and life satisfaction.

Levenkron, Cohen, Mueller, and Fisher, (1983) also found cognitive–behavioral techniques useful in modifying Type-A behavior. Thirty-eight male executives were taught to change their internal dialogues in situations they found stressful. They also practiced self-control methods such as taking less work home in the evening, adjusting personal schedules, and removing their wristwatches when unavoidably delayed. Another part of the therapy was relaxation training. The cognitive–behavioral therapy was compared with group support, which encouraged change in Type-A behavior but offered no specific techniques, and gave "brief information," which was limited to general advice on slowing down. The cognitive–behavioral technique was found the most effective and produced changes in both Type-A scores and free fatty acid reactivity, a measure of sympathetic arousal.

MANAGEMENT OF OTHER DISORDERS

As for management of medical problems other than coronary heart disease, one of the early attempts to treat physical illness by teaching cognitive and behavioral coping skills came in 1936 with a group of patients who had peptic ulcers (Chappell, Stefano, Rogerson, & Pike, 1936).

In this "psychological training" program, 32 patients were given lectures on "the influence of thinking on bodily processes" (Chappell & Stevenson, 1936, p. 593). In addition, they were taught how to disrupt worry and ruminations by such strategies as reflecting on pleasant recollections and altering their self-statements. They were given information on relaxation and avoiding conflict. Their training program was in conjunction with prescribed antacids and a controlled diet.

A comparison was made between these patients and a similar group who received only medication and the controlled diet. After 2 months, when both groups had returned to a regular diet, only one of the patients in the training program had a recurrence of ulcer symptoms. In the comparison group, 19 of the 20 patients had serious recurrences. At the end of 3 years, 10 of the patients in the cognitive-training group were symptom free, as opposed to none in the comparison group.

Some years later this early study was replicated in a program that taught cognitive restructuring, imaging, and relaxation training to a group of patients with duodenal ulcers (Brooks & Richardson, 1980). They were compared with a control group whose treatment focused on support and expression of emotion. After 2 months, the first group had fewer recurrences of symptoms and required less antacid medication. After 3½ years, the cognitive–behavioral treatment group had significantly lower rates of ulcer recurrence.

For both tension and migraine headaches, which are one of the leading problems mentioned by outpatients seeking medical attention, cognitive techniques, together with behavioral coping skills, have proved promising. In a program developed by Holroyd, Appel, and Andrasik (1983), training is divided into three phases. In the first phase, participants learn how chronic headaches originate, the part played by cognitions, and how precipitating factors are under the client's control.

The participants then learn to monitor their responses to stresses in their lives and to identify thoughts, feelings, and behavior that precede and accompany stressful situations. They learn to link upsetting situations (such as criticism from an employer) to resulting thoughts ("I can't do anything right") that produce symptomatic responses (depression, withdrawal, headache).

The third phase teaches cognitive and behavioral coping skills. Participants learn to ferret out the beliefs underlying the negative thoughts and feelings that accompany bad events. For example, when a headache and other symptoms develop after criticism, the individual might have the idea that he or she must do everything perfectly or it is awful. Participants are taught to correct such cognitive distortions and to stop believing that their self-worth depends on never making a mistake or being criticized.

In one study (Holroyd, Andrasik, & Westbrook, 1977), 31 persons with chronic tension headaches received either cognitive training or biofeedback for eight sessions. An index of headache occurrence was obtained from daily recordings for each of the two groups and from a control, waiting-list group. When an evaluation was made 15 weeks later, those who received cognitive training had markedly improved. Only about half of the participants who got biofeedback showed improvement. Headaches in the control group remained at the same level as before. On a 2-year follow-up, those in the cognitive-therapy group were still significantly improved. More than 80% were showing substantial reductions in headache occurrences. A second study (Holroyd & Andrasik, 1978), with 39 persons who had chronic headaches, produced similar results for those taught cognitive coping or cognitive coping plus relaxation training.

Another disorder that coping-skills training has been helpful in relieving is hypertension. Relaxation training could be of possible benefit in both primary and secondary prevention. For instance, a 12-week randomized study done by Peters, Benson, and Peters (1977) investigated the effects of the relaxation response on the blood pressure of 126 office workers. One group was taught relaxation training and was asked to practice it twice daily for 15 minutes. A second group was instructed simply to sit quietly during the 15-minute breaks. A matching third group was given no instructions.

Between the first baseline measurements and the last measurements 12 weeks later, the relaxation-training group experienced significantly greater reductions in both systolic and diastolic pressures. The mean change in systolic pressure for the training group was a decline of 11.6. Mean diastolic pressure was lowered by 7.9 mm Hg.

In England, promising results have been reported from teaching hypertensive patients "to discriminate between realistic and unrealistic fear and between appropriate and inappropriate physiological responses to situations in daily life" (Patel, 1977, p. 12). Coping methods to control physiological responses were taught. After 12 sessions, patients had reduced their systolic pressure by 26.1 mm Hg and their diastolic by 15.2 mm Hg. The improvement was maintained over a 3-month period and was significantly greater than the reduction achieved by a control group, which was only told to relax (Patel, 1975).

Chronic and acute pain is another problem area to which cognitive and behavioral coping techniques have been widely applied. A variety of strategies have been reported (Turk, Meichenbaum, & Genest, 1983) as useful in the control of pain including,

1. *Imaginative inattention*—conjuring up a scene incompatible with pain, such as lying on a beach or attending a party
2. *Imaginative transformation of pain*—relabeling the pain sensations as something else or minimizing the sensations
3. *Imaginative transformation of context*—picturing the intense stimulation as occurring in another context, such as playing football despite being injured or being wounded but carrying on
4. *Focusing attention on physical characteristics of the environment*—counting ceiling tiles or watching television

5. *Mental distractions*—reciting a poem or singing a song
6. Somatization—focusing attention on the affected area but doing so in a detached way, as if there were a barrier between the painful part and the rest of the person.

Meichenbaum and his colleagues (Meichenbaum & Jeremko, 1983) have developed a "stress inoculation" procedure that has proved promising in managing pain and other disorders. It combines relaxation training, cognitive reappraisal, and self-instructions with changing internal dialogue and using imagery.

The use of cognitive techniques in the treatment of cancer is also receiving increasing attention. The Simontons' cancer counseling program (Simonton & Simonton, 1975) was one of the first to teach patients to picture their lymphocytes devouring the cancerous cells. Although remissions have been reported, the effects of this imagery on malignancies have yet to be established through well-controlled studies.

Finally, managing the psychological impact of cancer once the disease occurs is the focus of several programs. Patients with melanoma, breast cancer and lung cancer were given individual coping instructions and counseling during hospitalization and 6 months afterward in one study (Gordon et al., 1980). Compared with a similar group of patients not in the program, they had a significant decline in anxiety, hostility, and depression. Some 1,700 women who underwent mastectomies participated in a psychosocial program at Memorial Sloan-Kettering Cancer Center in New York (Winick & Robbins, 1977) and reported they found it helpful. Most were able to resume normal activities within 4 months. In New Haven, another psychosocial program (Morgenstern, Gellert, Walter, Ostfeld, & Siege, 1984) seemed to have beneficial effects on quality of life and survival for women with breast cancer. The objectives of the program were to inspire hope and to get the patients to accept their disease and take charge of their lives.

In many of these examples, where improved outcomes have been reported in various diseases from the use of cognitive–behavioral techniques and stress management, conclusive statements cannot be made as to long-term effectiveness. More longitudinal studies are needed comparing intervention groups with matched nonintervention groups. Identification of biological mechanisms mediated by intervention must also be proposed to infer causal relationships.

We do have conceptual frameworks now for a better understanding of the effect of coping processes on health and medical problems. A reasonable start has been made on testing models and interventions with empirical studies and on demonstrating the influence of cognitive and behavioral techniques in the management of disease.

REFERENCES

Ader, R. (1980). Psychosomatic and psychoneurologic research. *Psychosomatic Medicine, 42*, 307–321.

Ahlqvist, J. (1981). Hormonal influences on immunological and related phenomena. In R. Ader (Ed.), *Psychoneuroimmunology*, New York: Academic Press.

Aldrich, C. K., & Mendkoff, E. (1963). Relocation of the aged and disabled: A mortality study. *Journal of the American Geriatrics Society, 11*, 185–194.

Antonovsky, A. (1979). *Health, stress, and coping.* San Francisco: Jossey-Bass.

Appley, M. H., & Trumbull, R. (1967). On the concept of psychological stress. In M. H. Appley & R. Trumbull (Eds.), *Psychological stress: Issues in research.* New York: Appleton-Century-Crofts.

Barefoot, J. C., Dahlstrom, W. G., & Williams, R. B. (1983). Hostility, coronary heart disease incidence, and total mortality: A 25-year follow-up study of 255 physicians. *Psychosomatic Medicine, 45*(1), 59–63.

Baum, A., Deckel, A. W., & Gatchel, R. J. (1982). Environmental stress and health: Is there a relationship? In G. S. Sanders & J. Suls (Eds.), *Social psychology of health and illness.* Hillsdale, NJ: Lawrence Erlbaum.

Baum, A., Singer, J. E., & Baum, C. S. (1981). Stress and the environment. *Journal of Social Issues, 37*, 4–35.

Beck, A. T. (1972). *Depression: Causes and treatment.* Philadelphia: University of Pennsylvania Press.

Benson, H., Kotch, J. B., & Crassweller, K. D. (1977). The relaxation response: A bridge between psychiatry and medicine. *Medical Clinics of North America, 61*, 929–938.

Berkman, L. F., & Syme, S. L. (1979). Social networks, host resistance, and mortality: A nine-year follow-up study of Alameda County residents. *American Journal of Epidemiology, 109*(2), 186–204.

Bourne, P. G., Rose, R. M., & Mason, J. W. (1967). Urinary 17-OHCS levels. *Archives of General Psychiatry, 131*, 792–797.

Bourne, P. G., Rose, R. M., Mason, J. W. (1968). 17-OHCS levels in combat. *Archives of General Psychiatry, 19*, 135–140.

Brooks, G. R., & Richardson, F. C. (1980). Emotional skills training: A treatment program for duodenal ulcer. *Behavior Therapy, 11*, 198–207.

Buell, J. C., & Eliot, R. S. (1979). The role of emotional stress in the development of heart disease. *Journal of the American Medical Association, 242*, 365–368.

Cannon, W. G. (1929). *Bodily changes in pain, hunger, fear and rage: An account of recent researches into the function of emotional excitement* (2nd ed.). New York: Appleton — Century Crafts.

Case, R. B., Heller, S. S., Case, N. B., Moss, A. J., & the Multicenter Post-Infarction Research Group. (1985). Type A behavior and survival after acute myocardial infarction. *New England Journal of Medicine, 312*(12), 737–741.

Cassel, J. (1974). Psychosocial processes and "stress": Theoretical formulation. *International Journal of Health Services, 4*(3), 471–482.

Cassem, N. H., & Hackett, T. P. (1971). Psychiatric consultation in a coronary care unit. *Annals of Internal Medicine, 75*, 9–14.

Chappell, M. N., Stefano, J. J., Rogerson, J. S., Pike, F. H. (1936). The value of group psychological procedures in the treatment of peptic ulcer. *American Journal of Digestive Diseases, 3*, 813–817.

Chappell, M. N., & Stevenson, T. I. (1936). Group psychological training in some organic conditions. *Mental Hygiene, 20*(4), 588–597.

Cherry, L. (1978, March). On the real benefits of eustress: An interview with Hans Selye. *Psychology Today*, 60–64, 69–70.

Chesney, M. A., Black, G. W., Chadwick, J. H., & Rosenman, R. H. (1981). Psychological correlates of the Type A behavior. *Journal of Behavioral Medicine, 4*(2), 217–230.

Corley, K. C., Mauck, H. P., & Shiel, F. O. M. (1975). Cardiac responses associated with "yoked chair" shock avoidance in squirrel monkeys. *Psychophysiology, 12*, 439–444.

Cromwell, R. I., Butterfield, E. C., Brayfield, F. M., & Curry, J. J. (1977). *Acute myocardial infarction: Reaction and recovery.* St. Louis: C. V. Mosby.

Davis, S. W. (1956). Stress in combat. *Scientific American, 194*, 31–35.

Derogatis, L. R., Abeloff, M. D., & Melisaratos, N. (1979). Psychological coping mechanisms and survival time in metastatic breast cancer. *Journal of the American Medical Association, 242*(14), 1504–1508.

Dimsdale, J. E. (1974). The coping behavior of Nazi concentration camp survivors. *American Journal of Psychiatry, 131*, 792–797.

Dubos, R. (1965). *Man adapting.* New Haven: Yale University Press.

Elliott, G. R., & Eisdorfer, C. (Eds.). (1982). *Stress and human health.* New York: Springer.

Ellis, A. (1973). Rational emotive therapy. In R. Corsini (Ed.), *Current psychotherapies.* Itasca, IL: Bantam, Peacock Press.

Engel, G. L., & Schmale, A. H. (1972). Conservation-withdrawal: A primary regulatory process for organismic homeostasis. In Symposium 8, *Physiology, emotion and psychosomatic illness, conducted at the meeting of the Ciba Foundation.* Amsterdam: Elsevier.

Folkman, S., & Lazarus, R. S. (1980). An analysis of coping in a middle-aged community sample. *Journal of Health and Social Behavior, 21*, 219–230.

Folkman, S., Schaefer, C., & Lazarus, R. S. (1979). Cognitive processes as mediators of stress and coping. In V. Hamilton & D. M. Warburton (Eds.), *Human stress and cognition: An information processing approach.* New York: John Wiley & Sons.

Frankenhaeuser, M. (1979). Psychobiological aspects of

life stress. In S. Levine & H. Ursin (Eds.), *Coping and health.* New York: Plenum.

Frankenhaeuser, M. B., Nordheden, B., Myrsten, A., & Post, B. (1971). Psychophysiological reactions to understimulation and overstimulation. *Acta Psychologica, 35*, 298–308.

French, J. R. P. Jr. (1974). Person-role fit. In A. A. McLean (Ed.), *Occupational stress.* Springfield, IL: Charles C. Thomas.

Friedman, M., Thoresen, C. E., Gill, J. J., Powell, L. H., Ulmer, D., Thompson, L., Price, V., Rabin, D. D., Breall, W. S., Dixon, T., Levy, R., & Bourg, E. (1984). Alteration of Type A behavior and reduction in cardiac recurrences in postmyocardial infarction patients. *American Heart Journal, 108*(2), 237–248.

Gal, R., & Lazarus, R. S. (1975). The role of activity in anticipating and confronting stressful situations. *Journal of Human Stress, 1*, 4–20.

Gordon, W. A., Freidenbergs, I., & Diller, L., Hibbard, M., Wolf, C., Levine, L., Lipkins, R., Ezrachi, O., & Lucido, D. (1980). Efficacy of psychosocial intervention with cancer patients. *Journal of Consulting and Clinical Psychology, 48*(6), 743–759.

Greer, S., Morris, T., & Pettingale, K. W. (1979). Psychological response to breast cancer: Effect on outcome. *Lancet, 2*, 785–787.

Haan, N. (1977). *Coping and defending: Processes of self-environment organization.* New York: Academic Press.

Hackett, T. P., & Cassem, N. Y. (1975). Psychological management of the myocardial patient. *Journal of Human Stress, 1*, 25–38.

Hamburg, D. A., & Adams, J. E. (1967). A perspective on coping behaviour: Seeking and utilizing information in major transitions. *Archives of General Psychiatry, 17*, 277–284.

Hamburg, D. A., Hamburg, B., & deGoza, S. (1953). Adaptive problems and mechanisms in severely burned patients. *Psychiatry, 16*, 1–20.

Haynes, S. G., Feinleib, M., & Kannel, W. B. (1980). The relationship of psychosocial factors to coronary heart disease in the Framingham study. III. Eight-year incidence of coronary heart disease. *American Journal of Epidemiology, 111*(1), 37–58.

Helsing, K. J., Szklo, M., & Comstock, G. W. (1981). Factors associated with mortality after widowhood. *American Journal of Public Health, 71*(8), 802–809.

Henry, J. P., & Stephens, P. M. (1977). *Stress, health, and the social environment: A sociobiologic approach to medicine.* New York: Springer-Verlag.

Hinkle, L. E. Jr. (1974). The concept of "stress" in the biological and social sciences. *International Journal of Psychiatry, 5*, 335–357.

Hinkle, L. E. Jr., Christenson, W. N., Kane, F. D., Ostfeld, A., Thetford, W. N., & Wolff, H. G. (1958). An investigation of the relation between life experience, personality characteristics and general susceptibility to illness. *Psychosomatic Medicine, 20*, 278–295.

Hinkle, L. E. Jr., Kane, F. D., Christenson, W. N., & Wolff, H. G. (1959). Hungarian refugees: Life experiences and features influencing participation in the revolution and subsequent flight. *American Journal of Psychiatry, 116*, 16–19.

Hinkle, L. E. Jr., & Wolff, H. G. (1957). The nature of man's adaptation to his total environment and the relation of this to illness. *Archives of Internal Medicine, 99,* 442–460.

Holroyd, K. A., & Andrasik. (1978). Coping and the self-control of chronic tension headache. *Journal of Consulting and Clinical Psychology, 46,* 1036–1045.

Holroyd, K. A., Andrasik, F., & Westbrook, T. (1977). Cognitive control of tension headache. *Cognitive Therapy and Research, 1,* 121–133.

Holroyd, K. A., Appel, M. A., & Andrasik, F. (1983). A cognitive–behavioral approach to psychophysiological disorders. In D. Meichenbaum & M. E. Jeremko (Eds.), *Stress reduction and prevention.* New York: Plenum.

Ilfeld, F. W. (1980). Coping styles of Chicago adults: Description. *Journal of Human Stress, 6,* 2–10.

Jacobs, M. A., Spilken, A., & Norman, M. (1969). Relationship of life change, maladaptive aggression, and upper respiratory infection in male college students. *Psychosomatic Medicine, 31,* 31–44.

Jarvik, L. F., & Russell, D. (1979). Anxiety, aging and the third emergency reaction. *Journal of Gerontology, 34,* 197–200.

Jennie, M. A., & Wollersheim, J. P. (1979). Cognitive therapy, stress management training and the type A behavior pattern. *Cognitive Therapy and Research, 3*(1), 61–73

Justice, B. (1987). *Who gets sick: Thinking and health.* Houston: Peak Press.

Kaplan, G. A., & Camacho, T. (1983). Perceived health and mortality: A nine-year follow-up of the Human Population Laboratory cohort. *American Journal of Epidemiology, 117*(3), 292–304.

Kasl, S. V. (1983). Pursuing the link between stressful life experiences and disease: A time for reappraisal. In C. L. Cooper (Ed.), *Stress research.* Chichester: John Wiley.

Katz, J. L., Weiner, H., Gallagher, T. G., & Hellman, L. (1970). Stress, distress and ego defenses. *Archives of General Psychiatry, 23,* 131–142.

Kobasa, S. C. (1979). Stressful life events, personality and health: An inquiry into hardiness. *Journal of Personality and Social Psychology, 37*(1), 1–11.

Kobasa, S. C., Hiker, R. R., & Maddi, S. R. (1979). Who stays healthy under stress? *Journal of Occupational Medicine, 21,* 595–598.

Kobasa, S. C., Maddi, S. R., & Courington, S. (1981). Personality and constitution as mediators in the stress-illness relationship. *Journal of Health and Social Behavior, 22,* 368–378.

Krantz, D. S. (1980). Cognitive processes and recovery from heart attack: A review and theoretical analysis. *Journal of Human Stress, 6,* 27–38.

Langer, E. J., Janis, I. L., & Wolfer, J. S. (1975). Reduction of psychological stress, in surgical patients. *Journal of Experimental Social Psychology, 11,* 155–165.

Lazarus, R. S. (1980). The stress and coping paradigm. In L. A. Bond & J. C. Rosen (Eds.), *Competence and coping during adulthood.* Hanover, NH: University Press of New England.

Lazarus, R. S., & Launier, R. (1978). Stress-related transactions between persons and environment. In L. A. Pervin & M. Lewis (Eds.), *Perspectives in interactional psychology.* New York: Plenum.

Levenkron, J. C., Cohen, J. D., Mueller, H. S., & Fisher, E. B. (1983). Modifying the type A coronary-prone pattern. *Journal of Consulting and Clinical Psychology, 51*(2), 192–204.

Levy S. M. (1983, August). *Emotional expression and survival in breast cancer patients: Immunological correlates.* Paper presented at the meeting of the American Psychological Association, Anaheim, CA.

Maddi, S. R., & Kobasa, S. C. (1984). *The hardy executive: Health under stress.* Homewood, IL: Dow Jones-Irwin.

Mason, J. W. (1975). A historical view of the stress field: Part II. *Journal of Human Stress, 1,* 22–36.

Matthews, K. A., Glass, D. C., Rosenman, R. H., & Bortner, R. W. (1977). Competitive drive, pattern A, and coronary heart disease: A further analysis of some data from the Western Collaborative Group Study. *Journal of Chronic Diseases, 30,* 489–498.

McClelland, D. C., Floor, E., Davidson, R. J., & Saron, C. (1980). Stressed power motivation, sympathetic activation, immune function, and illness. *Journal of Human Stress, 6,* 11–19.

McGrath, J. E. (1970). A conceptual formulation for research on stress. In J. E. McGrath (Ed.), *Social and psychological factors in stress.* New York: Rinehart and Winston.

Meichenbaum, D., & Jeremko, M. E. (Eds.). (1983). *Stress reduction and prevention.* New York: Plenum.

Meichenbaum, D. H., & Turk, D. C. (1976). The cognitive–behavioral management of anxiety, anger and pain. In P. O. Davidson (Ed.), *The behavioral management of anxiety, depression and pain.* New York: Brunner/Mazel.

Medalie, J. H., & Goldbourt, U. (1976). Angina pectoris among 10,000 men, II: Psychosocial and other risk factors. *American Journal of Medicine, 60,* 910–921.

Menninger, K. (1954). Regulatory devices of the ego under major stress. *International Journal of Psychoanalysis, 35,* 412–420.

Mikhail, A. (1981). Stress: A psychophysiological conception. *Journal of Human Stress, 7,* 9–15.

Morgenstern, H., Gellert, G. A., Walter, S. D., Ostfeld, A. M., & Siegel, B. S. (1984). The impact of a psychosocial support program on survival with breast cancer: The importance of selection bias in program evaluation. *Journal of Chronic Diseases, 37*(4), 273–282.

Mossey, J. A., & Shapiro, E. (1982). Self-rated health: A predictor of mortality among the elderly. *American Journal of Public Health, 72*(8), 800–808.

Murphy, L. B. (1974). Coping, vulnerability, and resilience in childhood. In G. V. Coelho, D. A. Hamburg, & J. E. Adams (Eds.), *Coping and adaptation.* New York: Basic Books.

Parens, H., McConville, B. J., & Kaplan, S. M. (1966). The prediction of illness from the response to separation. *Psychosomatic Medicine, 28*(2), 162–176.

Patel, C. (1975). Randomised controlled trial of yoga and biofeedback in management of hypertension. *Lancet, 2,* 93–95.

Patel, C. H. (1977). Biofeedback-aided relaxation and meditation in the management of hypertension. *Biofeedback and Self-Regulation, 2,* 1–41.

Peters, R. K., Benson, H., & Peters, J. M. (1977). Daily relaxation response breaks in a working population: II.

Effects on blood pressure. *American Journal of Public Health, 67*(10), 954–959.

Pines, A., & Aronson, E. (1980). *Burn out: From tedium to personal growth*. New York: Free Press.

Rodin, J. (1979). Managing the stress of aging: The role of control and coping. In S. Levine & H. Ursin (Eds.), *Coping and health*. New York: Plenum.

Roskies, E. (1985, March). *Approaches to alteration of Type A behavior pattern*. Paper presented at the meeting of the Society of Behavioral Medicine, New Orleans.

Roskies, E., & Lazarus, R. S. (1980). Coping theory and the teaching of coping skills. In P. O. Davidson & S. M. Davidson (Eds.), *Behavioral Medicine: Changing health lifestyles*. New York: Brunner/Mazel.

Roskies, E., Kearney, H., Spevack, M., Surkis, A., Cohen, C., & Gilman, S. (1979). Generalizability and durability of treatment effects on an intervention program for coronary-prone (type A) managers. *Journal of Behavioral Medicine, 2*(2), 195–205.

Roskies, E., Spevack, M., Surkis, A., Cohe, C., & Gilman, S. (1978). Changing the coronary-prone (type A), behavior pattern in a nonclinical population. *Journal of Behavioral Medicine, 1*(2), 201–216.

Schleifer, S. J., Keller, S. E., Camerino, M., Thornton, J. C., & Stein, M. (1983). Suppression of lymphocyte stimulation following bereavement. *Journal of the American Medical Association, 250*(3), 374–377.

Schmale, A. H. (1972). Giving up as a final common pathway to changes in health. *Advances in Psychosomatic Medicine, 8,* 20–40.

Schmale, A. H., & Engel, G. L. (1967). The giving up–given up complex illustrated on film. *Archives of General Psychiatry, 17,* 135–145.

Schmale, A. H., & Iker, H. (1971). Hopelessness as a predictor of cervical cancer. *Social Science & Medicine, 5,* 95–100.

Selye, H. (1976). Forty years of stress research: Principal remaining problems and misconceptions. *Canadian Medical Association Journal. 115,* 53–56.

Selye H. (1978a). *The stress of life*. New York: McGraw-Hill.

Selye, H. (1978b). General adaptation syndrome. Stress Management Symposium conducted at the meeting of the Institute for the Study of Human Knowledge and the University of Texas Health Science Center, Houston.

Shekelle, R. B., Gale, M. & Norusis, M. (1985). JAS Type A score and risk of recurrent coronary heart disease in the Aspirin Myocardial Infarction Study, *American Journal of Cardiology, 56,* 221–225.

Shekelle, R. B., Gayle, M., Ostfeld, A. M., & Paul, O. (1983). Hostility, risk of coronary heart disease, and mortality. *Psychosomatic Medicine, 45*(2), 109–114.

Shekelle, R. B., Hulley, S. B., Neaton, J. D., Billings, J., Borhani, N. O., Gerace, T. A., Jacobs, D., Lasser, M., Mittlemark, M., & Stamler, J. (1985). The MRFIT behavior study. II. Type A behavior and incidence of coronary heart disease. *American Journal of Epidemiology, 122*(4), 559–570.

Shekelle, R. B., Raynor, W. J., Ostfeld, A. M., Garron, D. C., Bieliauskas, L. A., Liu, S. C., Maliza, C., & Paul, O. (1981). Psychological depression and 17-year risk of death from cancer. *Psychosomatic Medicine, 43*(2), 117–125.

Simonton, O. C., & Simonton, S. S. (1975). Belief systems and management of the emotional aspects of malignancy. *Journal of Transpersonal Psychology, 7*(1), 29–47.

Singer, J. E. (1980). Tradition of stress research: Integrative comments. In I. G. Sarason & C. D. Spielberger (Eds.), *Stress and anxiety* (Vol. 7). Washington: Hemisphere.

Sinyor, D., Schwart, S. G., Peronnet, F., Brisson, G., & Seraganian, P. (1983). Aerobic fitness level and reactivity to psychosocial stress: Physiological, biochemical and subjective measures. *Psychosomatic Medicine, 45,* 205–217.

Turk, D. C., Meichenbaum, D., & Genest, M. (1983). *Pain and behavioral medicine: A cognitive-behavioral perspective*. New York: Guilford Press.

Vaillant, G. (1977). *Adaptation to life*. Boston: Little, Brown.

Wallace, L. M. (1984). Psychological preparation as a method of reducing the stress of surgery. *Journal of Human Stress, 10*(2), 62–77.

White, R. W. (1974). Strategies of adaptation: An attempt at systematic description. In G. V. Coelho, D. A. Hamburg, & J. E. Adams (Eds.), *Coping and adaptation*. New York: Basic Books.

Williams, R. B. Jr., Haney, T. L., Lee, K. L. Kong, Y-H., Blumenthal, J. A., & Whalen, J. E. (1980). Type A behavior, hostility and coronary arteriosclerosis. *Psychosomatic Medicine, 42,* 539–549.

Winick, L., & Robbins, G. F. (1977). Physical and psychologic readjustment after mastectomy: An evaluation of Memorial Hospital's PMRG program. *Cancer, 39,* 478–486.

Wolff, C. T., Friedman, S. G., Hofer, M. A., & Mason, J. W. (1964). Relationship between psychological defenses and mean urinary 17-hydroxycorticosteroid excretion rates: I. A predictive study of parents of fatally ill children. *Psychosomatic Medicine, 26,* 576–591.

Wolff, H. G. (1953). *Stress and disease*. Springfield, IL: Charles C. Thomas.

Wolf, S. (1967). The end of the rope: The role of the brain in cardiac death. *Canadian Medical Association Journal, 97,* 1022–1025.

Wolf, S. (1968). Disease as a way of life. In S. Wolf & H. Goodell (Eds.), *Harold G. Wolff's Stress and Disease* (2nd ed.). Springfield, IL: Charles C. Thomas.

Wolf, S., & Goodell, H. (1976). *Behavioral science in clinical medicine*. Springfield, IL: Charles C. Thomas.

Chapter 3

Stress and the Patient's Family

Donna R. Copeland

One of the most stressful situations a family encounters is the result of a chronic medical condition being diagnosed in one of its members. The problem is not restricted to the individual but touches each member of the family to varying degrees. The responses of the family unit to this type of stress depend to a great extent on the severity of the illness in terms of its life-threatening qualities and its disruption of life-style and on the family's effectiveness in coping with stress generally. This chapter will (a) review the contextual variables and research findings on the effects of physical illness on the family; (b) discuss the psychological issues that arise in the aftermath of diagnosis; (c) describe common patterns of family responses to the situation; and (d) suggest approaches the clinician might take in assisting the family. Case examples of the three issues and family responses are presented.

THE CONTEXT

With respect to disease factors, the visibility of the illness, the prognosis, and the limitations it imposes on daily activities and physical and emotional development partially determine the extent to which the family's life is altered.

Abe was 2 years old when his disease was diagnosed as malignant melanoma. Surgery was performed, which left his face severely disfigured. Although the long-term prognosis for cure was good,

Abe spent much of the next 5 years in the hospital receiving chemotherapy and undergoing follow-up surgeries, including plastic surgery to improve his appearance. In the meantime, however, his social development was impeded, and Abe and his mother developed a symbiotic relationship.

Treatment variables can have immediate and long-term effects on the family in terms of the amount of discomfort they produce, their complexity and the difficulty involved in administering them, their frequency, and their side effects. For example, the long-term effects of mutilating surgery, of some types of chemotherapy, and of radiotherapy are well documented (D'Angio, 1982; van Eys, 1984; van Eys & Sullivan, 1980). A child who received radiotherapy for leukemia prior to age 3 is not the same child she might otherwise have been, and the family must repeatedly adjust to this fact. A child who received this treatment at 21 months and is now an adult functions at an IQ level of less than 40. Prior to diagnosis, her birth and development had been normal. But today she is intellectually impaired, showing poor articulation, inability to understand verbal instructions, difficulty in understanding abstract concepts, poor memory, and poor fine-motor speed and dexterity. At each developmental stage, the family has mourned for the child they hoped she would be. She will require custodial care for the rest of her life, which will have a significant impact on the family's life-style.

Not all chronic diseases or treatments are so

invasive, and, in some cases, the potential for disruption in the family is much lower. For instance, children with leukemia who receive only chemotherapy, without irradiation, show little, if any, detrimental effect on their neurocognitive skills (Copeland et al., 1985).

Another factor contributing to the degree of stress experienced is the family's response to the illness, treatment, and long-term physical effects the patient will or might already have incurred. The manner in which families respond to stress is highly variable (Hansen & Hill, 1964). One mother had extreme difficulty accepting the surgery for her 5-year-old daughter that resulted in the child's sterility. The child was off treatment and doing well. However, each time the child played with dolls, the mother would sob, thereby conveying to the child that there was something wrong. The mother's tears discouraged the child from using adaptive coping mechanisms, such as playing with dolls, and the mother's attitude negatively influenced her child's self-image. Contrast this with the parents who had chosen amputation of their son's leg rather than a limb-salvage procedure because they realized that he could continue athletic activities more easily with a complete limb prosthesis. The opportunity for their child to fulfill his potential was more important to them than his outward appearance. They were able to cope with disfiguring treatment and guide their child toward active adaptation.

The parents' role is important, therefore, in that parents define for the child the meaning of the illness in terms of hopelessness versus active coping. This, in turn, influences the child's self-image. The parents who chose the amputation were saying to their son, "you *can* do it." The tearful mother was saying, "There is something wrong with you that cannot be fixed." The long-term consequences of these two approaches, given no intervention, are predictable.

When a family has difficulty accepting the reality of the disease and attempts to cope by denying its serious implications, the patient is likely to experience increased stress. David was a 13-year-old boy when his illness was diagnosed as T-cell leukemia. From the beginning, David had difficulty understanding that he had a serious, life-threatening disease that would require treatment for several years. It became apparent to the staff that defensive denial was interfering with his ability to cope. Upon further investigation, it was found that his parents were the source of the problem. His mother had "protected" him from information about the illness

from the time of diagnosis. He learned of his illness in an offhand manner, as staff assumed he knew of his disease prior to arriving at the cancer center. When he was brought to the hospital, the mother left him alone during the initial treatment, once again ignoring the severity of his condition and the anxiety he was experiencing. The father could not tolerate being at the hospital, as the memory of his father's recent death from cancer was still fresh in his mind. David became increasingly withdrawn, inactive, and uncommunicative. By denying the seriousness of her child's condition, the mother ignored his need for support and comfort during an extremely stressful period. At the same time, the father felt inadequate to support his son and used avoidance to cope with the situation. Contrast this family's responses with those of another family.

Ben was 11 years old when he was rushed to a cancer treatment center following the diagnosis of leukemia. His parents were extremely anxious for several weeks. They hovered over his bed and took turns staying with him during the initial treatment period. His brother visited him from time to time, as did his grandparents, and he received correspondence from acquaintances and friends at school and church. Although Ben and his family were fairly upset, they asked many questions, and Ben spoke openly about his worries and fears. After a few weeks, his parents and grandparents relaxed, and he began venturing out on the unit and participating in various ward activities. The outlook for the family's resumption of their usual life-style and long-term adjustment to the illness was optimistic.

The adaptive strengths of these two families are extremes on either end of a continuum, and they illustrate how families can facilitate adjustment and minimize stress or hinder adjustment by withholding information and support, thus increasing the stress of the illness on the patient.

Finally, the extent to which the family has additional stressors influences adjustment. Bedell, Giordani, Amour, Tavormina, and Boll (1977) tested the hypothesis that life stress is an important factor in the psychological functioning of chronically ill children. Forty-five children attending a summer camp for the chronically ill were assessed for life stress, self-concept, and anxiety. Those in the high-stress group were found to exhibit a lower self-concept and a higher number of illness episodes. Life stress apparently affects disease course as well. Ruberman, Weinblatt, Goldberg, and Chaudhary (1984) found that a high degree of life stress was associated with mortality in male survivors of acute myocardial infarction.

Pamela was a child who was born with severe congenital immune deficiency disease. The illness had required multiple transplants and almost continuous periods of hospitalization. This situation would be difficult for any family; however, in addition to the stress associated with Pamela's disorder, there were additional stresses. The father was an alcoholic who physically abused the mother when he was intoxicated, and he was noted to exhibit other signs of psychopathology. Still another stress on the family, particularly the mother, was the health of the aging maternal grandparents who cared for the mother's other three children when she had to be with Pamela at the hospital. The grandfather had had a stroke and was partially paralyzed. Clearly, the interaction of all these stresses took their toll on the family's functioning. Under these circumstances, the mother had to balance her time among mothering three children at home, earning a living, caring for her ill child in the hospital, and attending to her parents' needs.

Disease and treatment variables and family responses have interacting effects, compounding family stress. The Gray family cogently illustrates the point. In this family, the younger daughter was born with cerebral palsy, that required long-term treatment and various types of supportive care such as physical therapy. When this child was about 15 years old, her mother developed a chronic condition accompanied by continual pain, myofacial pain dysfunction syndrome. The woman tried numerous types of medical treatment, including biofeedback, but nothing was effective until she located a physician in New York City. The treatment consisted of steroids administered in 40–60 injections per visit. It was expensive and necessitated frequent trips to New York from the woman's home in the southwestern United States. Both the woman and her husband were apprehensive about her dependency on the medication and on "the only doctor in the world" who administered it. For additional help, the woman sought hypnotherapy and, subsequently, psychotherapy as a means of controlling pain and coping with increasing stress. Finally, the older daughter in the family, who had made several suicide attempts in recent months, was eventually hospitalized in a residential treatment center for unstable (borderline) personality disorder. The family braced themselves for 5 years of intensive psychotherapy and periodic hospitalizations. As these problems accumulated, stress in the family increased.

The responses of family members to these events underscore the complex interplay among the numerous contributing factors. The illnesses were all of a chronic nature, were difficult to treat, and disrupted the life-style and future plans of each family member. The treatments created friction in the family, as the father became more and more resentful of the mounting medical bills and more suspicious of health care professionals' motives and ability to cure illness. This response, in turn, increased the mother's stress, thereby exacerbating her chronic pain. Family therapy sessions held at the residential treatment center 150 miles from their home, although helpful, required effort, time, and expense. The teenage son in the family and the younger daughter became frustrated and bitter about the amount of family resources being diverted for medical treatment. They began to withdraw from the older daughter and withhold emotional support. In sum, disease, treatment, and family response variables interacted to create a highly stressful environment for this family.

REVIEW OF THE LITERATURE

There are differing points of view on the extent to which families are adversely affected by chronic illness. Earlier studies, as well as some of the more recent, report only slight adverse affects, given that the disease remains stable and given a certain amount of time after diagnosis (Boyle, Tebbi, Mindell, & Mettlin 1982; Brown, Rawlinson, & Hardin 1982; Chodoff, Friedman & Hamburg 1964; Croog & Levine, 1977; Futtermann & Hoffman, 1973; Korsch et al., 1973; Kupst et al., 1984; Venters, 1981; Zahn, 1973). The more positive reports from these studies might be attributed to improved treatment methods for most illnesses, thus reducing considerably the psychological stress on the family with respect to potential loss from death.

In a longitudinal investigation, Kupst and colleagues (Kupst & Shulman, 1980; Kupst et al., 1982; Kupst et al., 1984) followed 60 families for 2 years following the diagnosis of cancer in a child. Self-report measures and ratings by medical, nursing, and psychosocial staff indicated that the majority of families were coping well 2 years after diagnosis (Kupst et al., 1984). O'Malley, Foster, Koocher, and Slavin (1980) and Boyle et al. (1982) reported similar findings for families with children who have cancer. Korsch et al. (1973) assessed 35 children who successfully underwent kidney transplant for end-stage renal disease. According to the investigators these families had regained their prediagnosis equilibrium at the time of follow-up. They concluded that the potential for recovery of most children and families was good. Litman (1974) found that families are brought together as often as they are pushed apart by illness. Two studies have found that family members sometimes cope better with life when a family member is ill (Brown et al., 1982; Venters, 1981).

Nevertheless, many investigators point out that chronic illness inevitably places stress on the family system, and not all families are equipped to master the cumulative stresses and strains (Anthony, 1970; Binger et al., 1969; Kaplan, 1981; Kaplan, Smith, Grobstein, & Fischman, 1973; Magreb & Calcagno, 1978; Mattson, 1972; Petzel, Bugge, Warwick, & Budd, 1984; Richardson & Friedman, 1974; Spinetta, 1981a; Talbot & Howell, 1971). Binger's study showed that in 11 of 20 families studied, family members exhibited emotional problems requiring intervention. In studies by Kaplan et al. (1973), it was noted that over 80% of the families did not successfully master the initial coping tasks required of a family with an ill child. Parents in these investigations reported that problems either emerged or intensified after the child's illness was diagnosed. Pless, Roghmann, and Haggerty (1972) found in their assessments comparing 209 ill children with a group of 113 healthy children and their families that the combined effects of poor health and unfavorable family situation are cumulative over time. A recent study of adult cancer patients showed a prevalence rate of 47% for psychiatric disorders (Derogatis et al., 1983).

Chronic illness and disability in a child is distressing to the parents, as indicated by several recent investigations. Morrow, Hoagland, and Carnrike (1981) assessed 107 parents of children with cancer. Parents whose child had died and young parents (less than 30 years old) consistently demonstrated poorer psychosocial adjustment than the other parent groups. The importance of social support was demonstrated, in that parents' psychosocial adjustment correlated with perceived social support. Symptomatic distress (sleep disturbance and depression) in parents of children with leukemia was reported in a group of 25, when compared with 25 normal controls (Magni, Messina, DeLeo, Moasconi, & Carli, 1983). Breslau, (Staruch, and Mortimer (1982) examined the impact of child disability on psychological functioning in 369 mothers of children with various chronic diseases by comparing them with 456 mothers from a randomly selected sample. Mothers of disabled children showed significantly more distress than the controls; the more dependent the child, the greater the mother's distress.

Many clinicians and investigators have reported adverse effects on the parents' marriage as a result of a child's chronic illness (Bruhn, 1977; Crain, Sussman, & Weil, 1966; Hughes, 1976; Irvin, Kennell, & Klaus, 1982; Lawler, Nakielny, & Wright, 1966; Magreb & Calcagno, 1978; Silbert, Newburger, & Fyler, 1982; Tew, Laurence, Payne, & Rownsley, 1977; Tropauer, Franz & Dilgard, 1970). In their critique, Sabbeth and Leventhal (1984) found that in seven studies of marital distress in which a comparison group was used, four reported that parents of chronically ill children suffered more marital distress than did parents in the control group (Crain et al., 1966; Lansky, Cairns, Hassanin, Wehr, & Lowman 1978; Silbert et al., 1982; Tew, Payne, & Laurence, 1974). Some studies reported increased marital distress in families with chronically ill children but not necessarily a higher divorce rate (Begleiter, Burry, & Harris, 1976; Lansky et al., 1978; Sabbeth & Leventhal, 1984; Satterwhite, 1978). Still other studies indicated that increased marital distress is not a consequence of chronic illness in a child (Silbert et al., 1982; Vance, Fazan, Satterwhite, & Pless, 1980; Waisbren, 1979; Walker, Thomas, & Russell 1971). These latter studies were based on self-reporting, which reduces credibility, because patients and families of the ill typically fail to report difficulties in interpersonal relationships. For instance, the parents in Gath's (1977) study reported that the marital relationship had improved; however, rating scales indicated there was more tension, hostility, and distance between these couples, whose children had Down's syndrome, when compared with a control group of parents. Duration of the illness and intensity of treatment could account for at least some of the variability in these reports. Barbarin, Hughes, and Chesler (1985) found in their interviews of 32 married couples whose children had cancer that initially the family felt they were brought closer together. However, as the number of the child's hospitalizations increased, the perceptions of support from spouse and evaluation of marital quality decreased.

With respect to marital relationships in which a spouse is chronically ill, Lowry and Atcherson (1984) conducted follow-up interviews of 32 patients and 29 spouses who had been involved in home hemodialysis. In this investigation, it appeared that depression, anxiety, and marital distress were encountered less frequently than had been reported previously, such as in Shambaugh, Hampters, Bailey, Snyder, and Merrill (1967). No relation was found between degree of disability and marital satisfaction in three studies (Brown et al., 1982; Gibson & Ludwig, 1968; Kerns & Turk, 1984). Most studies, however, indicated increased stress on spouses of chronically ill patients (Braham, Hauser, Cline, & Posner, 1975; Crewe, Athelstan, & Krumberger, 1979; Klein, Dean & Bogdonoff, 1967; Skelton & Dominian, 1973; Toshihiko, Osborne, Swanson & Halling, 1981).

There are far fewer studies of the effects on children when a parent is chronically ill. One study of children whose fathers were paralyzed as a result of spinal cord injury showed that the children did not differ significantly from a group of children whose parents were not disabled (Buck & Hohmann, 1981). In contrast, three studies of children whose parents had multiple sclerosis (MS) reported deleterious effects on the children (Arnaud, 1959; Braham et al., 1975; Peters & Esses, 1985). Peters and Esses asked 33 children of MS patients and 33 children of nondisabled parents to complete a Family Environment Scale (FES) (Moos & Moos, 1980). The results showed that the index families scored higher on the Conflict scale and lower on scales of Cohesion, Intellectual-Cultural Orientation, Moral–Religious Emphasis, and Organization. Scores on the remaining five scales of the FES were not significant.

Siblings of chronically ill children apparently experience some degree of stress, according to a number of investigators (Binger, 1973; Cairns, Clark, Smith & Lansky, 1979; Cohen, Friedrich, Copeland, & Pendergrass, 1985; Crain, et al., 1966; Gath, 1973; Johnson, 1985; Kerns & Curley, 1985; Lask & Matthew, 1979; Lavigne & Ryan, 1979; Sourkes, 1980; Spinetta, 1981b; Vance et al., 1980). Breslau, Weitzman, and Messenger (1981) studied 239 families of pediatric patients with various chronic illnesses. The siblings in these families were compared with a random sample of 1,034 urban children. Siblings of disabled children did not differ from the control group in overall symptomatology, but their scores were significantly higher on two measures of interpersonal aggression with peers and within school. Although Vance et al. (1980) found few striking differences between 79 siblings of patients with nephrotic syndrome and 79 siblings of healthy children, several areas of increased vulnerability emerged, including low self-confidence and self-acceptance and greater inhibition in peer relationships and academic performance. Hoare (1984) made an interesting comparison between

siblings of children with newly diagnosed epilepsy and of children with chronic epilepsy. The siblings of children with newly diagnosed epilepsy were not disturbed when compared with the norms for their age. However, the siblings of chronic epileptics were, and they were significantly more disturbed than the other sibling group. The investigators concluded that chronic epilepsy places stress on other children in the family.

Over time, mothers too were shown to be more vulnerable, in that there was an association between disturbance in the child and disturbance in the mother when the illness was chronic. D. S. Cohen et al. (1985) surveyed 129 families of pediatric cancer patients to assess their adjustment and identify variables related to good and poor adjustment of siblings. Results indicated that the siblings did evidence significant adjustment problems when compared with norms of the child-behavior checklist utilized. The variables of parent depression, marital adjustment, income, social support, parent–sibling communication about the illness, and time since diagnosis emerged as significant predictors of sibling adjustment. Although many studies indicated that siblings are not severely affected by chronic illness in the family, other investigations have shown that there are areas of increased vulnerability and that siblings probably require attention from mental health staff.

Considered together, these investigative reports indicate that chronic illness places stress on family members individually and on the family system as a whole. Although most families manage to cope adequately with the situation, each family member is faced with the challenge of adaptation by adjusting her or his role, sharing the burdens of the illness, and accepting support from others in and outside of the family. It is also apparent from these investigations that some families are overwhelmed by the stress, partly because they are already vulnerable but perhaps also because the disease, treatment, or both are more severe. This raises questions about characteristics of families able to cope effectively with their circumstances and about those that require intervention from health care staff.

Family Characteristics

A number of writers have emphasized that, along with the type and degree of stress families experience, characteristics of family members and of the family system contribute to their adaptation to chronic illness (Battle, 1982, 1984; Bruch, 1949; Ferrari, Matthews, & Barabus, 1983; Hansen &

Hill, 1964; McCubbin & Figley, 1983; Turk & Kerns, 1985). Families that are coping functionally encourage open communication within the family; are cohesive as a unit, but flexible in their roles; are committed to one another and affectionate; are able to utilize resources available to them; take a solution-oriented approach to problems; and are able to identify specific stressors, accept them, and cope with them. Dysfunctional families, on the other hand, suppress communication; take an individualistic approach oriented toward blaming others; try to adhere rigidly to set roles; show little commitment or affection toward one another; make little use of available resources; perhaps use violence, drugs, or both to deal with problems; do not have a clear understanding of stresses they encounter; and perhaps use denial to cope with stress. These family characteristics predate the diagnosis of illness and form the basis for the family's particular coping responses.

Beyond the psychological and coping characteristics of families, socioeconomic status appears to be an important variable in family adaptation and adjustment to chronic illness. For instance, Ruberman et al. (1984) interviewed 2,320 male survivors of acute myocardial infarction. Results showed two variables to be strongly associated with mortality risk: social isolation and high degree of life stress. High levels of stress were most common among the least educated men. Numerous studies have shown that the financial burden that results from illness and treatment is great (Bodkin, Pigott, & Mann, 1982; Cairns, Clark, Black, & Lansky, 1981; Houts et al., 1984; Lansky, Black, & Cairns, 1983; Nelson, 1984; Salk, Hilgartner, & Granich, 1972; Satterwhite, 1978; Stein & Riessman, 1980). Costs for medical care can come to as high as 36% of the family income (Cairns et al., 1981; Lansky et al., 1983); nonmedical costs can range from 26% (Bodkin et al., 1982; Lansky et al., 1983) to 50% (Houts et al., 1984) of the family income. Additionally, lost wages for adults have been reported to be as high as 50% of the family income (Houts et al., 1984) during the treatment period. Satterwhite (1978) reported that 60% of parents of chronically ill children surveyed felt they had financial problems related to the child's illness.

PSYCHOLOGICAL ISSUES

Following the diagnosis of chronic illness in a family member, the family is faced with a number of psychological issues that arise as a result. These include separation and loss, emotional expression, value adjustments, developmental concerns, and alterations in the family system.

Separation and Loss

Along with the actual losses that occur as a result of chronic illness, the diagnosis reinvokes anxieties about earlier losses, especially if the illness is potentially life-threatening. Every family member experiences some type of loss. The patient might not feel well enough to engage in the usual family activities; hence, a sibling might lose a playmate or a spouse a sports partner. When the patient must obtain treatment out of town and is accompanied to the hospital or treatment center by another family member, those staying at home lose part of the family periodically. The two who go for treatment lose contact with other family members and friends. When the mother is one of the pair who leaves, those remaining at home sense the loss of her nurturing care. This is especially common when the mother invests her attention heavily in the ill person.

Loss of health, and loss of parts of the body when it occurs, is experienced not only by the patient but also by other family members. If the family is viewed as a system, a loss experienced by one is threatening to all. The parents might have to give up their dream that their son will play sports or their daughter will be a dancer. A child might have to accept the absence of a parent at school-sponsored performances and other events normally attended or supervised by parents. In the case of a life-threatening illness, the family is faced with the ultimate separation and loss: death.

Emotional Expression

The diagnosis of a chronic illness is emotionally upsetting, particularly immediately following the news. At first, the family feels shock and disbelief, closely followed by worry, fear, and even despair. Many report feeling out of control and helpless during this time. Feelings of guilt and blame surface; family members might feel responsible for delaying treatment by not having seen a physician sooner. Some might blame physicians who did not recognize the illness right away. Some feel that the illness is God's punishment for wrongdoing, such as breaking the law or having an extramarital affair. Virtually all parents feel guilty about not being able to fulfill the basic parental function of protecting their child from harm. When a parent becomes ill, the spouse and children worry about the threatened loss of financial and emotional support.

As the family recovers from the initial shock and

disappointment, they begin to grieve, not only for the present but also for the future, for what might have been. Then, for many, there is a period of renewed optimism and even exhilaration as the patient responds to treatment, the family becomes accustomed to the reality of chronic illness in their lives, and they develop more confidence in coping with the situation. Fluctuations in emotions occur in response to progress in treatment. The family is usually optimistic and cheerful when the patient is doing well or is between treatments and glum during periods of illness. This cycle can continue for years while the patient is in treatment, and it might contribute to chronic anxiety and depression. Some chronic diseases, such as diabetes, can be relatively well controlled, but others, such as cancer, always carry the possibility of recurrence, even in long-term survival. Fear of this diminishes over time, but it is not likely ever to disappear entirely.

Value Adjustments

Many families readjust their values about life, handicaps, illness, and religion and their attitudes toward aspects of day-to-day living following the diagnosis of a chronic illness. This is particularly apparent in religious beliefs. Many feel their faith in God is being tested and that they must somehow resolve the conflict of a loving God that allows pain and suffering to occur. They reorganize their priorities. Things that used to seem so important, such as a new car or academic and occupational achievement, are seen in a different perspective. This happens with children as much as with adults and could be a contributing factor in isolating them from their peers, especially in adolescence. Families might find themselves impatient with others whose concerns appear trivial compared with theirs. They complain when others do not seem to understand their situation or shun them due to the inability to tolerate difference, to not knowing what to do, or simply to being frightened by the illness itself.

Families report that the experience of illness makes them more sensitive to others' needs, and they feel more appreciation and more of a desire to be close to others and share life's experiences. In this sense, illness in a family can have a strengthening effect by reinforcing values such as caring, helping, and sense of community.

Developmental Concerns

The stress of chronic illness influences family members' accomplishment of developmental tasks (Drotar, Crawford, & Bush 1984). Children are most vulnerable, because they are in the phase of most rapid development. Social development might be restricted not only for the child who must receive extended treatment, but also for the sibling of the patient or for the child of an ill parent, in that transportation is more difficult and these children tend to withdraw from social activities. Intellectual and academic development is at risk for children who are ill or who must receive extended treatment. Adults' plans for educational and professional development can also be interrupted. A mother's plans for continuing education might have to be postponed if her husband or child becomes ill. A father might have planned to resign from his company and open a business of his own. Such a plan might be impossible if a family member becomes ill.

Alterations in Family Systems

Like any stress, chronic illness in a family tends to intensify preexisting patterns and problems and to elicit new patterns in the process of adaptation. The changes that take place can be neutral, beneficial, or maladaptive. For instance, if a family is basically strong and members turn to one another in times of stress, the illness intensifies this pattern, and members derive a great deal of comfort from one another. In one family, the father stated, "I let the kids crawl upon my lap whenever they want to, no matter what I'm doing. I figure if they come to me, there is a good reason for it." He recognized that the children had started coming to him more frequently since a family member had became ill. The illness thus reinforced the family's normal responses of support and comfort, and the father was prepared to allow a stronger bond with his children to develop. Unfortunately, chronic illness in the family also has the potential to reinforce problems. For instance, if marital discord already exists and the couple uses escape mechanisms as a means of coping, the long separations that could be required in the course of medical treatment provide the opportunity for increased distancing.

Sometimes the family's response to the illness solves a preexisting problem. Families often report that the illness brought them closer together. One might say, "I hadn't realized how important my family was to me until Leslie got sick." This was the case in one family in which the father had been pressured to spend more time with them. When a family member became ill, the father was convinced that God was sending him a message to devote more time to his family, which he did.

Very frequently, family members report shifts in alliances within the family following the diagnosis of chronic illness, particularly with respect to increased focus on the patient. One mother reported, "Betty and her father used to be at odds with one another and Mollie was his favorite; now Betty is his favorite and he allows her to do whatever she wants." Indulging a patient with gifts is common in families to "make-up" for the loss of health and, perhaps, to assuage guilt. The bestower of gifts is likely to develop a stronger relationship with the patient. The need for protective, intensive care of the patient reinforces the bond between the patient and whoever is administering the majority of care, usually the mother. This engagement is made at some cost to other family relationships. In one family, the older child, a son, was adopted. The younger child, a natural daughter, was stricken with cancer. Over time, the parents resented the boy more and more. The mother and daughter were in close alliance, and the father actively encouraged this relationship without aligning with his son. The son increasingly became a behavior problem, attracting the attention not only of his family but also of the community. Friends and extended family chided him for not being more considerate of his sister. He became very isolated, and no one seemed to realize that his parents' response to the other child's illness had pushed him away and made him feel justifiably deeply resentful.

Readjustment of roles might occur in a family with chronic illness. Fathers might have to take on a more nurturing position, preparing food for the family and providing more emotional support than is typical for them. Mothers might become more independent and autonomous as they meet the demands the illness presents and make more decisions on their own about family and treatment matters. Children in the family might be called upon to be parent substitutes in terms of caring for younger children and preparing meals. They might become more parental as well in their role of protection and comfort of a parent who feels overwhelmed by the illness and inadequate to face the problems encountered. More than one parent has said, "Johnny is stronger than I am; he makes me feel better and gives me hope."

PATTERNS OF RESPONSE

Families of the chronically ill must in some way come to terms with the disease. First, they must acknowledge the illness cognitively and emotionally (Kaplan, 1981) and allocate health care responsibilities to well members (Drotar et al., 1984). This includes acquiring a clear understanding of the disease and its treatments, as well as "anticipatory mourning" (Futterman & Hoffman, 1973; Lindemann, 1944) for the loss of health and the threat of fatality. They must come to accept long-term treatment and checkups (Drotar et al., 1984; Kaplan, 1981). They must balance the demands made by the illness with existing demands of academic and career goals (Drotar et al., 1984). Not all families are able to master these tasks successfully. In the beginning, their denial of the illness and, if applicable, its life-threatening aspects could be apparent to health care staff. Or they might overreact to these in a manner called *psychological euthanasia* and act as if the person is already dead or about to die (van Eys, 1977). Families might have unrealistic expectations of treatment or might not grasp the full impact of subsequent setbacks. They might lack awareness of the magnitude of the illness, maintaining strongly that "nothing has changed" and that their lives continue just as they did before. Although families adapt better if they maintain as normal a life-style as possible, it is also true that the diagnosis of a severe chronic illness is likely to have a lifetime impact on them (van Eys, 1982). Ignoring problems, that is, pretending they are not there, is more likely to prevent effective management than to reduce the pain of reality.

The adaptive capacities of the family, both immediately and over time, are clearly influential in long-term adjustment to the illness. Specific patterns of responses the family might employ include (P. Cohen, Dizenhuz, & Winget, 1977; Leonard, 1984; Minde, 1978; Prugh, 1983; Resnick, 1984):

1. Encouragement of the patient toward independence or increasing protectiveness and promoting dependency.
2. Acknowledgment of conflicts, followed by resolution or avoidance of conflict.
3. Flexibility or rigidity in coping and in roles.
4. Normalcy or specialness in relating to the patient.

If the family basically functions well, they find it easier to understand the patient's condition (the meaning of the disease and its treatment) and the limitations it imposes on everyone. They maintain a reasonable balance between dependency and encouragement toward independence and autonomous living. They encourage the patient to attend school or to work at a job when possible and to engage in social activities. When problems arise, such as anger toward the patient or marital strife, they acknowledge and discuss it as a means of working out solutions to the problems. They facilitate the patient's development of compensatory strategies and maintain attitudes of helpfulness and hopefulness. The family is aware that it is normal for people, even children, to become ill (van Eys, 1978), and they give the ill person special treatment only in response to objective needs (e.g., a wheelchair for a paralyzed patient) rather than on the basis of a sense of guilt or pity (e.g., overindulgence with gifts or privileges).

Those families who are vulnerable to stress and adapt poorly to chronic illness tend to be overly anxious and protective, promoting the patient's dependency and social withdrawal. They might deny the realities of the patient's condition by either minimizing its seriousness or exaggerating it. They try to avoid conflict, saying that it is unimportant in comparison with the patient's illness or that they ''just can't handle it anymore.'' They deny legitimate feelings, such as anger, out of guilt for having them or fear of hurting someone in the family. They adhere rigidly to their previously acquired roles and to coping mechanisms that are inappropriate for the situation. They have difficulty accepting the illness as a reality and, as a result, continue to harbor negative feelings about it. Continuing guilt and anger make it difficult for them to set appropriate limits with respect to the patient, both in terms of his or her behavior and in terms of the demands that he or she makes on the family.

Questions about coping responses and adjustment of the family arise when there is evidence of emotional immaturity, overdependency, inordinate fearfulness, social withdrawal, behavior problems, and problems at school or work, along with signs of depression, anxiety, and other emotional disorders.

CLINICAL INTERVENTION

In-depth assessment of the family's psychosocial functioning is important in long-term follow-up. Prompt recognition of problems and appropriate attention to them can make the difference between healthy and maladaptive adjustment. A family-focused approach to care for the chronically ill is sensible, in view of the many ramifications of the illness for the family. Further, it is very desirable for the care to be managed in a comprehensive-care

setting so that all the medical, psychological, and other supportive resources are available (Drotar et al., 1984).

Communication

Open communication about the illness between the health care team and the family and among family members is a basic element in reducing stress and furthering adjustment. This can be difficult for some families to accept, especially when the patient is a child. However, the patient who does not receive information is more likely to show signs of depression, anxiety, and fear. The patient almost always benefits from attending conferences about the disease and treatment. When a mental health professional is treating a family with a chronically ill member, and is independent of the medical team, communication about the illness with medical staff is advisable.

In communicating with the family, it is often necessary for health personnel to repeat the same information numerous times. It could be helpful for the physician to schedule several visits for such a purpose. Research has shown that individuals can process and comprehend only a limited amount of medical information at one time (Ley, 1976). Members of the health care team who have attended the information session, such as the nurse or social worker, might follow up with the family to determine if they understand what the physician told them, if they have any further questions, or if they require a repeat visit with the physician. The more anxious the family and the more limited their intellectual and educational background, the more this is necessary. During the course of a chronic illness, it might be useful to review medical information from time to time and provide the family with updated information, especially for children who might have been too young to understand fully what was told to them in the beginning. These sessions can be valuable as well to ascertain the family's progress in adjustment and to identify new problems that might arise. Family members should be encouraged to talk about the illness, discussing its meaning for each of them and any undesirable effects they are experiencing. Just getting them to talk to one another and provide support might be sufficient intervention, because many families are able to solve their problems once they have recognized and openly acknowledged them.

In view of the social stigma attached to illness, adults and children might experience stress at school or work as a result of shunning by others. The health care team might consider obtaining the family's permission to send a representative to the school or workplace to provide others with accurate medical information and promote more understanding and support of the patient.

In a comprehensive health care setting, close communication between the physician and the mental health staff is also very important. The mental health staff must have a thorough understanding of the illness, treatment, and prognosis in general, and specifically for the individual patient. The mental health staff can provide valuable information to the physician about the family in terms of their adjustment to the illness and about characteristics of the family system that could interfere with treatment. Most important, they can advise physicians and nurses about appropriate ways to approach the family and about how much information the family can tolerate. A family's stress during illness can be reduced considerably by a cohesive, well-organized, and cooperative health care team.

Family Therapy

Family therapy is useful throughout the treatment process, from diagnosis through relapses and family crises, to reduce stress, to assist the family in problem solving, to alter maladaptive patterns in the family system, and to help them identify and express their emotions in a more effective manner.

Minuchin and others' (Minuchin, 1981; Minuchin, Rosman, & Baker, 1978) technique of structural family therapy is particularly applicable to families with a chronically ill member (Friedrich & Copeland, 1983). With this approach, the therapist observes the interactions of family members and groups them into sets, identifying those that perpetuate a given problem. These become the focus of change-producing interventions. Minuchin et al. (1978) identified five family interaction patterns characteristic of families with an ill child who seek help. These include enmeshment, over-protectiveness, rigidity, difficulty in resolving conflicts, and involvement of a child in parental conflict. By identifying these characteristic patterns and altering them through interventions targeted toward the family system, the therapist is able to bring about change. Murray Bowen (1966) has worked toward helping families find a clearer definition of boundaries, particularly with respect to the self. This approach works well with families in which the patient has become fused with another family member. Because families with a chronically ill member are more prone to communication problems (out of a perceived need to protect one another), family therapy focusing on issues of communication and using the double-bind technique is readily applicable (Bateson, Jackson, Haley, & Weakland, 1956; Haley, 1963; Satir, 1964). In sum, there are a number of family therapy techniques suitable for psychological intervention with families with chronic illness. Following is an example.

Case Example

Mrs. Gee requested psychological intervention for her 15-year-old son, who was a long-term survivor of childhood leukemia and who returned to the clinic for checkups at regular intervals. She reported that they had received psychological assistance during his illness for behavior problems such as food refusal, manipulation (mother's term), and rudeness. Tom was an adolescent now, and these problems were recurring. The mother wondered if this behavior were related to his treatment for cancer. His twin brother, who had not been ill, was well behaved. Significantly, the mother also reported that, during the illness, the family had been brought closer together. Now it seemed they communicated less, particularly she and Tom, who had been very close during the illness.

In the initial interviews, first with the child and the mother, later with the entire family, it became apparent that the family (a) was deficient in communication; (b) exhibited unneccessary protect-iveness toward one another (c) had unresolved conflicts and unexpressed emotional needs, (d) was allowing triangulation to occur in various combinations, (e) was rigidly adhering to the notion that Tom was the "sick" child, and (f) was experiencing mounting separation anxiety as the children moved into adolescence and began developing their own identities.

The family belonged to a fundamentalist church that they had joined shortly after Tom became ill. Family conflicts often centered around the boys' activities at school. The mother preferred that they socialize primarily with their church group, dress in "nice" clothes (no jeans or sneakers), and date only girls from the church. During subsequent family sessions, the focus shifted from Tom as the patient to the family system. A certain degrees of rigidity was evident in the difficulty they experienced shifting from the child's ill state to one of physical health. The mother and Tom rigidly adhered to patterns of overinvolvement and overprotection. Triangulating interactions occurred among the father, the mother, and Tom and between the two boys and the mother. The father was overly protective of the mother out of guilt for not supporting her more during the early years of their marriage and the birth of their children. He continued to try to "make up" for this with overprotection and avoidance of confrontation.

Family therapy first addressed the parents' relationship, in which there was unacknowledged conflict, and later moved toward the issue of the boys' separation and individuation. The parents were encouraged to express their feelings more openly and directly with one another. The mother was angry with her husband for placing the responsibility on her for refusing social invitations and for overly sheltering her. The father was uneasy with some of the requests his wife made of him, but rather than telling her no, he would postpone acting on them, thus passively avoiding them. He disagreed with some of his wife's restrictions on the boys but would support her anyway, which irritated the boys. Tom and his brother enjoyed a more flexible relationship with their father, which they accounted for by the parents' differing backgrounds: Mother's was more protective and tight-knit; father's more casual.

During family therapy sessions, the father–son relationship was reinforced. The marital bond was also strengthened. This freed the mother from overinvolvement with her sons and allowed her to attend to her own individuation, which she had expressed an interest in doing. The tendency of family members to attribute decision making to others when they themselves did not want to take responsibility for it was another pattern that surfaced, particularly with regard to the father, who preferred that the mother be the strong one while he provided support rather than taking an assertive role. With regard to affect, the family tended to suppress anger, which was then expressed later through less direct, less effective ways. It was suggested that they experiment by approaching one another more directly and being more explicit about their feelings. They did so and found it to be highly gratifying.

This is an example of a family whose problems were long-standing and related to conflicts in the family system. Prior to family therapy, they displaced the source of the problem externally to factors beyond their control, to the illness and the treatment. It is apparent, however, that the illness merely accentuated problems that were at work long before it began. As family members began to identify

characteristic interaction patterns, to learn to express their thoughts and feelings more readily, and to allow normal development to proceed, stress was reduced considerably. They felt relieved and more comfortable in pursuing their individual interests and goals for achievement.

Relaxation and Hypnosis

Most clinicians employ some form of relaxation and hypnotic techniques in their stress-reducing programs. Their effectiveness with chronically ill patients is easily recognized. Harriet, a patient with chronic pain, requested hypnosis for control of her pain. When asked what was most troublesome to her about the pain, she replied, "the reactions of my family to it. They can't understand it and don't know what to do." Controlling the pain was, therefore, helpful not only to her but also to her family, in that they were relieved to know she was benefiting from intervention and that something could be done to help. In a family session in which the meaning of the woman's pain for each family member was explored, Harriet asked the therapist to demonstrate hypnosis for her family because they were curious about it. The therapist complied, telling other family members they might or might not experience changes inside themselves during the process of listening. A progressive relaxation technique followed by hand levitation was used for induction so that family members would be introduced to a technique (muscle relaxation) they could try on their own if they wished.

Relaxation and hypnosis are generally used as adjuncts in a comprehensive therapeutic program. "Instant" cures using these modalities alone are rare. Rather, change produced by these techniques is a process that takes place in the context of the therapeutic relationship. Before introducing hypnosis, the therapist should evaluate the patient, and the family when applicable, with regard to fantasies or hopes about cure, motivations for learning hypnosis and for change, and level of psychological functioning. Hypnosis is contraindicated for severely disturbed individuals except by professionals trained specifically for that type of therapy. In making the assessment, the therapist should note deficiencies in the family system, methods by which they maintain stability and self-esteem, ability to regulate tension, and quality of their relationships with one another and with the therapist. Gaining the family's trust and confidence and forming an alliance with them around their request for help is the primary task. At this point, the therapist emphasizes the controllability of the symptoms, while simultaneously placing limits on their expectations of the therapist's powers. Reinforcing their strengths and gaining their cooperation with one another, as well as with the therapist, is efficacious in producing change.

A multitude of techniques is available to the therapist who works with chronically ill patients (see Wain, 1980; Wester & Smith, 1984), and a number of them may be used concurrently in one session. For example, the fantasy technique of visualizing pain, or any type of problem, placing it in a box, and "hiding" it somewhere suggests that problems can be contained, that they can be temporarily dissociated from oneself, that they need not be overwhelming, and that one can regulate tension with the ability to relax and obtain at least temporary relief (Copeland, 1986). Hypnosis and relaxation may be used for a variety of purposes including symptom control, emotional support, ego strengthening, and therapeutic imagery.

Symptom control.

Symptoms of medical disorders, such as pain, nausea, vomiting, palsy, epileptic seizures, bleeding, muscle spasms, and vasomotor irregularities, as well as psychosomatic and psychiatric symptoms, respond to hypnotic techniques. Habit and appetite disorders are responsive to hypnotic intervention too. After the induction of relaxation, specific suggestions may be made to alter sensory perceptions. Distraction and dissociation are useful in helping the patient tolerate pain or undergo medical procedures. Families who are tense and high strung might find group inductions beneficial.

Emotional support.

Techniques of hypnosis and relaxation reinforce a sense of connectedness with the therapist, who can provide comfort and security. This can be especially helpful in chronic illnesses during periods of crisis or uncertainty. Strengthening suggestions might be used when a family member feels inadequate to cope or burdened by the patient's needs.

Ego strengthening.

Chronic illness might provoke a sense of helplessness and loss of control in family members. Hypnosis can be useful in helping them feel more worthwhile and more in control of their lives. This can be done simply by observing and remarking on their strengths, by teaching them self-relaxation and self-hypnosis, and by direct or indirect suggestions of growth and competency during trance.

Imagery.

Imagery may be used for a variety of purposes including relaxation, distraction, increased self-control, and mastery, and for compensatory gratification when the patient or family member is confined. It may be used as well to modify the disease process, although this has not yet been conclusively proven effective.

Case Example.

Joan was a 10-year-old girl with Hodgkin's disease. She had been treated for 9 to 10 months at a hospital near her home but was referred to a cancer treatment center following relapse. Soon after her admission to the cancer center, she was referred to the psychologist because she was very depressed, bitter, and resentful. She resisted treatment and tests vociferously. Not only did she resist physically, but she was also skillful in eliciting guilt feelings. She would say to her parents, "You don't know what it's like to have cancer."

During the initial psychological assessment, she was articulate in expressing her feelings and experiences from the time of diagnosis. She expressed anger at the injustice, fear at the thought of her family's abandoning her, shame about the disease, guilt about having committed a sin for which the disease was punishment, and guilt over the increased financial and emotional demands her disease placed on the family. She was puzzled and angry that the disease had stricken her rather than her cousin, toward whom she had feelings of rivalry and superiority. Much to her parents' dismay, she would say she wanted to stop treatment. Joan's insight into the psychological effects of cancer and her ability to verbalize her feelings and describe her problems was impressive and unusual for someone her age.

Psychological intervention for Joan consisted of providing a psychotherapeutic setting for her to vent her frustration and outrage and relaxation and hypnosis training to help her cope more effectively with procedures, to increase her appetite, and to reestablish emotional stability and a positive self-image. Family sessions were held periodically to improve family communication and to provide comfort and reassurance to the parents.

Joan readily responded to psychotherapy and

hypnosis. Five primary therapeutic goals were established, and her symptoms were addressed using various types of fantasy and suggestions.

The first goal was to develop a more positive self-image. Joan had expressed guilt about her disease as a result of transgressions she might have committed. Furthermore, she had lost a number of friends and had not been able to perform as well in school as she had previously. Thus, her self-esteem was very low, and she perceived of herself as a helpless victim. Guided fantasy in hypnosis focused on Joan as an active participant in the company of others (e.g., exploring an underwater cave with friends). Frequently, the therapist made direct reference during the trance to her "goodness through and through," her "good intentions," and her ability to accomplish goals she set for herself.

The second goal was to increase Joan's tolerance for pain. A finger puncture for blood withdrawal was selected as the first procedure with which to try hypnotic anesthesia. Following a posthypnotic suggestion, the procedure went well, for the most part, and she managed to use hypnotic anesthesia frequently thereafter. During bone marrow aspirations and spinal taps, she still felt pain, but her tolerance was increased, and she was much more cooperative.

An increased appetite was the third goal, as Joan was seriously malnourished. She regarded eating as another area in which others controlled her life. Initially, it was suggested to her that she imagine eating her favorite food with friends and family present. The success of this fantasy was probably due to her being allowed to select the food for the meal. Later, when she was again feeling helpless and isolated, the suggestion was made that she imagine that she and the therapist were preparing a banquet for friends. Frequently, images such as this accomplished more than one goal. For example, this image was intended not only to increase appetite but also to increase a sense of mastery and competency and reduce feelings of loneliness and isolation.

The fourth goal was to reduce Joan's nausea and vomiting. Probably the most successful hypnotic intervention was in diminishing this effect of chemotherapy. It was in this area that the psychotherapist learned that Joan was using autohypnosis. Her mother reported that after receiving a particularly potent drug, Joan liked to return home to her bed, above which she had hung a crystal ball. It was suspended from a string, and she would hit it with her foot and concentrate on it as a self-induction technique.

The final goal was to help Joan adjust to her chronic illness. The treatment for cancer is a long process, in Joan's case, 2½ years. During this time, there were long periods of hospitalization and restriction of activities. Joan liked to travel, but, due to the necessity of being near a treatment center, she could not do this. Fantasy trips while under hypnosis helped a great deal in restoring Joan's sense of freedom and discovery. Furthermore, these trips were refreshing for her and allowed her to endure long weeks in the hospital.

In response to Joan's claim that the illness had not been discussed in the family, the parents were invited to participate in sessions with Joan. They agreed and responded to her emotional outbursts with sensitivity, strength, and even some humor. They conveyed understanding and support for their daughter, acknowledging that this was the first time she had expressed some of her feelings to them. They, in turn, expressed their own sense of helplessness, feelings of inadequacy for not being able to restore her health, and concern that she continue with treatment. Prior to this time, the parents were unaware that one reason for Joan's desire to stop treatment was that she thought her family was doing too much for her and she did not feel worthy of this.

Although the parents had some questions about the medical treatment and the physician's judgments, they hesitated to ask questions for fear of offending her. They were encouraged to approach her, however, and, when they did, they found her to be open and responsive. From this time on, they regarded the physician with more confidence and saw her as a great source of strength.

This case illustrates the types of problems families of patients with chronic illness frequently encounter. Hypnosis was offered as an adjunct to individual and family therapy sessions and was a useful tool in helping Joan feel more comfortable. Problem areas for the family were primarily their hesitancy to communicate about some issues and a tendency to overindulge Joan and accede to her demands. Psychological intervention consisted basically of (a) providing a psychotherapeutic setting for Joan to vent her frustrations and outrage and in which to teach her relaxation techniques, (b) facilitating communication within the family and between family and physician, and (c) encouraging the parents to take a more assertive parental approach to their daughter. Facilitating communication about the illness and encouraging the parents to be more assertive in their normal parental role eased the burden of responsibility the illness placed on the child.

Group Therapy

If families are able to share their burdens with others, coping with a chronic illness is easier. Group therapy facilitates this process by encouraging family members to compare their experiences, express their feelings, and exchange ideas about solving problems. Some groups are led by professionals, but others, called self-help groups, are organized by laypeople around a common goal. "Curative" factors in the group experience are thought to be related to catharsis (expression of deeply felt emotions), therapeutic relationships in which members derive support and acceptance from others, problem solving, and acceptance following self-disclosure.

If the group is led by a therapist, attention should be focused on

1. Maintaining group cohesiveness
2. Facilitating group process
3. Setting limits
4. Providing technical information about illness or referring group members to the appropriate source of information

Group therapy can be highly effective in reducing the stress of chronic illness for the patient, for the spouse of a patient, for parents, and for siblings. In forming the group, some attention must be given to the criteria for inclusion in terms of the type of illness, its life-threatening aspects, and the degree to which it causes disruption in life-style. For instance, the issues involved in leukemia as a chronic illness are quite different from those of paralysis as a result of an automobile accident. As is true of other types of therapy, some might not be appropriate for group therapy, and it is the therapist's responsibility to screen prospective members prior to their attendance whenever possible. Those who have severe psychological problems or want to use the group for their own purposes (e.g., for religious conversion) should be discouraged from joining it.

In addition to facilitating the group process, the therapist might serve as a model in her or his role of supporting members, showing concern, and framing interpretations in a positive, ego-enhancing way. This promotes an atmosphere of spontaneous, free interaction among group members as they become more confident of themselves and develop feelings of acceptance by others. To further this process, relaxation procedures and hypnotic inductions might be worthwhile, either occasionally or on a regular basis.

The setting of limits involves seeing that the meetings start and end on time and encouraging members to attend regularly, if possible. It is usually wise to remind group members of the confidentiality of the group sessions and to caution them against revealing information when they are reluctant to do so. At times, the therapist intervenes to protect a group member from being made the scapegoat by another or from becoming overly dominant.

Prominent themes of groups organized around the stress of chronic illness include

1. Feelings of victimization
2. Dependency issues
3. Social isolation or ostracism
4. Anger toward medical staff
5. Expressions of helplessness
6. Effect of the illness on family members
7. Religious questions prompted by illness

CONCLUSION

A chronic patient's family constitutes one of the most vital elements in determining the course of the patient's adjustment to the illness. Well-functioning families contribute substantially to the patient's successful management of the disease and treatment. Alternatively, nonsupportive families increase the patient's burden. The illness can destroy a family already undergoing stress from other life events. The illness, the treatment, and the family system form an interacting circle of mutual influences (Figure 3.1).

Severe disease and its treatment place stress on the family and the patient. A dysfunctioning family can exacerbate the illness. A cooperative, cheerful patient who functions independently elicits positive regard from family members, whereas a demanding, bitter patient provokes resentment and hostility. Emotional reactions secondary to physical illness are common, and there is some evidence that stress contributes to the development of certain diseases and affects the disease process (Bammer & Newberry, 1982; Riley, 1981). Clinical observations and a review of the literature show that most families do experience some degree of stress as a result of

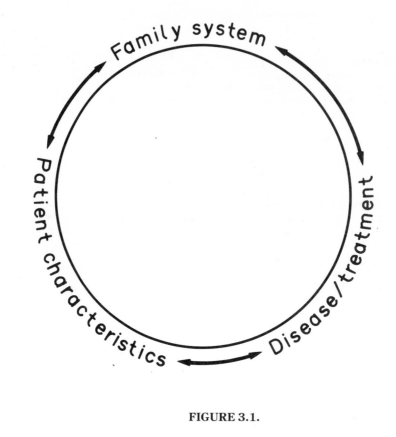

FIGURE 3.1.

chronic illness and benefit from the timely interventions of a comprehensive health care team (Copeland, Pfefferbaum, & Stovall, 1983). This team can help by doing the following two things:

Communicate and inform.

The team can make sure the patient and family have a clear understanding of the illness, its treatment, the potential side effects of treatment, and the prognosis. They can help the family give meaning to the illness by helping them explore their thoughts and feelings and communicate them to one another. The family should have some idea of the changes they can expect in their lives and the importance of minimizing these and maintaining normalcy as much as possible.

Provide Stress-reducing interventions.

The team can help the family come to terms with and work through their grief over loss, become more comfortable in expressing their emotional upset, and adjust the family system to the illness. Various types of therapeutic techniques can be used to assist them in managing anxiety and depression, coping with stress, and tolerating uncertainty about the future. Although some interventions are predictably worthwhile, such as family therapy sessions, most treatments must be tailored to the individual family's need, based on family characteristics and the nature of the disease and treatment. Some families require only brief, stress-reducing and problem-solving interventions on a one-time basis or intermittently (Pfefferbaum, in press). Others, whose family systems are characteristic of "psychosomatic families" (Minuchin et al., 1978) or are dysfunctional in other aspects, require more long-term treatment. When illness is extended, particularly if treatment involves frequent and long hospitalizations, virtually all families could benefit from psychological intervention.

REFERENCES

Anthony, E. J. (1970). The impact of mental and physical illness on family life. *American Journal of Psychiatry, 127,* 138–146.

Arnaud, S. H. (1959). Some psychological characteristics of children of multiple sclerotics. *Psychosomatic Medicine, 21,* 8–22.

Bammer, K., & Newberry, B. H. (1982). *Impact of stress on immunity and cancer.* Toronto: Hogrefe.

Barbarin, O. A., Hughes, D., & Chesler, M. A. (1985). Stress, coping, and marital functioning among parents of children with cancer. *Journal of Marriage and the Family, 47*(2), 473–480.

Bateson, G., Jackson, D. D., Haley, J., & Weakland, J. H. (1956). Towards a theory of schizophrenia. *Behavioral Science, 1,* 251–264.

Battle, S. (1982). *Psychosocial perspectives of sickle cell anemia patients.* Chicago: Eterna Press.

Battle, S. F. (1984). Chronically ill children with sickle cell anemia. In R. H. Blum (Ed.), *Chronic illness & disabilities in childhood & adolescence.* New York: Grune & Stratton.

Bedell, J. R., Giordani, B., Amour, J. L., Tavormina, J. & Boll, T. (1977). Life stress and the psychological and medical adjustment of chronically ill children. *Journal of Psychosomatic Research, 21,* 237–242.

Begleiter, M., Burry, V., & Harris, D. (1976). Prevalence of divorce among parents of children with cystic fibrosis and other chronic diseases. *Social Biology, 23,* 260–264.

Binger, C. M. (1973). Childhood luekemia: Emotional impact on siblings. In E. J. Anthony & C. Koupernik (Eds.), *The child in his family: The impact of disease and death.* New York: John Wiley & Sons.

Binger, C. M., Ablin, A. R., Feuerstein, R. C., Kushner, J. H., Zoger, S., & Mikkelsen, C. (1969). Childhood leukemia, emotional impact on patient and family. *New England Journal of Medicine, 280,* 414–418.

Bodkin, C. M., Pigott, T. J., & Mann, J. R. (1982). Financial burden of childhood cancer. *British Medical Journal, 284,* 1542–1544.

Bowen, M. (1966). The use of family therapy in clinical practice. *Comprehensive Psychology, 7,* 345.

Boyle, M., Tebbi, C. K., Mindell, E. R., & Mettlin, J. (1982). Adolescent adjustment to amputation. *Medical and Pediatric Oncology, 10,* 301–312.

Braham, S., Hauser, H. B., Cline, A., & Posner, M. (1975). Evaluation of the social needs of nonhospitalized chronically ill persons: One study of 47 patients with multiple sclerosis. *Journal of Chronic Diseases, 28,* 401–419.

Breslau, N., Staruch, K. S., & Mortimer, E. A., Jr. (1982). Psychological distress in mothers with disabled children. *American Journal of Diseases of Children, 132,* 682–686.

Breslau, N., Weitzman, M., & Messenger, K. (1981). Psychologic functioning of siblings of disabled children. *Pediatrics, 67,* 344–353.

Brown, J. S., Rawlinson, M. E., & Hardin, D. M. (1982). Family functioning and health status. *Journal of Family Issues, 3,* 91–110.

Bruch, H. (1949). Physiological and psychological interrelationships in diabetes in children. *Psychosomatic Medicine, 11,* 200–210.

Bruhn, J. (1977). Effects of chronic illness on the family. *Journal of Family Practice, 4,* 1057–1060.

Buck, F. M., & Hohmann, G. W. (1981). Personality, behavior, values and family relations of children of fathers with spinal cord injury. *Archives of Physical Medicine & Rehabilitation, 62,* 432–438.

Cairns, N. U., Clark, G. M., Black, J., & Lansky, S. B. (1981). Nonmedical costs of illness. In J. J. Spinetta & P. Deasy-Spinetta (Eds.), *Living with childhood cancer.* (pp. 121–132). St. Louis: C. V. Mosby.

Cairns, N. U., Clark, G. M., Smith, S. D., & Lansky, S. B. (1979). Adaptation of siblings to childhood malignancy. *Journal of Pediatrics, 95,* 484–487.

Chodoff, P., Friedman, S. B., & Hamburg, D. A. (1964). Stress, defenses and coping behavior: Observations in parents of children with malignant disease. *American Journal of Psychiatry, 120,* 743–749.

Cohen, D. S., Friedrich, W. N., Copeland, D. R., & Pendergrass, T. W. (1985, August). Pediatric Cancer: Predicting sibling adjustment. Paper presented at the meeting of the American Psychological Association, Los Angeles.

Cohen, P., Dizenhuz, I. M., & Winget, C. (1977). Family adaptation to terminal illness and death of a patient. *Social Casework, 58,* 223–228.

Copeland, D. R. (1986). The application of object relations theory to the hypnotherapy of developmental arrests: The borderline patient. *International Journal of Clinical and Experimental Hypnosis, 34*(3), 157–168.

Copeland, D. R., Fletcher, J. M., Pfefferbaum-Levine, B., Jaffe, N., Ried, H., & Maor, M. (1985). Neuropsychological sequelae of childhood cancer in long-term survivors. *Pediatrics, 75*(4), 745–753.

Copeland, D. R., Pfefferbaum, B., & Stovall, A. J. (Eds.) (1983). *The mind of the child who is said to be sick.* Springfield, IL: Charles C. Thomas.

Crain, A., Sussman, W., & Weil, W. (1966). Family interaction, diabetes, and sibling relationships. *International Journal of Social Psychiatry, 11,* 35–43.

Crewe, N. M., Athelstan, G. T., & Krumberger, B. A. (1979). Spinal cord injury: A comparison of pre-injury and post-injury marriages. *Archives of Physical Medicine & Rehabilitation, 60,* 252–256.

Croog, S. H., & Levine, S. (1977). *The heart patient recovers.* New York: Human Sciences Press.

D'Angio, G. J. (1982). The child cured of cancer: A problem for the internist. *Seminars in Oncology, 9*(1), 143–149.

Derogatis, L. R., Morrow, G. R., Fetting, J., Penman, D., Piasetsky, S., Schmale, A. M., Henrichs, M., & Carnicke, C. L. M. (1983). The prevalence of psychiatric disorders among cancer patients. *Journal of the American Medical Association, 249*(6), 751–757.

Drotar, D., Crawford, P., & Bush, M. (1984). The family context of childhood chronic illness: Implications for psychosocial intervention. In M. G. Eisenberg, L. C. Sutkin & M. A. Jansen (Eds.), *Chronic illness and disability through the life span: Effects on self and family.* (pp. 103–129). New York: Springer.

Ferrari, M., Matthews, W. S., & Barabus, G. (1983). The family and the child with epilepsy. *Family Process, 22,* 53–59.

Friedrich, W. N., & Copeland, D. R. (1983). Brief family-focused intervention on the pediatric cancer unit. *Journal of Marital and Family Therapy, 9*(3), 293–298.

Futterman, E. H., & Hoffman, I. (1973). Crisis and adaptation in the families of fatally-ill children. In E. J. Anthony & O. K. Koupernik (Eds.), *The child in his family: The impact of disease and death.* (pp. 127–143).

New York: John Wiley & Sons.

Gath, A. (1973). The school-age siblings of mongol children. *British Journal of Psychiatry, 123,* 161–167.

Gath, A. (1977). The impact of an abnormal child upon the parents. *British Journal of Psychiatry, 130,* 405–410.

Gibson, G., & Ludwig, E. G. (1968). Family structure in a disabled population. *Journal of Marriage and the Family, 30,* 54–63.

Haley, J. (1963). *Strategies of psychotherapy.* New York: Grune & Stratton.

Hansen, D., & Hill, R. (1964). Families under stress. In H. Christiansen (Ed.), *Handbook of marriage and the family.* (pp. 3–41). Chicago: Rand McNally.

Hoare, P. (1984). Psychiatric disturbance in the families of epileptic children. *Developmental Medicine and Child Neurology, 26,* 14–19.

Houts, P. S., Lipton, A., Harvey, H. A., Martin, B., Simmonds, M. A., Dixon, R. H., Longo, S., Andrews, T. Gordon, R. A., Meloy, J., & Hoffman, S. L. (1984). Non-medical costs to cancer patients and their families associated with outpatient chemotherapy. *Cancer, 53,* 2388–2392.

Hughes, J. G. (1976). The emotional impact of chronic disease. *American Journal of Diseases of Childhood, 130,* 1199–1203.

Irvin, N. A., Kennell, J. H., & Klaus, M. H. (1982). Caring for parents of an infant with a congenital malformation. In M. H. Klaus & S. H. Kennell (Eds.), *Parent-infant bonding.* (pp. 227–258). St. Louis: C. V. Mosby.

Johnson, S. B. (1985). The family and the child with chronic illness. In D. C. Turk & R. D. Kerns (Eds.), *Health, illness, and families.* (pp. 220–254). New York: John Wiley & Sons.

Kaplan, D. M. (1981). Interventions for acute stress experiences. In J. J. Spinetta & P. Deasy-Spinetta (Eds.), *Living with childhood cancer.* (pp. 41–49). St. Louis: C. V. Mosby.

Kaplan, D. M., Smith, A., Grobstein, R., & Fischman, S. E. (1973). Family mediation of stress. *Social Work, 18,* 60–69.

Kerns, R. D., & Curley, A. D. (1985). A biopsychosocial approach to illness and the family: Neurological diseases across the life span. In D. C. Turk & R. D. Kerns (Eds.), *Health, illness, and families.* (pp. 146–182). New York: John Wiley & Sons.

Kerns, R. D., & Turk, D. C. (1984). Depression and chronic pain: The mediating role of the spouse. *Journal of Marriage and the Family, 46*(4), 845–852.

Klein, R. F., Dean, A., & Bogdonoff, M. D. (1967). The impact of illness upon the spouse. *Journal of Chronic Diseases, 20,* 241–248.

Korsch, B. M., Negrete, V. F., Gardner, J. E., Weinstock, C., Mercer, A. S., Grushkin, C. M., & Fine, R. N. (1973). Kidney transplantation in children: Psychological follow-up study on child and family. *Journal of Pediatrics, 83,* 399–408.

Kupst, M. J., & Schulman, J. L. (1980). Family coping with leukemia in a child: Initial reactions. In S. L. Schulman & M. J. Kupst (Eds.), *The child with cancer: Clinical approaches to psychosocial care: Research in psychosocial aspects.* (pp. 111–128). Springfield, IL: Charles C. Thomas.

Kupst, M. J., Schulman, J. L., Honig, G., Maurer, H., Morgan, E., & Fochtman, D. (1982). Family coping

with childhood leukemia: One year after diagnosis. *Journal of Pediatric Psychology, 7,* 157–174.

Kupst, M. J., Schulman, J. L., Maurer, L., Honig, G., Morgan, E., & Fochtman, D. (1984). Coping with pediatric leukemia: A two-year follow-up. *Journal of Pediatric Psychology, 9*(2), 149–163.

Lansky, S. B., Black, J. L., & Cairns, N. U. (1983). Childhood cancer: Medical costs. *Cancer, 32,* 762–766.

Lansky, S., Cairns, N., Hassanin, R., Wehr, J., & Lowman, J. (1978). Childhood cancer: Parental discord and divorce. *Pediatrics, 62,* 184–188.

Lask, B., & Matthew, D. (1979). Childhood asthma: A controlled trial of family psychotheraphy. *Archives of Disorders of Childhood, 54,* 116–119.

Lavigne, J. V., & Ryan, M. (1979). Psychological adjustment of siblings of children with chronic illness. *Pediatrics, 63*(4), 616–627.

Lawler, R., Nakielny, W., & Wright, N. (1966). Psychological implications of cystic fibrosis. *Canadian Medical Association Journal, 94,* 1043–1046.

Leonard, B. J. (1984). The adolescent with epilepsy. In R. W. Blum (Ed.), *Chronic illness and disabilities in childhood and adolescence.* (pp. 239–263). New York: Grune & Stratton.

Ley, P. (1976). Toward better doctor–patient communications. In A. E. Bennett (Ed.), *Communications between doctors and patients.* (pp. 75–98). London: Oxford University Press.

Lindemann, E. (1944). Symptomatology and management of acute grief. *American Journal of Psychiatry, 101,* 141–148.

Litman, T. J. (1974). The family as a basic unit in health and medical care: A social behavioral overview. *Social Science & Medicine, 8,* 495–519.

Lowry, M. R., & Atcherson, E. (1984). Spouse-assistants' adjustment to home hemodialysis. *Journal of Chronic Diseases, 37*(4), 293–300.

Magni, G., Messina, C., De Leo, D., Mosconi, A., & Carli, M. (1983). Psychological distress in parents of children with acute lymphatic leukemia. *Acta Psychiatrica Scandinavica, 68,* 297–300.

Magreb, P. R., & Calcagno, P. L. (1978). Psychological impact of chronic pediatric conditions. In P. R. Magreb (Ed.), *Psychological management of pediatric problems.* Baltimore: University Park Press.

Mattson, A. (1972). Long-term physical illness in childhood: A challenge to psychosocial adaptation. *Pediatrics, 50,* 801–811.

McCubbin, H. I., & Figley, C. R. (1983). Bridging normative and catastrophic family stress. In H. I. McCubbin & C. R. Figley (Eds.), *Stress and the family: Vol. 1. Coping with normative transitions.* (pp. 218–228). New York: Brunner/Mazel.

Minde, K. K. (1978). Coping styles of 34 adolescents with cerebral palsy. *American Journal of Psychiatry, 135*(11), 1344–1349.

Minuchin, S. (1981). Structural family therapy. In R. J. Green & J. L. Framo (Eds.), *Family therapy: Major contributions.* (pp. 445–473). New York: International Universities Press.

Minuchin, S., Rosman, B. L., & Baker, L. (1978). *Psychosomatic families.* Cambridge, MA: Harvard University Press.

Moos, R. H., & Moos, B. S. (1980). *Family environment*

scale manual. Palo Alto, CA: Consulting Psychologists Press.

Morrow, G. R., Hoagland, A., & Carnrike, C. L. M., Jr. (1981). Social support and parental adjustment to pediatric cancer. *Journal of Consulting and Clinical Psychology, 49*(5), 763–765.

Nelson, R. P. (1984). Political and financial issues that affect the chronically ill adolescent. In R. W. Blum (Ed.), *Chronic illness and disabilities in childhood and adolescence.* (pp. 1–15). New York: Grune & Stratton.

O'Malley, J. E., Foster, D., Koocher, G., & Slavin, L. (1980). Visible physical impairment and psychological adjustment among pediatric cancer survivors. *American Journal of Psychiatry, 137*(1), 94–96.

Peters, L. C., & Esses, L. M. (1985). Family environment as perceived by children with a chronically ill parent. *Journal of Chronic Diseases, 38*(4), 301–308.

Petzel, S., Bugge, I., Warwick, W., & Budd, J. (1984). Long-term adaptation of children and adolescents with cystic fibrosis: Identification of common problems and risk factors. In R. W. Blum (Ed.), *Chronic illness and disabilities in childhood and adolescence,* (pp. 413–427). New York: Grune & Stratton.

Pfefferbaum, B. (in press). Common psychiatric disorders in children with cancer and their management. In J. Holland & J. Rowland (Eds.), *Psychological and psychiatric management related to cancer patients, family, and staff.* New York: Oxford Press.

Pless, I. B., Roghmann, K., & Haggerty, R. F. (1972). Chronic illness, family functioning and psychological adjustment: A model for the allocation of preventive mental health services. *International Journal of Epidemiology, 1,* 271–277.

Prugh, D. G. (1983). *The psychosocial aspects of pediatrics.* Philadelphia: Lea & Febiger.

Resnick, M. (1984). The teenager with cerebral palsy. In R. W. Blum (Ed.), *Chronic illness and disabilities in childhood and adolescence.* (pp. 299–326). New York: Grune & Stratton.

Richardson, D. W., & Friedman, S. B. (1974). Psychosocial problems of the adolescent patient with epilepsy: The epileptic's need for comprehensive care. *Clinical Pediatrics, 13*(2), 121–126.

Riley, V. (1981). Psychoneuroendocrine influences on immunocompetence and neoplasia. *Science, 212,* 1100–1109.

Ruberman, W., Weinblatt, E., Goldberg, J. D., & Chaudhary, B. S. (1984). Psychological influences on mortality after myocardial infarction. *New England Journal of Medicine, 311*(9), 552–559.

Sabbeth, B. F., & Leventhal, J. M. (1984). Marital adjustment to chronic childhood illness: A critique of the literature. *Pediatrics, 73*(6), 762–768.

Salk, L., Hilgartner, M., & Granich, B. (1972). The psychological impact of hemophilia on the patient and his family. *Social Science and Medicine, 6,* 491–505.

Satir, V. (1964). *Conjoint family therapy.* Palo Alto, CA: Science & Behavior Books.

Satterwhite, B. (1978). The impact of chronic illness on child and family: An overview based on five surveys with implications for management. *International Journal of Rehabilitative Research, 1,* 1–17.

Shambaugh, P. W., Hampters, C. L., Bailey, G. L., Snyder, D., & Merrill, J. P. (1967). Hemodialysis in the home: Emotional impact on the spouse. *Transactions of the American Society for Artificial Internal Organs, 13,* 41–45.

Silbert, A. R., Newburger, J. W., & Fyler, D. C. (1982). Marital stability and congenital heart disease. *Pediatrics, 69,* 747–750.

Skelton, M., & Dominian, J. (1973). Psychological stress in wives of patients with myocardial infarction. *British Medical Journal, 2,* 101–103.

Sourks, B. M. (1980). Siblings of the pediatric cancer patient. In J. Kellerman (Ed.), *Psychological aspects of childhood cancer.* (pp. 47–69). Springfield, IL: Charles C. Thomas.

Spinetta, J. J. (1981a). Adjustment and adaptation in children with cancer: A 3-year study. In J. J. Spinetta & P. Deasy-Spinetta (Eds.), *Living with childhood cancer.* (pp. 5–23). St. Louis: C. V. Mosby.

Spinetta, J. J. (1981b). The sibling of the child with cancer. In J. J. Spinetta & P. Deasy-Spinetta (Eds), *Living with childhood cancer.* (pp. 133–142). St. Louis: C. V. Mosby.

Stein, R., & Riessman, C. (1980). The development of an impact on the family scale: Preliminary findings. *Medical Care, 18,* 465–472.

Talbot, N. B., & Howell, M. C. (1971). Social and behavioral causes and consequences of disease among children. In N. D. Talbot & K. J. Eisenberg (Eds.), *Behavioral science in pediatric medicine.* (pp. 36–39). Philadelphia: W. B. Saunders.

Tew, B. J., Laurence, K. M., Payne, H., & Rownsley, K. (1977). Marital stability following the birth of a child with spina bifida. *British Journal of Psychiatry, 131,* 79–82.

Tew, B. J., Payne, H., & Laurence, K. M. (1974). Must a family with a handicapped child be a handicapped family? *Developmental Medicine and Child Neurology, 16,* 95–98.

Toshihiko, M., Osborne, D., Swanson, D. W., & Halling, J. M. (1981). Chronic pain patients and spouses: Marital and sexual adjustment. *Mayo Clinic Proceedings, 56,* 307–310.

Tropauer, A., Franz, M. N., & Dilgard, V. W. (1970). Psychological aspects of the care of children with cystic fibrosis. *American Journal of Diseases of Children, 119,* 424–432.

Turk, D. C., & Kerns, R. D. (Eds.) (1985). *Health, illness, and families.* New York: John Wiley & Sons.

van Eys, J. (1977). What do we mean by "the truly cured child"? In J. van Eys (Ed.), *The truly cured child: The new challenge in pediatric cancer cure.* (pp. 79–98). Baltimore: University Park Press.

van Eys, J. (1978). *The normally sick child.* Baltimore: University Park Press.

van Eys, J. (1982). Changing the world is not the best solution. In J. van Eys (Ed.), *Children with cancer: Mainstreaming and reintegration,* (pp. 129–150). New York: SP Medical & Scientific Books.

van Eys, J. (1984). The concept of rehabilitation in pediatric oncology. In A. E. Gunn (Ed.), *Cancer Rehabilitation.* (pp. 195–218). New York: Raven Press.

van Eys, J., & Sullivan, M. P. (Eds.) (1980). *Status of the curability of childhood cancers.* New York: Raven Press.

Vance, J. C., Fazan, L. E., Satterwhite, B., & Pless, I. B. (1980). Effects of nephrotic syndrome on the family: A controlled study. *Pediatrics, 65,* 948–956.

Venters, M. (1981). Familial coping with chronic and severe childhood illness: The case of cystic fibrosis. *Social Science and Medicine, 15,* 289–298.

Wain, H. J. (Ed.) (1980). *Clinical hypnosis in medicine.* Chicago: Year Book Medical Publishers.

Waisbren, S. (1979). Parents' reactions after the birth of a developmentally delayed child. *American Journal of Mental Deficiencies, 84,* 345–351.

Walker, J. H., Thomas, M., & Russell, I. T. (1971). Spina bifida and the parents. *Developmental Medicine & Child Neurology, 13,* 462–476.

Wester, W. C., & Smith, A. H. (Eds.) (1984). *Clinical hypnosis: A multidisciplinary approach.* Philadelphia: J. B. Lippincott.

Zahn, M. A. (1973). Incapacity, impotence, & invisible impairment: Their effects upon interpersonal relationships. *Journal of Health and Social Behavior, 14,* 115–123.

Chapter 4

Stress Management and the Elderly

ANITA M. WOODS
MICHELE J. RUSIN

INTRODUCTION

Stress is one of the most important, and yet most understudied, health factors in the aging process. Although much has been made of the relationship between stress and susceptibility to disease, stress management in the elderly has clearly taken a backseat to the treatment of disease. In a fairly recent critical review of the literature on stress and health (Parron, Solomon, & Rodin, 1981) the role of age received very little attention.

In working with older persons, it is as important for the professional to recognize stress and its effects as it is to recognize the existence of disease. Indeed, the increasingly complex interactions of health and behavior through the aging process necessitate ever more complex biopsychosocial approaches to assessment and treatment of the elderly.

RATIONALE

Demographics of aging

In recent years the proportion of older people in our society has risen dramatically, primarily because of the declining birth rate and the general increase in longevity. In 1900, only three million persons, or approximately 4% of the U.S. population, were 65 years of age or older. In 1980 there were over 25 million elderly, accounting for 11% of the population (National Center for Health Statistics, 1982).

The group generally identified as "old people" encompasses two generations, people ranging from age 65 to more than 100 years of age. About 40% of this group is older than 75, and 8% is older than 85. It is this group of "old old" people (over 75) who are most likely to be frail or to have serious health problems. They are also the most rapidly growing segment of the elderly population. Women outnumber men in the over-65 age group by 14.3 to 9.8 million, this disparity increasing with age. Among those older than 85, women outnumber men almost two-to-one (Shanas & Sussman, 1981).

Gerontophobia as a common disorder of health care professionals

The stereotypic view of aging is generally a negative one, and it is often linked with discrimination against the elderly. "Ageist" views are so pervasive in our society that health care professionals are apt to be as unenlightened about normal aging as any other group. Many physicians have negative attitudes about the medical and social conditions they associate with elderly patients (Geiger, 1978; Gorlin & Zucker, 1983; Klein, Najman, Kohrman, & Munro, 1982; Spence, Feigenbaum, Fitzgerald, & Roth, 1968). A recent large study of physicians in Michigan showed that 59% of general practitioners do not visit elderly patients in nursing homes, and nearly 20% said they

49

simply do not like old people (Mitchell, 1982). It is thus very important for professionals to carefully examine the assumptions they carry into their contacts with the aged and their families and to replace informally acquired biases with accurate information about the biopsychosocial dimensions of aging.

The elderly as a significant percentage of those seeking health care

The elderly patient might encounter a variety of difficulties in obtaining appropriate, comprehensive, and cost-effective health care. Some of these difficulties are related to negative stereotypes about the way aging affects health and the use of health care services.

A common belief in our culture is that old age is always associated with illness and loss of independence. Indeed, the occurrence of disease and disability rises sharply with age, but these two dimensions must be clearly differentiated. Illness in old age does not invariably mean loss of independence or even a restricted life-style. Although 80% of the elderly report at least one chronic health condition, only about 4% of people over 75 are bedfast at home, and about the same number are bedfast in institutions (Levy, 1980). Most elderly people are ambulatory, mentally alert, and self-sufficient.

Still, the stereotype about aging and illness bespeaks a certain truth: Because of the greater prevalence of illness in old age, old people are relatively heavy users of health care. Most primary-care physicians can expect to see a large proportion of elderly patients among their clientele. Although persons over 65 comprise only 11% of the population, they account for 29% of total personal health care expenditures ($41.2 billion out of $142.6 billion). The elderly are also the leading consumers of pharmaceuticals, purchasing 25% of all prescription drugs and approximately 40% of nonprescription drugs.

Persons over age 60 account for 40% of acute hospital bed days and 95% of bed days in long-term care. Once hospitalized, their length of stay during acute illnesses is 32% longer than that of middle-aged individuals (11.6 days, compared with 8.8 days). Nursing-home care costs are continuing to increase, going from $10 billion in 1976 to $21.6 billion in 1980 (Libow & Sherman, 1981; Wetle, 1985).

These numbers primarily reflect the fact that disease occurs disproportionately during the later years of life and that diseases tend to cluster with increasing age. The danger with stereotypic thinking that equates aging with disease and disability, however, is that it blurs the tremendous variations among older persons in terms of their health status and potential for successful treatment. Despite the increased risk of illness, many older persons stay healthy to advanced ages or can be successfully treated. The negative and ageist bias that is shared by so many elderly people, their families, and health care professionals (Butler & Lewis, 1977) can lead to inaccurate reporting of illness, to misdiagnosis, to complications in treatment, or, even worse, to self-fulfilling prophecies because of failure to treat the treatable.

Elderly persons as underutilizers of mental health services who often use the medical system for mental health needs

A popular stereotype of the aged is that they are hypochondriacal. Evidence, however, suggests the opposite. Much "suffering in silence" occurs in the elderly population. Brody, Kleban, and Moles (1983) sampled 132 old people to identify their day-to-day mental and physical symptoms and what was done about them. Those surveyed had an average of six diagnosed chronic health problems; yet, on a day-to-day basis, they reported virtually no symptoms of diagnosed or undiagnosed disorders to health care professionals. The patients and families tried to treat the symptoms themselves.

Some elderly persons *are* hypochondriacal complainers, just as others tend toward minimizing or denying their physical problems. Most elderly people, however, rate their own health accurately as compared with physicians' ratings and other behavioral indicators (Heyman & Jeffers, 1963; Maddox & Douglas, 1973). Underestimation of one's health in later life is abnormal and has been associated with a history of clinical depression and poor social adjustment (Maddox, 1962; Shanas et al., 1968). It could be a forerunner of frank hypochondriasis, which, in turn, is commonly considered an equivalent of depression (Maddox, 1964). According to Costa and his associates (1983), excessive somatic complaining at any age is linked with neuroticism, and the research evidence indicates that neither neuroticism nor complaining increases as a function of normal aging.

Actually, older people (at least the current generations) seem to emphasize somatic factors when they experience a general absence of well-being because they are not likely to identify and acknowledge contributing psychological, emotional, and interpersonal factors. Thus, they often present themselves and their difficulties as somatic. Some of the factors influencing this somatization include (a) the perception that physical ailments are more significant than emotional problems, (b) the cultural acceptability of physical problems in old age, (c) insensitivity to psychological notions, (d) inability to articulate emotions, and (e) distrust of the mental health profession.

Clearly, frank depression and milder feelings of demoralization or dysphoria are quite prevalent among the older population, but relatively few of these cases come to the attention of mental health professionals. The vast majority of elderly persons with such problems remain untreated or self-treated or are presented to primary-care physicians (Blazer & Williams, 1980; Regier, Goldberg, & Taube, 1978).

CHARACTERISTICS OF THE ELDERLY

Prevalence of stress-related disorders

A recurrent theme in the biopsychosocial dimensions of aging is the increased variability within the elderly population. On a wide array of measures, some older people manifest a great degree of decline in comparison with the young, whereas others show small or even negligible differences from the young. There does appear to be, however, a decrease in overall resistance to stress, as evidenced in the slowing of physiological responses of older organisms to such factors as cold temperatures and in the dramatic impact of illness on psychological and intellectual functioning. It is impossible to accurately estimate the prevalence of stress-related disorders, but the impact of the following on the physical and mental health of the aged should be considered: (a) Older people are often *not* subject to the same causes of stress as the younger population but do encounter many stress-producing factors in the area of loss, and (b) chronic diseases become more prevalent with advancing age.

Common illnesses

The relation of stress as a contributing factor to many commonly occurring diseases in older people should be noted. The three leading causes of death for people over 65 in this country are cardiovascular disease, stroke, and cancer. Perhaps the most common disorder of aging is hypertension, which is a major risk factor for stroke and coronary artery disease. Stress also plays a role in various

gastrointestinal disorders and in arthritis, which is the primary cause of limited activity in the elderly. The role of stress in cancer is currently a controversial topic, but stress is generally acknowledged to play some significant role in the function of the immune system. Frequent emotional consequences of stress are depression, anxiety, anger, and fear. Depression is the most common mental health problem of the elderly.

Cognitive functions

Contrary to popular belief, there is considerable stability in intellectual performance across the life span, in the absence of major illness or imminent death. Some research has noted that arteriosclerosis (Birren, 1963) and high blood pressure (Wilkie & Eisdorfer, 1973) adversely affect cognitive performance in older subjects.

Some aspects of intelligence appear sensitive to aging effects. It is typical for older persons to experience some decline in performance involving novel stimuli or problem-solving skills. There are, however, many individuals in their 70s and 80s whose performance on a wide range of psychological tests is at or near levels found in the young (Jarvik, 1975; Schaie, 1975). The effects of time appear to increase the risk that declines in intelligence will occur, most probably because of changes in the central nervous system or in other physiological processes and organ systems.

Rather than one pattern of test scores characterizing the aging population, individuals are likely to show varying degrees of change from earlier functioning. Some elderly manifest minimal or no decline whereas others have relatively extensive losses.

RESEARCH FINDINGS

Increased interindividual variability with age

Chronological age has proven to be a peculiar variable in the gerontologic literature. It can be used to group individuals in order to demonstrate age differences (as in cross-sectional studies) or age changes (as in longitudinal studies), but chronological age *per se* fails to predict performance on almost any psychological measure. If anything, chronological age predicts heterogeneity of variances. Studies show that within-group variability grows with increasing chronological age (Krauss, 1980). Simply stated, older individuals are more different from each other than are individuals at younger ages. Thus, careful assessment and consideration of individual differences is especially critical in work with elderly patients. Although one treatment technique might be inappropriate or ineffective for some older individuals, it might well provide significant therapeutic benefit to other elderly.

Use of biofeedback with the elderly

Biofeedback is a strategy that has been shown to be helpful in the treatment of a range of physical disorders across the life span, including headache, gastrointestinal disturbances, chronic pain, and certain cardiac problems. It is frequently included in a treatment regimen for stress-related disorders, although behavioral techniques in general have been largely ignored in the treatment of medical disorders prevalent in the elderly.

Siegler, Nowlin, and Blumenthal (1980) reported that less than 5% of the patients seen in the Biofeedback Laboratory at Duke University Medical Center were over 65 years of age. The reasons for this are unclear but might reflect attitudes on the part of health care professionals that are influenced by an equivocal literature. On the one hand, studies have shown that older persons do benefit from behavioral treatments in a wide variety of contexts (Richards & Thorpe, 1978); on the other hand, basic research on the relation of classical and instrumental conditioning to age suggests that older persons might learn more slowly than younger persons (for reviews, see Botwinick, 1967, 1973). Still other research using biofeedback with older persons shows that they master this skill more quickly than younger individuals (Woodruff, 1975).

Clearly, more empirical work needs to be conducted in the use of behavioral interventions such as biofeedback for stress management in the elderly. It could be that older people, having more years of experience than younger individuals, have learned ways to control levels of tension or to modify other physiologic processes. Thus their experiences in living might positively transfer to a structured therapeutic situation.

Exercise and stress management

Reviews of the literature relating physical activity to mental status (Tredway, 1978; Woods, 1981) have noted that older exercisers tend to feel less anxious, less tense, and less depressed and tend to experience enhanced feelings of well-being when compared with older nonexercisers. Other studies have reported that active older people have more

positive attitudes toward work, feel in better health, report increased stamina and greater ability to cope with stress and tension, and have a more positive self-image overall than inactive older people (Heinzelman & Bagley, 1970; Sidney & Shepherd, 1976).

There is increasing interest in the role of physical fitness in the performance of a wide variety of mental and physical tasks in older persons. Physical fitness implies a greater effectiveness of physiological processes in adapting to environmental demands. Selye (1974) considered this when proposing his *stress theory of aging*, which maintains that the cumulative wear and tear on physiological processes over a lifetime of adaptation to environmental demands gradually lessens the individual's ability to adapt to further stresses. Selye suggested that exercise, or physical conditioning, might protect an organism from the full brunt of environmental stresses.

Many people, particularly current cohorts of elderly persons, hold negative attitudes toward the role of exercise in health maintenance and stress reduction. They might be embarrassed by what they consider age-inappropriate behavior in the form of exercise. Older people also tend to underestimate their physical capabilities and exaggerate the danger that physical exertion poses to their health (Wiswell, 1980).

Aside from these impediments to physical activity, exercise in moderation seems to make good sense for elderly persons. Although its role in preventing heart disease and controlling arthritis in this age group is unclear, exercise has been shown to create positive physiological responses in elderly subjects (deVries, 1970; Shephard, 1983; Wiswell, 1980). A popular slogan for the maintenance of good health continues to be "use it or lose it," but this concept has more intuitive appeal than reliable scientific evidence. However, because some of the complications of immobility might be reduced and a sense of well-being enhanced through participation in physical activities, exercise programs for the elderly are beginning to be seen as important behavior interventions in the aging process.

Psychotherapeutic interventions with the elderly

Psychotherapy is a key ingredient in a stress-management program. Through therapy, individuals can identify sources of stress affecting their well-being, observe their typical coping responses, and learn new coping skills to expand their repertoire of adaptive responses. Given the range of interventions from behavioral to intrapsychic, psychotherapy can sharpen the individual's skills on many levels. Behavioral therapies tend to improve instrumental (active) strategies, those which directly alter the problem situation. Greater adeptness in the use of palliative (passive) strategies helps the individual perceive the problem differently so that its stress value is reduced (Lazarus & Launier, 1978).

George and Siegler (1985) studied the strategies used by subjects in a longitudinal aging study and found that an active approach was the one most commonly used to resolve conflicts and reduce stress. Those persons who felt they were most successful at coping, however, used a combination of active and passive methods. Passive methods used alone were also highly effective but not as helpful as the combination of active and passive. Thus, the most frequently used technique of active coping was not necessarily the most effective one for this sample of elderly.

Another factor influencing coping effectiveness was the perception of control. Persons who felt they had no control over the occurrence of the event, yet who did see themselves as in control of their responses to it, tended to view themselves as successful copers (George & Siegler, 1985).

Not far back in the history of gerontology there was a belief that older persons were not suitable candidates for psychotherapy. This viewpoint stemmed from the idea that cognitive rigidity, low energy, and a large store of unanalyzed material would render efforts toward psychoanalysis or insight-oriented therapies futile. Nonetheless, individual therapists sometimes accepted older persons for insight-oriented treatment and found they could work in this modality. These therapists tended to be embarrassed by such therapeutic irregularities, however, and shared their experiences with older patients only with trusted colleagues (Gatz, Popkin, Pino, & Vanden Bos, 1985).

The range of psychotherapeutic treatments is broader than traditional insight-oriented therapies. Behavior therapy, rational–emotive therapy, cognitive–behavioral therapy, and other modes of intervention have been shown to be useful with older patients. Life-review therapy (Boylin, Gordon, & Nehrke, 1976; Lewis, 1971) is a form of therapy that is used almost exclusively with older patients.

Numerous research studies have demonstrated the successful use of various psychological treatments with older patients (Eisdorfer & Stotsky, 1977; Knight, 1978; Richards & Thorpe, 1978); however, more research is needed. Levy and her associates (Levy, Derogatis, Gallagher, & Gatz, 1980) noted that there are few controlled outcome studies addressing the effectiveness of psychotherapeutic interventions with older adults. Even rarer are studies that compare one form of treatment with another. More recent work by Gallagher and Thompson (1983) comparing behavioral, cognitive-behavioral, and psycho-dynamic interventions for the treatment of major depressive disorders in elderly community residents has begun to provide substantive data. Other researchers are also contributing to our knowledge base. It is to be hoped that work in this field will later allow clinicians to select the most appropriate treatment for a particular patient.

Until this level of specificity is achieved, psychotherapy will continue to be used with elderly patients. We have no data that would indicate that any specific treatment is inappropriate for the elderly population. Selection of an intervention strategy is best guided by patient characteristics, problem type, and experience of the therapist. Therapies lending themselves easily to a time-limited format would seem particularly suitable for management of stress-related disorders.

Applicability of stress-management concepts with the elderly

Studies of normal, community-dwelling elderly indicate that they spontaneously use behavioral and cognitive techniques to manage stress (George & Siegler, 1985). That this is so should come as no surprise. However, the question remains as to whether older patients who have failed to learn or apply adequate stress-reduction techniques throughout their lives would be willing to do so at some later date. Adopting and utilizing stress-management techniques to treat medical illnesses might require a shift from a relatively passive to a more assertive style in their relationship with the medical system and modification of their beliefs regarding the causality of illnesses. It might also require them to overcome certain stereotypes that are more common in their generation; for example, that psychological interventions are meant only for "crazy" people.

Characteristics of successful copers

In the field of stress management, much can be learned from those who are functioning well.

Individuals who age well and happily can serve as models to help guide our interventions.

Elderly residents of Durham, North Carolina, were studied to determine the factors that produce "successful aging." Success was gauged by a composite score taking survival, health status, and life satisfaction into account. Not surprisingly, past behavior predicted current status. In other words, individuals who would have been labeled "successful agers" at the age of 75 would have been labeled "successful" at aging some years earlier. Specific factors that affected success were participation in church, community, or social activities; participation in physical activities; and (for men) work satisfaction. Furthermore, all participants tended to have a high amount of contact with family and close friends (Palmore, 1985).

When "successful aging" is defined in strictly medical terms (as one's having reached the age of 75 free of significant disease), some different factors emerge as predictors. Successful aging is then observed among those who have better cardiovascular status, lower serum cholesterol levels, higher levels of education, and higher scores on standard intelligence tests (Nowlin, 1985).

Those who are well integrated into their families and communities also seem to weather stresses more effectively. The negative impact of stressful life events was reduced among those persons having good psychological and social resources (Wilson, 1985).

Those individuals who are most satisfied with later years of life tend, then, to be active and involved. However, this type of life-style probably did not arise *de novo* in retirement. Whether older persons with histories of inactivity and isolation would benefit from changing established patterns remains to be seen. It is possible that patients feeling pressured to change activity patterns in later life would experience this influence as a deleterious stress. There is no basis for anticipating benefits from socializing individuals who have pursued an isolated life-style throughout most of their adulthood. A number of stress-reduction programs have been targeted for those elderly recently isolated by bereavement or other loss, but clear scientific evidence for reduced risk is not yet available (Kane, Kane, & Arnold, 1985). Caution must be exercised; perhaps the role of the successful ager is not appropriate for everyone. Individual choice must be respected and patients provided with assistance in creating their preferred life-styles.

Summary

Although there is no significant body of literature specifically addressing the applicability of stress-management techniques to the health problems of elderly patients, research concerning adaptation, psychotherapy, and biofeedback suggests that these components can be successfully applied to elderly patients. Significant alterations in techniques do not appear necessary in order to use these treatments effectively with the elderly. Sensitivity to individual differences and avoidance of stereotypic thinking enhance effectiveness in work with the elderly, just as with any other patient population.

ASSESSMENT ISSUES

A developmental view

The assessment of stress requires a careful listening ear; clinicians learn to hear points of stress as the patient speaks. They also attend to issues the patient dismisses too glibly or omits altogether. In working with elderly persons, therapists might need to be especially cautious about projecting their own fears about aging onto the older client.

A clinical investigation of stress is usually based upon items found on the Holmes and Rahe (1967) Schedule of Recent Events. This survey is based upon the assumption that any life change, whether positive or negative in tone, is stressful, because it disrupts the homeostasis of the organism. Each item is given a weighted value to indicate the degree of stress assumed to be imposed by that life change. (For reviews of this instrument see Masuda and Holmes, 1978; Rahe, 1979; and Dohrenwend, 1979).

This instrument could prove unsatisfactory when used without modification with older patients. *First*, many of the items on the Schedule of Recent Events concern issues that are no longer particularly relevant to the elderly. Older patients could grow annoyed when asked whether they have experienced a pregnancy within the last year. *Second*, the impact of various items appears to differ according to the life stage of the respondent (Masuda & Holmes, 1978). Older persons do not seem to feel the same degree of disruption that younger persons do with the occurrence of various events (Chiriboga & Cutler, 1980). It is likely that certain events are more stressful in later life than in young adulthood. For example, the loss of a driver's license might prove an annoying inconvenience to a young adult, but, to an older person, it could signal the beginning of a period of increased dependency. *Third*, it is not clear that older persons perceive positive change as stressful. Older participants in a Duke longitudinal study rejected across the board the idea that positive changes required emotional adaptations (George & Siegler, 1985).

Among those studies designed to discover age differences in reaction to stressors was one conducted at the University of California, San Francisco. When the reactions of high school seniors, newlyweds, middle-aged parents, and retirement-age individuals were compared, it was found that the oldest respondents reported higher levels of stress in the areas of family relationships and health problems. Levels of stress were lower than for younger groups for the occurrence of off-schedule events, personal disharmony, conflict with spouse, and time pressures. Responses in the areas of negative preoccupations (finances, legal issues), major stress occurrences, and stresses of the daily routine were similar among all age groups studied (Chiriboga & Cutler, 1980).

The reaction to the diagnosis of terminal illness seems also to differ by life stage. Mages and Mendelsohn (1979) have noted that older patients receiving a diagnosis of cancer often react with less anger than do younger patients. They also might use fewer active methods of coping. (See also Rosen & Bibring, 1966, for a discussion of the reaction to myocardial infarctions by men in different stages of their lives.)

Life stage can thus affect individuals' perceptions of the severity of given stresses. The finding that many events seem not to affect older persons as severely as younger ones might reflect the successful application of coping mechanisms acquired over decades. It could also reflect a philosophy that stressors are time-limited, a philosophy acquired through oft-repeated experience. However, individuals could face certain stressors for the first time in later life and find existing coping mechanisms ineffective. The therapist must remain attuned to all these possibilities in order to make accurate assessments of the stressors facing older patients. In reality, the therapist's task here is not different from the job to be done with younger patients, in which careful listening promotes rapport and leads to more accurate assessment of the patient's status.

Psychological assessment.

The comprehensive psychological evaluation should include examination of cognitive, emotional, and situational factors. A thorough clinical interview identifies those areas in which psychological testing might reduce ambiguity or help with treatment planning.

In the area of cognition, the clinician should be sensitive to signs of altered mental status that could signal an acute drug reaction or provide clues to an underlying medical disorder. A consideration of intellectual level helps the team know how to talk to the patient in order to have instructions understood. Evidence of substantial changes in intelligence from earlier levels should be noted. This occurrence might signal the need for a thorough neuropsychological evaluation.

The individual's affective expression, mood, and quality of thought processes should be noted. Significant unexplained deviations from normal could be further investigated through psychological testing. The assessment should review recent and current stressors; the person's repertoire of adaptive capabilities and resources; and, finally, environmental contingencies that might be affecting the manifestation of the problem.

Psychometric testing is frequently included in the initial assessment of the patient presenting for stress management. The selection of instruments is determined by the problem type and by patient characteristics. Use of the MMPI with older adults is controversial. One issue concerns the interpretation of clinical profiles, because scores on certain scales are observed to be correlated with age. For example, some researchers have found Scale 2 (Depression scale) to increase with age (Canter, Day, Imboden, & Cluff, 1962). Others have noted that elderly persons with either low or high intelligence levels tend to score lower than younger individuals on Scale F, which measures unusual responses not endorsed by the normal population (Gynther & Shimkunas, 1965). The interpretation of elevations on scale 4 (a measure of psychopathic deviance) is somewhat different for younger and older individuals (Good & Brantner, 1974). A final problem is that scores on scale 1 (Hypochondriasis) do rise somewhat in those individuals suffering from a physical illness (Carson, 1972).

The magnitude of these age-related differences seems not to be great. The mean profile obtained by a sample of 10,544 ambulatory medical outpatients, aged 60 through 69, treated at the Mayo Clinic in the early 1960s fell within the normal range. This finding was also true for 3,204 ambulatory outpatients above the age of 70 (Swenson, Pearson & Osborne, 1973). Thus, the MMPI can be appropriately used with the elderly patient. Review of the test results with the patient allows the therapist to correct errors in interpretation. It can also open the door to discussion of stressors or emotions the patient was keeping private.

Older patients with visual difficulties or cognitive changes might find the booklet form of the MMPI unwieldy or impossible to complete. In those instances, a shorter form may be administered by the therapist or by a staff person. The "OBD-168" (Sbordone & Caldwell, 1979) has the advantages of being shorter (168 items versus 566 items) and less trying to the patience of both the person reading the questions and the respondent. Statements are rephrased as questions, allowing the patient to answer yes or no. This format is more easily understood by those with cognitive impairments, perhaps yielding more valid results. Some caution must be used in profile interpretation. The correlation between the short and long forms is good for individual scale elevations; however, two- or three-point code types can differ between the forms.

Referral questions with elderly patients often concern the issue of depression. Obtaining an accurate diagnosis is important because depression can resemble dementia or can be masked by a somatic preoccupation. Diagnostic issues are discussed in detail in a number of sources (see Gallagher, Thompson, & Levy 1980; Herman & Barnes, 1982; Kane, Ouslander, & Abrass, 1984; Wang, 1980; Zung, 1980). Because depression can be effectively treated, it is important that it be detected.

The Rorschach and other projective techniques can provide useful data regarding emotional functioning, areas of conflict, and coping styles. Although the Rorschach was not designed or standardized to serve as a neuropsychological assessment instrument, patients' responses can yield useful information about cognitive functioning and provide clues to cognitive decline in instances where behavioral changes are slight. Inferences about cognitive decline would most appropriately be made by a psychologist who is also skilled in geriatric neuropsychology, because judgments about cognition would require that normal aging changes be taken into account. Other factors, such as level of intelligence, residential status, health status,

sensory deficits, and rapport with the examiner seem also to influence the types of responses given by older patients (Reichlin, 1984).

Questions regarding the presence of a dementing disorder are not likely to be directed to professionals involved in stress management. However, should such a question arise, those unfamiliar with geriatric neuropsychological testing issues should be careful to obtain consultation with professionals experienced in geriatric assessment. The use of age-corrected norms for performance on various tests and familiarity with the manner in which various dementias typically manifest are essential if an accurate diagnosis is to be made. Failure to take normal aging changes into account can lead to the diagnosis of dementia when none exists. A discussion of neuropsychological testing with elderly patients is beyond the scope of this chapter. Those wishing to read more about cognitive assessment will find Albert (1981), Filskov and Boll (1981), and Lezak (1983) useful resources.

Behavioral analysis

Mental health professionals have traditionally evaluated a patient's personality to understood problematic behavior. There are certain assumptions underlying this approach. Personality testing assesses what are thought to be intrapersonal factors, assumed to be consistent over time. Interventions based upon personality theories generally assume that the person's history is the prime determinant of current behavior. Change is expected to be slow and gradual.

A different slant on problematic behavior is obtained by assuming that behavior is determined by reinforcement contingencies. This approach assumes that behavior is purposeful, that individuals act in a way to maximize gain and minimize pain. Interventions based upon these theories tend to be present focused. Rapid, dramatic change is considered possible. Most behaviors are considered amenable to change. The application and power of these behavioral techniques is illustrated in Fordyce's (1976) work on the treatment of chronic pain.

A thorough evaluation of reinforcement contingencies is necessary for the development of an intervention strategy along behavioral lines. Investigating the circumstances preceding, accompanying, and following the occurrence of the targeted problem can yield clues to factors that might support the persistence of the "problem" behavior.

Friends and family members often provide useful information for this type of assessment.

The treatment plan follows directly from the results of the assessment. Altering the reinforcement contingencies can reduce or eliminate the targeted behavior. The problematic behavior should be replaced with one that is more functional. Sometimes patients require instruction and practice in problem-solving skills so they don't need to rely upon the power of the "sick role" to solve or excuse personal difficulties.

Family and social support systems

The quality of the patient's supportive network needs to be examined. The clinician will be interested in determining how the network is affected by the patient's problem, and, in turn, how the patient is affected by the network. Interviews with close friends and family members can add a perspective not available from talking with the patient alone. Because stress is not a problem that occurs in isolation, but involves a maladaptive relationship with the environment, interested parties can shed light on how the patient is functioning against his or her own best interests.

Environmental assessment also yields information about the quantity, quality, and diversity of resources available to the patient. In those instances in which failing health or other factors force the patient into a more dependent position, it is helpful to know what avenues of aid remain open to the patient.

Drug and alcohol use

The use of alcohol and other drugs should always be investigated. Improper use of medication can result in significant cognitive and medical problems for the elderly patient. Older persons tend to be at greater risk for such disorders because they are often treated by several physicians, each one prescribing medication for a specific disorder. The physician might fail to ask about other medications, or the patient might forget the names and purposes of medications she or he is using. Those patients with short-term memory deficits might fail to take medications as scheduled. Elderly patients might borrow medications from their neighbors or use medications that have been on their shelves for years. Although such practices are not unique to elderly patients, they are especially hazardous because of the longer time required for medications to be cleared from their major-organ and central nervous systems.

Alcohol use could account for some cases of confusion, unexplained falls, or memory deficits in older persons. Lifetime drinking patterns should be investigated, although alcohol abuse can also occur for the first time in later life. Families and patients might attempt to hide the problem, afraid of the stigma associated with alcoholism. However, the emergence of substance abuse for the first time in later life probably points to an underlying depressive disorder.

Medical evaluation

Evaluation of a patient's physical health status is important in dealing with any stress-related condition, but it is essential in work with elderly patients. Elderly persons, as noted earlier, list health problems as one of the major sources of stress in their lives. Widespread belief that failing health is a condition that invariably occurs with aging leads elderly persons (and sometimes health care professionals) to accept conditions that could be treated and cured. Medical conditions might also totally explain the presence of severe depression or cognitive deficits in elderly persons. Lacking proper diagnosis, organically based depressions fail to respond adequately to psychotherapeutic interventions; acute-dementia states are tolerated rather than treated.

Because normal aging brings about predictable changes in the functioning of organ systems, the absorption and metabolism of medications, and other physiological functions, the medical evaluation of geriatric patients should be carried out by a physician familiar with these age-related factors. (See Kane et al., 1984, for further information about medical evaluations of the elderly.)

Nutritional evaluation

There has been little scientific inquiry in the field of nutrition with special reference to metabolism and requirements during advancing old age in humans (Young, 1982). On the basis of quite limited knowledge, the nutrient needs of healthy aged subjects do not appear to differ significantly from those of young adults (Woods & Birren, 1984). It is necessary to keep in mind, however, that a characteristic of aging is increased disease incidence and morbidity, and these are conditions that could be far more important than age per se in determining practical differences between young adults and elderly people in their need for nutrients.

The effect of stressful events, ranging from

physical trauma to those of psychological origin, is of particular importance in consideration of diet and nutrient needs during old age. The net metabolic result in response to stress is a depletion of body nutrients, followed by a physiological increase in the need for nutrients to promote recovery and to compensate for earlier losses. Unfortunately, there are inadequate data to help determine how much nutrient intake should be increased to meet the additional demands created by such stressful conditions as infections, anxiety, pain, or physical trauma, which are frequent problems of older people.

Various drugs also can have profound effects on nutrient requirements by decreasing nutrient absorption or by altering the utilization of nutrients. Of particular concern in older people is their use of multiple drugs that might have synergistic effects, resulting in the additional loss of essential nutrients.

A broad range of conditions that accompany advancing age can have additional important effects on the nutritional status of the elderly. Depression, loneliness, poor vision, poverty, arthritis, mental impairment, inadequate knowledge of dietetic principles, and alcoholism can all contribute to inadequate nutrition. Those elderly most vulnerable to nutritional inadequacies need to be identified.

CASE EXAMPLES

The preceding sections have discussed issues related to theory, assessment, and intervention. This section, devoted to a discussion of two cases, will demonstrate how these principles can be applied in clinical practice. For comparison purposes, female patients with similar presenting complaints were selected. Differences in underlying dynamics demonstrate how psychological assessment and intervention can contribute to the formulation of an appropriate treatment plan.

Both women were admitted to the medical service of a large teaching hospital for evaluation and treatment of chronic pain. For both women, depression was a contributing problem. In both cases, the psychologist was consulted soon after admission. Thus, the psychological workup was presented to the patient as an integral part of the treatment. The coordination of medical and psychosocial care minimized the probability that the patient would see the psychological treatment as "a last ditch effort" to treat an otherwise resistant symptom. This coordination allowed the patient to see that she had not been abandoned by her physician, who might have believed that the pain was "in her head."

The psychological workup was similar in the two cases. It consisted of an initial evaluation composed of a clinical interview, behavioral analysis, and the MMPI. The behavioral treatment plan was communicated to the treatment team through chart notes and weekly team meetings. Short-term psychotherapy was conducted approximately three times per week, sessions occurring in the patients' hospital rooms. Outpatient follow-up was recommended; however, only one of the patients chose to continue psychotherapeutic work after discharge.

Case 1: *Masked depression with exacerbation of pain*

Martha R. was 61 years old at the time of admission. She sought medical attention from an internist following 3 months in which she had been excessively tired and had had disturbed sleep. She had been used to having pain in her legs and hands because of osteoarthritis. However, the pain had become worse in the months preceding admission. It became so severe that it interfered with her ability to care for her three-bedroom home and to manage her day-to-day needs.

The clinical interview revealed several significant events. Mrs. R's husband had died 1½ years earlier, after 37 years of a satisfying marriage. She seemed to have had the usual type of grief reaction. Six months after her husband's death, she began dating a man who had been a business associate of her husband's. She stated that her husband had not liked this man, but she did now know why this had been. This man had been pressuring the patient to marry him and had asked her to begin a sexual relationship. The patient refused to become sexually involved. She asked for 6 months to decide about marrying him. She had conflicting thoughts about the marriage. She thought the marriage would remove some responsibility from her children, because she would have someone to care for her. She had some reservations about this man, describing him as jealous and controlling. Although not voiced explicitly, there was also the issue of divided loyalties, because her husband had not approved of him.

The MMPI yielded a clinically valid profile characteristic of individuals often described as "smiling depressives." Concerned with external appearances, these persons tend to hide their sadness from others and fail to seek out needed support. The use of denial and repression often results in problems being ignored or tolerated rather than resolved. These individuals also tend to be sensitive to how their actions affect others' feelings. They usually find it difficult to behave in an assertive way, afraid of hurting others' feelings.

Other contributing factors include a tendency to worry and an obsessive, perfectionistic style. Low self-esteem is also likely to play a role. Some discomfort in social situations is expected. The critical-item analysis revealed that items clustered in the areas of somatic complaints and symptoms of pronounced anxiety.

From a psychological standpoint, several major issues emerged. First, there was a significant depressive disorder. Involvement in the new relationship with a man who in many ways was seen as "second best" to her husband reawakened grief and highlighted her sense of loss. However, because repression was a characteristic style of responding for this woman, she was not cognizant of the sadness and conflict. The physical symptoms worsened in response to the stress. There was significant secondary gain attached; the medical problems legitimized her sense of needing help. Interestingly enough, she sought out an internist who was highly empathic and holistic in his treatment. The pain also allowed her to delay the decision regarding deeper involvement with this man.

The medical history was significant for herniated discs. This problem was treated with chemopapain injections, with moderate success. She had arthritic pain in her hands. In the weeks prior to admission, she began having muscle spasms and intestinal spasms. With the pain problem and her low energy, she had paid less attention to her diet. The admitting workup revealed poor nutritional status.

A comprehensive treatment plan was developed and put into effect. It included a physical therapy program consisting of pain-relieving modalities and exercise, training in biofeedback and other relaxation skills through the occupational therapy department, consultation with a dietitian, and short-term psychotherapy. The physician conducted the medical evaluation, adjusted medications (antidepressant medications and muscle relaxants were used), oversaw the work of the consultants, and provided ongoing medical management.

The psychotherapeutic work allowed this woman to identify the conflicting forces operating on her and to make more informed decisions about her involvement in the relationship. Participation in an active therapy program also had a psychotherapeutic effect. Seeing herself regaining control of her physical functioning restored a sense of efficacy, breaking down patterns of depressive thinking.

This patient was discharged after 10 days of treatment. Her pain levels were markedly lowered, her mood was good, and her overall level of health was much improved. She returned for a follow-up session 2 weeks after discharge. The improvements in functioning were maintained. However, she noted she had not been keeping up with the exercise or dietary recommendations. Lack of follow-through raised the probability of relapse. The patient was aware of this and planned to readjust her schedule. Otherwise, she was dealing assertively with her partner and was reconnecting with old friends.

Overall, this was seen as a successful course of treatment. Given the relationship between the pain symptoms and the psychosocial issues, it is unlikely that the problem would have been resolved without some attention to the psychosocial issues.

Case 2. *Somaticization and the power balance in a marital dyad*

Bertha M. was 71 years of age at the time of admission. She had had back pain for 16 years. It resulted, she believed, from an injury incurred in an automobile accident when she was a child. The pain level had increased over the last 3 weeks, leading to admission to the physiatry service.

The clinical interview revealed multiple severe stressors over the previous 3 years. Her husband had undergone triple-bypass surgery, which was followed by kidney failure. He had gone into a coma, remaining comatose for 50 days. After recovering from this episode, he had developed pulmonary problems. The couple was told her husband had lung cancer. Surgery revealed it was tuberculosis. Her husband had developed pneumonia while recovering from this surgery. More recently he had developed hepatitis. Thus, his health continued to be poor. During the preceding years, she had twice faced the prospect of her husband's imminent death.

The patient reported that her husband was irritable and depressed. He had been impotent since the last surgery. He had withdrawn from regular friends and activities, spending most of his time in the house. He was unwilling to accompany his wife on trips or short vacations, so she, too, has spent more and more of her time at home.

The patient's husband reportedly said that the patient complained too much of her pain. Her son agreed. The patient stated that the son blamed her for the depressed state that she and her husband were in.

The scenario, then, seemed to be of a depressed couple staying at home, waiting to die. The husband could have been refraining from activity in an exaggerated attempt to protect his health. The unhappy patient, deprived of her social life, was vocal about how much she hurt (expressing the hurt somatically rather than emotionally).

The patient described her husband's condition in great detail. She seemed interested in getting *him* into treatment, though she acknowledged he would probably be unwilling to see a therapist. She thought that he might come if it was clear that he was coming to assist in her therapy.

The MMPI for this patient was also clinically valid, the results suggesting significant emotional disturbance. Similar individuals generally feel panicky, as if they are falling to pieces. Low scores on the K scale (measuring use of sophisticated defenses) and ego-strength scale (T score = 21) confirmed the impression that this woman had exhausted her internal resources and saw herself in need of outside help in order to go on.

The profile also indicated that this woman was likely to talk about health-related problems. By directing attention to her health complaints, she was able to get others involved with her while avoiding discussion of other issues that were in some ways more personal and intimate. There was also a severe depressive disorder. With this type of MMPI pattern (12), the depression often decreases as health improves.

The medical evaluation uncovered no active disease process requiring treatment. A psychiatric consultation was ordered, and she was begun on antidepressant medication. Physical therapy involved an exercise program. She learned relaxation techniques in occupational therapy. Psychotherapy focused on identifying those problems she had not yet discussed. Her husband was brought in for a session. In this session, the couple was encouraged to become more active socially and instructed as to how this would help the patient's mood and her pain.

Mrs. M. was discharged after 3 weeks of treatment. Her pain and her mood had both improved. Outpatient psychotherapy was recommended. She did not follow through, citing finances as a problem. The patient apparently relapsed. Several weeks after her discharge, a letter was received from the patient in which she angrily stated that the pain program had been misrepresented and she had failed to benefit from it.

Several factors seemed to have contributed to this treatment failure. The first was the patient's difficulty in engaging in a psychotherapeutic relationship. She seemed both attracted to and repelled by the idea. Perhaps she believed that all-out efforts in psychotherapy would prove that her husband and son were right and that she was, indeed, responsible for the problems at home. This problem might have been overcome had all psychotherapeutic work been done in a marital or family format. However, the reluctance of the patient's husband and son to actively participate interfered with this approach. Thus, the psychotherapeutic intervention failed to have a significant impact on the family dynamics. The patient was unwilling or unable (lacking good skills in assertiveness) to change the family structure by herself. Thus the patient could well have been on target when she said the program had accomplished nothing. Her participation in the program might even have reinforced the family's view that she, in fact, was the one with the problem.

REFERENCES

Albert, M. S. (1981). Geriatric neuropsychology. *Journal of Consulting and Clinical Psychology, 49,* 835–850.

Birren, J. E. (1963). Psychophysiological relations. In J. E. Birren, R. N. Butler, S. W. Greenhouse, L. Sokoloff, & M. R. Yarrow (Eds.), *Human aging: A biological and behavioral study,* Washington, D.C.: United States Government Printing Office.

Blazer, D. & Williams, C. D. (1980). Epidemiology of dysphoria and depression in an elderly population. *American Journal of Psychiatry, 137,* 439–444.

Botwinick, J. (1967). *Cognitive processes in maturity and old age.* New York: Springer.

Botwinick, J. (1973). *Aging and behavior.* New York: Springer.

Boylin, W., Gordon, S., & Nehrke, M. (1976). Reminiscing and ego integrity in institutionalized elderly males. *Gerontologist, 16,* 118–124.

Brody, J. A., Kleban, M. H., & Moles, E. (1983). What older people do about their day-to-day mental and physical health symptoms. *Journal of the American Geriatrics Society, 31,* 489–98.

Butler, R. N. & Lewis, M. (1977). *Aging and mental health* (2nd ed.) 2nd edition, St. Louis: Mosby.

Canter, R., Day, C. W., Imboden, J. B., & Cluff, L. E. (1962). The influence of age and health status on the MMPI scores of a normal population. *Journal of Clinical Psychology, 18,* 71–73.

Carson, R. (1972). MMPI profile interpretation. Paper presented at the Seventh Annual Symposium on the MMPI, Mexico City.

Chiriboga, D. A., & Cutler, L. (1980). Stress and adaption: Life span perspectives. In L. W. Poon (Ed.), *Aging in the 1980s* (pp. 347-362). Washington, DC: American Psychological Association.

Costa, P. T., Jr., McCrae, R. R., & Arenberg, D. (1983). Recent research on personality and aging. In K. W. Schaie (Ed.), *Longitudinal studies of adult psychological development*, (pp. 222-265). New York: Guilford Press.

deVries, H. A. (1970). Physiological effects of an exercise training regimen upon men aged 52 to 88. *Journal of Gerontology, 25*, 325-336.

Dohrenwend, B. P. (1979). Stressful life events and psychopathology: Some issues of theory and method. In J. E. Barrett (Ed.), *Stress and mental disorder* (pp. 1-15). New York: Raven Press.

Eisdorfer, C., & Stotsky, B. A. (1977). Intervention, treatment, and rehabilitation of psychiatric disorders. In J. E. Birren & K. W. Schaie (Eds.), *Handbook of the psychology of aging* (pp 724-748). New York: Von Nostrand Reinhold.

Filskov, S. B., & Boll, T. J. (1981). *Handbook of clinical neuropsychology*. New York: John Wiley & Sons.

Fordyce, W. (1976). *Behavioral methods for chronic pain and illness*. St. Louis: C. V. Mosby.

Gallagher, D., & Thompson, L. W. (1983). Cognitive therapy for depression in the elderly: A promising model for treatment and research. In L. D. Breslau & M. R. Haug (Eds.), *Depression and aging: Causes, care, and consequences* (pp. 168-192). New York: Springer.

Gallagher, D., Thompson, L. W., & Levy, S. M. (1980). Clinical psychological assessment of older adults. In L. W. Poon (Ed.), *Aging in the 1980s* (pp. 19-40). Washington, DC: American Psychological Association.

Gatz, M., Popkin, S. J., Pino, C. D., & Vanden Bos, G. R. (1985). Psychological interventions with older adults. In: J. E. Birren & K. W. Schaie (Eds.), *Handbook of the psychology of aging*, (pp. 755-788). New York: Van Nostrand Reinhold Company.

Geiger, D. L. (1978). How future professionals view the elderly: A comparative analysis of social work, law and medical students' perceptions. *Gerontologist, 18*, 591.

George, L. K., & Siegler, I. C. (1985). Stress and coping in later life. In E. Palmore, E. W. Busse, G. T. Maddox, J. B. Nowlin, & I. C. Siegler (Eds.), *Normal aging III* (pp. 148-159). Durham, NC: Duke University Press.

Good, P., & Brantner, J. (1974). *A practical guide to the MMPI*. Minneapolis: University of Minnesota Press.

Gorlin, R. & Zucker, H. D. (1983). Physicians' reactions to patients. *New England Journal of Medicine, 308*, 1059-1063.

Gynther, M., & Shimkunas, A. (1965). Age, intelligence, and MMPI F scores. *Journal of Consulting Psychology, 29*, 383-388.

Heinzelman, F., & Bagley, R. W. (1970). Response to physical activity programs and their effects on health behavior. *Public Health Report, 85*, 905-911.

Herman, S., & Barnes, D. (1982). Behavioral assessment in geriatrics. In F. J. Keefe & J. A. Blumenthal (Eds.), *Assessment strategies in behavioral medicine* (pp. 473-507). New York: Grune & Stratton.

Heyman, D., & Jeffers, F. (1963). Effects of time lapse on consistency of self-health and medical evaluations of elderly persons. *Journal of Gerontology, 18*, 160-164.

Holmes, T. H., & Rahe, R. H. (1967). The social readjustment rating scale. *Journal of Psychosomatic Research, 11*, 213-218.

Jarvik, L. F. (1975). Thoughts on the psychobiology of aging. *American Psychologist, 30*, 567-583.

Kane, R. L., Ouslander, J. G., & Abrass, I. B. (1984). *Essentials of clinical geriatrics*. New York: McGraw-Hill.

Kane, R. L., Kane, R. A., & Arnold, S. B. (1985). Prevention and the elderly: Risk factors. *Health Services Research, 19(6)*, 945-1006.

Klein, D., Najman, J., Kohrman, A. F., & Munro, C. (1982). Patient characteristics that elicit negative responses from family physicians. *Journal of Family Practice, 14(5)*, 881-888.

Knight, B. (1978). Psychotherapy and behavior change with the non-institutional aged. *International Journal of Aging and Human Development, 9*, 221-236.

Krauss, I. K. (1980). Between- and within-group comparisons in aging research, In L. W. Poon (Ed.), Aging in the 1980s: Psychological issues (pp. 542-551). Washington, D.C.: American Psychological Association.

Lazarus, R. S., & Launier, R. (1978). Stress related transactions between persons and environment. In L. A. Pervin & M. Lewis (Eds.), *Perspectives in interactional psychology* (pp. 287-327). New York: Plenum.

Levy, S. M. (1980). The psychosocial assessment of the chronically ill geriatric patient. In C. Phokopp & C. Bradley (Eds.), *Medical psychology: A new perspective* (pp. 259-277). New York: Academic Press.

Levy, S. M., Derogatis, L. R., Gallagher, D., & Gatz, M. (1980). Intervention with older adults and the evaluation of outcome. In L. W. Poon (Ed.), *Aging in the 1980s: Psychological issues* (pp. 41-61). Washington, DC: American Psychological Association.

Lewis, C. (1971). Reminiscing and self-concept in old age. *Journal of Gerontology, 26*, 2240-243.

Lezak, M. D. (1983). *Neuropsychological assessment* (2nd ed.). New York: Oxford University Press.

Libow, L. S., & Sherman, F. T. (1981). *The core of geriatric medicine: A guide for students and practitioners*. St. Louis: C. V. Mosby.

Maddox, G. L., & Douglass, E. B. (1973). Self-assessment of health: A longitudinal study of elderly subjects. *Journal of Health and Social Behaviors, 14*, 87-93.

Maddox, G. L. (1962). Some correlates of differences in self assessment of health status among the elderly. *Journal of Gerontology, 17*, 180-185.

Maddox, G. L. (1964). Self assessment of health status: A longitudinal study of selected elderly subjects. *Journal of Chronic Diseases, 17*, 449-460.

Mages, N. L., & Mendelsohn, G. A. (1979). Effect of cancer on patients' lives: A personological approach. In G. C. Stone, F. Cohen, & N. E. Adler (Eds.), *Health psychology: A handbook* (pp. 255-284). San Francisco: Jossey-Bass.

Masuda, M., & Holmes, T. H. (1978). Life events: Perceptions and frequencies. *Psychosomatic Medicine, 40*, 236-261.

Mitchell, J. (1982). *Medicare access to physician services in nursing homes*. Unpublished manuscript.

National Center for Health Statistics. (1982). *Changes in*

mortality among the elderly. Series 3, No. 22, 4.

Nowlin, J. B. (1985). Successful aging. In E. Palmore, E. W. Busse, G. T. Maddox, J. B. Nowlin, & I. C. Siegler (Eds.), *Normal aging III* (pp. 36-43). Durham, NC: Duke University Press.

Palmore, E. B. (1985). Predictors of successful aging. In E. Palmore, E. W. Busse, G. T. Maddox, J. B. Nowlin, & I. C. Siegler (Eds.), *Normal aging III* (pp. 29-36). Durham, NC: Duke University Press.

Parron, D. L., Solomon, R., & Rodin, J. (1981). *Health behavior and aging: A research agenda*. Washington, D.C.: Division of Mental Health and Behavioral Medicine, National Academy Press.

Rahe, R. H. (1979). Life change events and mental illness: An overview. *Journal of Human Stress, 5*(3), 2-10.

Regier, D. A., Goldberg, I. D. & Taube, C. A. (1978). The de facto U. S. mental health services system. *Archives of General Psychiatry, 35*, 685-693.

Reichlin, R. E. (1984). Current perspectives on Rorschach performance among older adults. *Journal of Personality Assessment, 48*, 71-81.

Richards, W. S., & Thorpe, G. L. (1978). Behavioral approaches to the problems of later life. In M. Storandt, I. C. Siegler, & M. F. Elias (Eds.), *The clinical psychology of aging* (pp. 253-276). New York: Plenum.

Rosen, J. L., & Bibring, G. L. (1966). Psychological reactions of hospitalized male patients to a heart attack: Age and social class differences. *Psychosomatic Medicine, 28*, 808-821.

Sbordone, R. J., & Caldwell, A. R. (1979). The "OBD-168": Assessing the emotional adjustment to cognitive impairment and organic brain damage. *Clinical Neuropsychology, 1*, 36-41.

Schaie, K. W. Age changes in adult intelligence. In D. S. Woodruff & J. E. Birren (Eds.), *Aging: Scientific perspectives and social issues*, (pp. 111-124). New York: D. Van Nostrand.

Selye, H. (1974). *Stress and distress*. New York: McGraw-Hill.

Shanas, E. & Sussman, M. B. (1981). The family in later life: Social structure and social policy. In R. W. Fogel, E. Hatfield, S. B. Kiesler, & J. March (Eds.), *Aging: Stability and change in the family* (pp. 222-237). New York: Academic Press.

Shanas, E., Townsend, P., Wedderburn, D., Friis, H., Milhoj, P., & Stehower, J. (1968). *Old people in three industrial societies*. New York: Atherton Press.

Shephard, R. J. (1983). Physical activity and the healthy mind. *Canadian Medical Association Journal, 128*, 525-530.

Sidney, K. H., & Shephard, R. J. (1976). Attitudes toward health and physical activity in the elderly: Effects of a physical training program. *Medicine and Science in Sports, 8*, 246-252.

Siegler, I. C., Nowlin, J. B., & Blumenthal, J. A. (1980). Health and behavior: Methodological considerations for adult development and aging. In L. W. Poon (Ed.), *Aging in the 1980s:* Psychological issues (pp. 599-612). Washington, DC: American Psychological Association.

Spence, D. L., Feigenbaum, E. M., Fitzgerald, F., & Roth, J. (1968). Medical students' attitudes towards the geriatric patient. *Journal of the American Geriatrics Society, 16*, 976.

Swenson, W. M., Pearson, J. S., & Osborne, D. (1973). *An MMPI sourcebook*. Minneapolis: University of Minnesota Press.

Tredway, V. A. (1978). Mood effects of an exercise program for older adults. *Unpublished doctoral dissertation*. University of Southern California.

Wang, H. S. (1980). Diagnostic procedures. In E. W. Busse & D. G. Blazer (Eds.), *Handbook of geriatric psychiatry*. (pp. 285-304). New York: Van Nostrand Reinhold.

Wetle, T. (1985). Future society's outlook toward aging, illness, and health care of the aged. In C. M. Gaitz, G. Niederehe, & N. Wilson (Eds.), *Aging 2000: Our health care destiny (Volume II: Psychosocial and policy issues)* (pp. 17-24). New York: Springer-Verlag.

Wilkie, F. L., & Eisdorfer, C. (1973). Systematic disease and behavioral correlates. In: L. Jarvik, C. Eisdorfer, & J. E. Blum (Eds.), *Intellectual Functioning in Adults* (pp. 83-93). New York: Springer.

Wilson, R. W. 1985. Assessing the impact of life change events. In E. Palmore, E. W. Busse, G. T. Maddox, J. B. Nowlin, & I. C. Siegler (Eds.), *Normal aging III* (pp. 356-372). Durham, NC: Duke University Press.

Wiswell, R. A. (1980). Relaxation, exercise and aging. In J. E. Birren & R. B. Sloane (Eds.), *Handbook of mental health and aging* (pp. 943-958). Englewood Cliffs, N. J.: Prentice-Hall, Inc.

Woodruff, D. S. (1975). Relationships between EEG alpha frequency, reaction time, and age: A biofeedback study. *Psychophysiology, 12*, 673-681.

Woods, A. M., (1981). *Age differences in the effect of physical activity and postural changes on information processing speeds*. Unpublished doctoral dissertation, University of Southern California, Los Angeles.

Woods, A. M. & Birren, J. E. (1984). Late adulthood and aging. In J. Matarazzo, S. Weiss, J. Herd, N. Miller, and S. M. Weiss (Eds.), *Behavioral health: A handbook of health enhancement and disease prevention* (pp. 91-100). New York: John Wiley & Sons.

Young, R. (1982). Nutrition. In J. W. Rowe & R. W. Besdine (Eds.), *Health and disease in old age* (pp. 317-333). Boston: Little, Brown and Company.

Zung, W. W. K. (1980). Affective disorders. In E. W. Busse & D. G. Blazer (Eds.), *Handbook of geriatric psychiatry*. New York: Von Nostrand Reinhold.

Part II
Common Procedures

Chapter 5

Relaxation Procedures for Stress Management

Edward A. Charlesworth
Ronald G. Nathan

RELAXATION PROCEDURES FOR STRESS MANAGEMENT

Stress Management is a collective term for a variety of techniques used to lessen the effects of stress, tension, and anxiety. Relaxation procedures are consistently included under this rubric and are, in many programs, the foundation for teaching effective stress management. Relaxation training has wide applicability, consistent effectiveness, and overall safety. This has tended to make it behavioral medicine's "aspirin." However, clinicians frequently counsel a patient to relax, without a true appreciation of the complexity of relaxation interventions.

Relaxation procedures for stress management can be classified into three general categories: muscle relaxation, autogenic relaxation, and imagery training. All three categories of intervention originated in the 1920s and 1930s. Edmund Jacobson (1929) developed the first behavioral technique for muscle relaxation in a procedure he named *progressive relaxation*. In the 1930s Johannes Schultz developed *autogenic training* to help relax the self-regulating systems of the body such as heart rate and blood circulation (Schultz & Luthe, 1959).

Carl Happich (1932) promoted the use of breathing and visual imagery exercises to help patients reach a level of consciousness where relaxation and a reasonable view of life stressors could be induced.

Self-control relaxation procedures were perceived of as less important with the advent of pharmacological interventions for tension, stress, and anxiety disorders. Then in the 1970s there was a resurgence of interest in relaxation treatments. This interest was spearheaded by work in the areas of systematic desensitization, biofeedback, behavior modification, relaxation, and meditation. One of the reasons for the renewed interest in relaxation procedures was related to research beginning in the late 1950s that discovered that people did have a certain amount of control over physical systems in their bodies that were once thought to be automatic. Other reasons were poor compliance in the areas of pharmacological treatments, side effects of medications, and dependency on certain medications. It had become clear that medications alone did not teach a person the skills needed to handle future stressors effectively.

In response to the need for a comprehensive, cost-effective system for relaxation training, the three major categories have been combined into different, progressive, training programs and presented in book form, *Stress Management: A Comprehensive Guide to Wellness* (Charlesworth & Nathan, 1984), and audiotape formats, *Relaxation Training Program* (Budzynski, 1974), *Stress Management Training Program* (Charlesworth & Peiffer, 1977), and *The Relaxation and Stress Management Program* (Charlesworth, 1981). Research has demonstrated the effectiveness of relaxation training programs in a variety of stress disorders including test anxiety (Charlesworth, Murphy, & Beutler, 1981); substance abuse (Charlesworth & Dempsey, 1982); withdrawal from benzodiazepine usage (Nathan et al., 1986); hypertension (Charlesworth, Williams, & Baer, 1984); and vascular disease and pain (Charlesworth & Harrington, 1984). This chapter will briefly describe the relaxation components utilized in a comprehensive stress-management program. Then a comparison of recorded and therapist-presented relaxation training will be discussed. The chapter will end with a section on applications, and contraindications for relaxation training.

MAJOR COMPONENTS OF RELAXATION TRAINING

Progressive Relaxation

The program's first behavioral technique was developed in the 1920s by Edmund Jacobson (1929). The *progressive relaxation procedure* trains a person to first tense and then relax the major muscle groups of the body in an orderly sequence. By following these instructions, a person can learn, in a experiential way, exactly where most muscles are located. In addition, the feelings of muscular tension and relaxation can be more fully differentiated and studied. With practice, the individual gradually learns to make this differentiation rapidly and to easily induce his or her own relaxation.

If a muscle is tensed, it relaxes more deeply when it is released. Muscular relaxation is the simple absence of tension. The initial tension–relaxation exercise appears to be one of the best starting places for relaxation training because the exercises not only teach a concrete skill for reducing tension and inducing relaxation, but also help people tune in to their own bodies.

Deep–muscle Relaxation

It is not always practical to tense and relax various muscles. The next procedure in the sequence is designed to help a person gain greater control over the same major muscle groups through cue-controlled mental awareness and suggestions.

Deep-breathing exercises are practiced to insure that respiration is regular and calm. Additionally, techniques of differential relaxation are introduced, so that some muscles can be relaxed even when a task requires other muscles to be in full use. Visual imagery exercises are practiced to aid still further in the development and maintenance of deep-muscle relaxation. Finally, key words and phrases are utilized to help a person recall and reinstate the feelings of relaxation experienced through progressive and *deep muscle relaxation*.

Thus, when people master deep muscle relaxation, they can recall feelings of muscular relaxation at any time by using the key words strongly associated with relaxation. To help them take full advantage of this, advice is given on the use of both deep-muscle and cue-controlled relaxation techniques in daily life.

Autogenic Training

Autogenic refers to self-generation. The autogenic relaxation techniques were designed to promote and give support to the self-regulating systems of the body. These are the systems that automatically regulate heart beat, blood circulation, and many other important biological functions. These systems respond to cues of potential danger by increasing visceral arousal to prepare for fight or flight. This was, and is, adaptive when the threat experienced is one requiring such action. However, for modern people, most threats are psychological or philosophical, and many of the resulting responses are maladaptive. Autogenic training helps control stress by teaching the self-regulating systems to be more relaxed when not faced with a real danger.

The introduction of autogenic training follows in a natural progression from learning to control tension in the major voluntary muscle groups. This is because the self-regulating system responses are generally more subtle than the voluntary system responses. Autogenic training involves "passive" concentration on different phrases, suggesting autonomic relaxation. This training can be conceptualized as helping to program the subconscious mind to create a state of internal calm. Alternatively, one can conceptualize it physiologically as reducing sympathetic arousal and triggering the parasympathetic nervous system via the hypothalamus. In either case, one hopes to replace most "fight- or-flight" responses with "stay-and-play" responses.

Visual Imagery Training

After successfully learning to relax those parts of the body that are under conscious control (gross musculature) and those systems of the body that are usually regulated automatically (heart rate, blood flow, and so on), the visual imagery part of the program teaches the individual a special cognitive technique to reduce and control mental anxiety. If one is physically exhausted and still unable to sleep, this could be due to disturbing thoughts. These thoughts and feelings could be repeatedly stimulating the autonomic fight-or-flight response.

Visual imagery training teaches the individual to produce relaxing images and thoughts. The images and thoughts can then be used to control mental anxiety by blocking out intruding and disturbing ideas. This is accomplished by employing visual imagery and pleasing ideas. The pleasant images and thoughts can trigger the calming parasympathetic nervous system. This imagery training also prepares an individual to use the systematic desensitization presented in the last phase of the relaxation training program.

Systematic Desensitization

Many people find it helpful to selectively rehearse coping with exceptionally difficult life stresses. In the 1950s Dr. Joseph Wolpe (1954, 1958) developed a scientifically viable technique for this aspect of anxiety management and called it *systematic desensitization* (1961). Theoretically, relaxation is incompatible with anxiety. For this reason, the individual is helped to imagine stressful scenes while in a profound state of relaxation. By progressively imagining more and more stressful scenes while relaxed, the individual learns to face these situations without incapacitating anxiety. Cognitive rehearsal of relaxed and effective coping skills (Goldfried & Trier 1974) can also be fostered during standard systematic desensitization. Such rehearsal has been shown to enhance the effects of the desensitization. Clinical guidelines for the application of these relaxation training procedures have been given elsewhere (Charlesworth & Nathan, 1984). It would be advantageous to study such issues as frequency of practice, settings, progression through the various forms of relaxation, compliance enhancement, generalization, and maintenance prior to practicing clinical applications of relaxation training.

RECORDED VERSUS THERAPIST PRESENTATION OF RELAXATION TECHNIQUES

Efficiency of Recorded Presentation

Recorded presentations of relaxation procedures have many clear advantages over therapist presentations in terms of efficiency. In terms of ongoing therapeutic work, the clinician can save herself or himself tremendous amounts of professional time and tedium. The patient, in turn, can save the cost of many office visits and increase his or her relaxation skills by engaging in home practice both during and after treatment. *The Relaxation & Stress Management Program* (Charlesworth, 1981) was designed to enhance client home practice (Freedman, 1981), which has been shown to be the primary predictor of successful stress management (Charlesworth, Williams, & Baer, 1984). These advantages and the clinician's cost effectiveness can make the difference between an affordable treatment and one beyond the means of many patients. For the researcher, the use of tapes virtually insures replicability of the taped part of her or his protocol.

Effectiveness of Recorded Presentations

The relative or absolute effectiveness and comparative efficiency of recorded presentations was not clear until recently. In fact, Bernstein and Borkovec "strongly advise against the routine use of such procedures in either research or clinical setting" (1973, p. 6). Their advice, however, was based almost entirely on interpretation of early research conducted by Paul and Trimble (1970) that has since been shown to be of questionable validity (Charlesworth & Doughtie, 1982). It should also be noted that Bernstein and Borkovec qualified their advice by ending the sentence previously quoted with the words "unless the particular tapes can be shown to be equivalent in effectiveness to live presentation." However, even their qualification regarding equivalent effectiveness should be reconsidered. Given the efficiency and cost-effectiveness of taped presentations, if one could demonstrate a clinically significant effectiveness, one might not require "equivalent" effectiveness. In this light, a brief review of the growing body of research using taped presentations will be presented before the comparative studies are reviewed.

Use of Recorded Presentations in Research

Many research studies have successfully used taped relaxation for training (Anton, 1976; Barlow, Leitenberg, Argas, & Wincze, 1969; Davidson, 1968). Other studies have used both recorded and live instructions (Gray, England, & Mahoney, 1965; Sherman, 1972; Weil & Goldfried, 1973; Zeisset, 1968). A large number of tapes and records is available offering relaxation training as part of a treatment program or as a separate focus (e.g., Budzynski, 1974; Cannistraci, 1975; Charlesworth, 1981; Charlesworth & Peiffer, 1977; Feher, 1962; Lupin, 1974; Proctor, 1975; Rappaport, 1974). In addition, a great deal of biofeedback training is augmented by taped relaxation instructions.

Taped Hypnotic Suggestions and Relaxation Techniques

Taped suggestions are also used to produce hypnotic phenomenon. These suggestions have been shown to be as effective as spoken ones (Barber & Calverley, 1966; Hokovec, Svorad, & Lanc, 1963). In addition, recorded relaxation instructions have been successfully utilized to improve hypnotic susceptibility (Leva, 1974). In fact, relaxation and hypnosis could be among the clinical techniques best suited for recorded presentation. Mikulas (1976) investigated a number of techniques in a self-control clinic using televised presentations. The results indicated that relaxation was more successful than other self-control techniques (such as self-desensitization, contingency contracting with self, token systems, thought stopping, and so on). Viewers of the televised presentation not only relaxed during the show but also reported continued practice and efficacy in a variety of anxiety-producing situations.

Taped Versus Live Progressive Relaxation

Older studies suggested modified presentations of Jacobson's progressive relaxation were statistically less effective in the taped modality than the live

modality for reducing physiological tension (Paul & Trimble, 1970; Russell, Sipich, & Knipe, 1976). However, these studies could have been based on an invalid baseline measurement such that physiological changes might have already occurred prior to actual measurement (Charlesworth & Doughtie, 1982), and they could have been biased by disparities in expectancy levels (Stefanek & Hodes, 1986). Current research has shown that no meaningful differences in relaxation measure were found between subjects receiving live and taped instructions (Hamberger & Schuldt, 1986). In addition, no significant difference has been shown between the two forms of induction with respect to their effects on subjective tension, as reported by the anxiety differential (Husek & Alexander, 1963). Current research and clinical opinion suggest that success in learning to relax should also be evaluated in terms of such cognitive skills as focusing, passivity, and receptivity (Smith, 1986). Somatic indicators might provide useful feedback as skills are being developed but might not be of primary importance for stress management.

Technical and Voice Quality of Recorded Relaxation

Other aspects of comparative research between live and recorded relaxation also deserve attention. Technical flaws (hissing, cracking noises, and other distractions) can make many taped instructions somewhat anxiety producing in themselves. The authors have noticed this problem even with professional tapes, on which a more concerted quality-control effort should have been made.

A clinical review of self-made and commercially available tape programs (Wysong, 1984) has recommended against therapist-produced relaxation tapes because of poor technical quality and presentation. Of those programs reviewed by Wysong (1984) *The Relaxation and Stress Management Program* (Charlesworth, 1981) was found to "far outdistance any of the other recorded relaxation programs on the market" (p. 12). In addition, this program combines instrumental music and environmental backgrounds for the taped relaxation, which research (Nathan, Nathan, Vigen, & Wellborn, 1981) has shown to significantly effect relaxation ratings and be preferred by over 90% of the researched subjects. Another factor that is suspect in experimenter-produced tapes is voice quality. This variable can be considered part of what psychologists have identified as "therapist warmth" in psychotherapy research. Therapist warmth has clearly been shown to be important in therapeutic interactions. Most relevant to the issue of taped versus live presentation of relaxation is a finding reported by Morris and Suckerman (1974). They clinically compared two recorded desensitization tapes and demonstrated that a "warm therapist" voice (soft, melodic, and pleasant) produced a significantly greater improvement with phobic individuals than a "cold therapist" voice (impersonal and businesslike). These technical variables could have been considered by various researchers, but the degree to which they were controlled is unknown.

Outcome Measures

Another important consideration in reviewing the comparative results involved the dependent measures. The two studies did not show the taped presentation to be statistically as effective in reducing electromyograph-recorded muscle tension as the live presentation, but it did show that the clients' anxiety differentials and cognitive reports of success and satisfaction with the treatment were equivalent (Paul & Trimble, 1970; Russell, Sipich, & Knipe, 1976). This is important because the need for profound *muscular* relaxation has not been demonstrated as a necessary condition for stress management, the reduction of anxiety, or the success of a psychotherapeutic intervention. A good example of this is found in a study by Braud (1978) involving hyperactive children. Biofeedback produced significantly greater decrements of an electromyographic *tension* than did taped relaxation. However, the taped relaxation produced a significant decrease in the target symptom of *hyperactivity*, and this decrease was not significantly different from that produced by biofeedback. Richard J. Morris and Kenneth R. Suckerman (1976) addressed this issue with respect to the use of tapes in live and automated desensitization. Their review is thorough and compelling.

> Though live relaxation may produce greater muscular relaxation than taped relaxation ... a substantial number of studies have used the taped relaxation method.... None of these studies have indicated that the use of taped relaxation had a negative effect on the outcome data that were generated (p. 486).

Taped Relaxation and the Treatment of Tension Headaches

Budzynski (1976) reviewed a number of studies comparing the efficacy of biofeedback, taped relaxation, placebo, and no-treatment controls for the adjunctive or sole treatment of tension headaches. In most of these studies, the taped relaxation alone was not as effective as biofeedback or biofeedback-assisted relaxation, but it was statistically and clinically more effective than placebo or no-treatment controls. Thus, when biofeedback instruments are not available, taped relaxation should be considered a useful adjunctive or a primary treatment for tension headaches.

Conclusions

Reviewing the research available at this time and granting the efficiency of recorded presentations, what conclusions can we reach regarding the comparative effectiveness of recorded versus live presentations of relaxation? If the goal or the target of one's intervention is *muscular* relaxation, there *might* be an advantage in the use of live therapist presentations over recorded presentations. It should be noted, however, that the ultimate treatment of choice might very well be biofeedback-assisted muscular relaxation rather than live therapist presentation of progressive relaxation.

If the goals of one's intervention involve such targets as general stress management, anxiety reduction, decreased hyperactivity, hypnotic induction, headache alleviation, or systematic desensitization, comparative effectiveness remains an important question. There is a clear need for more and better research comparing recorded presentations of high technical quality with live presentations under varied instructions and for multiple disorders before any final judgments can be made. Nonetheless, there seems to be considerable empirical support and practical need for the continued use of both approaches at this time. Many relaxation and biofeedback researchers have found that their normal, volunteer subjects "almost always report that their new skill is extremely useful to them on an everyday basis" (Bernstein & Borkovec 1973, p. 11). The physiological, psychological, and sociological data would certainly support the use of some sort of relaxation training for most people, on a preventive basis alone. Most psychiatric patients can benefit to some degree with or without concomitant care. However, given the limitations of present resources and motivation, what are the strongest indications and contraindications for the use of relaxation training?

INDICATIONS AND CONTRAINDICATIONS FOR USING RELAXATION TRAINING

The following section will attempt to provide an answer to the question of when to use relaxation training. It begins with a brief introduction to the use of relaxation training in biofeedback training. This is followed by a review of several stress-related psychiatric disorders, ulcers, hypertension, and other psychosomatic disorders will also be reviewed. Finally, a flowchart will outline steps that should help to insure patient selection.

Biofeedback

Biofeedback makes use of technologically complex machines to provide information about immediate physiological functioning in such a way that patients can learn to voluntarily increase or decrease their responses. The word *biofeedback* can be divided into three parts to make it more understandable. *Bio* refers to living organisms or tissues. *Feed* means to give or, in this case, display. *Back* refers to the direction in which this information is provided. *Feedback* is a compound that has grown popular with the widespread use of computer technology. It refers to a loop in which a system's output is used to make corrections and regulate the system. For example, a thermostat measures the heat a system puts out and feeds this information back into the system as an on or off signal. With biofeedback, life functions are monitored, and the data are fed back to the patient.

Many biological processes could not be measured and displayed rapidly and economically until quite recently. Equipment is now available that is able to amplify, analyze, and display this information directly or indirectly for a wide variety of biological functions. These include tension in the muscles (electromyograph), peripheral skin temperatures (electrothermograph), blood pressure (electro-sphygmomanometer), and even brain waves (electroencephalograph). The information about these bodily functions is fed back by visual or auditory signals, or both. The visual feedback includes the needle on a meter, an array of lights, or other sights. Auditory feedback includes clicks, tones, music, and other sounds. For the motivated patient, this visual or auditory information can be used as a reinforcer or reward to operantly condition his other physiological response in the desired direction. In this way, a person can increase awareness and self-control over the functions monitored. One of the most vivid and demystifying examples of biofeedback is that of the common bathroom scale. The bathroom scale monitors biological information that is not normally available to the individual and feeds this information back by displaying it on a meter. The patient can then use this information to reward or punish attempts at weight loss. Most biofeedback is far more immediate, but the concept is the same.

Many of the disorders discussed in this section are psychosomatic ones. They are functions of physical or emotional stress. As previously outlined, most of these disorders reflect chronic hyperarousal of the sympathetic nervous system and the body's failure to achieve homeostasis. The goal of treatment is to help the patient bring her or his body closer to homeostasis by reducing sympathetic arousal and activating the parasympathetic nervous system (Benson, 1976). This goal is often achieved through relaxation training. For this reason most biofeedback outside of neuromuscular rehabilitation is, to use Barbara Brown's 1977 term, biofeedback-assisted relaxation.

Biofeedback-assisted relaxation can be accomplished through trial and error, but this could be very time consuming and could limit generalization. A person learning relaxation only by responding to changes in visual or auditory signals might be unable to reproduce the results without the biofeedback machine. Most biofeedback clinicians use comprehensive relaxation instructions to help their patients build a bridge from the clinic and the machine to their everyday lives.

The most common clinical application of biofeedback involves the use of electromyograph and temperature feedback. Most patients begin biofeedback training using an electromyograph, with the electrodes placed on the forearm or frontalis muscle. This is true even in the case of migraine headaches, in which the final goal is cardiovascular changes as monitored by peripheral skin temperature. Learning muscle-tension feedback first makes it easier to learn from skin temperature feedback later. Relaxation training can be used with almost all biofeedback patients. It can be used to introduce the active participatory nature of the treatment. It can be used throughout a biofeedback program to augment the effects of office biofeedback through home practice.

Progressive relaxation and deep muscle relaxation are particularly useful for electromyograph training in many disorders including muscle tension headaches, bruxism, and spastic torticollis. Autogenic training and imagery training are both very useful for temperature biofeedback in such disorders as migraine headaches and Raynaud's disease. Furthermore, systematic desensitization can be augmented by the use of biofeedback instrumentation to monitor the level of stress that is evoked on each step of the hierarchy (Budzynski, 1976).

Phobic and Anxiety Neuroses

Given the integral part that anxiety seems to play in all repetitive, self-defeating patterns of behavior, Haugen, Dixon, and Dickel (1960), Wolpe (1958), and others have proposed that desensitization or relaxation training are the answers to *all* neuroses. However overinclusive such a proposal might be, patients with phobic and anxiety neuroses clearly deserve consideration for a trial of relaxation training. At this time, phobic and anxiety neuroses appear to be two of the most appropriate psychiatric disorders for relaxation training and, thus, two of the most responsive disorders to this form of treatment. One type of problem encountered with this type of patient is fear of loss of control should he or she become deeply relaxed. This can be minimized by working slowly with the patient, using the more concrete techniques such as progressive relaxation, and having good clinical skills for dealing with potential abreactions. An abreaction is a sudden release of emotional energy and disturbing memories. For example, an agoraphobic could have repressed conflicts such as past sexual abuse as a child, and deep relaxation might release supressed emotions and fears. Development of trust in the therapist and work on the abreaction would be necessary prior to continuation of relaxation training.

Anxiety Reactions

In assessing patients experiencing situational anxiety reactions, one must listen for common ways of describing hyperarousal and the fears that it often evokes. Complaints can include references to some or all of the following: tightness in the chest or the throat, forced breathing, fast or slow pulse, and cold or clammy hands or feet. Similarly, patients might report that their vision is blurred, that their mouths are frequently dry, and that their stomachs are jittery or "full of butterflies." They might complain of burping, gassiness, and frequent urination. Knotted shoulder muscles and tight stomach muscles are also reported. Patients find themselves flushed or sweaty and their skin oily. Many complain of feeling wound up, or unsteady, or dizzy. Patients often report getting upset all the time, or bracing themselves for the worst. They find themselves easily startled or irritated and unable to sit still or concentrate. Some feel they are losing control and fear they are going crazy or cracking up. They might talk about strong urges to cry or run away. Others mask their anxieties with giddiness or seductiveness.

Long stretches of hyperarousal can lead to complaints of distractability, frustration, procrastination, chronic fatigue, loss of confidence, or irritability. Diarrhea and loss of appetite are common symptoms. Sexual difficulties are often reported, including loss of interest, orgasmic dysfunction, vaginismus, and impotence. Patients might describe long bouts with insomnia including initial, intermittent, and terminal sleep disturbances. Some anxiety-related insomnias are multifaceted. Contributing factors can include residual muscle tension from the events of the day, self-generated cognitive anxiety, and tension evoked from stimuli in the sleeping environment.

Tension-Related Disorders

Headaches, backaches, and earaches are not a direct result of chronic hyperarousal but can often result from striated muscle tension. Haugen et al. (1960) hypothesized that this tension arises from atavistic reflexes like those displayed by other animals when they are startled: The head is lifted and the fur is ruffed up. Some of these contracting muscles insert into the galea aponeurotica and result in bandlike headaches. Backaches associated with arthritis or prior injury can be aggravated, and a local spasm can result if the patient's back muscles are stiff and tight for long periods of time. In some cases of low back pain, strengthening is preferable to relaxation, and these cases must be differentiated from tension backaches by a qualified physician. Cracking, ringing, or buzzing in the ears could be due to contractions of the tensor tympani or, more likely, the pharyngeal muscles that control the openings of the eustachian tubes.

An additional symptom of anxiety involves heightened menstrual distress, often leading to primary dysmenorrhea. This syndrome, involving debilitating uterine cramps, can be accompanied by headaches, intestinal disturbances, water retention, increased menstrual flow, and emotional variability. Research (Filler & Hall, 1970) suggests that dysmenorrhea results more from dysrhythmic patterns of contractions than from the intensity of the contractions alone. The elevated muscle tonus and dysrhythmic contractions cause focal ischemia (a deficiency of blood) and hypoxia (inadequate oxygen) in the myometrium, or smooth muscle tissue, of the uterine wall. Work by Heczey (1978) and others has shown the clear relationship of stress to menstrual distress. Heczey (1978) has also demonstrated the efficacy of biofeedback, as well as of relaxation and autogenic training alone, for the treatment of primary dysmenorrhea.

Anxious Patients in Medical Care

Physicians, as well as other clinicians, find that anxious patients tend to worry about their health and often somatize. It has been reported that the anxious patient is more likely to make late or early appointments for periodic physical examinations (Frazier et al., 1979). Complaints vary with specialty, and many functional patients legitimately want to be reassured that nothing is physically wrong with them. Medical educators (Frazier et al., 1979) are suggesting that the differential diagnosis of anxiety should be moved up to earlier phases of patient evaluation, rather than being relegated to the tail end of an examination. Furthermore, all physicians are encouraged to go well beyond the approach characterized by statements such as "There is nothing organically wrong with you, so it must be your nerves." The diagnosis and explanation should be made on the basis of inclusion as well as exclusion. Strong affect, particularly anxiety, can also interfere with cognitive functioning and interpersonal trust. Thus, the rapid identification and clarification of anxiety can improve the accuracy of the history taken and facilitate a better doctor–patient relationship.

The prevalence of anxiety in the general population is estimated to be between 15% and 20%. The number of male and female psychiatric patients is roughly the same. However, among general medical patients with primary anxiety, women outnumber men two to one. Men tend to suffer in silence unless severely disabled or fearful of serious disease such as heart problems. Among patients seen by cardiologists, 10% to 14% have functional symptoms as their only presenting problem (Frazier et al., 1979). Adolescents, on the other hand, often reveal their anxiety in school failure, act it out through rebellious behavior, or medicate themselves for it through the use of alcohol, marijuana, or other central nervous system depressants.

Bachrach (Frazier et al., 1979), a gastroenterologist, provided a list of characteristics he looks for in patients he suspects of functional anxiety. These patients present with atypical symptoms that do not fit organic illnesses, often presenting with peculiar symptoms such as aerophagia or belching. The symptoms and syndromes tend to shift over time. The patients "doctor shop" and often carry a veritable pharmacy with them from doctor to doctor. Sexual conflicts are common. These patients are suggestible and tend to respond almost too well to brief hospitalization. They seem ready to "jump on the operating table" but are loathe to accept psychiatric referral.

Many patients do not report anxiety symptoms without some prompting. The clinician is advised to look for nonverbal signs of anxiety such as the jittery patient with dilated pupils whose palm is wet upon handshaking. Inappropriate affect is also a common sign of anxiety. Here the loss of a job or loved one might be described by a patient who is smiling. Finally, the clinician does well to monitor her or his own feelings and be intuitive. An anxious patient tends to make one anxious, just as a depressed patient evokes sad feelings. An inquiry into possible stressors, conflicts, and anxiety symptoms can be brief, but it is often critical to patient care.

Anxious Patients in Psychotherapy

Another major use of relaxation training is as a catalyst or adjunct to group or individual psychotherapy for patients with stress or tension-related disorders. Some therapists find such patients are then able to talk about their deeper interpersonal and intrapsychic conflicts.

Pain patients, particularly those with headaches, often perceive a stress-management intervention as concrete evidence that the therapist acknowledges their pain as real and not as proof that they are crazy. Once trust is established and some relief obtained, many of these patients are ready to discuss the psychosocial aspects of their pain.

Therapists can also use the training as an alternative to anti-anxiety medication during therapy. Some psychoanalytically oriented therapists find the technique useful but refer their patients to another therapist, so as to preserve the ongoing power of a purely analytic approach. In either case, relaxation training can be a useful adjunct to most forms of psychotherapy.

Alcohol and Drug Abuse

Numerous theories have been proposed to explain the causes of alcoholism and drug addiction. One position proposes that alcohol and drugs are reinforcing because they have tension-reducing properties (e.g., Kingham, 1958). This view assumes that the organism is in a state of increased arousal and that the effects of the drug serve to reduce this arousal. The subjective interpretation of this arousal state has been identified as anxiety (Conger, 1956), and people might drink or ingest drugs to reduce this anxiety or tension (Bandura, 1969). There is a complex interaction of alcohol consumption with objective and subjective measures of tension (Steffan, Nathan, & Taylor, 1974). Research supporting the relevancy of tension and anxiety reduction to alcoholism and other drug-abuse health problems is extensive.

It is generally accepted that *drug dependence* as a term should not be used independently of the type of agent involved (Catanzaro, 1968). Many studies have been undertaken to establish similarities or differences among and within various groups of drug abusers. The data are often confused and discordant. Researchers can draw different conclusions from the same data. Nevertheless, certain factors seem to be consistently involved whether the abused substance is alcohol or drugs. One such factor is the failure of whatever adaptive resources the person uses to manage the stress, tension, and anxiety encountered in modern life.

Shibuya (1974) employed the 16PF with individuals using marijuana and LSD and concluded that a major motivation for drug use was to prepare one for stress. C. P. Cohen, White, and Schoolar (1971) utilized the Leary Interpersonal System with a group of drug abusers. They concluded that addicts might not have a cognitive label for the tension they experience, but they are experiencing significant amounts of tension. Pittel (1971) characterized both heroin addicts and psychedelic drug users as lacking impulse control and the psychological resources needed to deal adequately with environmental frustrations.

Researchers have attempted to delineate homogeneous subgroups within populations of drug abusers. Frequently, anxiety is not only a general factor but also a specific factor in typologies. For example, Nerviano and Gross (1973) described Type

I alcoholics as being high in anxiety and introversion and concluded that they drink to control tension. On the other hand, Type II alcoholics tend to conform and use alcohol to control unacceptable impulses. Stein and Rozynko (1974) delineated 10 alcoholic types. They conducted research on a detoxification ward and concluded that anxiety contributed to the difficulty of these patients in functioning adaptively and effectively. Berzins, Ross, and Monroe (1971) sampled over 800 hospitalized narcotic addicts and conceptualized their nonconformity as related to acute subjective distress and disturbed thinking. Later Berzins et al. speculated that this group of addicts might be employing drugs to control or attenuate feelings of anxiety, depression, and distress. Another approach, by A. Cohen (1971), utilized a conceptual model based on the basic motivational forces leading to drug abuse. Cohen characterized those individuals using drugs for the physical experiences as having a strong desire for physical relaxation. Many drug abusers experience a prolonged and distinct preference for a particular drug. Milkan and Frosch's (1973) data indicate that the drug of choice was syntonic with the abuser's characteristic modes of adaption. The heroin addict utilized repression and withdrawal to reduce anxiety, whereas the amphetamine abuser commanded a variety of compensatory maneuvers to maintain a posture of active confrontation with the environment. Thus, addicts reduce anxiety by using drugs to bolster their characteristic modes of defensive functioning. The heroin addict bolsters satiation, and the amphetamine addict bolsters activation. Other researchers explored the preferential use of marijuana (Hendin, 1973; Segal & Feger, 1973) and concluded that it is used to relax, to reduce emotions, and to avoid vicious feelings aroused in competitive situations.

Others (Fischer, 1973; Prendergast, Preble, & Fennant, 1973) have concluded that disorders of habit as manifested by cigarette smoking, overuse of food, excessive alcohol consumption, or drug abuse are interrelated. The data were consistent with the hypothesis that some individuals respond to stress through these activities and supported their recommendation that the psychotherapeutic approach of choice should facilitate a transformation from helplessness to self-control.

A. Cohen (1971) pointed out that drug use is not a minority, but a majority, phenomenon and suggested that we need to find alternatives to it, rather than just to promote abstinence. Although no clear and distinct type of personality or typology of personalities has been identified in the literature, many alcoholics and addicts lack adaptive resources to manage their life stresses and their subjective distresses. A void is created when they are asked to give up their chemical resources. Teaching an individual self-control techniques of relaxation and stress management to reduce anxiety and nervousness could give that person increased psychological and adaptive resources to deal effectively with stress without the help of chemicals. The systematic and effective use of relaxation training in the treatment of stress, tension, and anxiety, as an adjunct to the standard therapies for substance abuse, is relatively new. National (Brown, 1977; Green 1977) and international (Cordeiro, 1974; Heinemann et al., 1974) reports have emerged indicating the success of such an approach.

Psychosomatic Disorders

The neurotic disorders and anxiety reactions just reviewed are quite debilitating both socially and psychologically, but the so-called psychosomatic disorders have the added complication of clear physiological change generally involving demonstrable tissue damage. Examples of the stress-related psychosomatic disorders include bruxism, hypertension, and ulcers.

Bruxism involves the habit of clenching or grinding one's teeth, often at night and during sleep. Such a habit places harmful strain on the teeth's supportive tissues and can lead to muscular spasm and bite disorders. Hypertension or high blood pressure, is a complex disease with regard to both its etiology and process. As a precursor to heart attacks and strokes, it is part of a health problem reaching epidemic proportions in the United States. Differences in diet, exercise, genetics, personality patterns, stress, and other phenomena have been implicated as causes of hypertension. Except for genetic predisposition, all of these factors have become the target of treatments of hypertension and heart disease. Ulcers, the open, bleeding sores of the gastrointestinal tract, are often stress related. During certain stages of the disease, ulcer patients are appropriate for relaxation training in conjunction with appropriate medication. The effects of pharmacological and psychological interventions are often synergistic for such disorders, if timed appropriately.

An important aspect of patient selection for relaxation training involves assessing all patients for multiple disorders. Just as psychotherapists can overlook physical disorders, physicians can inadvertently overlook unrelated or accompanying anxiety reactions. We must all appreciate the complexity of illness. Many anxiety responses are related to physical disorders. For example, pain almost always involves anxiety and tension. The reduction of this anxiety and tension, particularly in chronic-pain patients, has proven to be quite effective. Relaxation training is often a way of avoiding or decreasing the use of painkillers, with their harmful side effects and potential for addiction. The ongoing assessment and treatment of anxiety should be an integral part of comprehensive medical care. Please refer to figure 5.1.

Contraindications

A medical clearance is mandatory to rule out anxiety-masked disorders that would respond more readily and effectively to other interventions. There are a number of organic diseases that present as seemingly pure anxiety states. It is best for the clinician to be particularly aware of these, so as to make appropriate referrals before beginning treatment, or during treatment should they appear after training is initiated. Many of these can be life threatening if left untreated.

Hyperthyroidism is a fairly common disease that is known to mimic anxiety neuroses. These patients might present complaining of jumpiness, and some "simply" present asking for tranquilizers. The constellation of weight loss, sweating, hyperactivity, and grandiose behavior can be accompanied by symptoms of heat intolerance, such as not wearing a coat in bitterly cold weather. Differentially, the tremor of the thyrotoxic patient is fine rather than gross; his or her pulse remains the same during sleep, rather than tending to abate; and his or her extremities are warm and pink, rather than cold and clammy. Laboratory tests are also important aids in the differential diagnosis (Frazier et al., 1979).

Martin (1977), in reviewing some of these diseases, pointed to tumors of the adrenal gland, particularly in middle-aged men. These tumors are usually benign but secrete adrenalin. The resulting symptoms include panic, fear, flushing, trembling, headache, and elevated blood pressure during episodic and transient attacks. Turning to the pancreas, islet cell adenoma can cause hypoglycemia that can produce episodic anxiety, sweating tremor, hunger, dizziness, fatigue, and sometimes rather bizzare behavior. Acute intermittent porphyria, a hereditary disease, can present with sudden anxiety

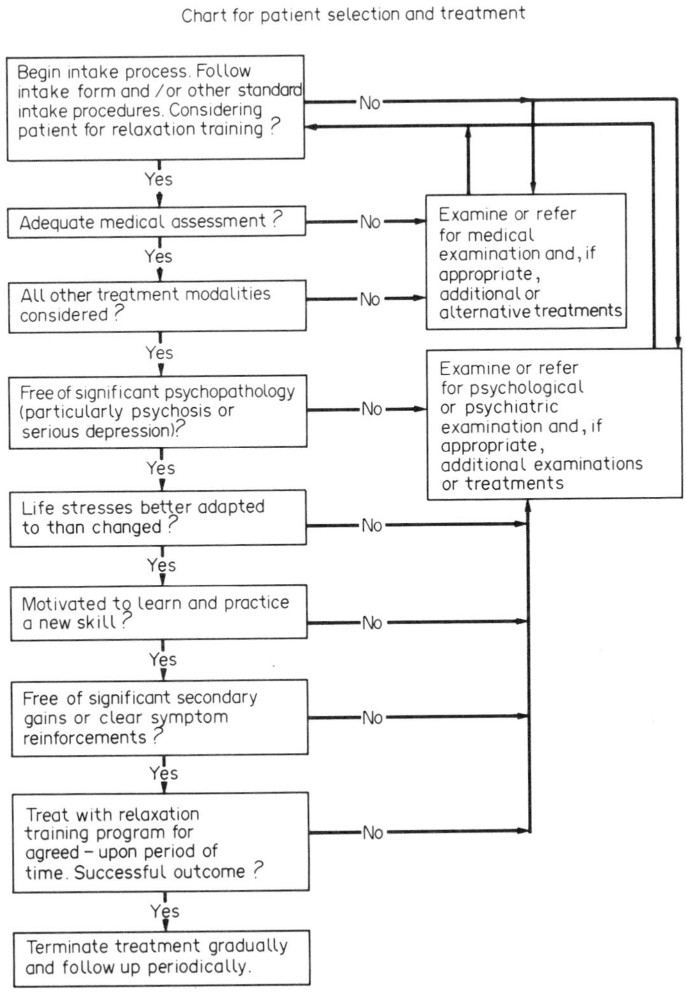

Chart for patient selection and treatment

```
┌──────────────────────────────┐
│ Begin intake process. Follow │
│ intake form and /or other    │──── No ────────────────┐
│ standard intake procedures.  │                        │
│ Considering patient for      │                        │
│ relaxation training ?        │◄───────────────────────┤
└──────────────────────────────┘                        │
              │ Yes                                      │
              ▼                                          │
┌──────────────────────────────┐      ┌─────────────────┴──────┐
│ Adequate medical assessment ?│─ No ─│ Examine or refer       │
└──────────────────────────────┘      │ for medical            │
              │ Yes                    │ examination and, if    │
              ▼                        │ appropriate,           │
┌──────────────────────────────┐      │ additional or          │
│ All other treatment          │─ No ─│ alternative treatments │
│ modalities considered ?      │      └────────────────────────┘
└──────────────────────────────┘
              │ Yes
              ▼
┌──────────────────────────────┐      ┌────────────────────────┐
│ Free of significant          │      │ Examine or refer       │
│ psychopathology (particularly│─ No ─│ for psychological      │
│ psychosis or serious         │      │ or psychiatric         │
│ depression)?                 │      │ examination and, if    │
└──────────────────────────────┘      │ appropriate,           │
              │ Yes                    │ additional examinations│
              ▼                        │ or treatments          │
┌──────────────────────────────┐      └────────────────────────┘
│ Life stresses better adapted │─ No ─►
│ to than changed ?            │
└──────────────────────────────┘
              │ Yes
              ▼
┌──────────────────────────────┐
│ Motivated to learn and       │─ No ─►
│ practice a new skill ?       │
└──────────────────────────────┘
              │ Yes
              ▼
┌──────────────────────────────┐
│ Free of significant secondary│─ No ─►
│ gains or clear symptom       │
│ reinforcements ?             │
└──────────────────────────────┘
              │ Yes
              ▼
┌──────────────────────────────┐
│ Treat with relaxation        │─ No ─►
│ training program for         │
│ agreed - upon period of      │
│ time. Successful outcome ?   │
└──────────────────────────────┘
              │ Yes
              ▼
┌──────────────────────────────┐
│ Terminate treatment gradually│
│ and follow up periodically.  │
└──────────────────────────────┘
```

FIGURE 5.1. Chart for patient selection and treatment

attacks and emotional outbursts. These are often accompanied by abdominal pain and paresthesia. Martin suggested that the often maligned King George III of England might have suffered from this disorder during the American Revolution.

Coronary insufficiency or ischemia must also be ruled out by the history and the physical. One clue involves the strong relationship of the symptoms to sustained effort, which is more likely to be found in the history of the cardiac patient than the anxious patient. Paroxysmal atrial tachycardia can be grossly differentiated from anxiety by taking the patient's pulse. A pulse rate over 140 beats per minute is unlikely to be the result of anxiety alone.

Mitral valve prolapse (MVP) might also contribute to stress and anxiety symptoms. Charlesworth, in a recent unpublished study, found approximately 80% of agoraphobic patients had MVP, and a similar number of MVP patients with no phobic history scored with significant stress, anxiety, and depression on the MMPI. Relaxation training might be appropriate for treating MVP symptoms, but more severe cases need to be followed by a cardiologist, for possible medications.

Caffeinism involves the overuse of coffee, tea, colas, and other substances containing caffeine. As a stimulant, coffee can produce tachycardia, insomnia, and most of the symptoms associated with anxiety. This condition can be ruled out by asking the patient to cut back on caffeine consumption and having her or him monitor symptoms. Other forms of drug abuse should also be ruled out. Patients taking amphetamines or cocaine often present with anxiety like symptoms. This is also true of the active chronic alcoholic. In addition, those patients abruptly withdrawn by choice or by circumstances from central nervous system (CNS) depressants or analgesics (pain medications) exhibit many symptoms of anxiety.

Other organic disorders that might masquerade as anxiety are psychomotor epilepsy and hypoglycemia. The list is a long one, and an adequate physical examination is required. The clinician is advised to properly request and obtain previous medical records and to review earlier workups to insure their thoroughness. One should also be convinced that all appropriate forms of treatment have been attempted or are in progress. If any doubts about the diagnosis or treatment remain after consultation with the referring or primary-care physician, one could consider encouraging the patient to seek a second opinion.

Patients affected by long-term stressors can develop a sense of hopelessness, learned helplessness, and depression. Some writers recommend relaxation training for even the depressed patient (Haugen, et al., 1960), but most compare its effects on the depressed patient to those of tranquilizers. If given to a patient with agitated depression, tranquilizers are said to bring out the depression still further because they take away the agitation as a defense. Relaxation training given alone can also have this adverse affect. In addition, depression tends to decrease patient cooperation, involvement, and motivation. Relaxation training given alone could also have this adverse effect. For this reason, relaxation training could lead to disappointment and possibly exacerbate the depression. The program could be used as an adjunctive procedure, but, at this time, to pursue the program alone with the clearly depressed patient should be considered experimental and is thus best left to carefully controlled research settings. If a patient develops a depression during treatment, a referral for concomittant or alternative psychiatric or psychological care is in order.

Given these caveats, it might be helpful to review the symptoms of depression and how to differentiate depression, particularly a masked or an anxious one, from anxiety itself. This is also important because depression is a reaction to or a part of most psychiatric disorders, even some of those most responsive to stress-management training. Such secondary depression is not a contraindication for stress-management intervention. Depression is also a difficult disorder to define (Levitt & Lubin, 1975). Depression's most consistent symptom is a sad or depressed mood. Neurovegetative signs, however, are present in most moderate to severe neurotic or psychotic depressions. These signs include disturbances in sleep, appetite, elimination, and sexuality. Most of these functions are decreased or blocked, but some could be increased. Psychomotor slowing and crying episodes are also common. Most patients suffer from unipolar depressions and do not have swings into mania, as in bipolar depression. Depressions typically follow loss of a loved one, a job, or another important psychological object. Guilt, lowered self-esteem, apathy, hopelessness, and helplessness are other psychological factors. Depression can often be differentiated from anxiety by its diurnal cycles. These cycles involve early morning awakenings, accompanied by heightened emotional difficulties, with improvements in depressed mood as the day progresses. Most anxious patients have more problems with initial insomnia, but, once asleep, they typically sleep for their usual length of time. In addition, age is a criterion. Older patients tend to exhibit more agitated depressions and younger patients more anxiety states, particularly on the first presentation of a psychiatric illness. A careful, initial and ongoing diagnosis can help one detect masked depressions, so one can refer for concomitant or alternative care.

There are many other medical situations in which relaxation training might be contraindicated and referral or consultation necessary. In the case of a bleeding ulcer, for example, relaxing the viscera might be expected to increase the loss of blood. Certain parts of relaxation training, such as progressive relaxation, might be contraindicated in patients who have been advised not to tense their muscles. In these cases, consultation with a physician or physical therapist is absolutely necessary before proceeding with or continuing a relaxation program.

When patients are receiving anxiolytic (anti-anxiety) medications, antihypertensive preparations, antidepressant medications, any CNS depressant, or insulin, it is important to work closely with the prescribing physician to titrate the drug so as to optimize its effectiveness and avoid the possibility of an overdose. Some theories and clinicians claim that relaxation training is state specific and somewhat faster for the more motivated, drug-free patient. They recommend discontinuation of psychotropic medication if at all possible. In all of these situations, thorough, ongoing consultation is most important. The use of relaxation training with the psychotic individual is still at an experimental stage. Parts of the program, such as visual imagery, could be particularly upsetting to one who is experiencing hallucinations. Other parts, such as progressive relaxation, are more concrete and have shown clinical promise for use with psychotics. The patient with moderate ego strength should be monitored for signs of deterioration requiring referral or even hospitalization. Once again, a consultative model with medical and psychiatric backup cannot be recommended too strongly.

A psychosocial contraindication involves a situation in which a person is experiencing chronic hyperarousal but needs to make a change rather than to adjust to life circumstances. Examples include the unassertive employee who deserves a raise or the slum tenant whose landlord is taking advantage of his or her ignorance. Relaxation training has been clinically useful in preparing some people for alternative treatment such as assertiveness training, but without appropriate guidance, relaxation training might dull the person to the need for change in her or his behavior. To borrow parts of an ancient saying, we must help the patient to change that which can be changed, to accept that which cannot be changed, and to gain the wisdom to recognize the difference.

SUMMARY AND CONCLUSIONS

In summary, a comprehensive program for relaxation training involves muscle, autonomic, and cognitive relaxation components. Such a program can be presented in a recorded format and be as effective as live presentations (Hamberger & Schuldt, 1986). This yields replicability of research and intervention programs, cost-effectiveness, convenience, and client compliance. Many chronic diseases might be appropriate to receiving trial relaxation training as part of a comprehensive, interprofessional, collaborative model of stress management for chronic diseases.

REFERENCES

Anton, W. N. (1976). An evaluation of outcome variables in the systematic desensitization of test anxiety. *Behaviour Research and Therapy, 14,* 217–224.

Bandura, A. (1969). *Principles of behavior modification,* New York: Holt, Rinehart and Winston.

Barber, T. X., & Calverley, D. S. (1966). Toward a theory of "hypnotic" behavior: Experimental analysis of suggested amnesia. *Journal of Abnormal Psychology, 71,* 95–107.

Barlow, D., Leitenberg, H., Argas, W., Wincze, J. (1969). The transfer gap in systematic desensitization: An analog study. *Behavior Research and Therapy, 7,* 191–196.

Benson, H. (1976). *The relaxation response,* New York: William Morrow.

Bernstein, D. A., & Borkovec, T. D. (1973). *Progressive relaxation training: A manual for the helping professions.* Champaign, IL: Research Press.

Berzins, J., Ross. W., & Monroe, J. (1971). A multivariant study of the personality characteristics of hospitalized addicts on the MMPI. *Journal of Clinical Psychology, 27,* 174–181.

Braud, L. W. (1978). The effects of EMG biofeedback and progressive relaxation upon hyperactivity and its behavioral concomitants. *Biofeedback and Self-Regulation, 3,* 68–80.

Brown, B. B. (1977). *Stress and the art of biofeedback.* New York: Harper & Row.

Budzynski, T. H. (1974). *Relaxation training program.* New York: Biomonitoring Applications.

Budzynski, T. H. (1976). *Biofeedback stress management and headache pain control.* New York: Biofeedback Application.

Cannistraci, A. (1975). *Auto-induction procedures for relaxation.* New York: Biomonitoring Applications.

Cantanzaro, R. (1968). *Alcoholism: The total treatment approach.* Springfield, IL: Charles C. Thomas.

Charlesworth, E. A. (1981). *The relaxation and stress management program.* Houston: Stress Management Research Associates.

Charlesworth, E. A., & Dempsey, G. (1982). Trait anxiety reductions in substance abuse population trained in stress management. *Journal of Clinical Psychology, 9,* 191–201.

Charlesworth, E. A., & Doughtie, E. B. (1982). Modification of baseline by differential task presentation as either hypnosis or "learned" relaxation. *Perceptual and Motor Skills, 55,* 1131–1137.

Charlesworth, E. A., & Harrington, R. (1984). Autogenic training and biofeedback assisted hand warming in the treatment of Buerger's Disease: A case study. *American Journal of Clinical Biofeedback, 7,* 107–111.

Charlesworth, E. A., Murphy, S., & Beutler, L. E. (1981). Stress management skill for nursing students. *Journal of Clinical Psychology, 37,* 284–290.

Charlesworth, E. A., & Nathan, R. G. (1984). *Stress management: A comprehensive guide to wellness.* New York: Atheneum.

Charlesworth, E. A., & Peiffer, A. L. (1977). *Stress management training program* (Audio-therapeutic Cassette Series). Houston: Stress Management Research Associates.

Charlesworth, E. A., Williams, B. J., & Baer, P. E. (1984). Stress management at the worksite for hypertension: Compliance, cost-benefit, health care and hypertension related variables. *Psychosomatic Medicine, 46,* 387–396.

Cohen, A. (1971). The journey beyond trips: Alternatives to drugs. *Journal of Psychedelic Drugs, 3,* 16–21.

Cohen, C. P., White, E. H., & Schoolar, J. C. (1971). Interpersonal patterns of personality for drug abusing patients and their therapeutic implications. *Archives of General Psychiatry, 24,* 353–358.

Conger, J. (1956). Alcoholism: Theory, problem and challenge: II. Reinforcement theory and the dynamics of alcoholism. *Quarterly Journal of Studies on Alcohol, 17,* 296–305.

Cordeiro, S. B. (1974). Le relaxation chez les toxicomanes: Bilan de quatre ans. (Corporal relaxation with drug addicts: A four-year survey). *Toxicomanes, 7,* 197–212.

Davidson, G. C. (1968). Systematic desensitization as a counterconditioning process. *Journal of Abnormal Psychology, 73,* 91–99.

Feher, M. (1962). *Relaxing body and mind: The relaxation record.* Folkways Records FX 6191.

Filler, W. W., & Hall, W. C. (1970). Dysmenorrhea and its therapy *American Journal of Obstetrics and Gynecology, 106,* 20–26.

Fischer, H. (1973). Some aspects of psychotherapy in patients with addictive personality traits. *Psychosomatics, 14,* 27–32.

Frazier, S. H., Bachrach, W. H., Detre, T. P., Freedman, D. X., Shader, R. I., Swan, H. J. C., & Stephens, G. G. (1979). *Anxiety: A clinical view.* New Jersey: Health Learning Systems.

Freedman, J. (1981). Stress management training program. *American Journal of Clinical Biofeedback, 2,* 156–158.

Goldfried, M. R., & Trier, C. S. (1974). Effectiveness of relaxation as an active coping skill. *Journal of Abnormal Psychology, 83,* 348–355.

Gray, B. B., England, G., & Mahoney, J. L. (1965). Treatment of benign vocal nodules by reciprocal inhibition. *Behaviour Research and Therapy, 3,* 187–193.

Green, E. (1977, April 4) Biofeedback: What it is and how it can help you. *U. S. News and World Report.* pp. 63–64.

Hamberger, L. K., & Schuldt, W. J. (1986). Live and taped relaxation instructions: Effects of procedural variables. *Biofeedback and Self-Regulation, 11,* 31–46.

Happich, C. (1932). Das Bildbewusstsein als Ansatzstelle Psychischen Behandlung. *Zentralblatt fur Psychoanalyse und Psychotherapie, 5,* 663–677.

Haugen, G. B., Dixon, H. H., & Dickel, H. A. (1960). *A therapy for anxiety-tension reactions.* New York: MacMillan.

Heczey, M. D. (1978). *A behavioral approach to the treatment of dysmenorrhea and menstrual distress: Research results.* Houston: Biobehavioral.

Heinemann, C. et al. (1974). Treatment of narcotic addicts. *Praxis der Kinderpsychologie und Kinderpsychiatrie, 23,* 292–299.

Hendin, H. (1973). Marijuana abuse among college students. *Journal of Nervous and Mental Disease, 156,* 259–270.

Hokovec, J., Svorad, D., Lanc, O. (1963). The comparative effectiveness of spoken and tape recorded suggestions of body sway. *The International Journal of Clinical and Experimental Hypnosis, II,* 163–166.

Husek, T. R., & Alexander, S. (1963). The effectiveness of the anxiety differential in examination stress situations. *Educational and Psychological Measurement, 23,* 309–318.

Jacobson, E. (1929). *Progressive relaxation.* Chicago: University of Chicago Press.

Leva, R. A. (1974). Modification of hypnotic susceptibility through audio-tape relaxation training: Preliminary report. *Perceptual and Motor Skills, 39,* 872–874.

Levitt, E. E., & Lubin, B. (1975). *Depression: Concepts, controversies, and some new facts.* New York: Springer.

Lupin, M. (1974). *Peace harmony awareness,* Houston: Biobehavioral.

Martin, M. J. (1977). *Anxiety and depression. Audio-Digest Psychiatry, 4* (6), Audio-Digest Foundation: Glendale, CA.

Mikulas, W. L. (1976). a televised self-control clinic. *Behavior Therapy, 7,* 564–566.

Milkan, H., & Frosch, W. (1973). On the preferential abuse of heroin and amphetamines. *Journal of Nervous and Mental Disease, 156,* 243–248.

Morris, R. J., & Suckerman, K. R. (1974). Therapist warmth as a factor in automated desensitization. *Journal of Consulting and Clinical Psychology, 42,* 244–250.

Morris, R. J., & Suckerman, K. R. (1976). Studying therapist warmth in analogue systematic desensitization research: A reply to McGlynn. *Journal of Consulting and Clinical Psychology, 44,* 485–489.

Nathan, R. G., Nathan, M. M., Vigen, M. P., & Wellborn, J. G. (1981). Relaxation training tapes: Preferences and effects of gender and background. *Perceptual and Motor Skills, 53,* 927–934.

Nathan, R. G., Robinson, D., Cherek, D. R., Sebastian, C. S., Hack, M., & Davidson, S. (1986). Alternative treatments for withdrawing the long-term benzodiazepine user: A pilot study. *International Journal of the Addictions, 21,* 195–211.

Nerviano, V., & Gross, W. (1973). Multi-variate delineation of two alcoholic profile types on the 16PF. *Journal of Clinical Psychology, 29,* 37.

Paul, G. L., & Trimble, R. W. (1970). Recorded vs. "live" relaxation training and hypnotic suggestions: Comparative effectiveness for reducing physiological arousal and inhibiting stress response. *Behavior Therapy, 1,* 285–302.

Pittel, S. (1971). Psychological aspects of heroin and other drug dependence. *Journal of Psychedelic Drugs, 4,* 40–45.

Prendergast, T. J. Jr., Prebel, M. R., & Fennant, F. S. (1973). Drug use and its relation to alcohol and cigarette consumption in the military community of West Germany. (Drugs, alcohol, cigarettes in a military setting) *International Journal of the Addictions, 8,* 741–754.

Proctor, J. (1975). *Relaxation and meditative techniques.* New York: Biomonitoring Applications.

Rappaport, A. J. (1974). *Relaxation Procedures.* New York: Biomonitoring Applications.

Russell, R. K., Sipich, J. R., & Knipe, J. (1976). Progressive relaxation training: A procedural note. *Behavior Therapy, 7,* 566–568.

Schultz, J. H., & Luthe, W. (1959). *Autogenic Training.* New York: Grune & Stratton.

Segal, B., & Feger, G. (1973). Drug use and fantasy processes in college students. *Journal of Altered States of Consciousness 1,* 5–14.

Sherman, A. R. (1972). Real-life exposure as a primary therapeutic factor in the desensitization treatment of fear. *Journal of Abnormal Psychology, 79,* 19–28.

Shibuya R. R. (1974). Categorizing drug users and nonusers on selected social and personality variables. *Journal of School Health, 44,* 442–444.

Smith, J. C. (1986). Meditation, biofeedback, and the relaxation controversy: A Cognitive–Behavioral Perspective. *American Psychologist, 41,* 1007–1009.

Stefanek, M. D., & Hodes, R. L. (1986). Expectancy effects on relaxation instructions: Physiological and self-report indices. *Biofeedback and Self-Regulation, 11,* 21–29.

Steffan, J., Nathan, P., & Taylor, H. (1974). Tension reducing effects of alcohol: Further evidence and some methodological considerations. *Journal of Abnormal Psychology, 83,* 542–547.

Stein, K. B., & Rozynko, V. (1974). Psychological and social variable and personality patterns of drug abusers. *International Journal of the Addictions, 9,* 431–446.

Weil, G., & Goldfried, M. R. (1973). Treatment of insomnia in an eleven year-old child through self-relaxation. *Behavior Therapy, 4,* 282–294.

Wilson, G. T., & Thomas, M. (1973). Self- versus drug-produced relaxation and the effects of instructional set in standardized systematic desensitization. *Behaviour Research and Therapy, 11,* 279–288.

Wolpe, J. (1954). Reciprocal inhibition as the main basis of psychotherapeutic effects. *Archives of Neurology and Psychiatry, 72,* 205–226.

Wolpe, J. (1958). *Psychotherapy by reciprocal inhibition.* Stanford, CA: Stanford University Press.

Wolpe, J. (1961). Systematic desensitization of neuroses. *Journal of Nervous and Mental Diseases, 132,* 189–203.

Wysong, J. (1984). A review of tape recorded stress management programs. *Psychotherapy Newsletter, 2* (3), 10–13.

Zeisset, R. M. (1968). Desensitization and relaxation in the modification of psychiatric patients' interview behavior. *Journal of Abnormal Psychology, 73,* 18–24.

Chapter 6

Nutritional Interventions for Stress Management

Rebecca S. Reeves

Stress response in humans is provoked by a variety of stressful conditions including nervous tension, physical injury (trauma and shock), infection, muscular work, mental anguish, and environmental conditions. Within the category of environmental conditions, prolonged exposure to heat and cold and famine and starvation and the reverse, prosperity and obesity, activate a general response syndrome in people. Research has discovered that all of these stressor conditions impact upon our nutritional status in various ways. As a result of the stress, our nutritional profile is compromised.

Selye (1970) described several examples of the "disease, of adaptation" (p. 5) which he hypothesized can result from "a faulty adaptive response to the stress" (p. 5). Malignant hypertension, nephrosclerosis, periateritisnodosa, and some lesions resembling rheumatic diseases can be produced experimentally in animals by administering an overdose of aldosterone. Stress also promotes oversecretion of this hormone in the body and could contribute to the exacerbation of the disease condition, depending on duration of hormone action, diet, and hereditary predisposition. Stress has also been implicated in the development of hypertension with cardiovascular disease, gastric ulcers, headache, and neurosis. According to Selye, "emotional tension is the most common human

stressor" (p. 6), leading ultimately to the previously mentioned conditions. In his opinion, these disease states are intensified when the organs involved are conditioned by a poor diet. In his words, "When stress is superimposed on a nutritional disorder, the effect is to make a bad condition worse" (p. 5).

Because research on reducing stress through nutritional interventions is so limited, this chapter will approach the topic from another perspective. Much interest is currently focusing on the effect of nutrition on behavior. Does the food we eat influence mood, sleep patterns, ability to remain alert, or activity levels? Recent developments in this field will be explored and discussed from a nutritional viewpoint.

CAFFEINE

Caffeine, theophylline, and theobromine are classified chemically as methylated xanthines that pharmacologically act as stimulants in the body. Caffeine, primarily found in coffee, produces its greatest effect on the central nervous system. The xanthine in tea, theophylline, exerts its strongest action on the cardiovascular and musculoskeletal systems. Common pharmacologic reactions to xanthines include "stimulation of the central nervous system, action on the kidneys to produce diuresis, stimulation of cardiac muscle and relaxation of smooth muscle'' (Stephenson, 1977 p. 240). Excessive consumption of xanthines can increase susceptibility to caffeinism, a medical term for ''coffee nerves.'' Symptoms of this condition are often mistaken for those of an anxiety neurosis and include restlessness and insomnia, nervousness, heart palpitations, irritation of the stomach, diuresis, irritability, tremulousness, muscle twitchings, and arrhythmias (Stephenson, 1977). Various investigators have reported alleviation of these anxiety like symptoms by restricting caffeine-containing foods and beverages from the food intake.

Overconsumption of caffeine by some people can lead to a mild addictive state. Withdrawal of the substance can produce headache, often extreme in severity. Several studies have demonstrated that large intakes of caffeine can also activate headache. If caffeine-containing analgesics are taken to relieve the headache, they produce only temporary relief.

It is hard to categorize caffeine intake into normal and excessive amounts because of its variable effect on people. The threshold amount for stimulant effects in a sensitive individual could be as low as 150–250 mg per day, the amount of caffeine in about 1½ cups of brewed coffee (Caffeine: What it does, 1981). To produce the symptoms of caffeinism, approximately 800–1000 mg per day must be consumed. One study has shown that caffeine is fatal if taken at doses of 3,000–10,000 mg within a brief time (Stephenson, 1977). Caffeine is metabolized by the body at the rate of 15% per hour, the average half-life being 3.5 hours (Stephenson, 1977).

Americans consume their caffeine primarily in the form of beverages, although many over-the-counter drugs contain a substantial amount of the substance. Coffee remains the nation's largest source of caffeine, even though per capita consumption declined from three cups in 1962 to two cups in 1980. What has increased substantially over the years is the sale of soft drinks, which have replaced coffee as our country's number one beverage. What most Americans are not aware of is the caffeine content of carbonated beverages. Soft-drink manufacturers add caffeine to their products to give them that special ''lift.''

Caffeine affects not only the behavior of adults but also the behavior of school age children, which has recently received much attention. In a preliminary study sponsored by the National Institute of Mental Health, children who consumed a large amount of caffeine were compared with those who took only a small amount (Pollitt & Read, 1985). Significant differences in behavior patterns were demonstrated between the two groups, as judged by their teachers. Within the high caffeine-consuming group, nine children would have been considered clinically hyperactive, with the remaining 21 demonstrating more hyperactive-type behavior than the low-consuming group.

A determination of the caffeine consumption of adults and children should be considered in the routine evaluation of a person demonstrating the behavioral abnormalities just discussed. Table 6.1 lists the average amount of caffeine found in beverages and over-the-counter drugs available in the marketplace.

VITAMINS

''Probably no single class of drugs has been the target of as much quackery, misunderstanding, misrepresentation and misuse as the vitamins despite the fact that far more is known about these compounds ... than about any other group in the U.S.'' (Greengard, 1970, p. 1643).

This statement accurately reflects the mania in America over popping vitamin pills. We take vitamins for everything, from hyperactivity and stress to mental illness and sexual impotency. Furthermore, we believe that, if one capsule containing the Recommended Daily Allowance of vitamins is considered nutritional insurance, then 10 times that amount on a daily basis should provide nutritional immunity for all ailments and diseases. Unfortunately, these claims are not true and not substantiated with hard scientific fact. In Herbert and Barrett's (1982) book, *Vitamins and Health Foods: The Great American Hustle,* the authors describe in great detail the vitamin hoax and health fraud that has fooled the American public. What we should remember is that vitamin supplements are not needed if a person consumes a wide variety of foods daily from all of the food groups. The only rationale for vitamin therapy is documented vitamin deficiency.

Taking high-potency stress vitamins to alleviate ''stress'' is another example of Madison Avenue marketing. The idea for this product was probably derived from a report in 1952 on therapeutic nutrition by two scientists representing the Food and Nutrition Board, National Academy of Sciences, National Research Council. Soon after the release of this report, the National Academy of Sciences declared it invalid on the grounds of inadequate evidence and recalled it. It is known that synthesis of

TABLE 6.1. CAFFEINE CONTENT OF BEVERAGES AND FOODS

ITEM	AMOUNT	AVERAGE mg	RANGE mg
COFFEE			
Brewed, drip method	5 oz	115	60–180
Brewed, percolator	5 oz	80	40–170
Instant	5 oz	65	30–120
Decaffeinated, brewed	5 oz	3	2–5
Decaffeinated, instant	5 oz	2	1–5
TEA			
Brewed, major U.S. brands	5 oz	40	20–90
Brewed, imported brands	5 oz	60	25–110
Instant	5 oz	30	25–50
Iced	12 oz	70	67–76
COCOA			
Cocoa Beverage	5 oz	4	2–20
Chocolate milk beverage	8 oz	5	2–7
Milk chocolate	1 oz	6	1–15
Dark chocolate, semisweet	1 oz	20	5–35
Baker's chocolate	1 oz	26	26
Chocolate-flavored syrup	1 oz	4	4
SOFT DRINKS			
Sugar-Free Mr. PIBB	12 oz	58.8	
Mountain Dew	12 oz	54.0	
Mello Yello	12 oz	52.8	
TAB	12 oz	46.8	
Coca-Cola	12 oz	45.6	
Diet Coke	12 oz	45.6	
Shasta Cola	12 oz	44.4	
Shasta Cherry Cola	12 oz	44.4	
Shasta Diet Cola	12 oz	44.4	
Mr. PIBB	12 oz	40.8	
Dr. Pepper	12 oz	39.6	
Sugar-Free Dr. Pepper	12 oz	39.6	
Big Red	12 oz	38.4	
Sugar-Free Big Red	12 oz	38.4	
Pepsi-Cola	12 oż	38.4	
Aspen	12 oz	36.0	
Diet Pepsi	12 oz	36.0	
Pepsi Light	12 oz	36.0	
RC Cola	12 oz	36.0	
Diet Rite	12 oz	36.0	
Kick	12 oz	31.2	
Canada Dry Jamaica Cola	12 oz	30.0	
Canada Dry Diet Cola	12 oz	1.2	
PRESCRIPTION DRUGS			
Cafergot (for migraine headache)		100	
Fiorinal (for tension headache)		40	
Soma Compound (pain relief, muscle relaxant		32	
Darvon Compound (pain relief)		32.4	
NONPRESCRIPTION DRUGS			
Weight-control Aids			
Dex-A-Diet II		200	
Dexatrim, Dexatrim Extra Strength		200	
Dietac capsules		200	
Maximum Strength Appedrine		100	
Prolamine		140	

Alertness Tablets
  Nodoz ... 100
  Vivarin ... 200
Analgesic and Pain Relief Medicine
  Anacin, Maximum Strength Anacin ... 32
  Excedrin ... 65
  Midol ... 32.4
  Vanquish ... 33
Diuretics
  Aqua-Ban ... 100
  Maximum Strength Aqua-Ban Plus ... 200
  Permathene H2 Off ... 200
Cold and Allergy Remedies
  Coryban-D capsules ... 30
  Triaminicin tablets ... 30
  Dristan Decongestant tablets and
  Dristan A-F Decongestant tablets ... 16.2
  Duradyne-Forte ... 30

Note: Food and Drug Administration (1984, March). *The Latest Caffeine Scorecard.* (DHHSS publication No. (FDA) 84–2184.) Washington DC: U.S. Government Printing Office.

the "stress" hormones epinephrine and norepinephrine is dependent on Vitamin C. However, no current scientific studies document the efficacy of increasing vitamin C dosage to reduce stress.

ALCOHOL

Recommendation of an alcoholic beverage as a therapeutic measure to relieve stress requires a complete knowledge of the client's social and medical history. Even after evaluation of this information, a recommendation to take alcoholic beverages for medicinal purposes should be given cautiously.

The primary effect of alcohol on the body is to depress the central nervous system, but the initial subjective feeling in most people is euphoria. This is a release of natural inhibitions and a feeling of escape from reality. The total quantity of alcohol and the rate of consumption determine the effect. Alcohol is metabolized by the liver on the average of from 7 to 10 g an hour. On the basis of this fact, the liver of an average adult male would require from 5 to 6 hours to fully oxidize the alcohol in 4 oz of whiskey or 2½ pt of beer. An excess of alcohol passes into the circulatory system and is transplanted to the brain, where it begins to slow down brain activity. If the amount of alcohol ingested increases, the symptoms of intoxication become more pronounced.

According to an analysis of the USDA Nationwide Food Consumption Survey, 1977–1978 (Windham, Wyse, & Hansen, 1983), suggesting alcohol as a therapeutic measure to reduce stress could be redundant. Their figures indicate that two-thirds of the U.S. population already consume some form of alcohol. Those who drink consume ½ oz of ethanol

SMCD–D

(alcohol) daily. This figure is calculated on the "drinking age population" defined as individuals 14 years old or older. The Nationwide Food Consumption Survey also reported that Americans prefer beer as their form of ethanol, rather than wine or distilled spirits. Of alcoholic beverages consumed in our country, beer represented 49%, distilled spirit 39%, and wine 12%. "Average apparent consumption equals nearly 30 gall of beer, which is equivalent to 320 12 oz cans of beer each year per person 14 years old and older" (p. 365). For the same drinking age population, per capita consumption of wine was 2.5 gall, distilled spirits 2.6 gall.

Before a suggestion to use alcohol as a mechanism for reducing stress, the client's present alcohol consumption should be carefully documented. Moderation in alcohol consumption is strongly encouraged, and this is defined as two servings per day. A serving is equal to 12 oz of beer, 4 oz of wine, or 1–1½ oz of distilled spirits. Table 6.2 lists the calories and grams of alcohol found in a standard serving of an alcoholic beverage.

SUGAR

Many claims in recent years have associated dietary sugar intake with delinquent and criminal behavior. The studies upon which these claims are based do not provide conclusive evidence that sugar caused the aberrant behavior. The majority of these studies suffer from poor experimental design, which invalidates the published results. An extensive review of the literature on this topic was published recently by Gray and Gray (1983). In their article, the authors critiqued the studies and programs that

TABLE 6.2. Composition of Alcohol Beverages

BEVERAGE	SERVING SIZE oz	ALCOHOL gm/svg	CARBOHYDRATE gm/svg	kcal per svg
Beer				
regular	12	13.0	13.7	151
light	12	10.1	6.0	90
extra light	12	8.1	3.3	70
near	12	1.5	12.3	60
Liquor				
distilled spirits, 86-proof (gin,				
rum, vodka, whiskey, scotch)	1.5	15.3	Trace	105
dry brandy or cognac	1.0	10.7	Trace	75
Wine				
table				
red or rosé	4	11.6	1.0	85
dry white	4	11.3	0.4	80
sweet	4	11.8	4.9	102
light	4	6.4	1.3	48–58
sparkling				
champagne	4	11.9	3.6	98
sweet kosher	4	11.9	12.0	132
appetizer/dessert				
sherry	2	9.4	1.5	73
sweet sherry, port, muscatel	2	9.4	7.0	94
vermouth				
dry	3	12.6	4.2	105
sweet	3	12.2	13.9	141

From Franz, M. J. (1983). Diabetes Mellitus: Considerations in the development of guidelines for the occasional use of alcohol. Journal of the American Dietetic Association, *83,* 147–152.

have been conducted to prove the effect of sugar on delinquency. Several failed to include well-defined control groups, so their reported results could not be attributed to dietary change. Experimental designs of other studies were invalidated by the "pygmalion effect," produced when an influential teacher molds a pupil's behavior to conform to his or her expectations. Random assignment to treatment groups and strict interpretation of hypoglycemia flawed the design of the study by Yaryura-Tobias and Neziroglu (1975). Breaking the double-blind technique and failing to match treatment and control participants on a variety of variables undermined the study by Schoenthaler (1982). Because well-controlled and well-designed studies have not been conducted in this field to date, conclusive evidence relating sugar intake to behavior is lacking.

In response to the claims that consumption of high sugar foods or reactive hypoglycemia is contributing to the crime rate of America, the California Council Against Health Fraud formed a Task Force on Diet and Criminal Behavior. This group conducted an exhaustive study on the subject and issued a position paper that was adopted by the council. Recently, The American Dietetic Association (1985) endorsed this position paper as their official stand on diet and criminal behavior.

Sugar has been implicated not only in criminal behavior but also in hyperactivity in children. Because the research that has been conducted in this field is limited and the results conflicting, scientific agreement on this topic has not been reached. Studies conducted by C. K. Conners, Goyette, Southwick, Lees, and Andrulonis (1976); Behar & Rapoport et al. (1984); and Gross (1984) indicate no effect of sugar on heightened activity levels in children. In contradiction to their work, Prinz, Roberts, and Hantman (1980) and Chiel and Wurtman (1981) have found highly significant correlations between the carbohydrate–protein ratio in the diet and the amount of hyperactivity. Until conclusive studies are conducted to document this effect, it should not be assumed that a child's sugar intake causes increased activity levels.

Sugar is not the only substance that has been named a cause of hyperkinesis. In 1974, Feingold (1985) proposed that salicylates, artificial colors, and artificial flavors were the cause of hyperactivity. As he refined his theory, he deemphasized the role of salicylates but intensified his claims that artificial additives and the preservative BHT and other antioxidants were the causative agents. If Feingold's claims were correct, the impact they would exert on the national food supply and the public health of children would be significant. Therefore, the Nutrition Foundation established an advisory committee and the National Institutes of Health organized an Interagency Task Force to examine his claim and recommend a method of testing its scientific merit. Diet crossover studies and specific challenge experiments were the recommended approaches to test the hypothesis. The major findings of the numerous studies that were conducted have been compiled into a report by the National Advisory Committee on Hyperkinesis and Food Additives to the Nutrition Foundation (Wender & Lipton, 1980). The following recommendations are in agreement with the conclusions reached by the Advisory Committee to the National Institutes of Health and also by K. Conners (1980) in his book *Food Additives and Hyperkinetic Children*. Based on the National Advisory Committee report and results of further studies, Lipton and Mayo (1983) have formulated these recommendations:

1. There is no indication for the continuation of high priority, specially funded programs for further investigation in this area. Individual research, based upon an investigator's personal motivations and subject to the competitive peer review system, should go on, however.
2. There seems to be no need for changes in public policy with regard to the use of artificial food colorings in the food industry on the basis of a presumed relationship between artificial colorings and behavior problems in children. There is no evidence to recommend a ban of food containing artificial food colorings in federally supported school lunch programs.
3. There is no special need for a symbol on food labels indicating the presence or absence of food additives for the purpose of treating behavioral disorders like hyperkinesis or learning disability. There may be other reasons for indicating the presence of certain food additives on food labels, but behavioral disturbance is not among them.
4. Since the food additive-free diet has no apparent harmful effects and since the nonspecific placebo effects of this dietary treatment are frequently very beneficial to families, there is no reason to

discourage families that wish to pursue this type of treatment as long as they continue to follow other therapy that is helpful. (p. 133–34).

The exact causes of hyperkinesis still elude us, but, in treating this problem, certain etiologies should be considered. The disorder could be due to anxiety, subclinical seizure disorder, or lead encephalopathy. In these instances appropriate medical or psychological treatment would be advised. If the hyperactivity is idiopathic, central nervous stimulants like methylphenidate can be prescribed (Lipton & Mayo, 1983).

BRAIN NEUROTRANSMITTERS

Neurotransmitters are the critical messengers that enable one neuron or group of neurons in the brain to communicate with another. Presently, 20 to 30 compounds have been identified as neurotransmitters. Of interest, each group of neurons produces only a single neurotransmitter, and the syntheses of some of these neurotransmitters are precursor dependent. In other words, the synthesis of the neurotransmitter is regulated by the availability of circulating precursors, which in turn is influenced by food consumption.

Serotonin synthesis demonstrates how this phenomenon operates. Serotonin is dependent on tryptophan, an essential amino acid, for its production. Protein metabolism releases tryptophan, a large neutral amino acid, which enters the circulation and joins a pool of amino acids waiting for transportation to the brain. The molecule that carries tryptophan also transports other large neutral amino acids.

Because tryptophan is competing for a position on this molecule, the higher the levels of this amino acid circulating in the blood, the greater the amount of this substance reaches the brain. Consumption of protein-rich meals does not increase serotonin production because the increased amount of circulating tryptophan is not delivered to the brain. Consumption of carbohydrate-rich meals does stimulate the production of serotonin. This occurs because carbohydrate-rich meals trigger insulin production, which influences uptake of all amino acids by body tissue *except* tryptophan. Therefore, greater amounts of tryptophan reach the brain, stimulating increased production of serotonin.

Research into the function of serotonin in the body has identified several behaviors that it appears to influence, including sleep, appetite, mood, and pain sensitivity. The role of serotonin in sleep regulation is undergoing extensive investigation. In animals, repeated studies have demonstrated that the destruction of neurons that produce serotonin or the blockage of serotonin synthesis markedly interrupts sleep patterns. Human research with insomniacs has produced more conclusive results with the mild insomniac than with normal good sleepers or seriously ill insomniacs. Hartmann and Spinweber (1979) concluded that doses of at least 1g of tryptophan significantly decrease the time it requires a mild insomniac to fall asleep and the number of times this person might awake during the night.

Further research is investigating the effect of tryptophan administered in accompaniment with a carbohydrate-rich meal. Because serotonin is identified in sleep regulation, greater production of this substance by the brain evokes greater drowsiness in the individual. Based on the previously described synthesis of serotonin, carbohydrate-rich meals should demonstrate in people a greater drowsiness than protein-rich meals. Studies conducted by Holman, Elliott, and Barchas (1975) and Clancy, Caldwell, Oberleas, Sangiah, and Villeneuve (1978) have supported this hypothesis. Richard Wurtman, an investigator in this field, theorizes that supplementing a carbohydrate-rich meal with low doses of tryptophan could prove very beneficial in treating insomnia (Fernstrom & Wurtman, 1971).

Yogman (Yogman & Zeisel, 1985) has applied these theories of sleep regulation to infants. In his studies, he fed infants a tryptophan-rich formula and discovered that the infants' sleep patterns were altered, that they entered quiet and active sleep more quickly. Although research in this area is promising, it remains in the preliminary stages of investigation. Recommendations to self-medicate with tryptophan for sleep disorders are not warranted, especially not in infants. The other clinically important neutotransmitters and their precursors are

Precursor	Neurotransmitter
Tyrosine	Catecholamines (dopamine and norepinephrine)
Choline	Acetylcholine

The synthesis of catecholamines by physiologically active specific brain neurons is influenced by circulating levels of its precursor tyrosine. These levels can be increased by taking pure tyrosine alone or with a carbohydrate-rich meal. Research elucidating the role of catecholamine in behavior-related disorders is very limited. Gelenberg, Wojcik, Growdon, Sved, and Wurtman (1980) have been investigating the theory that lack of catecholamines is involved in depression. Their clinical results from a small pilot study suggest that administering tyrosine might help alleviate depression in some patients. Other investigators have demonstrated beneficial effects using tyrosine with patients suffering mild Parkinson's disease.

The level of choline in the brain and therefore the production of its neurotransmitter, acetylcholine, can be manipulated by the ingestion of pure choline or phosphatidylcholine. Choline is found in food in the form of phosphatidylcholine or, its common name, lecithin. Lecithin is distributed widely in foods, but the richest sources include liver, eggs, soybeans, and peanuts. The human body also manufactures choline. Because of these reasons, a choline deficiency syndrome has never been documented in humans. Many people in our society take lecithin as a magic cure-all for various health problems. In most instances, lecithin has not been proven efficacious in reversing these disease processes. Moreover, investigators question the repeated intakes of large doses of the substance and suggest that the continued practice could disturb the cholinergic–dopaminergic–serotinergic balance in the brain. Daily doses averaging over 20 times the usual content of a mixed diet can produce adverse side effects such as gastrointestinal distress, sweating, salivation, and anorexia. Research into the role that choline and its neurotransmitter play in behavior disorder is in its infancy.

Preliminary studies have documented some beneficial success in treating tardive dyskinesia (Growdon, Gelenberg, Doller, Hirsch, & Wurtman 1978), mania, and ataxias with choline (Barbeau, Growdon, & Wurtman, 1979). Administering choline to patients with advanced Alzheimer's disease did not improve their condition. Prescribing choline in conjunction with either of the drugs phipostigmine or piracetom might prove more successful.

DIETARY TRIGGERS IN MIGRAINE HEADACHES

Stedman's Medical Dictionary (Stedman, 1982) defines migraine as ''a symptom complex occurring periodically and characterized by pain in the head, vertigo, nausea and vomiting, photophobia, and scintillating appearances of light (p. 879). A migraine is diagnosed as a vascular disorder resulting from a series of physiological events.

Research has identified various triggers that initiate a migraine attack (Perkin & Hartje, 1983). Included on this list are stress, vasoactive foods, oral contraceptive use, fatigue, menstruation, and exposure to glaring light. Based on this research, a "dietary" migraine has been described, in essence, a migraine headache produced by the consumption of certain foods. Estimates of the prevalence of dietary migraine in terms of the total number of clinical migraines range from 5% to 25%. Because of the debilitating and stressful nature of most migraine attacks, all efforts should be made to assist clients in reconstructing the events leading up to their attacks, to try to identify the triggering mechanism. If the "trigger" can be isolated, the chances of reducing these painful and stress-related attacks from a client's daily life are good.

Various dietary triggers have been implicated in migraine headaches. In early research, certain foods were thought to produce an allergic reaction, thus inducing the migraine. This theory is no longer widely accepted. What is receiving greater attention is the role of chemical reactions affecting the vascular system that might relate food ingestion to migraine. The primary reaction under investigation involves monoamine oxidases, which function as barriers to vasoactive chemicals in food. If the monoamine oxidases were defective, increased absorption of vasoactive substances could induce a migraine attack. Two prominent monoamine substrates, tyramine and phenylethylamine, have been implicated in dietary migraines. If the degradation process of these substances is malfunctioning, an excess of norepinephrine is released from nerve endings, causing increased blood pressure and eventual headache. Large quantities of these substrates have been found only in aged, fermented, or spoiled products. Tyramine-rich foods include aged cheeses (concentrated near the rind), fermented sausages, sour cream, pickled herring, yeast extracts, sauerkraut, beer, ale, vermouth, and wine. Phenylethylamine is found in chocolate, a food implicated in inducing migraines. The amount of these compounds required to produce a migraine varies. One researcher reported 3 mg of phenylethylamine induced a migraine attack 12 hours after ingestion in susceptible individuals. The same researcher found that the amount of tyramine in 3½ oz of aged cheese (100 mg) was enough to cause a headache 3–12 hours after ingestion (Perkin & Hartje, 1983).

Sodium is another dietary component linked to migraine headaches, due to its effect on blood pressure and volume in relation to blood vessel dilation. If this can be documented as a dietary trigger, then foods concentrated in sodium should be eliminated from the diet. This list would include salty snack foods, many cheeses, processed meats, canned soups, meat products, vegetables, most crackers, and pickled foods. More investigation is needed in this area.

Other foods linked to migraines are monosodium glutamate (MSG) and alcohol. One survey discovered that 30% of persons who ate Chinese food prepared with MSG developed symptoms that included headache 20 minutes after ingestion. In another study, 159 individuals out of 414 reported having headaches after eating Chinese food. Soy sauce contains MSG and should be considered a trigger food in susceptible persons.

Presently, the only form of alcohol that susceptible migraine sufferers have been able to consume is vodka. Wine is not recommended because it contains histamine, tyramine, and phenethylamine, chemicals associated with migraine attack (McCabe, 1986).

Because there are many foods implicated as triggers of migraine headaches, the following procedure is suggested for professionals who are consulting with clients suffering from migraines. First, ask the client to keep a food and symptom diary indicating food consumption, times of headache onset, and duration relative to food and beverage consumption. Upon examination of the diary, patterns might begin to emerge relating food intake to migraine episodes. If the offending food is clearly defined by the records, then it could be eliminated. If there are several foods implicated, then a more sophisticated food-sensitivity test may be prescribed.

CONCLUSION

In summary, certain food-related substances such as caffeine and the monamine substrates do appear to produce stress-related behavior in humans. Removing these substances from a person's diet who is complaining of symptoms might indeed improve her or his overall disposition. Otherwise, the research in this field is so preliminary and somewhat conflicting that to make conclusive statements based on published results would be unadvisable. Continued investigation in this field might one day establish a documented link between human behavior and diet, but for now, making recommendations or policy changes based on current evidence is not warranted.

REFERENCES

American Dietetic Association. (1985). Position paper on diet and criminal behavior. *Journal of the American Dietetic Association, 85,* 361–362.

Barbeau, A., Growdon, J. H., & Wurtman, R. J. (Eds.) (1979). *Nutrition and the brain; Vol V. Choline and lecithin in brain disorders.* New York: Raven Press.

Behar, D., Rapoport, J. L., et al. (1984). Sugar challenge testing with children considered behaviorally "sugar reactive." *Nutrition and Behavior, 1,* 277–288.

Caffeine: What it does. (1981, October). *Consumer Reports,* 585–599.

Chiel, H. J., & Wurtman, R. J. (1981). Short-term variations in diet composition change the patterns of spontaneous motor activity in rats. *Science, 213,* 676–678.

Clancy, J., Caldwell, D. F., Oberleas, D., Sangiah, S., & Villeneuve, M. J. (1978). Effect of chronic tryptophan dietary deficiency on the sleep–wake cycle. *Brain Research Bulletin, 3,* 83–87.

Conners, C. K., Goyette, C. H., Southwick, D. A., Lees, J. M., & Andrulonis, P. A. (1976). Food additives and hyperkinesis. A controlled double-blind experiment. *Pediatrics, 58,* 154–166.

Conners, K. (1980). *Food additives and hyperkinetic children.* New York: Plenum.

Feingold, B. F. (1985). *Why your child is hyperactive.* New York: Random House.

Fernstrom, J. D., & Wurtman, R. J. (1971). Brain serotonin content: Increase following ingestion of carbohydrate diet. *Science, 174,* 1023–1025.

Gelenberg, A. J., Wojick, J. D., Growdon, J. H., Sved, A. F., & Wurtman, R. J. (1980). Tyrosine for the treatment of depression. *American Journal of Psychiatry, 137,* 622–623.

Gray, G. E., & Gray, L. K. (1983, May–June). Diet and juvenile delinquency. *Nutrition Today,* 14–22.

Greengard P. (1970). The vitamins: Introduction. In L. S. Goodman and A. Gilman (Eds.), *The Pharmacological basis of therapeutics* (4th ed). NY: MacMillan.

Gross, M. D. (1984). Effect of sucrose on hyperkinetic children. *Pediatrics, 74,* 876–878.

Growdon, J. H., Gelenberg, A. J., Doller, J., Hirsch, M. J., & Wurtman, R. J. (1978). Lecithin can suppress tardive dyskinesia. *New England Journal of Medicine, 298,* 1029–1030.

Hartmann, E., Spinweber, C. L. (1979). Sleep induced L-tryptophan: Effect of dosages within normal dietary intake. *Journal of Nervous and Mental Disease, 167,* 497–499.

Herbert, V., & Barrett, S. (1982). *Vitamins and health foods: The great American hustle.* Philadephia: George F. Stickley.

Holman, R. B., Elliott, G. R., & Barchas, J. D. (1975). Neuroregulators and sleep mechanisms. *Annual Review of Medicine, 26,* 499–520.

Lipton, M. A., & Mayo, J. P. (1983). Diet and hyperkinesis: An update. *Journal of the American Dietetic Association, 83,* 132–134.

McCabe, B. J. (1986). Dietary tyramine and other pressor amines in MAOI regimens: A review. *Journal of the American Dietetic Association, 86,* 1059–1064.

Perkin, J. E., & Hartje, J. (1983). Diet and migraine: A review of the literature. *Journal of the American Dietetic Association, 83,* 459–463.

Pollitt, E., & Read, M. S. (1985). Bridges between nutrition, neuroscience, and behavior. *American Journal of Clinical Nutrition, 42,* 348–351.

Prinz, R. J., Roberts, W. A., & Hantman, E. (1980). Dietary correlates of hyperactive behavior in children. *Journal of Consulting and Clinical Psychology, 48,* 760–769.

Schoenthaler, S. J. (1982). The effect of sugar on the treatment and control of antisocial behavior: A double-blind study of an incarcerated juvenile population. *International Journal for Biosocial Research, 3,* 1–9.

Selye, H. (1970, Spring). On just being sick. *Nutrition Today,* 2–10.

Stedman's medical dictionary, illustrated. (1982). Baltimore: Williams and Wilkins.

Stephenson, P. E. (1977). Physiologic and psychotropic effects of caffeine on man. *Journal of the American Dietetic Association, 71,* 240–247.

Wender, E. H., & Lipton, E. H., (1980). *National Advisory Committee on Hyperkinesis and Food Additives: Final report to the Nutrition Foundation.* Washington, DC: The Nutrition Foundation.

Windham, C. T., Wyse, B. W., & Hansen, R. G. (1983). Alcohol consumption and nutrient density of diets in the Nationwide Food Consumption Survey. *Journal of the American Dietetic Association, 82,* 364–370.

Yaryura-Tobias, J. A., & Neziroglu, F. (1975). Violent behavior, brain dysrhythmia, and glucose dysfunction: A new syndrome. *Journal of Orthomolecular Psychiatry, 4,* 182–188.

Yogman, M. W., & Zeisel, S. H. (1985). Nutrients, neurotransmitters and infant behavior. *American Journal of Clinical Nutrition, 42,* 352–360.

Chapter 7

Hypnosis for Stress Management

I am a part of all that I have met;
Yet all experience is an arch wherethrough
Gleams that untravell'd world, whose margin fades
For ever and for ever when I move.
— Alfred Lord Tennyson

Eva S. Stubits

INTRODUCTION

Historical Perspectives

Hypnosis and hypnotic phenomena have been described since the evolution of consciousness, and they continue to intrigue those interested in exploring the limits of human potential. Hypnosis has been practiced under different labels by tribal medicine men, witch doctors, and religious healers. Passages from the 3,000-year-old Egyptian Book of the Dead describe hypnotic induction procedures similar to those used today. The concept of the laying on of hands described in the Bible and the Talmud can be considered a hypnotic technique. In the middle ages, kings and princes were described as having the "magic touch" and often achieved seemingly miraculous cures.

Our contemporary understanding of hypnosis begins during the Age of Reason with Franz Anton Mesmer, an 18th-century physician faith healer who attempted to develop a scientific understanding of the powerful curative forces he had learned to use. Borrowing from the ideas of the Viennese Jesuit, Maximilian Hell, Mesmer believed that he had discovered a cosmic fluid present in all things whose blockage resulted in disease. Mesmer attempted to redirect this fluid by inducing a "crisis" through the use of magnets. Due to widespread interest in Mesmerism, the French government appointed a royal commission to study the process. The commission disproved Mesmer's theories and concluded that patient cooperation and expectancies were the basis of Mesmer's cures.

Despite the official denunciation of Mesmerism, interest in the phenomenon continued to spread throughout the world. The first recorded use of hypnoanesthesia was by Recamier in 1821, who performed surgery on patients in a mesmeric coma. James Esdaile, a Scottish surgeon practicing in India, reported hundreds of painless operations between 1840 and 1850 (Esdaile, 1850). Another Scottish physician, James Braid, coined the terms *hypnotism* and *hypnosis* from the Greek word *hypnos*, meaning sleep (Braid, 1843). His belief that an individual's expectancy increased susceptibility to suggestion earned him the title Father of Modern Hypnotism. Sigmund Freud became interested in hypnosis in the 1890s and contributed to its development with his discovery of the unconscious mind and psycho-dynamic processes.

Unfortunately, Freud's subsequent rejection of hypnosis and its affiliation with showmen and showwomen and psychic phenomena led to its loss of respectability. This loss was partially regained when Milton Erickson presented a graduate seminar on hypnosis in 1923 and Clark Hull published his classic book *Hypnosis and Suggestibility: An Experimental Approach* in 1933. Since then, hypnosis has become the subject of legitimate scientific experimentation and was officially accepted by the American Medical Association in 1958 as a therapeutic tool. Interest in hypnosis has continued to grow and mature, coinciding with a resurgence of interest in the area of behavioral medicine in the 1970s.

Theories of Hypnosis

Increased scientific scrutiny of hypnosis has led to the development of numerous theoretical formulations. The atavism, or death feint, theory (Meares, 1960) describes hypnosis as a type of immobilization reflex in which a powerful stimulus such as fright can cause an animal or individual to "freeze." However, this theory is unable to explain how symbolic meanings and increased repetition can produce hypnosis in humans. Psychophysiological theories unsuccessfully attempted to differentiate hypnosis on the basis of unique physiological criteria or to define hypnosis as a type of sleep. Other theorists have characterized hypnosis as selective hypersuggestivity (Weitzenhoffer, 1953, 1957), adaptive regression of the ego (Gill, 1972), trance (Erickson, 1967), or a state (Hilgard, 1965; Orne, 1959). Barber (1969, 1974) argued that postulation of a special trance state is unnecessary and proposed that behavioral and experiential changes occur through a process of "cognitive–perceptual restructuring." Haley (1973) defined hypnosis as an interpersonal event requiring a special type of exchange between two people.

Tart (1975) distinguished between a baseline state of consciousness characterized by ordinary waking, sleeping, and dreaming states and a discrete altered state of consciousness, defined as a state different from baseline consciousness. External reality provides a set of cues to stabilize baseline consciousness, whereas trance induction helps the hypnotic subject focus on inner reality as a means of achieving the discrete altered state of consciousness of a hypnotic trance. Wall (1984) conceptualized hypnotic induction as a strategy to distract left-hemisphere functioning, followed by a shift to right-brain processes through utilization of repatterning suggestions.

The coexistence of numerous models of hypnosis reflects continued ambiguity and disagreement. However, most theorists view hypnosis as a trance, or state, involving heightened acuity and concentration and less critical acceptance of suggestions through the bypassing of conscious or higher cortical controls. Although acknowledging the importance of expectancy and demand characteristics, trance theorists propose that an altered state, possibly with increased right-brain involvement, best accounts for hypnotic phenomena. The neo-dissociation theory (Hilgard, 1979) softens the chasm between state and nonstate theories by proposing a continuum of dissociative experiences ranging from superficial responses to suggestion, to deep, widespread, subjective dissociations. Individual differences in dissociative capacity can explain divergencies in hypnotic responsivity, with more profound dissociations suggestive of an altered state of consciousness, or trance.

Common Misconceptions about Hypnosis

Despite continuing advances in our scientific understanding of hypnosis, many professionals and patients view hypnosis as mystical and dangerous. This perception is encouraged by media misrepresentation of hypnosis and the sensationalism promulgated by showwomen and showmen. Because fears and false expectancies can impede success, it is essential prior to trance induction, to discuss and dispel myths and fallacies. Some of the most commonly held misconceptions are listed next.

1. The hypnotist is a person gifted with unusual, mysterious, and magical powers. In fact, the hypnotist, or operator, is a person who has learned skills that can facilitate the development of a hypnotic trance. Hypnotic subjects actually hypnotize themselves through their own convictions.

2. The experience of hypnosis involves being asleep, unconscious, or in a mystical state. In fact, hypnosis bears little resemblance to sleep. The hypnotic state is often characterized by heightened acuity, concentration, and receptivity to the operator's suggestions.

3. Hypnosis is a surrender of will. In fact, subjects cannot be forced to do anything against their wishes or moral codes. Subjects will accept *only* suggestions they wish to accept and will not do anything they do not want to do. The hypnotic subject is the one in control.

4. Subjects in a hypnotic trance reveal all their secrets. In fact, subjects are capable of choosing what to reveal and what to withhold. Subjects are also able to lie while in a trance.

5. If the operator dies or leaves while the subject is in a trance, the subject cannot be dehypnotized. In fact, hypnotic subjects put themselves into a trance by their own beliefs. Therefore, they can bring themselves out of a trance in a split second, if need be.

6. People who are easily hypnotized are weak-minded or weak-willed. In fact, people who are imaginative, of above average intelligence, and capable of intense concentration are usually the most easily hypnotized.
7. Many people cannot be hypnotized. In fact, under the right conditions, and given enough motivation, almost everyone can be hypnotized.
8. A person has to be put into a deep state of hypnosis to achieve results. In fact, many excellent results can be achieved while the subject is in a light hypnotic trance.
9. Cures can be achieved in just one or two hypnotic sessions. In fact, hypnosis is a therapeutic adjunct and not a miracle cure. Although some habits can be broken in a few hypnotic sessions, given sufficient motivation, in most cases, a number of hypnotic sessions combined with other psychotherapeutic techniques are needed to solve problems.

In sum, hypnosis is not a mysterious state in which a powerful operator exerts control over a gullible or weak-minded subject. The operator's job is to facilitate development of a trance state and subsequent hypnotic phenomena. However, the subject is the one in control, can accept or reject the operator's suggestions, and actually puts himself or herself into a trance. Thus, heterohypnosis, in which the operator helps the subject develop a trance state, is really a form of auto- or self-hypnosis.

Trance Phenomena

Theorists disagree on whether behaviors frequently associated with hypnosis are unique (Orne, 1959, 1977) or not unique (Barber, 1969) to the hypnotic state. Hilgard (1979) proposed that profound subjective changes can occur during deep hypnosis, with the degree of change dependent upon the extent of dissociative experiences. He suggested that hypnosis can alter central cognitive executive functions, to reduce the criticality associated with the subject's usual "reality orientation" but without her or his totally relinquishing normal cognitive controls. This relative lack of criticality allows the hypnotized individual to experience an altered subjective state, with potential changes in memory, perception, cognition, and behavior. Examples of these hypnotic phenomena include catalepsy, ideomotor activities, ideosensory activities, hallucinations, hyperesthesia, hypnotic analgesia and anesthesia, dissociative experiences, time distortion, hypnotic amnesia, hypermnesia, age regression or pseudorevivification, revivification, and acceptance of posthypnotic suggestions (Kroger & Fezler 1976; Kroger 1977).

Catalepsy is a common hypnotic phenomenon that involves involuntary muscle tonicity. Ideomotor activities refer to the involuntary capacity of muscles to respond spontaneously to images or ideas outside of conscious awareness. This ability can be used to deepen a trance, as hypnotic subjects do not realize that involuntary muscle movements are a function of their own thoughts in response to external suggestions. Ideomotor signaling, in which a hypnotic subject answers a question by lifting the appropriate finger (designated as "yes," "no," "I don't know," or "I don't want to answer") is an example of ideomotor activity.

Ideosensory activity is based on the brain's capacity to produce visual, auditory, tactile, gustatory, olfactory, and kinesthetic images. Although a natural capacity, as in a person's ability to visualize faces and forms when gazing at clouds, ideosensory processes can be enhanced during hypnosis and can result in the development of positive or negative hallucinations. Positive hallucinations consist of an experience of a suggested sensory event, that does not exist in external reality. For example, a hypnotic subject might "see" a person who is not actually in the room, "hear" the strains of a Brahms lullaby, or "taste" a nonexistent apple. Negative hallucinations involve an inability to sense the obvious. A subject might accept the suggestion that the five other people in the room are no longer there or be unaware of a putrid odor. Posthypnotic hallucinations can be either positive or negative and refer to ideosensory suggestions given during the hypnotic trance, but they are carried out after termination of the hypnotic state.

Hypnotic suggestions can also affect tactile experiences. *Hypnotic hyperesthesia* describes an increased sensitivity to touch in response to hypnotic suggestion. Analgesia and anesthesia can be suggested during trance and refer to decreased sensitivity to or lack of awareness of pain, respectively. Dissociative experiences can also be suggested as a means of pain control. For example, subjects can "see" themselves from across the room or experience themselves at the beach, thus detaching from the part of self experiencing pain. Parts of the body, such as a limb, can also be dissociated such that the hypnotic subject does not have to "feel" the "separated" part of the body.

Successful levitation suggestions are examples of lesser degrees of dissociation. Time distortion refers to a person's ability to expand or contract his or her experience of time. For example, suggestions can be given to stretch out and savor a pleasant moment or to contract an experience of pain into the space of a few seconds.

Hypnotic suggestions can also affect memory processes. Hypnotic amnesia involves a subject's ability to forget trance or other life events. Although amnesia might be spontaneous in deep trance, it is usually suggested. Hypermnesia refers to increased memory recall or retrieval of information. In response to suggestions, hypnotic subjects can often recall details of scenes that are otherwise outside of conscious awareness. Subjects can also re-experience past life events. In age regression or pseudorevivification, subjects reexperience past events in the framework of the present such that they are aware of their actual age. Revivification refers to the actual reliving of past experiences in response to suggestions, such that the subjects have no memory of events following the age to which they were regressed. For example, if bilingual subjects are regressed past the age when they initially learned English, they lack knowledge of the English language while in this stage of the trance.

These examples of hypnotic phenomena involve enhancement of naturally ocurring processes within an individual. Highway hypnosis or daydreaming are everyday examples of dissociative experiences. Forgetting and remembering are normal cognitive processes that can be enhanced or diminished during trance. The challenge of clinical hypnosis is to help an individual experience enhancement of capacities normally outside of conscious control, in order to achieve a desired goal.

CLIENT SUITABILITY

General Considerations

Hypnosis can be successfully employed with a wide variety of psychological, physical, and psychophysiological disorders. Examples of conditions that have improved through use of hypnosis are anxiety disorders, phobias, psychophysiological disorders such as ulcers and headache syndromes, chronic and acute pain conditions, habit disorders such as obesity and smoking, and depressive disorders.

Determination of the appropriateness of hypnosis is based upon thorough patient assessment. Questions posed are similar to questions asked in intitial interviews. Data are gathered regarding the patient's current reasons for seeking treatment, major presenting complaints, symptoms, history and etiology, possible organic involvement, possible reinforcement for symptoms, prior treatment attempts, motivation for change and overall personality structure, and conceptions of and attitudes toward hypnosis. The intake process provides valuable information and helps establish the rapport that is essential for good therapeutic work.

Following a through assessment, the clinician can formulate a treatment plan. Patients with physical symptoms who have not been seen by a physician need to be referred for a medical evaluation. Unrealistic treatment expectations should be discussed. Issues related to low motivation or fears and misconceptions regarding hypnosis need to be dealt with prior to attempting hypnotic interventions.

The clinician also needs to determine if hypnosis will be used as part of a longer term psychotherapy program or as the primary treatment modality. For example, relatively intact patients with stress-related psychophysiological disorders that are receiving minimal reinforcement respond well to brief hypnotherapeutic interventions. A more careful assessment of the appropriateness and timing of hypnotic procedures would be made with patients who are severely disturbed or who are receiving a great deal of reinforcement for their symptoms. In such cases, if hypnosis is employed, it is usually adjunctive to other types of psychotherapy. Patients' conflicts and personality issues need to be understood, such that hypnotic procedures can be tailored to the individual. For example, patients with a major fear of loss of control might need continued reassurance that they are in charge of the hypnotic process and that they can choose to terminate their trances at any time.

Susceptibility Tests

Tests of hypnotic susceptibility have been developed both for research purposes and to help determine client suitability for hypnosis. Informal tests of hypnotic susceptibility include the handclasp test, the backward postural sway test, and the hand levitation test. More formal tests of hypnotizability with psychometric features include the Stanford Hypnotic Susceptibility Scale, Form A & B (Weitzenhoffer & Hilgard, 1959); the Stanford Hypnotic Susceptibility Scale, Form C (Weitzenhoffer & Hilgard, 1962); the Abbreviated Stanford Hypnotic Clinical Scale (Hilgard & Hilgard, 1975);

the Stanford Hypnotic Clinical Scale for Children (Morgan & Hilgard, 1973); the Harvard Group Scale of Hypnotic Susceptibility, Form A (Shor & Orne, 1962); and the Barber Suggestibility Scale (Barber & Wilson, 1978/1979). The Hypnotic Induction profile developed by Spiegel (1972, 1973b) is based on clinical observations.

Informal tests of hypnotic susceptibility are easy to administer, and the results are easy to gauge. In the handclasp test, subjects are asked to clasp their hands firmly together either at eye level or overhead. They are then asked to press their fingers tighter and tighter together and to imagine that their hands are glued together. Following several repetitions of these suggestions, the subjects are told they will soon be asked to pull their hands apart but will be unable to do so if they really wish to follow other suggestions. Difficulty with unclasping is indicative of high susceptibility.

In the backward postural sway test, susceptibility is measured by the degree to which a subject allows herself or himself to fall backward in response to suggestions. Prior to beginning the test, the subject is asked to practice falling backward into the operator's arms to insure that he or she will be caught. She or he is next asked to stand erect with arms at the sides and eyes closed. The operator stands behind the subject with hands lightly on the subject's shoulders. The operator suggests falling backward. Suggestions for body catalepsy are also given, and the operator's hands are gently drawn back from the subject's shoulders. The falling backward and swaying suggestions are repeated several times. A highly susceptible subject frequently falls into the operator's arms.

In the hand levitation test, the subject is seated with hands in lap and asked to relax, to stare at one of the hands, and to focus on any feelings or sensations in the selected hand, not matter how minute. The subject is then told that, as he or she relaxes, his or her hand and fingers will probably feel lighter and lighter, and even begin to lift. Lightness or floating suggestions are given repeatedly, perhaps using analogies such as "your hand and fingers are so light ... so light that it's almost as if they were a feather floating in a breeze ... floating upward, ever upward." The degree of hypnotic susceptibility is assessed by the degree to which the subject's hand or fingers lift.

More formal tests of hypnotic susceptibility employ a series of subtests similar to the tests just mentioned. The Stanford Hypnotic Susceptibility Scale, Forms A and B, originally consisted of 12 tasks that were scored simply for passing or failure. Tests items included postural sway, eye closure, hallucination, and amnesia tasks. The Stanford Hypnotic Susceptibility Scale, Form C, utilizes items that require increased use of imagery and cognitive distortion. Examples include mosquito hallucination, age regression, and negative visual hallucination tasks. The Abbreviated Stanford Hypnotic Scale consists of five items: moving hands, dream, age regression, posthypnotic suggestions, and anmesia. The Stanford Hypnotic Clinical Scale for Children is a short, seven-item hypnotic susceptibility scale developed by modifying some of the items in the adult scales for use with children. The Harvard Group Scale of Hypnotic Susceptibility, Form A, is a modification of the original Stanford scales for group administration. The Barber Suggestibility Scale is an eight-item test that measures an individual's responsivity to suggestions. Because the test is not meant to be a measure of hypnotizability, a subject's positive response to a test item does not have to be defined as hypnosis. However, the test content is similar to that of the other scales. Test items include arm levitation, thirst hallucinations, and a posthypnoticlike response. All of these tests have standardized administration protocols and scoring instructions.

The Hypnotic Induction Profile (Spiegel, 1972, 1973) was designed to be a rapid induction and testing procedure, which takes 5 to 10 minutes to administer. It consists of three major elements: an upward roll of the subject's eyeballs, hand levitation, and the control differential, defined as the subject's difference in sense of control over the levitated arm versus the other arm. Test administration is brief, but scoring is intricate and requires practice. Test items and scoring procedures are standardized, and the subject's score is thought to be indicative of various personality characteristics as well as hypnotizability.

Although few clinicians use standardized scales in day-to-day practice, the scales are valuable for experimental research, as they offer standardized criteria for assessing hypnotic susceptibility and depth. It is important to note that tests of hypnotizability consist of a set of direct, authoritarian suggestions set up in such a manner that the subject knows immediately if he or she has passed or failed a test item. These factors can influence a subject's expectancies regarding future experiences with hypnosis and affect her or his performance on remaining test items. Proponents of more naturalistic, permissive techniques of hypnotic induction refute the view of hypnotizability as a stable, enduring personality trait and argue against the use of any tests in a clinical setting. The focus of most clinicians is on helping the client discover his or her unique capacities for experiencing trance.

DEPTH OF HYPNOTIC STATE

Hypnotic susceptibility refers to a subject's degree of responsiveness to hypnotic suggestion and hypnotic depth refers to a subject's place on a hypothesized continuum. Depth can be measured by behavioral, clinical, subjective, and phenomenological methods (Shor, 1979).

Research Perspectives

For experimental purposes, depth of hypnotic state is usually measured by behavioral methods, although some researchers view subjective reports and phenomenological measures as interesting data sources. Measurements of hypnotic depth are frequently classed into the following five categories:

1. Nonsusceptibility
2. Hypnoidal (precurser to hypnosis) or borderline
3. Light stage
4. Medium stage
5. Deep stage

Behavioral measures of hypnotic depth use a standardized set of test items that are administered using a standardized set of instructions and are scored on a pass or fail basis according to objective behavioral criteria. Subjects who successfully perform more of the test items are judged to have achieved a greater depth of hypnosis than those who successfully perform fewer test items within a standardized set. Examples of tests using the behavioral methods include the Stanford Hypnotic Susceptibility Scale (Forms A, B, and C), the Harvard Group Scale of Hypnotic Susceptibility, and the Stanford Hypnotic Clinical Scale.

Subjective methods of measuring hypnotic depth are based on subjects' experiential reports rather than on behavioral performance criteria. In this method, hypnotized subjects are asked to call out numbers that best corresponds to the depth of their experience of hypnosis. Examples of self-report scales of depth include the LeCron Scale (LeCron, 1953), the North Carolina Scale (Tart, 1962), the Brief Stanford Scale (Hilgard & Tart, 1966; Tart, 1966a; Tart & Hilgard, 1966), and the Long Stanford Scale (Larsen, 1965; Tart, 1966b).

The phenomenological measure of hypnotic depth (Shor, 1979) uses retrospective reports by hypnotic subjects that can be used to make two types of measurements. One type is based on the traditional assumption that hypnotic depth is positively correlated with difficulty of hypnotic phenomenon. For example, eyes-open age regression is considered a more difficult task than hand levitation. Consequently, subjects able to experience eyes-open age regression are assumed to achieve greater trance depth than subjects who are unable to experience this phenomenon but do experience hand levitation. The phenomenological approach differs from traditional approaches in that the ratings are based on retrospective experiential reports rather than behavioral criterion. The second type of measurement assesses eight variables related to psychological processes considered important in the author's theory of hypnosis. The two measurements are nontranslatable, explore two different meanings of hypnotic depth, and are proposed to help clarify our understanding of the complexities of the hypnotic experience.

Clinical Aspects

Standardized tests or scales are not used in clinical assessments of hypnotic depth. Hypnotic phenomena are ranked according to presumed level of difficulty and depth of hypnosis needed to achieve successful performance. Depth of hypnosis is usually classified as light, medium, or deep. All items within a classification do not have to be performed in order to be gauged at a particular depth. Clinical observations of depth are usually based on a small subset of possible observations. For example, the experience of visual hallucination is considered a difficult task, indicative of a deep state of hypnosis. Consequently, a subject who convincingly reports experiencing a visual hallucination is considered to be in a deep state of hypnosis during that time.

The light stage of hypnosis is characterized by a pleasant feeling of restfulness and a decrease in muscle tension. Breathing often becomes slow, regular, and deep. Facial muscles loosen. Eyelids might tremble involuntarily, and the head might spontaneously move forward or sideways. Limbs are limp and fall unimpeded when picked up and released, and the subject might experience eyelid catalepsy. Manifestations of a medium hypnotic depth include increased relaxation and depth of breathing. Arm catalepsy and the ability to follow simple posthypnotic suggestions are also characteristic of medium depth.

Phenomena associated with a deep hypnotic state include the ability to develop positive and negative hallucinations and to follow complex posthypnotic suggestions. Development of "glove" anesthesia, age regression, revivification, and spontaneous amnesia are also indicative of a deep trance. Somnambulism is the deepest level of hypnosis and is characterized by a masklike face, staring eyes, slow speech, hyperesthesia, spontaneous amnesia, and the ability to develop hypnotic anesthesia.

HYPNOTIC INDUCTION

Practical Suggestions

When considering hypnosis as a therapeutic adjunct, it is important to have a thorough understanding of the individual patient and his or her problem. Following a decision to use hypnosis, it is essential to have a preinduction talk with the patient that includes a definition of hypnosis, a rationale for the use of hypnosis, a discussion of common misconceptions, and a brief description of the induction process. The patient's own concerns and theories should also be explored.

Once the patient has agreed to participate, comfort is important. The patient should be instructed to get into a comfortable position, to loosen any tight clothing, and to feel free to change position if desired. Subdued lighting contributes to a relaxing effect. Soundproofed rooms are desirable. A patient with contacts might feel better with the lenses removed. It might be best to postpone an initial induction if the patient has a severe cough or cold or is unusually anxious. Reticent patients might need additional discussion of possible fears and apprehensions.

The operator's attitude, skill, and degree of rapport with the patient strongly influence treatment efficacy. An induction based on the patient's own expectations, past experiences, and experiential style is the most likely to be successful. A calm, confident, supportive demeanor enhances trance development. The precise wording of the induction is less important than the operator's flexibility and familiarity with hypnotic procedures that will enhance suggestion.

Although suggestibility is not synonymous with hypnotizability, increased suggestibility is associated with hypnosis and can partially account for the development of hypnotic phenomena. Kroger (1977)

defined suggestion as "the uncritical acceptance of an idea" and described four modes of communication that affect suggestion. Verbal communication refers to information transmitted through sounds or words. Careful phrasing and selection of words and sound (such as mmm, hmm) is important. Short, simple words and sentences are usually more effective. Nonverbal communication refers to gestures, facial expressions, and other body movements. A relaxed countenance and deep rhythmic breathing can be used to model desired behaviors. Intraverbal communication deals with voice tone, inflection, and modulation. A soft, rhythmic, slow tone usually enhances relaxation and suggestibility. Extraverbal communication consists of the implied meanings of words and phrases. For example, the command "Close your eyes. Now!" is more likely to meet with resistance than the indirect suggestion "It might seem like an effort to keep your eyes open. Wouldn't it be nice to relax and let your eyes close and rest?"

In general, indirect, permissive suggestions without a definite time for completion are better accepted. Positive suggestions such as "you can find yourself feeling more and more relaxed and confident" are better than negative suggestions such as "you can find that you won't feel as anxious."

Acceptance of suggestions is also enhanced by increased repetition. Ideas repeated over and over tend to be acted upon. It is best to start with simple suggestions such as asking the subject to get into a comfortable position and take a deep breath. Suggestions should be given slowly, to give the patient a chance to respond, and they can gradually be built up to increased complexity.

A patient should also be asked to *allow* hypnotic phenomena and experiences to occur. "Don't fight it, but don't try either — just allow it to happen." This suggestion is based on the principle of reversed effect, which states that the harder a person tries to do something, the less likely their probability of success. Imagery helps to bypass conscious trying. For example, instead of directly suggesting numbness in the right hand, the operator can say "Imagine that your right hand is in a pail of icy, very cold water. Really feel the coldness and numbness of your hand. So cold, so numb, a wooden feeling . . . almost as if your hand fell asleep from sitting on it . . . or as if you had an anesthetic injected in your right hand . . . really, really numb." The idea is to enhance the patient's focus on internal feelings and processes, so as to loosen the anchor of outer reality. Use of all five senses (visual, auditory, olfactory, gustatory, and kinesthetic or tactile) is the most likely to be productive.

Reinforcement is also important, both in trance and consciously. Tell the patients how well she or he is doing and that she or he will do better next time. Never tell a patient that he or she is a poor hypnotic subject. Notice small cues exhibited by the patient during the induction. For example, if you notice a fluttering of the eyelids, tell the patient "you can begin to notice the fluttering of your eyelids and, as you do, you can drift even deeper into a very safe, pleasant, and secure state of hypnotic relaxation." Utilize everything you see to aid trance development.

Relaxation Induction

Hypnosis is frequently induced via some type of relaxation induction. Versions of relaxation induction vary, ranging from minimal modifications of traditional progressive relaxation procedures to inductions using a great deal of imagery. The following modification of a progressive relaxation induction was developed by the author. The induction was designed to include deep-breathing exercises, which facilitate physiological relaxation; to focus the patient's awareness on bodily sensations; and to help develop the patient's imagery capacities. Most of the imagery suggestions were designed to evoke the patient's own experiences and expectancies. Allusions to "a magical cloud" and a "perfect day" are used to indirectly suggest the possibility of "magic" and to enhance the patient's own capacities. General posthypnotic suggestions are given to enhance the patient's general well-being and to aid in the development of the next trance. Due to its simplicity, pleasantness, and nonthreatening nature, this induction succeeds with most patients.

Cloud Relaxation Induction

"Allow yourself to get into a comfortable position, close your eyes, and begin to allow yourself to relax. Take a deep breath . . . hold it . . . relax and let go. Really, really relax. There is no way that you can fail because all you have to do is to do nothing at all." General relaxation instructions are continued with the gradual introduction of imagery. "In a moment or so, I will probably ask you to imagine some things on that movie screen in your mind's eye, and it really will be quite easy to do. For example, if I asked you to imagine a red rose on a white tablecloth, you could do so very quickly and easily indeed." Here the patient's capacity for imagery is reinforced.

"Now, as you continue to breathe deeply and to relax, perhaps you can imagine in the very far corner of the room ... a very thin porous fluffly cloud ... more like a mist than a cloud ... so thin and misty that you can barely see it at all. And you can become aware that this is a very special cloud ... a magical cloud ... with a very special quality. It is a tension-absorbing cloud ... it attracts tension, absorbs it, and releases it into the atmosphere. And you can begin to imagine this cloud slowly ... gently ... drifting toward you ... toward your feet ... slowly enveloping your feet up to your ankles ... so thin ... so misty, you can barely feel it at all. And as the cloud envelops these muscles ... you can begin to feel those foot and ankle muscles loosen ... really, really loosen ... tension drifting away ... melting away ... absorbed by this wonderful, soft, and magical cloud that gradually and gently drifts ... up to envelop your calves, up to your knees." Here, the same general muscle-relaxation instructions can be repeated for the calves and knees, thighs, hips and pelvic area, abdominal region, chest, back, shoulders, facial and scalp area, arms, hands, and fingers. "As you continue to relax more and yet more and even more, this magical cloud gradually drifts off into the atmosphere. You can almost see the last vestiges of tension flowing out through your fingertips trailing after this wonderful cloud as you relax more and yet more and even more ... more relaxed than you ever thought possible ... drifting deeper into a very, very pleasant, safe, and secure state of hypnotic relaxation." At this point, the operator can suggest imagery, use other trance–deepening techniques, or begin therapeutic work.

This progressive relaxation-induction approach is offered as an example and is not to be followed verbatim. With practice, each operator will develop her or his unique version of a relaxation induction. Examples of other common induction techniques include the coin technique, the eye fixation technique, and the arm levitation methods (Smith & Wester, 1984).

Utilization Theory

Utilization theory refers to a broad theoretical approach to both trance induction and treatment, in which the therapist utilizes the patient's own motivation, cognitive processes, associations, perceptual style, and symptomatology to facilitate trance development and therapeutic change. This attunement to and use of the patient's own capacities forms the cornerstone of Ericksonian hypnosis and psychotherapy. Successful hypnotherapy is based on the therapist's ability to use words, intonations, gestures, and metaphors to evoke the patient's own behaviors and mental processes. Trance development is seen as a depotentiation of external realities, with an increased focus on inner processes. Learning in trance is thought to be primarily subconcious, as submergence of critical ego functions allows development of new perspectives and modification of old associations. Although Ericksonian hypnotherapy eschews formal induction techniques in favor of a permissive style that utilizes individual potential, a number of general induction approaches have evolved.

In the casual conversational approach, carefully framed suggestions for trance development are woven into a seemingly innocuous chat. The approach involves distracting the patient's conscious mind and creating uncertainty about outer reality, thus facilitating internal awareness. Shaggy-dog stories are one variant of the confusion approach, in which a long, nonsensical, boring story is told. The patient becomes so bored that she or he goes into trance. Questioning can be used to focus attention, suggest indirectly, and establish expectancies for behavioral responses. For example, the question Which hand is lighter? focuses attention on the hands, depotentiates waking consciousness, indirectly suggests that one hand is lighter, and puts the patient in a double bind such that a hypnotic response is required about whichever hand is lighter. Trance development can also be facilitated by evoking recall of previous inductions or by a naturally occurring trance state. Other general approaches include the use of surprise, pantomime, and heightened awareness of inner processes. More specific induction approaches include the early learning set, eye fixation, hand levitation, and mutual handshake inductions, which combine several general approaches (Erickson & Rossi, 1979).

DEEPENING TECHNIQUES

A variety of approaches can be used to increase trance depth. In the permissive-imagery approach, patients can imagine themselves in a very beautiful, special place. Following general relaxation instructions, patients are asked to envision themselves in their own very special place. It can be some place they've been or always wanted to go. The choice of scenery is left to the patients. The operator then adds suggestions that personalize the experience and enhance the vividness of the scene.

"You can see yourself there on a gorgeous spring day. You know what kind of day I mean ... the kind of day in which the sky is just a perfect shade of blue, and the sun is warm but not too warm, and there is a touch of magic in the air ... a gentle breeze is blowing, and you can feel the pleasant warmth of the sun on your hands and feet ... and really enjoy the lovely blue of the sky ... and smell and tase the clear fresh air ... so real ... so vivid, it's almost as if you were there now." Suggestions that employ the subject's five senses are repeated, followed by general relaxation suggestions.

Another popular deepening technique is the elevator technique. However, it is important to determine if the patient has a fear of elevators prior to using this technique. "As you remain comfortably relaxed, perhaps you can imagine yourself in a store or building on the 10th floor and you can see yourself stepping into the elevator, a very plush elevator, with a comfortable chair in which to sit. And you know that, as the elevator descends to the first floor, you can relax more and more, deeper and deeper with each floor. And when the door opens on the first floor, you can find yourself in your own beautiful special place. And in your mind's eye, you can see the lights go on as you go down floor by floor. And you're now reaching the ninth floor and relaxing more and yet more, and even more. And the eighth floor, deeper and deeper ... and the seventh floor ... deeper and deeper still." Continued relaxation suggestions are given as the elevator slowly descends, floor by floor. "And one ... you are very deeply relaxed and you can see the door open and see yourself stepping out into a very beautiful, gorgeous place." At this point, the therapist can continue with additional imagery or begin to employ therapeutic suggestions.

The escalator technique is a variant of the elevator technique in which the patient is asked to imagine himself or herself standing at the top of a very safe, slowly moving, plushly carpeted escalator. The patient is instructed to step onto the escalator and to relax more and more deeply as the escalator slowly moves down, with the expectation of finding a plushly carpeted room with a door at the bottom of the escalator. Behind the door is a beautiful garden (or whatever type scene the patient finds beautiful and relaxing), and, upon opening the door, the patient can be in the beautiful restful garden.

Trance can also be deepened by utilizing ideomotor signaling or by suggesting the development of various hypnotic phenomena. "If you are feeling pleasantly relaxed and would like to relax even more, your unconscious mind can let me know by allowing one of the fingers of your right hand to lift … any finger at all … or perhaps one of the fingers of your left hand. You're really not sure just which finger will lift … you really don't know at all … and you're really not sure just when it will lift … but your unconscious mind knows, and it will be interesting for you to find out as you continue to relax more and yet more and even more and begin to wonder about which of your fingers will lift.'' This technique is particularly effective if the therapist has noted spontaneous finger twitching or ideomotor signaling during the initial trance induction. In that case, one of the patient's fingers will probably lift again, and the patient will take it as evidence of trance enhancement. Other popular trance-deepening techniques include evocation of hand levitation or arm catalepsy.

Vogt's fractionation technique (Vogt, 1896) consists of asking the patient to describe the thoughts, feelings, and sensations that were experienced at the point of maximum relaxation prior to dehypnotization. The patient is then dehypnotized, and subsequent trance inductions utilize the information provided by the patient. For example, if the patient describes a light, floating feeling when deeply relaxed, she or he can be told that, as soon as she or he feels light and floaty, she or he will drift deeper and deeper into an even more pleasant state of hypnotic trance and relaxation.

The foregoing are examples of basic trance-deepening procedures. With increased skill and understanding of the basic tenets of hypnosis, the therapist can develop his or her own deepening techniques. As with basic hypnotic inductions, it is important to take the individual characteristics of the patient into consideration.

HYPNOSIS IN MEDICINE

Although hypnosis has only been accepted as a therapeutic tool by the American Medical Association since 1958, hypnotic techniques have long been used as a treatment adjunct in many branches of medical practice. These include neurology, psychosomatic medicine, physical rehabilitation, obstetrics and gynecology, dermatology, internal medicine, opthalmology, orthopedics, oncology, surgery, and genitourinary practice. Hypnotic techniques have also helped patients cope with chronic pain syndromes, learn stress-management techniques, and modify behaviors such as overeating, excessive alcohol intake, and smoking, which are associated with an increased incidence of health problems.

Hypnosis and Psychophysiological Disorders: An Overview

Psychophysiological disorders are defined as physical diseases that are precipitated or exacerbated by psychological factors, including stress. These disorders usually affect organs innervated by the autonomic nervous system, such as those of the gastrointestinal, endocrine, cardiovascular, and respiratory systems. Examples of psychophysiological disorders include neuro-dermatitis, psoriasis, hives, peptic ulcers, chronic gastritis, colitis, tachycardia, hypertension, migraine and tension headaches, backaches, muscle cramps, bronchial asthma, hyperventilation, and urinary retention.

The diathesis–stress model (Sternbach, 1966) of the development of psychophysiological disorders proposes that individuals have a unique constitutional pattern of responding to stress such that specific organs or physiological systems are activated; certain organs or systems are predisposed to disease due to genetic influences, diet, or previous illness or injury; or both. Environmental or emotional stressors might combine with this physiological predisposition, to produce a psychosomatic episode. Examples of environmental stressors include injury, non-optimal environmental conditions such as extremes of heat or cold, natural catastrophies such as an earthquake, loss experiences such as bereavement or divorce, and stressors in the social environment. Individual's coping skills can affect the magnitude of the stress response or serve as stressors. For example, individuals who are hypervigilant or perfectionistic or who utilize a great deal of denial can be thought of as placing stress on themselves. People who cope with environmental stressors by catastrophizing or using maladaptive coping mechanisms such as overeating or abusing alcohol are also placing additional stress on themselves.

In sum, psychophysiological disorders can be seen as the end result of a complex interplay of factors including physiological predispositions and responses to stress, environmental factors, and an individual's personality characteristics and coping skills. Hypnotic intervention can be made at a number of points along this continuum, depending upon the needs of the individual patient. One general aim of hypnotherapy with psychophysiological disorders is to reduce anxiety and regulate autonomic arousal. Hypnotherapy can also be used to help the patient modify maladaptive beliefs, perceptions, and behaviors that contribute to excessive stress, including habit patterns that can aggravate or precipitate the development of a psychophysiological disorder. Because psychophysiological disorders involve actual organic problems, it is important to coordinate hypnotherapy with a medical treatment program.

Hypnosis and Relaxation Training

Although hypnosis per se has not been equated with specific physiological parameters, suggestions given while in a hypnotic state can be used to elicit the relaxation response. The relaxation response (Benson, Beary, & Carol, 1974) is defined as a physiological response associated with decreased sympathetic nervous system activity, and it is thought to be the counterpart of the stress, or flight-or-fright, response, which is usually associated with increased sympathetic nervous system activity.

Benson, Arns, and Hoffman (1981) described four basic elements associated with elicitation of the relaxation response: a passive attitude, with disregard for distracting thoughts; decreased muscle tone; a quiet environment, with decreased sensory stimulation; and constant mental stimulus such as a sound, a word, or a phrase. These elements are frequently found in hetero- and autohypnotic techniques. In a review of the literature, Benson et al. (1981) concluded that neutral states of hypnosis, or hypnotic states elicited prior to the giving of specific suggestions, are characterized by many of the physiological changes associated with the relaxation response. The authors suggested that individuals experiencing a hypnotic state might experience the relaxation response prior to the elicitation of other hypnotic phenomena. Suggestions specific to the relaxation response can also be given during trance. Posthypnotic suggestions to facilitate increased daily relaxation and autohypnosis can also be given. Home practice should be stressed.

Hypnosis and Pain Control

Until recently, scientific theories have focused on the physiological and anatomical aspects of pain. In contrast, Melzack and Wall's (1965) gate control theory of pain attempts to account for physiological, psychological, and anatomical facts regarding pain perception. The theory hypothesizes a central gating function in the spinal cord whose effects can be modified by cognitive processes. Consequently, this theory accounts for the role of psychological factors including past experience, anxiety, emotion, and an individual's personal pain perception and response. Hypnotic techniques can modify pain experiences through modification of cognitive processes.

Acute Pain

Acute pain is usually defined as pain that lasts for less than 6 months, has a specific organic etiology, and is minimally influenced by social, psychological, or environmental factors. The pain associated with a broken leg is an example of acute pain. Because most individuals experiencing acute pain are highly motivated to reduce the intensity of their pain experience, hypnotic techniques are often highly successful. General relaxation inductions coupled with anxiety-reduction suggestions can modify anxiety-related increases in pain intensity. The decreased muscle tonicity associated with relaxation might help reduce pain that is aggravated by muscle spasms. Other hypnotic techniques include dissociative suggestions, utilization of imagery, and hypnotic analgesia.

To enhance dissociation, a patient can be asked to close her or his eyes and imagine herself or himself in a different place. For example, a patient might be asked to imagine himself or herself experiencing such pleasant events as relaxing by the beach, snow skiing, or fantasying a science fiction adventure. Suggestions can also be given that the painful body part no longer exists. For example, a patient with a broken ankle can be told ''Pretend that you have no left ankle. When you look down at your left leg, you can see no ankle or foot. You can find this experience of a lack of a foot interesting and amusing because you know that your ankle and foot are gone only temporarily. But for a time, it is interesting to notice that you have no left leg.''

A patient's perception of pain can also be modified by using imagery techniques. For example, pain can be visualized as a large red circle on a blank screen, and that circle can grow smaller and smaller, until it is just a tiny dot. A patient can also be asked to visualize a number from 1 to 10 that represents her or his current experience of pain. He or she can then be asked to watch the number become lower and lower. Another technique involves having the patient imagine that the nerves to the painful area are connected to a box in her or his mind. Within the box, is a switch that controls each group of nerves, with ''on'' and ''off'' positions. A patient can be instructed to find the appropriate switch and switch it to the ''off'' position.

Hypnotic analgesia suggestions can also be used to decrease the intensity of pain experiences. A patient can be asked to remember a time when he or she received an anesthetic or took medication for pain, then asked to imagine receiving the anesthetic or the painkiller at the present time, and told to become aware of the sensations of tingling and numbness as the anesthetic takes effect. In the glove–hand anesthesia technique, a patient is instructed to imagine her or his hand immersed in a pail of cold, icy water and to experience a ''wooden'' numb feeling. Suggestions for numbness are repeatedly given. The patient can then be asked to imagine experiencing a minor pain in the other hand, such as the pain experienced after touching a hot stove. The patient is next instructed to transfer the feeling of numbness to the hand that hurts. This experiential demonstration gives credence to the idea that the feeling of numbness can also be transferred to the injured body part.

The previous examples are only a few of many possible hypnotic pain-reduction techniques. Because not all of these techniques work for all patients, an individual might need to be taught a variety of techniques and be encouraged to use the ones that work best. Once a patient has learned these procedures, she or he can use them alone through autohypnosis.

Chronic Pain

Chronic pain can be defined as pain that persists for 6 months or more and resists traditional medical efforts at diagnosis and treatment (Fordyce & Steger, 1979). In contrast to acute pain, chronic pain is incredibly complex. The role of psychological and social environmental influences is thought to be major. These influences include cognitive factors such as expectancy and coping strategies (Turk, Meichenbaum & Genest, 1983), culturally conditioned response patterns (Fordyce & Steger, 1979), and an individual's personality or anxiety state.

Prior to using hypnosis with a chronic pain patient, it is important to determine the role of psychological and social factors in the development and maintenance of the individual's pain behaviors and experiences. For example, an individual who is experiencing a great deal of reinforcement for pain behaviors and viewing the pain as strictly physiological is unlikely to respond well to hypnotherapeutic procedures without other types of psychological interventions. Data obtained through a thorough history, through psychological testing, or from pain diaries are useful in formulating a treatment plan.

It is essential to educate the patient about the role of psychological processes in pain perception and to reassure him or her that the pain is real. If conditioning factors are considered important, a behavioral treatment program should be set up with the help of significant others in the patient's environment. Anxiety and muscle tension can be reduced by teaching the patient self-hypnosis and eliciting the relaxation response. Cognitive strategies such as attention diversion and dissociation techniques can be taught, using some of the hypnotherapeutic procedures described for use with acute pain patients. Hypnoanalgesic procedures can also be used. In a situation where the person's pain serves as a warning signal for over exertion, posthypnotic suggestions can be given such that the person will only be able to do as much as is within her or his capacity without causing further tissue damage.

If use of several procedures does not result in pain reduction, questions can be asked in trance to help determine if there is a part of the person that is sabotaging change or if there are subconscious reasons for keeping the experience of pain. If the person is unwilling to give up the pain, it might be possible to modify the pain experience. For example, mild pain in the little finger for 10 minutes a day might be substituted for a continual excruciating headache.

HABIT DISORDERS

A habit can be defined as a disposition or tendency to act in a certain way, usually accompanied by frequent repetitions of the same act. Examples of habit disorders include nail biting, bruxism, overeating, smoking, tics, hair pulling, stuttering, and chemical substance abuse. Some habits are initiated or maintained by underlying emotional issues, whereas others have never been associated with underlying emotional problems. Some habits might have begun as responses to emotional conflicts and are maintained even though the original reasons for their development are no longer there. Such habits are often referred to as *empty habits*. Other habits might continue to serve important emotional functions.

When treating a habit disorder, the significance of a habit needs to be considered. The patient's motivation to change and frustration tolerance also needs to be assessed. For example, if excessive smoking is thought to be a primary means of dealing with unexpressed anger, it is important to assess whether or not the patient would be able to deal with the anger without smoking. The possibility of an underlying organic disorder should be considered with some habits such as tics or enuresis.

If hypnosis is part of the treatment plan, it might be useful to ask the patient's unconscious mind, under hypnosis, if there is any part of the person that would object to elimination of the habit or that would sabotage treatment efforts. Use of time-progression techniques, in which the patient sees himself or herself as giving up the habit, can provide useful information. For example, a patient can be asked to describe hypnotic suggestions she or he has found useful in changing habits. Screening of a potential patient through a phone interview might also be helpful. During a phone screening, a patient can be asked if he or she really wants to give up the habit. When external factors such as a spouse's insistence are the primary sources of motivation, treatment is unlikely to succeed.

Smoking

Data on the use of hypnotic techniques for smoking cessation are mixed. Holroyd (1980), in a comprehensive literature review, reported on studies with abstinence rates ranging from 4% to 88% during a 3- to 12-month follow-up period. The 17 programs reviewed were examined in terms of six methodology variables thought to be possible contributants to treatment outcomes: subject population, individual versus group hypnosis treatment, standardized versus tailored treatment suggestions, self-hypnosis, number of sessions, and adjunctive treatments. The best results were associated with individualized suggestions, an increased number of treatment sessions, and adjunctive treatment or follow-up telephone contact. Development of an intense interpersonal relation between the client and the therapist was also positively related to treatment outcome.

Pederson, Scrimgeour, & Lefcoe (1979) randomly assigned 65 habitual smokers to four treatment groups, to determine the variables that were related to successful smoking cessation. The groups consisted of counseling alone, hypnosis plus counseling, videotape hypnosis plus counseling, and relaxation hypnosis plus counseling. The hypnosis-plus-counseling group was the most effective, with a 53% abstinence rate at 6 months posttreatment. Saunders (1977) viewed smoking as a multidetermined habit that is affected by the smoker's characteristics, belief system about smoking, and environment. Her program employed mutual group hypnosis, in which hypnotized group members gave suggestions to each other, time-progression suggestions to evaluate the possibility of change in the future, imagery in which they were successfully able to resist future temptations, and were taught self-hypnosis to decrease anxiety and aid in nonsmoking imagery rehearsal. She reported a 68% abstinence rate at a 10-month follow-up. Spiegel (1970) and Spiegel and Spiegel (1978) used a one-session cessation approach, in which smoking behaviors were viewed as a means of respecting the body and preserving health. His reported success rate was 20% at a six-month follow-up.

Other techniques can be used depending on the needs of the patient. For example, during trance, environmental cues that used to be connected with smoking can be suggested to be associated with nonsmoking behaviors and relaxation. Underlying emotional needs for smoking can be assessed and suggestions given to associate the need with nonsmoking behaviors. For example, Lait (1973) described a patient who began smoking at age 10 in order to feel important. In trance, it was suggested that he could experience this feeling of importance in the future whenever he refused a cigarette or did not smoke when others were smoking. Other authors have recommended the use of covert conditioning procedures, in which smoking behaviors are associated with noxious stimuli such as a horrible smell, nausea, or grotesque imagery (Kroger, 1977; Watkins, 1976).

Obesity

Overeating is another habit disorder that is frequently treated with hypnosis. Spiegel and Debetz (1978) suggested use of self-hypnosis to restructure eating habits and asked patients to use a three-part self-affirmation consisting of the following phrases: (a) For my body, overeating is a poison; (b) I need my body to live; and (c) I owe my body this respect and protection. Lindner (1963) suggested restructuring situations that are typically associated with the eating of the wrong foods. Posthypnotic suggestions are given that evoke a desire to eat healthy, unfattening foods when faced with these situations. Suggestions are also given to program a thin body image. Covert sensitization techniques, in which fattening foods are mentally associated with noxious stimuli, are frequently used. Cooke & Van Vogt (1956) combined covert sensitization with suggestions associating healthy foods, small portions, and slow eating with pleasure. They also suggested that eating small quantities of healthy foods would result in a sensation of fullness, as if the patient had eaten a big Thanksgiving dinner.

Direct suggestions to alter eating and exercise patterns can also be given during hypnosis. These include suggestions to avoid snacks between meals, adhere to diets, increase exercise, and eat smaller portions. Time-progression suggestions and hypnotherapeutic work to uncover possible underlying reasons for overeating can also be used. Some treatment programs combine behavioral interventions with hypnosis and emphasize self-hypnosis (Kroger, 1970; Stanton, 1975).

Despite the wide variety of hypnotic techniques available to treat obesity, Mott and Roberts (1979), in a review of the literature on hypnosis and obesity, found few good experimental studies, with much of the literature consisting of anecdotal reports and case histories. Terms and measures were not well defined, and procedures were frequently not standardized. Additionally, many of the studies reviewed combined hypnosis with other treatment approaches such as behavior modifications, exercise programs, and diets. However, several more recent studies have found that standardized measurements of hypnotizability were positively correlated with weight loss for hypnotized subjects (Anderson, 1985; Deyoub & Wilkie, 1980).

Ethical Considerations

Although hypnosis is generally viewed as safe, a number of ethical considerations apply. Practitioners should use hypnosis only within the limits of their training. For example, a surgeon should not use hypnosis within a psychotherapeutic framework without proper training in psychotherapy. Traumatic and buried material should not be uncovered unless the operator is highly trained and knows how to deal with the material. Hypnosis should always be used for the good of the patient and never for entertainment purposes.

Careful patient selection and evaluation are important when determining the appropriateness of hypnosis. Prior to using hypnosis, the therapist needs the patient's consent or the consent of the parents when dealing with minors. A preinduction talk to clarify procedures and correct misconceptions

is helpful. It is essential to obtain a medical consultation prior to using hypnosis with medical conditions or psychophysiological disorders.

CASE HISTORIES

Colitis Patient

The patient was a 60-year-old, divorced woman with colitis who was referred for psychological evaluation and treatment by her physician. She stated that she had first developed stress-related problems when she was married. Her marriage was described as very stressful, due to poor communication with her husband. Her husband was pictured as a man who avoided conflicts, agreed to compromises, and never changed his behaviors. Consequently, the patient reported that she had stopped trying to discuss her feelings, had begun holding them inside, and had developed a coping style with which she blocked negative feelings out of conscious awareness.

The patient reported that her colitis had become worse 4 years before when her husband left her for another woman. Her parents had died the following year. At the time of the initial consultation, the patient reported that she was still trying to straighten out her parents' estate. Her divorce, which had taken 3 years, had just become final.

Results of psychological assessment procedures were suggestive of intense dependency needs, high anxiety levels, depression, and utilization of repression as a predominant coping style. Treatment recommendations included cognitively oriented psychotherapy to help the patient become aware of, and deal with, conflicts and concerns instead of repressing or avoiding them and hypnosis to decrease anxiety and tension levels. The initial induction was a relaxation induction procedure, and ego strengthening suggestions were given. The patient was taught self-hypnosis as a means of eliciting the relaxation response and instructed to spend at least 15 minutes a day relaxing. She was seen for a total of 20 sessions and reported considerable alleviation of her symptomatology. During a 2- year follow-up visit, she stated that she continued to use her self-hypnosis exercises and reported feeling fine.

Dermatology Patient

The patient was a 34-year-old, divorced Latin American female who presented with a 1-year history of excessive hair loss for which no organic cause could be found. She described herself as a nervous, anxious person who did not think very highly of herself. At the time of her initial visit, she had just begun a new job, following a 3-year history of several job changes. She also reported feeling angry about her 7-year relationship with a separated man.

The patient described a difficult childhood. She saw her father as a brilliant but stubborn man who had continually worked and found little time for his family. Her mother was described as a martyr with a history of depression and vague physical complaints. She stated that her mother thrived on illness because it was her sole means of getting attention from her husband. The patient fought identification with her mother because her mother was symbolic of dependency and weakness. Interestingly, the patient reported that her mother had a 10-year history of excessive hair loss, and the patient worried that she might be using her own hair-loss symptoms to gain sympathy from, and express anger at, her boyfriend.

Results of psychological assessment procedures were suggestive of a moderate degree of depression, high anxiety levels, low self-esteem, lack of assertiveness, excessive need for approval, and obsessive ruminative thought processes. Major defenses included repression, denial, and intellectualization.

Treatment recommendations included fairly long-term, cognitively oriented psychotherapy to help the patient resolve her identity conflicts and utilization of hypnotherapeutic procedures for relaxation training and to aid in unconscious learning. Given the symbolism associated with the hair loss, and possible secondary gain factors, it was felt that use of hypnosis without a therapeutic framework would not be effective.

The patient was seen for 70 sessions. At the end of treatment, she reported increased self-confidence, better coping skills, alleviation of much of her anxiety and tension, and resolution of her conflicts between dependence and independence. She was also able to work through her ambivalence regarding intimacy and became engaged. These factors, along with her ability to separate psychologically from her mother, contributed to a significant reduction in hair loss.

Hypnosis was used initially to facilitate relaxation training and to help the patient cope more effectively with stressful situations. Time-progression techniques were used in which the patient was asked to imagine herself as the type of woman she would like to be at a future time and to reflect on the steps she would have to take to reach her goal. Hypnosis was frequently employed during the therapeutic process to help the patient deal with previously repressed material. Dreams were occasionally induced while she was in a trance state, with the suggestion that they would contain significant material she could begin to understand. Imagery techniques in which the patient saw herself symbolically merge with, and later from, her mother were also used to aid the process of individuation. Ideomotor signaling techniques were used to help her understand some of the symbolic reasons behind her hair loss. During a 1-year follow-up telephone conversation, the patient reported doing well, with no recurrence of her symptomatology.

TMJ Patient

The patient was a 35-year-old, married, Caucasian male who presented with a 3-year duration of pain in the temporomandibular joint. Other complaints included depression, anxiety, inferiority feelings, sleep-onset insomnia, irritable bowel syndrome, and headaches. He also reported nocturnal bruxism (clenching of his jaw) and daytime bruxism when under stress. Dental treatment consisted of occlusal equilibration and the wearing of an acrylic occlusal appliance. Although the patient reported some alleviation of his symptoms from the dental treatment, he still reported pain, anxiety, and bruxism.

The patient stated that he had been experiencing intense, free-floating anxiety for the past several months and that his insomnia had worsened since he had started his own business 8 months earlier. He stated that he had been working 100 to 120 hours per week and that he had never taken a real vacation. He described himself as a critical and angry individual who was unable to relax and had difficulty establishing close relationships. Determined to overcome social snubbery, which he had experienced as a teenager, he continually drove himself to excel.

Results of psychological assessment procedures were suggestive of an intense degree of psychological distress, excessive preoccupation with physical symptomatology, depression, very high anxiety levels, and social withdrawal. The patient was a very compulsive, driven individual with deep-seated inferiority feelings. Despite his life's successes, he was unable to give himself credit and felt that he needed to live up to his own rather grandiose expectations. Although he was a very sensitive person, he found it extremely difficult to get close to others, due to a great deal of mistrust. Major defenses included repression, denial, and projection.

The patient was seen for 30 treatment sessions. Treatment consisted of a combination of cognitively oriented psychotherapy and utilization of hypnotherapeutic procedures. Treatment goals were to help the patient alter his driven life-style, build self-esteem, modify negative self statements, learn relaxation skills, and eliminate his bruxing habit. Hypnosis was used to help the patient develop relaxation skills. He responded well to relaxation inductions and exhibited good visual imagery. He practiced self-hypnosis at home for relaxation and to help decrease tension and anxiety levels. He was able to use glove anesthesia transfer techniques to help numb his pain when it became too intense. His bruxing habit was modified through suggestions in which the onset of bruxing or clenching was paired with jaw relaxation. Imagery during trance was used to modify some of his negative self-concepts and compulsive behaviors. Although the patient terminated treatment without resolving many of the underlying psychological issues, he was able to modify his life-style somewhat and reported a decrease in somatic symptomatology including jaw joint pain and excessive bruxing.

SUMMARY AND CONCLUSIONS

Once seen as a quasi-magical, mystical phenomenon, hypnosis is now accepted as a legitimate therapeutic tool and subject for scientific inquiry. Although theoretical disagreements abound regarding the nature of hypnosis, most theorists view hypnosis as a "trance" or state, with probable increased right-brain involvement, which enhances a subject's concentration, acuity, and involvement with inner, subjective feelings and experiences. These factors serve to reduce critical ego functions and facilitate the acceptance of suggestions.

Through increased understanding of the trance state and the logic of the subconscious mind, therapists can easily learn to enhance trance development. Although numerous standard induction procedures exist, inductions work best when tailored to meet the individual needs of the patient. Following a thorough assessment process, suggestions can be devised and administered to patients in the trance state in an attempt to facilitate therapeutic change in the cognitive, affective, or behavioral arenas.

In sum, hypnosis is a therapeutic tool that can be used as a treatment method for a wide variety of psychological and psychophysiological disorders. These include anxiety disorders; depression; habit disorders including smoking, alcohol abuse, and obesity; chronic pain syndromes; and numerous psychophysiological conditions. Due to its versatility, the uses of hypnosis are limited only by the therapist's imagination.

REFERENCES

Andersen, M. S. (1985). Hypnotizability as a factor in the hypnotic treatment of obesity. *International Journal of Clinical and Experimental Hypnosis, 33,* (2), 150–159.

Barber, T. X. (1969). *Hypnosis: A scientific approach.* New York: Van Nostrand Reinhold.

Barber, T. X. (1974). Implications for human capabilities and potentialities. In T. W. Barber, N. P. Spanos, & J. F. Chaves (Eds.), *Hypnosis, Imaginations, and Human Potentialities.* Elmsford, NY: Pergamon Press.

Barber, T. X., & Wilson, S. C. (1978/1979). The barber suggestibility scale and the creative imagination scale: Experimental and clinical applications. *American Journal of Clinical Hypnosis, 21,* 85.

Benson, H., Arns, P. A., & Hoffman, J. W. (1981). The relaxation response and hypnosis. *International Journal of Clinical and Experimental Hypnosis, 29,* (3), 259–270.

Benson, H., Beary, J. F., & Carol, M. P. (1974). The relaxation response. *Psychiatry, 37,* 37–46.

Braid, J. (1843). *Neurypnology, or the rationale of nervous sleep considered in relation to animal magnetism.* London: Churchill.

Cooke, C. E., & Van Vogt, A. E. (1956). *The hypnotism handbook.* Alhambra, CA: Borden.

Deyoub, P. L., & Wilkie, R. (1980). Suggestion with and without hypnotic induction in a weight reduction program. *International Journal of Clinical and Experimental Hypnosis, 28,* 333.

Erickson, M. H. (1967). Deep hypnosis and its induction. In J Haley (Ed.), *Advanced techniques of hypnosis and therapy-selected papers of Milton H. Erickson.* New York: Grune & Stratton.

Erickson, M. H., & Rossi, E. L. (1979). *Hypnotherapy: An exploratory casebook.* New York: Irvington.

Esdaile, J. (1850). *Mesmerism in India.* Hartford, England: S. Andrus & Son.

Fordyce, W. E. (1976). *Behavioral methods for chronic pain and illness.* St. Louis: C. V. Mosby.

Fordyce, W. E., & Steger, J. C. (1979). Chronic pain. In O. F. Pomerleau, J. P. Brady (Eds.), *Behavioral medicine: Theory and practice.* Baltimore: Williams & Wilkins.

Gill, M. M. (1972). Hypnosis as an altered and regressed state. *International Journal of Clinical and Experimental Hypnosis, 20,* 224.

Haley, J. (1973). *Uncommon therapy: The psychiatric techniques of Milton H. Erickson, M. D.* New York: W. W. Norton.

Hilgard, E. R. (1965). Hypnosis. *Annual Review of*

Psychology, 16, 157.

Hilgard, E. R. (1979). Divided consciousness in hypnosis: The implications of the hidden observer. In E. Fromm & R. E. Shor (Eds.), *Hypnosis: Developments in research and new perspectives* (2nd ed.). New York: Aldine.

Hilgard, E. R., & Hilgard, J. R. (1975). *Hypnosis in the relief of pain.* Los Altos, CA: William Kaufmann.

Hilgard, E. R., & Tart, C. T. (1966). Responsiveness to suggestions following waking and imagination instructions and following induction of hypnosis. *Journal of Abnormal Psychology, 71,* 196–208.

Holroyd, J. (1980). Hypnosis treatment for smoking: An evaluative review. *International Journal of Clinical and Experimental Hypnosis, 28,* 4, 341–357.

Hull, C. L. (1933). *Hypnosis and suggestibility: An experimental approach.* New York: Appleton-Century-Crofts.

Kroger, W. S. (1970). Comprehensive Management of Obesity. *American Journal of Clinical Hypnosis, 12,* 165–176.

Kroger, W. S. (1977). *Clinical and experimental hypnosis in medicine, dentistry and psychology,* (2nd ed.). Philadelphia: J. B. Lippincott.

Kroger, W. S., & Fezler, W. D. (1976). *Hypnosis and behavior modification: Imagery conditioning.* Philadelphia: J. B. Lippincott.

Lait, V. S. (1973). Smoking. In The American Society of Clinical Hypnosis Education and Research Foundation, *A syllabus on hypnosis and a handbook of therapeutic suggestions.* Des Plaines. IL: Editor.

Larsen, S. (1965). *Strategies for reducing phobic behavior.* Unpublished doctoral dissertation, Stanford University.

LeCron, L. M. (1953). A method of measuring the depth of hypnosis. *Journal of Clinical and Experimental Hypnosis, 1,* (2), 4–7.

Lindner, P. G. (1963). *Mind over platter.* North Hollywood, CA: Wilshire Book.

Meares, A. (1960). *A system of medical hypnosis.* Philadelphia: W. B. Saunders.

Melzack, R., & Wall, P. (1965). Pain mechanisms: A new theory. *Science, 150,* 971.

Morgan, A. H., & Hilgard, E. R. (1973). Age differences in susceptibility to hypnosis. *International Journal of Clinical and Experimental Hypnosis, 21,* 78.

Mott, T., & Roberts, J. (1979). Obesity and hypnosis: A review of the literature. *American Journal of Clinical Hypnosis, 22,* 3.

Orne, M. T. (1959). The nature of hypnosis: Artifact and essence. *Journal of Abnormal Psychology, 58,* 277.

Orne, M. T. (1977). The construct of hypnosis: Implications of the definition for research and practice. In W. E. Edmonston Jr. (Ed.). *Conceptual and investigative approaches to hypnosis and hypnotic phenomena.* New York: Academy of Sciences.

Pederson, L. L., Scrimgeour, W. G., & Lefcoe, N. M. (1979). Variables of hypnosis which are related to success in a smoking withdrawal program. *International Journal of Clinical and Experimental Hypnosis, 27,* 14.

Saunders, S. (1977). Mutual group hypnosis and smoking. *American Journal of Clinical Hypnosis, 20,* 131.

Shor, R. E. (1979). A phenomonological method for the measurement of variables important to an understanding of the nature of hypnosis. In E. Fromm & R. E. Shor (Eds.), *Hypnosis: Developments in research and new perspectives* (2nd ed.). New York: Aldine.

Shor, R. E., & Orne, E. C. (1962). *The Harvard group scale of hypnotic susceptibility, form A.* Palo Alto, CA: Consulting psychologists Press.

Smith, A. H., Jr., & Wester, W. C., II., (1984). Techniques of induction and deepening. In W. C. Wester II. & A. H. Smith Jr. (Eds.), *Clinical hypnosis: A multidisciplinary approach.* Philadelphia: J. B. Lippincott.

Spiegel, H. (1972). An eye-roll test for hypnotizability. *American Journal of Clinical Hypnosis, 15,* 25–28.

Spiegel, H. (1973). *Manual for hypnotic induction profile: Eye-roll levitation method* (rev. ed.). New York: Soni Medica.

Spiegel, H. (1970). A single-treatment method to stop smoking using ancillary self-hypnosis. *International Journal of Clinical and Experimental Hypnosis, 18,* 235–250.

Spiegel, H., & Debetz, B. (1978). Restructuring eating behavior with self-hypnosis. *International Journal of Obesity,* 287.

Spiegel, H., & Spiegel, D. (1978). *Trance and treatment.* New York: Harper & Kow, Basic Books.

Stanton, H. E. (1975). Weight loss through hypnosis. *American Journal of Clinical Hypnosis, 18,* 34–38.

Sternbach, R. A. (1966) *Principles of psychophysiology.* New York: Academic Press.

Tart, C. T. (1962). *A comparison of suggested dreams occurring in hypnosis and sleep.* Unpublished master's thesis, University of North Carolina.

Tart, C. T. (1966a). Types of hypnotic dreams and their relation to hypnotic depth. *Journal of Abnormal Psychology, 71,* 377–382.

Tart, C. T. (1966b). Thought and imagery in the hypnotic state: Psychophysiological correlates. Paper presented at the meeting of the American Psychological Association, New York.

Tart, C. T. (1970). Self-report scales of hypnotic depth. *International Journal of Clinical and Experimental Hypnosis, 18,* 105–125.

Tart, C. T. (1975). *States of consciousness.* New York: E. P. Dutton.

Tart, C. T., & Hilgard, E. R. (1966). *Responsiveness to suggestions under "hypnosis" and "waking-imagination" conditions: A methodological observation. International Journal of Clinical and Experimental Hypnosis, 14,* 247–256.

Turk, D. C., Meichenbaum, D., & Genest, M. (1983). *Pain and behavioral medicine.* New York: Guilford Press.

Vogt, O. (1896). Zur Kenntnis des Wesens und der psychologischen Bedeutung des Hypnotismus. *Zeitschrift fur Hypnotismus* (pp. 4, 32, 122, 229).

Wall, T. W. (1984). Hypnotic Phenomena. In W. C. Wester II. & A. H. Smith Jr. (Eds.), *Clinical hypnosis: A multidisciplinary approach.* Philadelphia: J. B. Lippincott.

Watkins, H. H. (1976). Hypnosis and smoking: A five-session approach. *International Journal of Clinical and Experimental Hypnosis, 24,* 381–390.

Weitzenhoffer, A. M. (1953). *Hypnotism: An objective study in suggestibility.* New York: John Wiley & sons.

Weitzenhoffer, A. M. (1957). *General techniques of hypnosis*. New York: Grune & Stratton.

Weitzenhoffer, A. M., & Hilgard, E. R. (1959). *Stanford hypnotic susceptibility scales: Forms A and B*. Palo Alto, CA: Counseling Psychologists Press.

Weitzenhoffer, A. M., & Hilgard, E. R. (1962). *Stanford hypnotic susceptibility scale, Form C*. Palo Alto, CA: Consulting Psychologists Press.

Part III

Applications with Medical Patients

Chapter 8

Stress Management and the Treatment of Chronic Pain Syndrome

Arthur R. Tarbox
Gerard J. Connors

INTRODUCTION

Pain as a symptom is the most common chief complaint offered by patients seeking a physician's help, and chronic pain has been described as an enormously costly problem in both human terms and financial expenditures. For example, it has been estimated that medical costs, compensation, lost wages, and related expenses due to chronic pain total nearly $70 billion annually (Bonica, 1980). Not too surprisingly, such a ubiquitous and costly problem has received increasing attention in both the clinical and experimental literature.

From a medical standpoint, pain serves a useful purpose as part of the body's alarm system, alerting us to the fact that something harmful is going on. However, because the word *pain* is used in so many different ways, scientists have had difficulty agreeing on a unifying definition of this clinical concept. Recent heuristic efforts have been focused on pain as a behavior (e.g., Fordyce, 1976), and several research groups have proposed a respondent model of chronic pain in which classical conditioning of the

pain response occurs when muscle tension levels are elevated in acute stressful situations, leading to a pain–tension–stress cycle and subsequent intractable chronic pain (e.g., Gentry & Bernal, 1977). The proposal and investigation of such models has led to increased attention to the role of stress in assessing chronic pain and to the importance of stress management in clinically treating patients diagnosed as having chronic pain syndrome.

The recognition that chronic pain patients constitute a distinct clinical population is a relatively new finding; it is really only since the mid 1970s that chronic pain has been admitted to the medical lexicon and chronic pain units established across the country. These pain centers are almost without exception multimodal in their treatment approach. It is perhaps not surprising that such increased clinical awareness occurs in the same period during which there has been a rapid burgeoning of attention to the role of stress in medical illness. This clinical interest is timely, as it has been estimated that nearly one third of the American population has persistent or recurrent chronic pain (Bonica, 1980), and perhaps one half to two thirds of these people are partly or totally disabled for periods of weeks, months, or even years. According to a fairly recent article in *Time* (June 11, 1984), there are now more than 36 million who suffer from arthritis in the United States, 70 million with back pain, 20 million who suffer from migraine headaches, 5 million patients diagnosed as having sciatica, and nearly 1 million Americans suffering from pain associated with cancer.

Chronic low back pain is probably the most prevalent chronic pain syndrome. It is estimated that lower-back pain has chronically disabled over 7 million Americans and accounts for more than 8 million office visits to physicians annually in the United States. Thus, the majority of patients found in chronic pain units present with low back pain. For that reason, much of the focus of this chapter will be on the treatment of chronic low back pain.

Theoretical Approaches to The Nature of Chronic Pain

Aristotle defined pain as "a passion of the soul." Ancient Egyptians, although they believed chronic pain was due to spirits and the gods, began treating it with opium by the 16th century B.C. The ancient Greeks correctly placed the center of pain perception in the brain, but this knowledge was lost to us during the Middle Ages, when superstition once again took hold. It was not until the Renaissance and the advent of such theorists as Leonardo de Vinci that pain was once again understood in terms of the nervous system.

Pain, like the stress response itself, can be discussed in terms of stimulus and response. Perhaps the most commonly utilized working definition is that provided by the International Association for the Study of Pain, which described pain as "an unpleasant sensory and emotional experience associated with actual or potential tissue damage, or described in terms of such damage" (1979 p. 249). Thus, pain begins physiologically as nociception, the neural response to noxious stimuli. Pain is the conscious perception of that event. The event begins neurochemically with the release of neurotransmitters stored in nociceptors for just such protective purposes. Among these chemicals are prostaglandins, histamines, bradykinin, and substance P (for pain). Such a limited model of pain, however, yields only a limited range of treatments, and most such treatments focus on removal of the cause of pain. Unfortunately, this is rarely, if ever, possible in chronic pain sufferers, and some clinicians have even described chronic pain as any failure of extensive therapy directed at eliminating nociception.

Clinicians and researchers have attempted to differentiate pain based on such categories as acute versus chronic (Holden, 1979), malignant versus benign (Gildenberg & DeVaul, 1985), and pain as masked depression (Blumer & Heilbronn, 1982). Sternbach (1974) differentiated somatogenic pain from psychogenic pain, although he acknowledged that it was a difficult differentiation at best. From a psychophysiological point of view, Sternbach (1968) defined pain as "an abstract concept which refers to (1) a personal, private sensation of hurt; (2) a harmful stimulus which signals current or impending tissue damage; (3) a pattern of responses which operate to protect the organism from harm. The responses can be described in terms which reflect certain concepts, i.e., in neurological, physiological, behavioral and affective languages" (p. 12).

The theoretical rationale proposed for chronic pain in this chapter is that the subjective experience of pain experienced over time leads to a complex syndrome of behaviors that can be viewed as the end stage of a progression that began with nociception, as described. Thus, it is less a question of when pain complaints begin to intrude on an individual's life-style than of *how*. To be sure, pain can be discussed in objective physiological and behavioral terms, but the patient tends to think of her or his pains as feelings of distress. At that point in the individual's life, when pain becomes "chronic," even if the pain itself follows the expected dermatome map or a recognizable pattern of visceral/and neurological pain, other factors have become important. Individual factors in the development of chronic pain include the pain syndrome itself, physical disability associated with that complaint, and psychological dysfunction that accompanies the pain syndrome. Psychological dysfunction centers around that constellation of symptoms describing the intensity, quality, duration, and locus of the pain. It is argued herein that it is difficult, if not futile, to attempt to differentiate somatogenic from psychogenic pain. Rather than visualize a series of unique, chronic pain syndromes along a single axis throughout this chapter, we will present a multidimensional model defining chronic pain on the basis of the patient's current physiological functioning, psychological functioning, and environmental reality (see Figure 8.1). In the assessment and treatment of chronic pain, all three factors must be equally weighted.

Development and treatment of chronic pain: a multiaxial model

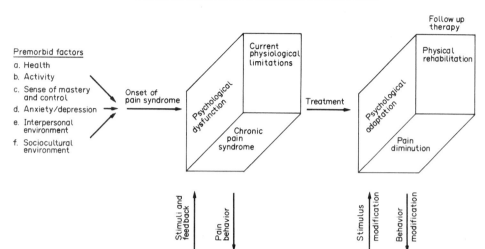

FIGURE 8.1. Development and Treatment of Chronic Pain: A Multiaxial Model

Note: From *Chronic Pain: A Multiaxial Approach to Psychosocial Assessment and Intervention.* (p. 203, 205) by Blazer, 1981, *Southern Me Journal, 74,* 203–207, 214. Copyright 1981 by Southern Medical Association. Adapted by permission.

TABLE 8.1. Biopsychosocial Assessment of Chronic Pain

A. Current Physiological Functioning
   1. Amount of physical damage
   2. Level of activity
   3. Degree of pain behaviors
B. Current Psychological Functioning
   1. Level of anxiety and depression
   2. Expectancies
   3. Competing sensory stimuli
   4. Suggestion
C. Pain Syndrome and Environmental Aspects
   1. Meaning and context of dysfunction
   2. Interpersonal factors
   3. Sociocultural factors

ASSESSMENT: DETERMINANTS OF THE PAIN RESPONSE

Given the previously mentioned multiaxial approach to chronic pain as a clinical syndrome, one can see that pain as a perception is determined by a multiplicity of biopsychosocial factors. Table 8.1, based on Melzack's discussion of pain perception (1970), outlines the determinants to be assessed in evaluating chronic pain. Melzack noted that pain perception was more than a function of the amount of physical damage inflicted on a person and that factors

such as expectancies and suggestion can significantly affect the total pain response.

Current Physiological Functioning

Medical Evaluation.

The comprehensive evaluation of a patient complaining of chronic pain begins with a skilled physician. It is within the physician's expertise to assess the underlying neurochemical determinants of the pain response, that is, the amount of physical damage. Within the context of taking a thorough medical history, this portion of the assessment focuses on determining the nature of the pain complaints encompassing, (a) character, (b) intensity, (c) distribution, (d) activities that ameliorate or exacerbate pain, (e) prescription and nonprescription drug use with regard to the pain complaints, (f) origin including when and how the pain began, (g) prior treatments and subsequent response, (h) the patient's perception of the problem, and (i) the patient's and family's past medical and surgical history.

Following the history-taking portion of the physician's interview is the physical examination. The results of a general physical examination are then correlated with the pain symptomatology, in an effort to ascertain the validity of physical findings, such as sensory and motor functions. This includes careful examination of the area of the pain: observing its appearance, palpating the area, and manipulating to determine such aspects as range of motion. All of this is designed to identify the specific area or tissue that might be the origin of the pain, in an effort to determine a specific treatment plan (Gildenberg & DeVaul, 1985).

Physical therapists are often consulted in an effort to further define the relative range of motion, muscle tonus, and role of progressive exercise in the patient's treatment plan. Premorbid levels of physical activity are compared with current levels of activity tolerance. This examination is particularly important in that one of the most common chronic pain syndrome is that of myofascial pain syndrome, which has been defined as pain that follows local injury to an area of muscle or attachment of muscle to bone, resulting in a stretching or tearing of muscle (Gildenberg & DeVaul, 1985).

Psychophysiological Evaluation: The Role of Stress in Chronic Pain.

Several researchers (e.g., Wolf, Nacht, & Kelly, 1982) have proposed psychophysiological evaluations utilizing electromyographic (EMG) measures for chronic pain. The importance of the interaction between psychological and physiological factors has been highlighted, due to the lack of empirical evidence indicating a straightforward organic pathology for many chronic pain syndromes, especially chronic back pain (Flor & Turk, 1984). To therefore explain myofascial pain syndrome, for example, one might invoke a social-learning-theory model, in which the initial experience of pain due to muscular strain or inflammatory process is followed by increased musculoskeletal tension as a function of this stress response, leading to a vicious cycle of pain–tension–stress (Gentry & Bernal, 1977). In turn, this pain might then be exacerbated by conditioned anxiety about physical activity, leading to relative immobilization and muscular atrophy (e.g., Lethem, Slade, Troup, & Bentley, 1983).

Empirical support for such a diatheses–stress model has been somewhat limited. For example, several reports have noted that chronic back-pain patients do indeed demonstrate higher EMG levels in various body positions or during differential relaxation, compared with control subjects (e.g., Grabel, 1973, Hoyt et al., 1981; Kravitz, Moore, & Glaros, 1981). In contrast, Collins and his colleagues (Collins, Cohen, Naliboff, & Schandler, 1982) found

lumbar EMG levels lower, compared with normal subjects in certain body positions. Collins and his colleagues went one step further and examined EMG levels in the lower backs of such patients following exposure to various stressors, and the results did not support the hypothesis that stress elevates EMG levels specifically in the back muscles of chronic back-pain patients. Instead, the authors observed elevation of frontalis muscle tension levels both during baseline testing and in response to laboratory stressors.

Before discarding the hypothesis that chronic pain is a stress-related syndrome, there are several methodological limitations that should be noted regarding the previously mentioned studies. Flor, Turk, and Birbaumer (1985) suggested that EMG studies should be bilateral rather than unilateral (e.g., Grabel, 1973), should include both EMG elevations and return to baseline levels, and should examine the individual responses of patients to personally relevant stressors rather than nonspecific, more global measures of laboratory stress. In a well-designed study, those authors reported support for their diathesis–stress model of chronic back pain. Only the chronic back-pain patients investigated demonstrated abnormal back-muscle reactivity to personally relevant stressors, and these patients alone demonstrated prolonged delay in returning to baseline levels of muscle tension. They concluded that identification of muscular hyperactivity could serve as a useful clinical criterion for the inclusion of a stress-management component within a comprehensive treatment program.

Behavioral Assessment and Observation.

Clinicians involved in assessing chronic pain in patients have also turned to direct behavioral observations, in an effort to determine baseline levels of function and response to treatment. Such behaviors may be assessed in a wide variety of settings pertinent to the life-style of the patient, and the clinician can then become directly involved in helping the patient establish on a contractual basis what his or her goals and expectations should be regarding treatment outcome. Keefe and Block (1982) have described an observation method for recording behaviors of chronic low-back-pain patients, including guarded movement, bracing, rubbing, grimacing, and sighing. They examined the validity of these behaviors in four separate experiments and reported that pain patients behaved significantly differently from healthy and depressed control subjects. Pain behaviors correlated well with estimates of pain obtained from both the patient and observers. Other researchers have utilized an observational approach to chronic pain by emphasizing the systematic assessment of categories of pain behaviors such as "uptime" (Sanders, 1980), medication intake (Halpern, 1977), and self-reports of pain to ancillary health care (Keefe, Block, Williams, & Surwit, 1981).

Questionnaire Measures of Chronic Pain.

A number of questionnaire measures have been proposed to aid the clinician in assessing chronic pain. Most of these have been rating scales geared to grouping pain complaints into sensory, affective, and evaluative categories, (Melzack, 1975; Melzack & Torgerson, 1971). The treatment goal derived from these questionnaires has been that of teaching the patient to self-monitor and to begin to discriminate incremental shifts in her or his subjective experience of pain. Such measures are also useful in explicating precipitating stressors and their consequent involvement in chronic pain as a syndrome.

Early measures consisted of simple self-rating scales such as that first proposed by Bond and Pilowski (1966), which consisted of a simple, graphic, 10-cm line anchored with the statements "I have no pain at all" and "My pain is as bad as it could possibly be" at the end points. The patient was simply instructed to make a mark on the line corresponding to the intensity of his or her pain.

A number of researchers have followed the lead of Sternbach (1974), who asked his patients to estimate their own pain levels by marking a point on a line scaled from 0–100. He went further by using a tourniquet on the patient's nondominant arm, so as to produce ischemic pain, and this procedure was used to obtain three measures of pain response. *First*, the patient was asked to estimate when the ischemic pain matched his current clinical pain level. *Second*, the patient was asked to match the degree of ischemic pain with his worst level of clinical pain. *Third*, Sternbach obtained a maximum tolerance level by asking the patient to report when he could no longer stand the ischemic pain produced in the tourniquet test. He reported the discrepancy between the subjective self-rating of pain and the tourniquet-matched clinical pain level to be important in the assessment of the patient's chronic pain syndrome. Sternbach was able to assess the range of ischemic pain response on the basis of the average response latency of a specific category of pain patients (e.g., the average maximum tolerance time

for patients with low back pain was reported to be 7 minutes).

Another popular questionnaire approach is that developed by Melzack and his colleagues at McGill University. They have constructed the McGill-Melzack Pain Questionnaire, which yields three major measures: (a) a pain rating index, (b) a number of descriptive words chosen for the pain complaint, and (c) the present pain intensity, based on a 5-point scale. The scale appears to be a valid and reliable instrument (see Graham, Bond, Gerkovich, & Cook, 1980; Hunter & Philips, 1981; Reading, 1979) for assessing the degree and nature of pain in a clinical setting, and it is of great value in assessing the degree of change in subjective pain during and after treatment (e.g., Melzack & Perry, 1975).

One interesting and comprehensive approach has been the Emory Pain Estimate Model (Brena, 1984; Brena & Koch, 1975). The model is essentially comprised of rating scales for physical function, on the one hand, and pain behaviors on the other. These two sets of data are then correlated and assigned to one of four different classes of chronic pain. The degree of organic pathology is based on four different factors: physical examination, neurological evaluation, radiological studies, and other studies (e.g., trigger point injections). Pain behaviors are rated on a scale based on three factors: (a) pain intensity (measured by rating scales as described, (b) self-reports of physical activities of daily living, and (c) the MMPI. These two separate factors are then correlated, and four classes are derived. In Class I, pain behavior scores are high, but organic pathology scores are low. Thus, Class I patients display conditioned pain behaviors in excess of demonstrable medical findings. At the other extreme, Class IV patients demonstrate high organic pathology scores and low pain-behavior scores. Treatment plans are assigned on the basis of specific class assignment (Brena, 1984). By operationally defining pain in such a fashion, this would appear to be a particularly clinically relevant and heuristic model. It is also apparent in this rather comprehensive model of assessment that psychological factors become more pertinent, and this is exemplified by use of the MMPI, which will be described below.

Current Psychological Functioning

The dichotomy between physiological and psychological functioning is largely arbitrary, and this should be readily apparent to clinicians who have dealt with chronic pain. Dualistic notions in medicine are being rapidly displaced by more holistic biopsychosocial approaches (Engel, 1960, 1980). However, questionnaire measures for comprehensively assessing pain can be divided into those assessing subjective aspects and pain behaviors (as described earlier) and those that evaluate affective aspects.

Level of Anxiety and Depression.

In an effort to assess the role of anxiety and depression in defining a chronic pain syndrome, most clinicians have relied on the clinical interview and on personality measures. Unfortunately, early attempts to improve diagnostic skills focused on ways to differentiate organic problems from pain that was more functional, or due to anxiety, depression, or both. The psychological explanation was that pain and the inability to experience or anticipate pleasure could be viewed as a central phenomenon of depression (Klein & Davis, 1969). It was believed that any measure for differentially diagnosing organic pain from functional complaints would be of immense value.

Psychodiagnostic Measures: the MMPI

Of all psychometric instruments, the MMPI has enjoyed the widest usage, and this is especially so in research investigating psychological functioning of chronic pain patients. Two early studies (Gentry, Shoers, & Thomas, 1974; Hanvik, 1951) concluded that the MMPI could be reliably discriminate somatogenic from psychogenic pain. Hanvik reported that pain patients whose complaints were clearly organic in etiology had essentially "normal" profiles, and patients whose pain etiology could not be documented had elevated scores on scales for hypochondriasis (Hs), depression (D), and hysteria (Hy). Thus, the latter group was considered to be suffering from "neurotic traits"; hence, their back pain was labeled as psychogenic.

Although other studies were cautious in statements about causality regarding the legitimacy of pain complaints, many authors (Maruta, Swanson & Swenson, 1976; Polley, Swenson, & Steinhilber, 1970; Sternbach, Wolf, Murphy, & Akeson, 1973) have consistently reported marked elevations on the three scales constituting the so-called neurotic triad (the Hs, D, and Hy scales). Phillips (1964) reported that scores on these three scales were higher in patients with low back pain than among patients with fractures of the extremities. Beals and Hickman (1972) have suggested that, as the number of surgical procedures on these patients increases or

rehabilitation is delayed, the exacerbation of symptoms becomes greater. Sternbach and his colleagues (1973) demonstrated that, although acutely ill patients had elevated scores on these scales, they were not as high as the scores of chronic patients. The authors concluded that chronic pain patients were emotionally disturbed, that the disturbances were neurotic, and that patients felt hopeless and totally focused on their pain complaints (Sternbach, 1974).

The implied assumption, thus, is that chronic pain patients whose scores on the first three scales (Hs, D, and Hy) of the MMPI are elevated are probably neurotic and have functional or psychogenic pain. As to current clinical and research utilization of the MMPI, we agree with Sternbach and his colleagues (1973, 1974), who regard the dichotomy between functional and organic as useless at best and destructive to patients at worst. Careful review of their results reveals "striking profile similarities" and no important profile differences between comparison groups. Their research has attempted to identify more pertinent dimensions that could account for systematic variations among pain patients' MMPI profiles. For example, they discovered significant MMPI differences between pain patients with less than 6 months of pain and with pain for longer than 6 months. Such advances can aid clinicians in more readily indentifying patients with chronic pain syndromes and thus minimize the frustrations encountered by patients and clinicians alike when an acute pain model of treatment fails to provide relief.

With affective correlates of pain being so important, the majority of questionnaire measures have attempted to psychometrically evaluate anxiety and depression through the use of adjective checklists (e.g., Flor, Turk, & Birbaumer, 1985). A complete review of such measures is beyond the scope of this chapter, but some of the most commonly employed questionnaires will be described.

Anxiety Measures.

Several researchers and clinicians have theorized that anxiety is the primary reaction to acute pain and that depression might be the response to chronic pain (e.g., Meichenbaum & Turk, 1976). Some research has suggested that the elevated levels of anxiety observed in back-pain patients are associated with relatively high levels of recent life-change events and stress (Leavitt, Garron, & Bieliauskas, 1980). One of the most common measures employed to assess levels of anxiety is the State-Trait Anxiety Inventory (Spielberger, Gorsuch, & Lushene, 1970), a measure comprised of two separate self-report scales. The trait scale is designed to measure anxiety proneness relevant to how a subject generally feels, and the state aspect is more situationally determined. Test–retest reliabilities on the measure are quite adequate, and several researchers have found significantly elevated levels on state anxiety only prior to treatment (e.g., Flor et al., 1985), with a consequent reduction in that scale following treatment in a chronic pain unit (e.g., Capka, Griffin, Harris, & Pinsky, 1979).

Depression Measures.

Far more attention has been paid to the role of depression in chronic pain as a syndrome (Fordyce, 1976; Sternbach, 1974). However, there is considerable controversy regarding the extent to which depression and chronic pain are associated and the mechanism of such an association, if it does indeed exist (for a fairly recent comprehensive review, the reader is referred to Romano & Turner, 1985). Briefly, much of the interest in depression as a causal factor in chronic pain stems from theories of depression proposed by Beck and his colleagues, who have argued that cognitions and beliefs are essential elements in the production and maintenance of depression (Beck, 1967).

Attempts to understand why only certain pain syndrome patients become clinically depressed have stemmed from the aforementioned cognitive model of depression (e.g., Lefebvre, 1981), and the dependent measure most commonly employed in these studies has been the Beck Depression Inventory (Beck, Ward, Mendleson, Mock, & Erbaugh, 1961). This is a 21-item self-report inventory of depressive symptoms, including disturbances of sleep, appetite, and energy level, that has been widely used in numerous psychiatric studies. There is empirical support for Beck's theory and its involvement in chronic pain (Lefebvre, 1981), in that patients with both depression and chronic low back pain showed more cognitive distortions on questionnaire items specifically related to back pain than did depressed subjects without pain. Further research is needed to clarify whether such tendencies would predispose patients with chronic pain to develop depressive symptomatology or whether cognitive distortions occur as a consequence of being depressed and in pain.

Depression has been diagnosed in chronic pain patients by a wide range of other self-report

instruments (Pilowsky, Chapman & Bonica, 1977) and clinical interviews, ranging from structured (Lindsay & Wyckoff, 1981) to nonstructured (Lascelles, 1966; Wilson, Blazer, & Nashold, 1976). Few studies have used Research Diagnostic Criteria (Spitzer, Endicott, & Robins, 1978) or the third edition of the Diagnostic and Statistical Manual of Mental Disorders (American Psychiatric Association, 1980) to diagnose depressive symptoms, and a comprehensive review of methodological issues involved in assessing such depression can be found in Romano and Turner (1985).

Despite numerous methodological problems, some trends are apparent in the research literature. The majority of published reports suggest that rates of depressive symptomatology are clearly higher in chronic pain syndrome patients than in other populations. In general, results indicate that about 50% of patients with chronic pain and depression developed the two disorders simultaneously, and about 40% became depressed sometime after the onset of pain. Such data await further confirmation in prospective longitudinal designs.

Evaluation of Expectancies, Distractability, and Suggestibility.

Much has been written in the research literature on the effects of expectancy set on psychotherapy outcome (Garfield & Bergin, 1978), and clinicians involved in the treatment of chronic pain syndrome frequently discuss the importance of evaluating a patient's expectancies regarding treatment outcome for the purpose of setting accurate goals. However, very little research has been conducted to evaluate the effects of expectancies on the part of patients and how they might interact with chronic pain syndrome and its treatment.

One of the few such studies to evaluate the effects of patient expectations was reported by Thomas and Lyttle (1980). Expectancies regarding potential success from various treatments for chronic low back pain were measured in 95 subjects, and the potential effects of certain moderator variables, including self-concept, depressive symptoms, and demographic variables, were correlated. Results indicated that, prior to treatment, patients had very high expectations for positive outcome; on a 7-point rating scale, patients checked to a mean value of 5.7 (7 being the most expected success). As to experienced relief provided by treatment, there was a distinct bimodal distribution. There was a significant negative correlation between expectancy of relief before treatment and reported satisfaction with outcome, regardless of the treatment modality employed. In other words, the greater the expectancy for complete relief, the greater the likelihood the patient will be dissatisfied with the treatment. The authors interpreted their data to mean that patients with expectancies based on few relevant health experiences tended to set goals for recovery that would not be met by current treatment practices for back pain. Unfortunately, further studies investigating the effects of expectancy on treatment response and outcome are sorely lacking, and future work directed at the interaction between expectancies and other psychological variables insofar as their impact on treatment outcome goes should prove heuristic.

The diathesis–stress model of chronic pain endorsed by the authors herein would predict that increased stress exacerbates pain, and one mechanism for enhanced pain responsivity would be increased attention to or focus on sympathetic nervous system arousal. Consequently, researchers have hypothesized that the ability to distract oneself cognitively might prove effective in diminishing pain complaints. In an early study, Gardner and Lacklider (1959) found that dental patients reported little or no pain during extractions and drilling when subjected to intense auditory stimuli (white noise; Melzack, 1973). However, the results of this study could have been due to expectancy effects, distraction, suggestion, anxiety reduction, or a combination of all four variables.

Given the potential efficacy of distraction, suggestion, and relaxation in reducing pain, it is not surprising that many clinicians have employed various relaxation techniques and hypnotic-induction methods in attempts to relieve or at least diminish pain complaints. Much research has fairly well established that both experimentally induced pain and clinical pain can be quickly and completely eliminated, at least for the short term (Crasilneck & Hall, 1975; Hilgard & Hilgard, 1975). Barber (1982) has stated the case strongly: "Hypnosis is clearly an effective way to modify perception so that a person can be unaware of pain" (p. 42). Many researchers and clinicians have explained the ability of some patients to distract themselves from the pain messages on the basis of gate control theory of pain (Melzack & Wall, 1965), using a notion of competing sensory stimuli. However, there is considerable controversy over whether hypnosis and distraction techniques can be learned by most patients.

To enhance the clinical applicability of such approaches, there has been a great deal of research attempting to address the susceptibility or suggestibility of patients to hypnosis and distraction techniques. For example, Hilgard and his colleagues designed the Stanford Scale of Hypnotic Susceptibility (Weitzenhoffer & Hilgard, 1959). These researchers have reported that population scores do indeed fall along a normal curve (Hilgard & Hilgard, 1975), but other investigators have argued that suggestibility and hypnotizability are not stable biological traits but modifiable ones (e.g., London, Cooper, & Engstrom, 1974). Barber (1980) reported that people who score low on suggestibility and hypnotizability tests can, on other occasions, respond to different approaches sufficiently to experience competing sensory stimuli including perceptual modification of sensory input and amnesia. Given the controversy that remains in the field, it would appear that the clinical use of such evaluation techniques in a chronic pain unit would be questionable indeed at this time but worthy of more research.

Environmental and Demographic Factors Chronic Pain Syndrome Meaning and Context of the pain

Mechanic (1962) has researched what is termed *illness behavior*. He described this behavior as consisting of the ways in which given symptoms are perceived, evaluated, and acted (or not acted) upon by a given individual. Illness behavior might or might not lead to help-seeking behavior, depending to a large degree on the severity and quality of the symptoms, as well as on the context in which they occur. Figure 8.2 presents a schema for understanding illness behavior and the sick role.

In evaluating the meaning of a patient's pain syndrome, as well as the context in which it occurs, the clinician must obviously take into account numerous variables, as depicted in Figure 8.2. A significant body of research literature concerning the effects of various life-change events indicates that the most important stressors in terms of disease processes in general and pain complaints in particular are interpersonal stressors such as loss of a loved one, divorce, and separation. Therefore, some clinics have proposed the use of life-change event scales and other measures of overall stress in the process of evaluating a chronic pain patient. Fordyce (1976) has discussed in great detail the evaluation of pain behavior as an operant and the subsequent reinforcement that patients might receive in their environments for such pain behaviors.

Pain and illness

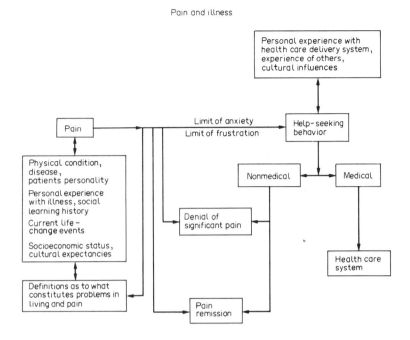

FIGURE 8.2. Pain and illness.

Demographic Factors and Socioeconomic Class.

How an individual chooses to cope with pain, whether it be acute or chronic, is to a large degree influenced by a variety of factors that include socioeconomic class. Koos (1954) has reported that people from higher socioeconomic classes tend to report themselves ill more frequently than do those in lower socioeconomic brackets. Some researchers have attributed such class differences to realistic economic considerations, whereby the upper class are seen as more easily able to afford medical bills and loss of days at work in order to see physicians. Furthermore, some have speculated that some individuals with higher educational levels and greater awareness of medical problems seek help earlier. On the other hand, the very poor on public assistance programs can afford to engage in medical-help-seeking behavior more readily than the working-class individual who cannot afford to lose hourly wages in order to make use of such medical care facilities. Finally, it should be noted that there is evidence that these social class differences in medical care utilization are rapidly diminishing (e.g., Ross, 1962).

Mechanic (1968) and others have speculated that

socioeconomic class interacts with attitudes and orientation toward illness in general and toward pain in particular. Deasy (1956) reported results of a survey indicating that lower-class populations were more fatalistic about contracting disease and thus less likely to be open to accepting a preventive-medicine approach (Rosenstock, 1969). Gentry and his colleagues (Gentry et al., 1974) represent the typical chronic pain patient as of lower-middle-class socioeconomic background, with limited formal education. Frequently employed in physically strenuous or overly routinized jobs, most began work at an early age, dropping out of school. Pain patients are further described as having experienced unmet dependency needs early in life and as working at relatively hard jobs for a long period of time prior to the onset of their symptoms. At the time of initial symptom onset, these patients generally had support available from others, although significant loss often preceded the symptom picture. In addition, many of the patients in their study had familiar models of pain and disability present in their early life experiences. Gentry and his colleagues concluded, "Thus, by virtue of providing for others and not being able to fully depend on their own parents as children, they had postponed gratification of such needs until a minor injury provided rational and socially acceptable means of depending on others for emotional and economic support'' (p. 176).

Merskey (1972) added to this clinical picture the observation that patients with chronic pain tend to come from large families, to be engaged in unskilled or semiskilled work at best, to typically have a hard life and, as such, to be prone to depression and hypochondriasis. Given these cognitive and personality limitations, it is not surprising that such patients manifest little insight into the nature of their illness and, consequently, expect the physician to take away the pain. It is difficult at first for patients to adopt a collaborative, mutualistic approach to the problem. These observations are in line with earlier data reported by Hollingshead and Redlich (1958), who found psychiatric diagnoses of personality disorders and neuroses to be more common among middle- and upper-class individuals and diagnoses of severe psychoses and ''psychosomatic'' reactions to be more commonly associated with lower-class populations.

Ethnic and Religious Factors.

As is widely known, there are certain religions in Western society that absolutely forbid medical help-seeking behavior. Certainly religion and ethnic origin are important aspects of one's perception of pain and the sick role, as well as of one's tendency to engage in medical or nonmedical help-seeking behavior. For example, some cultural groups (e.g., Hispanic populations as encountered in the Southwest) are more likely to seek family care and support first and rely on nonmedical help-seeking behavior second when they accept the sick role (Saunders, 1954). Native English-speaking people studied in the same general region of the United States, on the other hand, tend to seek modern medical treatment first. Mechanic (1962) reported that religious differences appear to influence acceptance of the sick role independent of social class; furthermore, he reported that Jewish and Episcopalian patients reported that they would be more likely to use medical facilities for various symptoms than would Catholics and Christian Scientists surveyed in a large university area.

A number of researchers have looked at ethnic and religious factors and how they mediate one's response to pain (for a comprehensive review, the reader is referred to Wolff and Langley, 1968). From a methodological standpoint, some of the best data have been gathered by Zborowski (1952; 1969).

During the exploratory phase of that research, he interviewed a wide variety of physicians whose practices included high proportions of Irish, Italian, and Jewish patients. Those physicians reported that both Italian and Jewish patients tended to ''exaggerate'' their pain and were more ''emotional'' than other ethnic groups, whereas those of Anglo-Saxon background (what Zborowski termed ''Old Americans'') had a more ''accepting'' attitude toward pain, with the Irish found to be more stoic in their approach to pain. Consequently, the four groups of male patients (the Irish, Italian, Jewish, and ''Old Americans'') were studied more intensely regarding their pain responses. Many of the observations made by the physicians in their contacts with those patients were then verified by statistical analyses of a structured questionnaire administered to those groups of patients. For example, Italian and Jewish patients did tend to be more expressive and emotional than Old Americans when experiencing and expressing pain. The Italians and Jewish patients tended to emphasize or heighten their perception of pain, but the Irish and Old Americans tended to deemphasize the pain. Wolff and Langley (1968) have concluded in their review, ''Cultural factors in terms of attitudinal variables, whether explicit or implicit, do indeed exert significant influences on pain and its perception'' (p. 500).

Cultural factors and their impact on pain complaints have been examined in a laboratory setting by Sternbach and Tursky (1965). They utilized a methodology investigating palmar skin potentials and pain response in reaction to electrical shock. The use of these reactive measures, in which subjects were asked to identify the levels of intensity of pain (i.e., sensation threshhold, discomfort, pain, and tolerance), did show ethnic differences. However, no differences were observed in the magnitude estimation procedure where, for example, a standard electric shock of 30 volts was presented to a subject and given a numerical rating of 10. Other presentations of shock stimuli above and below that standard were then rated by the subject, who provided a numerical estimate to be compared with the standard. Their results suggested that sensory evaluation of shocks did not differ as a function of ethnic grouping, but the reactive and motivational component did indeed differ in the ways suggested by previous research (Zborowski, 1952; 1969).

Cultural and racial differences in the reaction to pain appear to be related not only to differences in underlying attitudes but also to anxiety reactions (see Weisenberg, 1976). For example, Weisenberg and his colleagues (Weisenberg, Kreindler, Schachat, & Werboff, 1975) examined anxiety responses among North American blacks, and whites and Puerto Rican patients. Significant differences were observed among these three groups on trait anxiety (Speilberger et al., 1970) and overall anxiety in response to dentistry. Attitudinal differences were also obtained that reflected the relative willingness of the patient to either deny or avoid dealing with the pain or to get rid of the pain. Puerto Rican patients showed the strongest endorsement of such items (e.g., "the best way to handle pain is to ignore it"), whites the weakest endorsement; black patients were in between. Other laboratory experiments have also documented the powerful effect of social influence processes and modeling on response to experimental pain (e.g., Craig & Weiss, 1971). For a review of the impact of sociocultural variables on the pain response, the reader is referred to Weisenberg (1976).

TREATMENT ISSUES

Physiological Dysfunction and Medical Management

The treatment of pain from a medical standpoint ideally consists of removal of the underlying organic cause. Unfortunately this is rarely, if ever, possible in chronic pain syndrome; indeed, as noted earlier, some clinicans begin conceptualizing chronic pain syndrome as any failure of extensive therapy, including surgeries, directed toward elimination of nociception. Nevertheless, a variety of medical and surgical techniques have been proposed to treat chronic pain, and these will be briefly reviewed. The most common medical intervention, of course, is the prescription of pain medications.

Detoxification and Withdrawal of Medications.

Most chronic pain sufferers take many drugs for symptomatic relief and, yet, typically complain that such medications do not offer significant diminution of pain (Gildenberg & DeVaul, 1985). In addition, almost all medications used for the treatment of acute pain tend to add to the depression manifested by many chronic pain patients. On the basis of years of clinical experience, Gildenberg and DeVaul (1985) stated the case strongly, "In all patients who have had pain relief after admission to the chronic pain unit, the most significant step toward that relief was the withdrawal of narcotics" (p. 97). Guidelines for medical management of withdrawal were then offered by these authors, and they justified why they recommended abrupt withdrawal of opiate narcotics and gradual detoxification for barbiturate abuse or addiction to diazepam (to prevent the potential for seizures).

Analgesic Compounds. Virtually all analgesic compounds, with the exception of several aspirinlike medications, are chemically related to opiates in their structure. Thus, they possess the ability of narcotics to produce tolerance, habituation, and addiction. Although useful for acute pain, analgesics are not useful for the treatment of chronic pain and, in fact, can potentiate chronic pain suffering (Gildenberg & DeVaul, 1985). Some researchers have speculated that the long-term administration of exogenous opiates directly disturbs central mechanisms for pain tolerance by depleting endogenous opiates (endorphins and enkephalins).

Tricyclic Antidepressants. As noted earlier, the emotional responses most commonly associated with pain are anxiety and depression, the former related more to acute, the latter more to chronic pain (Sternbach, 1976). Although controversial, there is empirical support, reviewed earlier, for distinct association between the two syndromes of chronic pain and depression, suggesting that coexisting pain and depression might be a final common symptom cluster reached by a number of pathways (Romano & Turner, 1985). Thus, psychotropic medication for the alleviation of anxiety or depression has been employed for a number of years and investigated in several studies. Three controlled double-blind studies, for example, have examined the efficacy of tricyclic antidepressants in the management of chronic pain (Jenkins, Ebbutt, & Evans, 1976; Johansson & van Knorring, 1979; Ward, Bloom, & Freidl, 1979). Results of these studies indicate that chronic pain patients treated with antidepressants show significant improvement in both depression and pain relative to placebo controls. Patients who are the most severely depressed (Jenkins et al., 1976) and who show high serum levels of antidepressant medication respond well (Ward et al., 1979), whereas patients who do not show such characteristics respond poorly to antidepressant medication.

Apart from treating depressive symptoms, it has also been suggested that psychotropic medication might decrease pain complaints by modulating nociception. Results of uncontrolled clinical studies suggest that either tricyclic antidepressants alone (Beaumont, 1973, 1976), phenothiazines alone (Chavanne, 1960; Panaccio, 1959; Paradis, 1962), or a combination of tricyclic antidepressants and phenothiazines (Merskey & Hester, 1972) can alleviate chronic pain. The underlying neurochemical mechanics by which such psychotropic medications might alter pain are not known at this time.

Impulse Augmentation.

Pain perception can be changed medically by increasing or decreasing incoming neuronal input. Afferent nervous impulses can be augmented with nerve stimulation procedures. In chronic pain units, this is most typically accomplished by applying electrodes connected to a suitable generator to the skin, a method known as transcutaneous electral nerve stimulation (Long, 1976, 1980). According to Long and his colleagues (Long, Campbell, & Guzer, 1979), transcutaneous stimulation has been successful in moderating pain complaints in myofascial pain syndrome and peripheral nerve injury. On the other hand, patients with central nervous system pain and peripheral neuropathies appear to do poorly. Clinicians have also suggested more permanent stimulation via surgical implants close to selected neural structures (Gildenberg & DeVaul, 1985). Electrodes are more or less permanently connected to a radio receiver implanted under the skin, and pain relief is dependent on the production of stimulation paresthesia referred to the painful area of the body (Nashold & Friedman, 1972). Spinal cord stimulation has also been achieved by surgical implantation of electrodes close to the dorsal columns during laminectomy (Gildenberg & DeVaul, 1985; Long, 1976, 1980). In such patients, long-term results have demonstrated some moderation of pain in roughly 25% to 30% of patients operated upon (Long, 1976; Urban & Nashold, 1978). There have been no reports of major complications due to the surgical procedures (Urban, 1982).

Impulse Reduction.

The most common method of reducing pain impulses is via nerve blocks with local anesthetics. Such blockage involves the introduction of an anesthetic injection to a neural pain pathway, resulting in temporary analgesia, reflex interruption, and nociceptive blockage (Urban, 1982). Bonica (1959) has suggested treating chronic pain syndrome with repeated blocks, contending that subjective pain relief often outlasts the duration of local anesthetic action. Other clinicians (Breivik, Hesla, Molner, & Lind, 1976) have suggested that therapeutic efficacy might be enhanced by the addition of corticosteroids to such nerve blocks. Brena and Unikel (1976) found nerve blocks to be efficacious within a contingency management program; symptomatic pain relief from nerve blocks was used as a reinforcer for decreased pain behaviors.

More permanent impulse reduction methods, whether chemical (Katz, 1974) or neurosurgical (Long, 1980), are utilized far less because of poor long-term results and potential complications. Exceptions might be sympathectomies for causalgia and dorsal root lesions (Urban, 1982).

Psychological Management

Stress Education and Reconceptualization of Pain.

As noted earlier, the typical chronic pain sufferer expects some sort of "medical cure," is not psychologically minded, and is apprehensive about any psychiatric or psychological evaluation or treatment. As such, a primary and critical goal is to explain to the chronic pain patient that the pain is indeed "real" and is the primary focus of treatment. The chronic pain patient must then be educated that pain is a function of stress, and we typically do that by discussing stress from a physiological standpoint and pain as an underlying neurochemical event. The clinical goal is to reach some shared conceptualization of the problem so that therapist and patient can mutually collaborate on appropriate treatment.

Once the patient begins to accept the notion that pain is "in my head" (i.e., a neurochemical event) and a function of the physiology of stress, the role of emotions and cognitions can be entertained. The second phase of education and reconceptualization begins as patients are taught to self-monitor. Whether the clinician chooses to employ hierarchies, diaries, or whatever is not critical; the important concept appears to be identification of relevant interpersonal and environmental stressors that exacerbate the pain response and make the patient more at risk for depressive symptomatology such as withdrawal, isolation, and feelings of hopelessness and helplessness.

The third step in education and reconceptualization of pain is to examine the role of depressive symptomatology as it might be exacerbating pain behaviors. Issues of expectancies, degree of helplessness and hopelessness, and limitations in activity (work, recreation, sexual relations, etc.) are focal.

As the patient's conceptualization of chronic pain broadens, he or she could be educated in family systems theory (Minuchin, 1974). Despite an absence of empirical support, family or spouse involvement appears to have been widely accepted as an essential ingredient in many pain treatment programs (Roy and Tunks, 1982). Fordyce (1976), theorizing that spouses and families are intrumental in reinforcing dysfunctional behaviors, recommended that some patients not be admitted to treatment if spouses were unwilling or unavailable to participate in treatment. Apart from the operant reinforcement of pain behaviors by family members, a second rationale for involving family in the treatment program is to help them, as well as the patient, cope with the effects of pain on their lives. Turk, Meichenbaum, and Genest (1983) have described many of the consequences that pain has on family members, including financial loss, decreased family outgoings, fewer vacations, disruptive sexual relationships, shifted burdens of responsibility, and a wealth of emotional reactions.

To experimentally assess the efficacy of spouse involvement in treatment for chronic pain, Moore and Chaney (1985) randomly assigned 43 chronic pain patients and their spouses to either couples group treatment, patient-only group treatment, or a waiting-list control group. Results indicated significant gains for patients in both treatment groups, gains that were maintained at follow-up (3 and 7 months), but spouse involvement did not facilitate response to treatment on any variable. The authors concluded that patients can realize positive gains from treatment with or without spouse participation and that no patient should be refused treatment solely on the basis of spouse nonparticipation. The authors noted that some spouses reported how helpful treatment was for them in learning how to cope with chronic pain on the part of their spouses, and future studies are recommended to more completely assess change within the spouse of chronic pain patients.

Physical Activity.

During treatment, patients monitor degree of mobility and activity. Frequently patients are prescribed a highly structured, gradually increasing regimen of physical exercise and activity through the aid of physical therapists. Family members might also be involved, in order to encourage and reinforce activity levels. From a cognitive standpoint, the overall goal is to deemphasize pain complaints and reinforce increased coping skills and activity on the part of the patient.

Biofeedback.

In clinical practice, biofeedback therapy is a blend of physiological and psychotherapeutic intervention. The specific physiological applications of biofeedback training are actually quite limited, and the relative efficacy of biofeedback training for certain specific disorders has been well documented insofar as modification of muscle tension (e.g., Nuechterlein & Holroyd, 1980) and alterations in blood flow (e.g., Budzynski, 1979) are concerned. Several review articles in recent years have critically evaluated the usefulness of biofeedback interventions for the treatment of specific pain disorders, but the nonspecific effects of biofeedback therapy have not been carefully researched as yet. Such a review is beyond the scope of this chapter, but a justification for the inclusion of biofeedback training in a comprehensive chronic pain program will be provided.

At this time, it can be stated that biofeedback training is employed by most chronic pain programs, despite the fact that the mechanism of its effectiveness in pain management is still undetermined. Most clinicians would now argue that biofeedback training is most useful with pain disorders when used in conjunction with other treatment modalities within a cognitive and behavioral treatment program (Turk et al., 1983). Such programs will be described later in this chapter.

In biofeedback training, a physiological process is electronically monitored and fed back to the patient via an easily discriminable signal, auditory, visual, or both. Although training varies somewhat, depending on the specific target organ system (e.g., vascular changes in the treatment of migraine headaches, skeletal muscle tension in the treatment of muscle-contraction headaches), there is sufficient similarity across training regimens to permit scrutiny of the commonalities involved in such an approach.

Following a careful history taking and medical evaluation, as described earlier, the patient is educated about the role of stress and how it might contribute to his or her pain complaints. At that point, a rationale for the use of biofeedback training in ameliorating the patient's specific symptoms is offered. The next critical phase of biofeedback training involves increasing the patient's awareness of the specific physiological process and teaching the patient to not only monitor but also control that activity to some predetermined level. The patient is reinforced for this operant behavior via diminution or normalization of the feedback signal. The major mode employed to control that signal is relaxation techniques.

It has been argued (Turk et al, 1983) that researchers evaluating biofeedback therapy have paid insufficient attention to what actually happens prior to implementing specific treatment procedures. Those authors argue persuasively that events that occur prior to such treatments are rarely discussed (e.g., patient's conceptualization of the problem, treatment expectancies). The research literature on biofeedback training tends to focus more on definable aspects including the relative merits of certain relaxation techniques, placement of electrodes, and quality of feedback provided.

In our clinical experience, biofeedback training provides a unique opportunity to aid the patient in reconceptualizing her or his pain complaints. Because it is inherently technical in nature, provides "objective data," and allows the patient to acquire skill and sense of control, the context of biofeedback training provides the patient with an opportunity to collaborate in his or her treatment program. Required to be more active than passive, the patient practices relaxation techniques and begins to achieve a sense of control in monitoring and altering some physiological response. As this locus of control becomes more internal, the patient's perceptions, attributions, and appraisals (the patient's internal dialogue; see Turk et al., 1983) begin to shift. We have often seen this shift accompanied by enhanced motivation for treatment and hope for the future.

Probably the most commonly employed method of biofeedback training for chronic pain syndrome has been EMG involving either frontalis muscle or lower back muscle. Several reports have described increased frontalis muscle tension levels among chronic back pain patients during resting baseline and in response to different laboratory stressors (Collins et al., 1982). Recent research has stressed the importance of cognitions in assessing muscle tension (Flor et al., 1985). In that study, the relationship of a paraspinal EMG reactivity to personally relevant stressors was compared among chronic back-pain sufferers, nonback pain patients in a medical setting, and healthy controls. The authors reported that chronic back-pain patients alone displayed elevations and delayed return to baseline levels only in the paravertebral musculature and only when discussing personally relevant stressors. In addition, abnormal muscular reactivity was best predicted by

depression and manner of cognitive coping strategies rather than by any organic variables (e.g., extent of trauma, physical damage). The authors concluded that the assessment of stress-related responses could serve as a useful criterion for the inclusion of a stress-management component within a comprehensive treatment program for chronic back pain.

The final goal in biofeedback training is that of transfer of treatment and generalization of relaxation cues to the patient's "real" environment. To achieve such transfer of training, the patient must first recognize through self-monitoring techniques the presence of his or her maladaptive responses (e.g., tensing the paraspinal musculature) and any accompanying cognitions or emotions that serve as antecedents. Prior to such evaluation and monitoring, patients typically report that pain is omnipresent and constant, undifferentiated, and overwhelming. The resulting response on the part of the patient is anxiety to the point of panic. As a result of self-monitoring techniques and biofeedback training, the patient is almost forced to reconceptualize her or his problem differently, noting that certain antecedents precede more intense or less intense pain messages and thus viewing pain along a continuum of stress. The patient's reactions and coping strategies (sense of control and responsibility) become paramount. Relaxation cues are then generalized, so that patients begin to relax frequently and on an almost unconscious level, to intercept and minimize severe pain episodes. Obviously much more is going on in biofeedback training than simply reduced muscular tension; in fact, several researchers have reported that reduction in pain complaints among chronic back pain sufferers does not correlate with decreases in muscular tension (e.g., Nouwen & Solinger, 1979; Philips, 1977). As noted by Schuman (1982), biofeedback treatment for chronic pain sometimes has no specific physiological basis but becomes instead a psychotherapeutic context for teaching relaxation, exploring the mind–body relationship or both.

Relaxation Techniques.

Self-regulation techniques under the rubric of *relaxation training* are numerous and vary significantly in their focus. Relaxation in varied forms has been reported to reduce pain problems and complaints in many clinical settings, but a thorough review of that literature is beyond the scope of this chapter. However, a brief overview of the various proposed modes of relaxation will be provided.

Passive Meditation.

Historically, perhaps the oldest technique for relaxation is passive meditation. This approach has a rich tradition in both Eastern and Western religions and philosophies. In more modern times, yoga techniques and transcendental meditation have become popular in the Western world. A growing body of experimental data substantiates the clinical observation that experienced meditators can produce relatively specific and consistent physiological changes that are incompatable with stress responses, and these techniques have been widely popularized in the lay literature (e.g., Benson, 1975). For a comprehensive review of that research literature, the reader is referred to Edmonston (1981).

Progressive Muscle Relaxation.

In more modern times, progressive muscle relaxation (PMR) was one of the first relaxation procedures based on physiological research (Jacobson, 1929). In PMR, patients are taught to contrast the difference between muscle tension and complete relaxation by progressively tensing and then relaxing one muscle at a time while moving from one region of the body to another. The goal is to permit finer discrimination of extreme muscle states that can lead to stress-related illnesses. This technique appears to be one of the most popular relaxation strategies used, but we have found PMR to be of very limited use in dealing with chronic pain sufferers.

First of all, PMR is a very overt and active method of relaxation, one that does not lend itself to generalization in a wide range of environments. *Second*, many patients view progressive muscle relaxation as being somewhat simplistic and might respond with resistance. Perhaps most important, chronic pain patients, especially those with underlying myofascial involvement, sometimes report feeling much more pain following tensing of muscle groups. Such a negative response at the very beginning can lead to decreased optimism and hope and to negative expectancies that will be difficult to overcome.

Autogenic Training.

Autogenic training, a technique first developed in Europe in the 1930s (Shultz & Luthe, 1959), is another widely used relaxation technique. More passive and autosuggestive in nature, this technique is also based on physiological research. The patient is trained to subvocally repeat standardized phrases

(e.g., "My hands feel warm and heavy"), because the sensations of warmth and heaviness have been found to be most commonly associated with deep-muscle relaxation. The patient is then trained to progressively move through striated, skeletal muscle groups to visceral, smooth-muscle function, in an effort to gain conscious control over a variety of target organ systems. This technique has received much empirical support (e.g., Luthe, 1972), and, because of its passive nature and focus on easily generalized verbal cues, lends itself to working with chronic pain syndrome patients.

Visual Imagery.

Another common practice for inducing relaxation is to suggest that a patient focus on a specific visual image. Obviously the patient must be carefully evaluated beforehand so as to suggest the correct image, (one that will be relaxing, pleasant, and distracting). An additional common practice is to focus on "disease-specific imagery" which, for the chronic pain patient, might include focusing on certain muscle groups' changing shape, color, and so on as they go from "distressed, painful, and inflammed" to "relaxed, cool, and flexible." For an excellent clinical guide to the use of imagery conditioning in a variety of stress-related illnesses, the reader is referred to Kroger and Fezler (1976).

Hypnosis.

As noted earlier, hypnosis has been widely touted as a method of providing relief from various pain disorders. Considerable research has found that both experimentally induced pain and clinical pain can be quickly and sometimes completely eliminated (e.g., Crasilineck & Hall, 1975; Hilgard & Hilgard, 1975). However, there is considerable controversy and a growing literature that argue that hypnosis is essentially synonymous with relaxation (Edmonston, 1981), and relaxation can be brought about by any or all of the techniques already discussed.

Although the boundaries between relaxation and hypnosis are still not clearly delineated, it is apparent that introducing the concept of hypnosis to a chronic pain patient has a very distinct impact. Once a person is physiologically relaxed, hypnotic training involves the presentation of a wide variety of possible experiences that could be associated with "hypnosis." These include analgesia, paralysis, time distortion, and distraction techniques as suggested and directed by the hypnotherapist.

Melzack and Perry (1975) examined the pain-reducing properties of alpha biofeedback training coupled with hypnosis. They reported that enhancing the feelings of the patient's control over pain was the major affective ingredient in their study, in which they compared three groups of patients with chronic pain. The patients in Group I received alpha biofeedback training and hypnosis, Group II patients received hypnosis only, and the third group received alpha biofeedback training alone. Results indicated that the combined hypnosis and alpha biofeedback training significantly relieved pain from the baseline measures, with 58% of the patients reporting a decrease in pain of at least one-third or greater. Hypnosis alone achieved substantial but less significant changes from baseline, and alpha biofeedback training alone was ineffective. The authors interpreted the result to indicate that relaxation and suggestion, coupled with the ability to distract attention, gave the patients a sense of control over pain.

In brief, although much has been written about the use of clinical hypnosis for pain (cf. Barber, 1982; Crasilineck & Hall, 1975), the mechanisms by which hypnosis works to reduce pain are as yet unclear, and the relative efficacy of hypnosis, as opposed to the techniques mentioned earlier, is not known at this time. However, given the clinical case studies that indicate the therapeutic effectiveness of hypnosis with certain patients by certain therapists, hypnosis as a technique is worthy of further scrutiny.

Cognitive–Behavioral Therapies.

Another key clinical goal for chronic pain patients is the development of cognitive–behavioral coping skills. The development of these skills is central to any subsequent reduction of stress and possibly also to pain levels. Effective utilization of coping skills also serves to increase the patient's sense of self-efficacy and control over life functioning (see Bandura, 1977). In addition, it is also helpful for patients to learn that these skills are intended, perhaps most importantly, to minimize the extent to which pain affects overall life functioning, regardless of whether any significant reduction in pain is realized. This is an important point, because it places the core focus within the treatment on increasing life functioning capability and not solely on reducing pain.

Several cognitive–behavioral treatment approaches have been described in training patients to reduce stress and pain. We have chosen to describe three such training strategies in this section as representative of a broader array of approaches. It should be noted that there are several areas of

overlap in these approaches, but each has unique aspects in presentation.

Kendall et al. (1979) have described a treatment protocol for reducing anxiety among hospitalized male patients scheduled for cardiac catheterization procedures. Kendall and his colleagues utilized a five-step stress management intervention within their key experimental condition. Specifically, the treatment initially involved labeling stress and identifying stress-related cues. Patients then identified their own coping strategies, and the therapist in turn reinforced the patient's use of her or his coping style. Finally, training, modeling, and rehearsing of such coping strategies were provided. Their data indicated that this approach yielded markedly higher levels of adjustment and lower levels of anxiety during the subsequent medical procedure. It is of interest that the coping skills reinforced and rehearsed were those identified by the patient as those he or she used to deal with stress; no specific training in the use of particular coping strategies was provided. Thus, the identification and rehearsal of personal stress-management techniques engendered positive effects in addressing a stressful situation.

A second protocol, and one that deals more directly with chronic pain, is that described in detail by Turk et al. (1983), who delineated three central phases in treating chronic pain. Their initial phase of treatment includes two components. The first is a situational and cognitive–affective analysis of the chronic pain complaint. This preliminary phase is multifaceted and includes such components as determining pain-related cognitions, identifying behaviors associated with pain, keeping a pain diary, and assessing the extent of efficacy expectations. The second component of their preliminary phase entails determining the role of significant others in the presenting complaint, as well as the effect of the patient's pain on his or her relationships with significant others. This initial phase of treatment closes with a "reconceptualization process" that is intended to "recast the pain experience in terms that imply hope and resourcefulness" (p. 247). In addition, pain is not presented by Turk et al. as a global phenomenon, but instead is reframed to include controllable physical sensations, pain-related cognitions and images, pain-related feelings, and pain-related behaviors.

The second phase of these investigations' approach entails skills acquisition and consolidation. In this phase of treatment, patients receive exposure to a variety of cognitive-behavioral coping skills:

relaxation procedures, distraction techniques, and instruction in self-statements. In addition, the patient is given the structure of a four-stage strategy for breaking into an episode of pain or exacerbated pain: ''(1) preparing for the onset of pain, (2) confrontation and handling the sensations, (3) coping with your feelings and sensations at critical moments, and (4) thinking about how you handled the situation and praising yourself for your efforts'' (p. 297). Finally, the third phase of the model is the application in the natural environment of the strategies developed in the previous phase. Included are graded exposure to pain-related situations, decisions regarding life-style changes, and strategies for preventing or minimizing relapse (see Marlatt & Gordon, 1985).

A third strategy for dealing with stress and pain complaints is being used in our own clinical setting. In this regard, we have been proposing to our chronic pain inpatients a three-component approach. The first component is developing awareness. Patients are given instruction on becoming more aware of the antecedent consequences of stress and their pain or changes (increases or decreases) in the preception of their pain. The goal of this effort is to obtain a sense of the topography of their pain syndrome. Strategies used in this effort include daily logs, pain ratings, duration records, recordings of concommitant cognitions, and situational information. This information is then used in the second part of the strategy, which is the development of *danger signals*. Danger signals are defined as any thoughts, feelings, events, or situations that in the past or now have been associated with increases in their pain or with decreases in their ability to cope with their existing pain. It is suggested that patients use their danger signals the way caution lights are used on a highway trip. Finally, the third component is the development and utilization of coping skills designed to deal with the identified danger signals. These skills include relaxation procedures, cognitive restructuring and self-talk procedures, assertiveness training, self-monitoring, and development of social supports. It is emphasized throughout that the three components of this approach must be used in concert, given their interdependence. For example, the potential benefits of knowing one's danger signals are greatly diminished if the patient is not sufficiently aware or able to foresee problem situations. Likewise, the benefits of having a repertoire of coping skills are diminished when situations are not foreseen and addressed.

Before closing, it is worth noting that these approaches are representative of a broader array of strategies for increasing the patient's ability to deal with stress or pain complaints and with factors that exacerbate these difficulties. Even among the three approaches described, there exists considerable overlap, in that behavioral analysis and coping skills development are emphasized. The intended end result is to place in the hands of the patient as much control over her or his overall effective life functioning as possible.

Case Illustration

Mr. B. was a 63-year-old, black, married man who was admitted to a 3-week inpatient chronic pain-treatment program. Mr. B. had been in pain since an industrial accident approximately 22 months prior to admission. The onset of his pain followed an accident in which several tons of grain were dropped on him. He described resultant upper body pain that began at the base of his neck and radiated across his shoulders, especially on the left side. When the pain was severe, it radiated down his left arm to the forearm. The pain was worse when bending over or when using his left arm. The patient also described right leg and hip pain that made walking difficult and quite painful. Nothing seemed to ease the pain. Mr. B. underwent three surgeries during the year following his injury; two of these were surgical laminectomies and one was a lumbar laminectomy. The interventions provided no noticeable relief.

During the year following his accident, Mr. B. underwent four other surgeries. Three of these were procedures involved with a triple coronary bypass operation. Another type of pain followed these procedures. Specifically, Mr. B. began to experience additional leg pain while walking. The fourth surgical procedure was bladder surgery for urinary retention.

In terms of social history, Mr. B. was born and raised on a small farm in the south. He left school during the eighth grade and began to work full-time. He joined the service at age 18 and saw action in World War II in Europe. Following this duty, the patient began a job as a laborer. He had held this job with the same organization for 28 years. He noted that he worked long hours, and all indications were that he was a valued employee. The patient had been married for the previous 29 years and had three children (a son, age 18, and daughters, ages 20 and 22), each of whom was living at home and attending college. The patient's job and his children were the central foci of his life. His relationship with his wife while he was still working was not good; they did not communicate much with each other and frequently went several months with little, if any, conversation. This situation became much worse when the patient was placed on disability (he also retired after the accident) and was not helped by the fact that, according to the patient, his wife was drinking quite heavily.

At intake, Mr. B. presented as a depressed and tense individual. His physical examination revealed obvious atrophy and fasciculations of both arms, greater on the left. He had marked muscle tenderness of the posterior neck and the trapezius muscle in the proximal left arm. His medication included acetaminophen with codeine (Tylenol # 3), prednisone, and heart medications. He had been sleeping only 15 to 20 minutes at a time and had been isolating himself at home. His pain was constant and was rated by the patient as being 90 on a 100-point scale (with 100 being the worst pain he could imagine). The impression at intake was of chronic pain syndrome complicated by severe depression.

Over the course of the hospitalization, the patient was exposed to several therapeutic techniques, including physical therapy and occupational therapy. In addition, the patient terminated his use of the acetaminophen with codeine and the prednisone and was placed on an antidepressant (Nortriptyline). Mr. B. also initiated participation in biofeedback and in a stress-management and coping skills group for chronic pain patients. It was these later treatments that Mr. B. identified as most beneficial to him. In particular, he reported that the relaxation procedures were the key component for him, because their use was the first evidence to him that he could exert some control over his physiological state. As a result, he was soon able to master the EMG biofeedback apparatus and to generalize the relaxation procedure through breathing exercises, self-talk, and imagery techniques. Mr. B. also found that his pain level decreased significantly and that he was able to sleep 5 or 6 hours per evening.

Mr. B.'s group involvement also appeared to be of significant benefit. Changes in medication seemed to permit a greater degree of involvement and awareness. In particular he found the identification of danger signals a realistic and helpful strategy for anticipating and avoiding problem situations or for coping with situations he could not avoid. The key danger signals he identified, among others, were contacts with his wife and social isolation. For example, contacts with his wife were seen as a danger signal because most of his recent contacts

with her were associated with tension and an increase in his pain. He soon became able to use interactions with his wife to cue in a relaxation response and other coping strategies, such as self-talk or assertiveness, whereas in the past these interactions elicited tension and an increase in his pain. By the end of treatment, the patient indicated that his pain level on the 100-point scale generally stayed at around 30. Thus, the patient continued to experience pain associated with his injuries, but it was less than pretreatment levels. In addition, the patient's overall life-functioning capability was very much increased.

GENERAL CONCLUSIONS

The assessment and treatment of stress and chronic pain are complex and have just since the mid 1970s been receiving increased attention from clinicians and researchers. The clinical procedures and research data described herein suggest strongly that promising strides are being made, but much additional research needs to be initiated before confident conclusions can be set forward regarding our understanding and treatment of stress and chronic pain and their interaction. Whatever conclusions are eventually drawn, it does appear that positive treatment outcomes will be largely dependent on a comprehensive and multimodal assessment and a multifaceted treatment protocol.

REFERENCES

American Psychiatric Association. (1980). *Diagnostic and statistical manual of mental disorders* (3rd ed.). Washington, DC: Author.

Bandura, A. (1977) Self-efficacy: Toward a unifying theory of behavior change. *Psychological Review, 84,* 191–215.

Barber, J. (1980). Hypnosis and the unhypnotizable. *American Journal of Clinical Hypnosis, 23,* 4–9.

Barber, J. (1982). Incorporating hypnosis in the management of chronic pain. In J. Barber & C. Adrian (Eds.). *Psychological approaches to the management of pain* (pp. 40–59). New York: Brunner/Mazel.

Beals, R. K., & Hickman, N. W. (1972). Industrial injuries of back and extremities: Comprehensive evaluation — aid in prognosis and management: Study of one hundred eighty patients. *Journal of Bone Joint Surgery (AM), 54,* 1593–1611.

Beaumont, G. (1973). Clomipramine (Anafranil) in the treatment of pain, enuresis, and anorexia nervosa. *Journal of International Medical Research, 1,* 435.

Beaumont, G. (1976). The use of psychotropic drugs in other painful conditions. *Journal of International Medical Research, 4,* 56–57.

Beck, A. T. (1967). *Depression: Clinical experimental and*

theoretical aspects. New York: University of Pennsylvania Press.

Beck, A. T., Ward, C. H., Mendelson, M., Mock, J. E., & Erbaugh, J. K. (1961). An inventory for measuring depression. *Archives of General Psychiatry, 4,* 561–571.

Benson, H. (1975). *The relaxation response.* New York: William Morrow.

Bernstein, D. A., & Borkovec, T. D. (1973). *Progressive relaxation training: A manual for the helping professions.* Champaign, IL: Research Press.

Blumer, D., & Heilbronn, M. (1982). Chronic pain as a variant of depressive disease. *Journal of Nervous and Mental Disease, 170* (7), 381–406.

Bond, M. R., & Pilowsky, I. (1966). Subjective assessment of pain and its real relationship to the administration of analgesics in patients with advanced cancer. *Journal of Psychosomatic Research, 10,* 203–208.

Bonica, J. J. (1959). *Clinical applications of diagnostic and therapeutic nerve blocks.* Springfield, IL: Charles C Thomas.

Bonica, J. J. (1980). Pain research and therapy: Past and current status and future needs. In L. Ng & J. J. Bonica (Eds.), *Pain, discomfort, and humanitarian care* (pp. 1–46). New York: Elsevier North-Holland.

Breivik, H., Hesla, P. E., Molnar, I., & Lind, B., (1976). Treatment of chronic low back pain and sciatica: Comparison of candal epidural injections of bupivicaine and methylprednisolone with bupivicaine followed by saline. In J. J. Bonica & D. G. Albe-Fessard (Eds.), *Advances in pain research and therapy* (Vol. 1). New York: Raven Press.

Brena, S. F. (1984). Chronic Pain States: A model of reclassification. *Psychiatric Annals, 14*(11), 778–782.

Brena, S. F., & Koch, D. L. (1975). A pain estimate for quantification and classification of chronic pain states. *Anesthesiology Review, 2,* 8–13.

Brena, S. F., & Unikel, I. P. (1976). Nerve blocks and contingency management in chronic pain states. In J. J. Bonica & D. G. Albe-Fessard (Eds.), *Advances in pain research and therapy* (Vol. 1). New York: Raven Press.

Budzynski, T. H. (1979). Biofeedback strategies in headache treatment. In J. V. Bosmajian (Ed.), *Biofeedback: Principles and practice for clinicians* (pp. 132–152), Baltimore: Williams & Wilkins.

Capka, D., Griffin, S., Harris, G., & Pinsky, J. J. (1979). Selected psychometric evaluations before and after treatment on a pain unit. In B. L. Crue (Ed.), *Chronic pain* (pp. 373–384). New York: Simon & Schuster, Spectrum.

Chavanne, J. (1960). Treatment of pain with a group of phenothiazine amines. *Presse Medicale, 68,* 2347.

Collins, G. A., Cohen, M. M., Naliboff, B. D., & Schandler, S. L. (1982). Comparative analysis of paraspinal and frontalis EMG, heart rate and skin conductance in chronic low back pain patients and normals to various postures and stress. *Scandinavian Journal of Rehabilitation Medicine, 14,* 39–46.

Craig, K. D., & Weiss, S. M. (1971). Vicarious influences on pain-threshold determinations. *Journal of Personality and Social Psychology, 19,* 53–59.

Crasilneck, H. B., & Hall, J. A. (1975). *Clinical hypnosis: Principles and applications.* New York: Grune & Stratton.

Deasy, L. (1956). Socioeconomic status and participation in the poliomyelitis vaccine trial. *American Social Review, 21,* 185–191.

Edmonston, W. E. Jr. (1981). *Hypnosis and relaxation: Modern verification of an old equation.* New York: John Wiley & Sons.

Engel, G. L. (1960). A unified concept of health and disease. *Perspectives in biological Medicine, 3,* 459–485.

Engel, G. L. (1980). The clinical application of the biopsychosocial model. *American Journal of Psychiatry, 137,* 222–231.

Flor, H., & Turk, D. C. (1984). Etiological theories and treatments for chronic back pain: I. Somatic models and interventions. *Pain, 19,* 105–121.

Flor, H., Turk, D. C., & Birbaumer, N. (1985). Assessment of stress-related psychophysiological reactions in chronic back pain patients. *Journal of Consulting and Clinical Psychology, 53*(3), 354–364.

Fordyce, W. E. (1976). *Behavioral methods for chronic pain and illness.* St. Louis: C. V. Mosby.

Gardner, G. G., & Lacklider, L. (1959). The use of distraction in dental applications. *International Journal of Clinical and Experimental Hypnosis, 7,* 203–214.

Garfield, S. L., & Bergin, A. E. (1978). *Handbook of psychotherapy and behavior change: An empirical analysis.* New York: John Wiley & Sons.

Gentry, W. D., & Bernal, A. (1977). Chronic pain. In R. B. Williams & W. D. Gentry (Eds.), *Behavioral approaches to medical treatment* (pp. 173–182). New York: Ballinger.

Gentry, W. D., Shoers, W. D., & Thomas, M. (1974). Chronic low back pain: A psychological profile. *Psychosomatics, 15,* 174–177.

Gildenberg, P. L., & DeVaul, R. A. (1985). *The chronic pain patient: Evaluation and management.* Switzerland: Karger.

Grabel, J. A. (1973). Electromyographic study of low back pain muscle tension in subjects with and without low back pain. *Dissertation Abstracts International, 34,* 2929B–2930B.

Graham, C., Bond, S. S., Gerkovich, M. M., & Cook, M. R. (1980). Use of the McGill Pain Questionnaire in the assessment of cancer pain: Replicability and consistency. *Pain, 8,* 377–387.

Halpern, L. M. (1977). Analgesic drugs in the management of pain. *Archives of Surgery, 112,* 861–869.

Hanvik, L. J. (1951). MMPI profiles in patients with low back pain. *Journal of Consulting Psychology, 15,* 350–353.

Hilgard, E. R., & Hilgard, J. R. (1975). *Hypnosis in the relief of pain.* Los Altos, CA: William Kaufmann.

Holden, C. (1979). Pain, dying, and the health care system. *Science, 203,* 984–985.

Hollingshed, A. P., & Redlich, F. C. (1958). *Social class and mental illness.* New York: John Wiley & Sons.

Hoyt, W. H., Hunt, H. H., DePauw, M. A., Bard, D., Shaffer, F., Passias, J. N., Robbins, D. H., Reunyon, D. G., Semrad, S. E., Symonds, J. T., & Watt, K. C. (1981). Electromyographic assessment of chronic low back pain syndrome. *Journal of the American Osteopathic Association, 80,* 722–730.

Hunter, M., & Philips, C. (1981). The experience of headache: An assessment of the qualities of tension headache pain. *Pain, 10,* 209–219.

International Association for the Study of Pain, Subcommittee on Taxonomy. (1979). Pain terms: A list with definitions and notes on usage. *Pain, 6,* 249–252.

Jacobson, E. (1929). *Progressive relaxation.* Chicago, IL: University of Chicago Press.

Jenkins, D. G., Ebbutt, A. F., & Evans, C. D. (1976). Tofranil in the treatment of low back pain. *Journal of International Medical Research, 4,* 28–40.

Johansson, F., & von Knorring, L. (1979). A double-blind controlled study of a serotonin uptake inhibitor (zimelidine) versus placebo in chronic pain patients. *Pain,* 69–78.

Katz, J. (1974). Current role of neurolytic agents. In J. J. Bonica (Ed.), *Advances in Neurology* (Vol. 4). New York: Raven Press.

Keefe, F. J., & Block, A. R. (1982). Development of an observation method for assessing pain behavior in chronic low back pain patients. *Behavior Therapy, 13,* 363–375.

Keefe, F. J., & Block, A. R., Williams, R. B., & Surwit, R. S. (1981). Behavioral treatment of chronic low back pain: Outcome and individual differences in pain relief. *Pain, 11,* 221–231.

Kendall, P. C., Williams, L., Pechacek, T. F., Graham, L. E., Shisslak, C., & Herzoff, N. (1979). Cognitive–behavioral and patient education interventions in cardiac catheterization procedures: The Palo Alto Medical Psychology Project. *Journal of Consulting and Clinical Psychology, 47,* 49–58.

Klein, D. F., & Davis, J. M. (1969). *Diagnosis and treatment of psychiatric disorders.* Baltimore: Williams & Wilkins.

Koos, E. (1954). *The health of Regionville: What the people thought and did about it.* New York: Columbia University Press.

Kotarba, J. A. (1983). *Chronic pain.* New York: Sage. Kravitz, E., Moore, M. E., & Glaros, A. (1981). Paralumbar muscle activity in chronic low back pain. *Archives of Physical Medicine and Rehabilitation. 62,* 172–176.

Kroger, W. S., & Fezler, W. D. (1976). *Hypnosis and behavior modification: Imagery conditioning.* Philadelphia: J. B. Lippincott.

Lascelles, R. G. (1966). Atypical facial pain and depression. *British Journal of Psychiatry, 112,* 651–659.

Leavitt, F., Garron, D. C., & Bieliauskas, L. A. (1980). Psychological disturbance and life event differences among patients with low back pain. *Journal of Consulting and Clinical Psychology, 48,* 115–116.

Lefebvre, M. F. (1981). Cognitive distortion and cognitive errors in depressed psychiatric and low back pain patients. *Journal of Consulting and Clinical Psychology, 49*(4), 517–525.

Lethem, J., Slade, P. D., Troup, J. D. G., & Bentley, G. (1983). Outline of a fear-avoidance model of exaggerated pain perception. *Behavior Research and Therapy, 21,* 401–408.

Lindsay, P., & Wyckoff, M. (1981). The depression-pain syndrome and its response to antidepressants. *Psychosomatics, 22,* 511–577.

London, P., Cooper, L. M., & Engstrom, D. R. (1974). Increasing hypnotic susceptibility by brain wave feedback. *Journal of Abnormal Psychology, 83,* 554–560.

Long, D. M. (1976). Use of peripheral and spinal cord stimulation in the relief of chronic pain. In J. J. Bonica & D. G. Albe-Fessard (Eds.), *Advances in pain research and therapy* (Vol. 1). New York: Raven Press.

Long, D. M. (1980). Surgical therapy of chronic pain. *Neurosurgery, 6,* 317–328.

Long, D. M., Campbell, J. N., & Guzer, G. (1979). Transcutaneous electrical stimulation for relief of chronic pain. In J. J. Bonica, J. C. Liebeskind, & D. G. Albe-Fessard (Eds.), *Advances in pain research and therapy* (Vol. 3). New York: Raven Press.

Luthe, W. (1972). Autogenic therapy: Excerpts on applications to cardiovascular disorders and hypercholesteremia. In J. Stoyva, T. X. Barber, L. DiCara, J. Kamiya, N. E. Miller, & D. Shapiro (Eds.). *Biofeedback and self-control* (pp. 437–462). Chicago: Aldine-Atherton.

Marlatt, G. A., & Gordon, J. R. (1985). *Relapse prevention.* New York: Guilford Press.

Maruta, T., Swanson, D. W., & Swenson, W. M. (1976). Low back pain patients in a psychiatric population. *Mayo Clinic Proceedings, 51,* 57–61.

Mechanic, D. (1962). The concept of illness behavior. *Journal of Chronic Disease, 15,* 189–194.

Mechanic, D. (1968). *Medical sociology: A selective view.* New York: Free Press.

Meichenbaum, D., & Turk, D. (1976). The cognitive–behavioral management of anxiety, anger, and pain. In P. Davidson (Ed.), *The behavioral management of anxiety depression, and pain.* New York: Brunner/Mazel.

Melzack, R. (1970). The perception of pain. In perception and its disorders. *Research Publication of the Association for Research in Nervous and Mental Disease, 48,* 272–285.

Melzack, R. (1973). *The puzzle of pain.* New York: Harper & Kow, Harper Torchbooks.

Melzack, R. (1975). The McGill Pain Questionnaire: Major properties and scoring methods. *Pain, 1,* 277–299.

Melzack, R., & Perry, C. (1975). Self-regulation of pain: The use of alpha-feedback and hypnotic training for the control of chronic pain. *Experimental Neurology, 46,* 452–469.

Melzack, R., & Torgerson, W. S. (1971). On the language of pain. *Anesthesiology, 34,* 50–59.

Melzack, R., & Wall, P. D. (1965). Pain Mechanisms: A new theory. *Science, 150,* 971–979.

Merskey, H. (1972). Personality traits of psychiatric patients with pain. *Journal of Psychosomatic Research, 16,* 163–166.

Merskey, H., & Hester, R. A. (1972). The treatment of chronic pain with psychotropic drugs. *Postgraduate Medical Journal, 48,* 594–598.

Minuchin, S. (1974). *Families and Family therapy.* Cambridge, MA: Harvard University Press.

Moore, J. E., & Chaney, E. F. (1985). Outpatient group treatment of chronic pain: Effects of spouse involvement. *Journal of Consulting and Clinical Psychology, 53*(3), 326–334.

Nashold, B. S., & Friedman, H. (1972). Dorsal column stimulation for pain: A preliminary report on thirty patients. *Journal of Neurosurgery, 36,* 590–597.

Nuechterlein, K. H., & Holroyd, J. C. (1980). Biofeedback in the treatment of tension headaches. *Archives of*

General Psychiatry, *37*, 866–873.

Nouwen, A., & Solinger, J. W. (1979). The effectiveness of the EMG biofeedback training in low back pain. *Biofeedback and Self-Regulation*, *4*, 103–111.

Panaccio, V. (1959). Trimeprazine: A new phenothiazine derivative for treatment of pruritic dermatoses. *Canadian Medical Association Journal*, *80*, 885.

Paradis, B. (1962). Analgesic and anaesthetic properties of levomepromazine (Nozinan) (7044 R. P.) *Canadian Anaesthetists Society Journal*, *9*, 153.

Philips, C. (1977). A psychological analysis of tension headache. In S. Rachman (Ed.), *Contributions to medical psychology* (Vol. 1). Oxford, England: Pergamon Press.

Phillips, E. L. (1964). Some psychological characteristics associated with orthopaedic complaints. *Current Practices in Orthopaedic Surgery*, *2*, 165–176.

Pilowsky, I., Chapman, C. R., & Bonica, J. J. (1977). Pain, depression, and illness behavior in a pain clinic population. *Pain*, *4*, 183–192.

Polley, H., Swenson, W., & Steinhilber, R. M. (1970). Personality characteristics of patients with rheumatoid arthritis. *Psychosomatics*, *11*, 45–49.

Reading, A. E. (1979). The internal structure of the McGill Pain Questionnaire in dysmenorrhea patients. *Pain 7*, 353–358.

Romano, J. M., & Turner, J. A. (1985). Chronic pain and depression: Does the evidence support a relationship? *Psychological Bulletin*, *97*(1), 18–34.

Rosenstock, I. (1969) Presentation of illness and maintenance of health. In J. Kosa, A. Antonovksy, & I. K. Zola (Eds.), *Poverty and health* (pp. 168-190). Cambridge M A: Harvard University Press.

Ross, J. (1962). Social class and medical care. *Journal of Health and Human Behavior*, *2*, 35–40.

Roy, R., & Tunks, E. (1982). *Chronic pain: Psychosocial factors in rehabilitation*. Baltimore: Williams & Wilkins.

Sanders, S. H. (1980). Toward a practical instrument for the automatic measurement of "uptime" in chronic pain patients. *Pain*, *9*, 103–109.

Saunders, L. (1954). *Cultural differences and medical care*. New York: Russell Sage Foundation.

Schultz, J. H., & Luthe, W. (1959). *Autogenic training: a psychophysiologic approach to psychotherapy*. New York: Grune & Stratton.

Schuman, M. (1982). Biofeedback in the management of chronic pain. In J. Barber, C. Adrian (Eds.). *Psychological approaches to the management of pain.* (pp. 150-167). New York: Brunner/Mazel.

Spielberger, C. D., Gorsuch, R. L., & Lushene, R. E. (1970). *Manual for the State-Trait Anxiety Inventory.* Palo Alto, CA: Counsulting Psychologist Press.

Spitzer, R. L., Endicott, J., & Robins, E. (1978). Research diagnostic criteria: Rationale and reliability. *Archives of General Psychiatry*, *35*, 773–782.

Sternbach, R. A. (1968). *Pain: A psychophysiological analysis.* New York: Academic Press.

Sternbach, R. A. (1974). *Pain patient: Traits and treatment.* New York: Academic Press.

Sternbach, R. A. (1976). Psychological factors in pain. In J. J. Bonica & D. G. Albe-Fessard (Eds.), *Advances in pain research and therapy* (Vol. 1). New York: Raven Press.

Sternbach, R. A., & Tursky, B. (1965). Ethnic difference among housewives in psychophysical and skin potential responses to electric shock. *Psychophysiology 1*, 241–246.

Sternbach, R. A., Wolf, S. R., Murphy, R. W., & Akeson, W. H. (1973). Aspects of chronic low back pain. *Psychosomatics*, *14*, 52–56, 226–229.

Thomas, M. R., & Lyttle, D. (1980). Patient expectations about success of treatment and reported relief from low back pain. *Journal of Psychosomatic Research*, *24*, 297–301.

Turk, D. C., Meichenbaum, D., & Genest, M. (1983). *Pain and behavioral medicine: A cognitive–behavioral perspective.* New York: Guilford Press.

Urban, B. J. (1982). Therapeutic aspects in chronic pain: Modulation of nociception, alleviation of suffering, and behavioral analysis. *Behavior Therapy*, *13*, 430–437.

Urban, B. J., & Nashold, B. S., Jr. (1978). Percutaneous epidural stimulation of the spinal cord for relief of pain: Long-term results. *Journal of Neurosurgery*, *48*, 323–328.

Wallis, C., Mehrtens, Galvin R., Thompson, B., & Thompson, D., (June 11, 1984). Unlocking pain's secrets. *Time*, pp 58-66.

Ward, N. G., Bloom, V. L., & Friedl, R. O. (1979). The effectiveness of tricyclic antidepressants in the treatment of co-existing pain and depression. *Pain*, *7*, 331–341.

Weisenberg, M. (1976). Cultural and racial reactions to pain. In M. Weisenberg (Ed.), *The control of pain.* New York: Psychological Dimensions.

Weisenberg, M., Kreindler, R., Schachat, R., & Werboff, J. (1975). Pain: Anxiety and attitudes in black, white and Peurto Rican patients. *Psychosomatic Medicine*, *37*, 123–135.

Weitzenhoffer, A. M., & Hilgard, E. R. (1959). *Stanford Hypnotic Susceptibility Scale: Form A and B.* Palo Alto, CA: Consulting Psychologists Press.

Wilson, W. P., Blazer, D. G., & Nashold, B. S. (1976). Observations in pain and suffering. *Psychosomatics*, *17*, 73–76.

Wolf, S. L., Nacht, M., & Kelly, J. R. (1982). EMG biofeedback training during dynamic movement for low back pain patients. *Behavior Therapy*, *13*, 395–406.

Wolff, B. B., & Langley, S. (1968). Cultural factors and pain response: A review. *American Anthropologist*, *70*, 494–501.

Zborowski, M. (1952). Cultural components in response to pain. *Journal of Social Issues*, *8*, 16–30.

Zborowski, M. (1969). *People in pain.* San Francisco: Jossey-Bass.

Chapter 9

Pain and Stress Management and Temporomandibular Joint Dysfunction

Roberta M. Diddel

Temporomandibular joint dysfynction syndrome and other related pain syndromes of the head and neck have become familiar to dentists and oral surgeons only recently. Although there is evidence that TMJ's symptoms are experienced by a significant number of people, the general public is unaware of or poorly informed about its causes and treatments. It is not uncommon for TMJ sufferers to receive treatment for migraines, brain tumors, ear infections, and cervical disc problems or to be labeled hypochondriacs or conversion hysterics. It is usually the family dentist who recognizes the problem, but not before a great deal of time, money, and frustration has been spent.

Because of the complex musculature in the head and neck, muscle tension is usually a prominent feature in TMJ. A recent review of psychological research indicates that much of this tension and accompanying pain are stress related, and clinical stress management is becoming a well-accepted form of treatment for TMJ. Despite studies on personality, psychopathological traits, and muscle reactivity, little has been published on treatment methods or as guidelines for developing stress-management programs for TMJ. The purpose of this chapter is to share a subjective viewpoint of stress management with TMJ patients, in the hope of stimulating more interest and qualitative work in this clinical field.

PHYSICAL AND EMOTIONAL DIMENSIONS OF THE PROBLEM

It will be helpful to begin with a description of TMJ, its theoretical etiology, and some information about those who suffer from it. TMJ is called a syndrome because it refers to a panoply of symptoms centered in and around the temporomandibular joint (that which hinges the jaw) and the surrounding musculature. When X rays or arthrograms indicate that the joint itself is dysfunctional due to displacement, dysfunction in the condyle, stretched ligament, arthritic inflammation, or other joint-related difficulties, the resulting symptoms of pain and dysfunction are usually referred to as temporomandibular joint dysfunction syndrome (TMJ). When chronic muscle tension and unremitting spasm occur without actual joint involvement, it is sometimes called myofascial pain dysfunction syndrome. Other more recent titles include masticatory pain and dysfunction (Rugh, 1983) and mandibular stress syndrome (Thomas, Tiber, & Shireson, 1973). For convenience in this paper, this entire group of syndromes will be referred to as TMJ.

With or without joint problems, sufferers of TMJ complain of some or all of a long list of symptoms. The most common physical complaints include headache; neck, shoulder, and jaw pain; popping or clicking in the joint; earache; swelling in the face; upper body weakness; pain on chewing and swallowing; and frozen jaw (open or shut). TMJ sufferers also frequently complain of physical symptoms generally associated with emotional distress: dizziness, panic attacks, and vegetative signs of depression such as sleep disturbance, gastrointestinal complaints, and weight loss (sometimes due to inability to eat). As many as 80% of those presenting with TMJ also report a history of other psychophysiological conditions such as asthma, ulcers, colitis and stress-related skin conditions (Lupton, 1966). Along with the physical symptoms, a group of related psychological complaints often includes anxiety, depression, irritability, difficulties with attention and concentration, social alienation, diminished energy, and general decreases in activity levels, social, familial, and sexual.

The etiology of TMJ is generally accepted as being linked to a group of causes involving both functional–structural and psychological contributions (Rugh, 1983). In the physical category, TMJ problems can be brought on by injury, as in a blow to the jaw or whiplash. Malocclusion, or the misalignment of the teeth and jaw, is another important physical factor know to influence TMJ development. Damaging oral habits like bruxing, clenching, or grinding the teeth have been estimated to occur in 80% of all TMJ patients (Speculand, Goss, Hughes, Spence, & Pilowsky, 1983) and are clearly implicated in its etiology. Stress-related muscle hyperactivity has been suggested as a major cause of TMJ (Yemm, 1979) as a culprit in the maintenance of habits like nocturnal bruxism and as sustaining myofascial irritation and muscle spasms in patients with problems in the structure of their jaw. TMJ researchers have observed that prolonged masticatory muscle tension alone can lead to the severe complaints of TMJ pain and dysfunction. Studies indicate that TMJ sufferers not only respond to stress with increased masticatory muscle tension (Johnson, Shipman, & Laskin, 1972; Perry, Lammie, Main, & Teuscher, 1960), but they also do not show the same degree of muscular habituation in situations causing anxiety and frustration as do nonpatients (Thomas et al., 1973). TMJ patients appear to be more likely to convert psychological distress into muscle tension, which, over a period of time, causes pain and dysfunction. This psychophysiologic process creates a self-renewing cycle in which stress causes muscle tension, which causes pain, which increases the stress, increasing the tension and pain, and so on. Even when structural problems in the jaw are treatable, if such a pain–stress–pain cycle is present, it can interfere substantially with dentists' attempts to change the bite. It is the pain–stress–pain cycle that most often leads patients, in desperation, to psychological consultation.

There have been numerous studies attempting to address the question of who is most susceptible to developing the psychophysiologic cycle of TMJ pain and dysfunction. A number of authors have tried to establish descriptive personality types, possibly hoping to generate work like Sternbach's low-back profiles for TMJ (Sternbach, 1974). The resulting range of characteristics associated with TMJ is so broad as to be conceptually confusing and clinically unreliable. Terms used to describe patients in these studies include dependent, neurotic, obsessive, rigid, perfectionistic, restrained aggressive, hypernormal, hypochondriacal, and insecure (Rugh, 1983). It has been shown that TMJ patients deny stress, are more likely to complain, have a greater disease conviction (Rothwell, 1972), and show impairment of capacity for interpersonal contact (Speculund et al., 1983).

It is difficult to sort out the meaning of these descriptors without acknowledging that 75%–90% of the TMJ sufferers who present for treatment are women. Although epidemiological studies suggest that men and women suffer symptoms equally as often, women present for treatment of the condition three to four times more frequently (Lupton, 1966). Traditional female role characteristics influence these personality findings considerably and probably result in an overly stereotypic picture of the classic woman in distress. Lupton described his female TMJ subjects as bossy and managerial, covering up their submissive-dependent characters in a counter-phobic style. These women were seen by others as emotionally strong, proud, and unwilling to admit weakness, but their "matriarchal" qualities involved inflexible overgenerosity and a tendency to martyrdom, which they eventually came to resent or regret. This supports a fairly recent finding (Diddel,

1985) on MMPI profiles that an unusual number of women with TMJ produce a "high 4, low 5" profile. Women with this profile frequently withhold anger and are self-effacing or masochistic, manipulating and engendering anger and guilt in others. The way this might manifest itself in chronic pain is exemplified by the woman who repeatedly engages in self-injurious behavior, taking satisfaction in the fact that her subsequent pain causes suffering to others. But this is generally the extreme. Given the well-documented conflict in women today between stereotypic passive dependence and the drive to achieve and excel like men (Dowling, 1974) the observed personality characteristics of TMJ patients are neither surprising nor necessarily abnormal. However, the presence of such conflict in women with TMJ pain could necessarily become a focal point in treatment. This will be discussed more later.

The issue has not been resolved of just how emotionally disturbed TMJ patients are. Writers agree that the majority of TMJ patients, especially those with tension-related myofascial pain, are "psychologically different" (Rugh, 1983), but this is as likely to be the result of the common experience of chronic pain as it is indicative of premorbid psychological disturbance. Estimates on the degree of severe emotional disturbance range from 10% to 76% (Dell, 1969; Speculund, et al., 1983). In the sample of patients seen, MMPI results suggest that the majority of TMJ patients do not show much psychopathology, although 25% indicate significant depression, somatic preoccupation, and anxiety and appear to be somewhat disturbed in two other areas of psychopathology as measured by the MMPI (See Figure 9.1). These data and other studies point up the importance of adequate psychological screening, by interview or testing, because many patients do not need psychological intervention, and a few need it badly. TMJ patients, who usually present themselves to their dentists for initial treatment, will never receive stress management unless the psychological consultant has educated the dentists and oral surgeons in basic screening procedures. Good history taking and even routine psychological screening, using the MMPI or Illness Behavior Questionnaire (Heloe & Heiberg, 1980), provide invaluable assistance to dental professionals in deciding whom to refer.

Once the appropriate patients have been referred, the clinician can expect to see a broad spectrum of emotional distress. Anxiety is the most often described psychological symptom in the literature, and nervous, worried, fretful patients are common in TMJ clinics. Some authors feel strongly that this anxiety is a result of the pain and disruptive dysfunction of TMJ rather than a cause of its development (Gale, 1978; Marbach, Lipton, Lund, Delahanty, & Blank, 1978). Regardless of the source of origin, TMJ patients do seem to be more affected by anxiety than the average person and more affected by frustration (Thomas et al., 1973) and anticipatory anxiety or apprehension. It is too simple to assume that one conflict or stressor has created the anxiety and concomitant physical symptoms. Some patients have had TMJ symptoms since childhood or adolescence, and others, presenting with recent, sudden onset of symptoms, were free from anxiety or unusual stress before their symptoms began. In stress management too much focus on establishing evidence of premorbid symptoms might not be appropriate, and it generally alienates the patient. How it developed is less important than the fact that, when they present for treatment, they look anxious, feel anxious, and desperately need to learn how to interrupt the cycle of physical and emotional hyperactivity.

For anyone who has experienced pain for an extended period of time, it should not be surprising that fearful anxiety results. Pain is a physiologic warning system, and we are programmed neurologically to respond by becoming alert to the danger the pain implies. Touch your finger to a hot stove and observe how quickly the muscles in your arm respond to the warning signal of pain. Pain information travels along neural pathways to the brain, where it is processed perceptually, assigned a meaning based on past experience and stored memory, and results in a response. In most cases this includes a hyperalert state, created mainly by an excitatory response in the reticular activating system. This feeds and, sometimes, creates the kind of anxiety expressed by TMJ patients. It also sets up conditions for development of the other psychological sequelae of TMJ: somatic preoccupation (hypochondriacal thinking), mental confusion or distractibility, episodic anger and irritability, depression, and social alienation. Whether or not the TMJ patient is more hypochondriacal than the average person before the onset of symptoms, he or she nearly always is after it develops. The chronic pain experience creates a tendency to be somatically hypervigilant and to interpret each twinge or spasm as a threat of renewed or increased pain. This produces a conscious or unconscious need to "do something" (e.g., pull the hand away from the stove). The

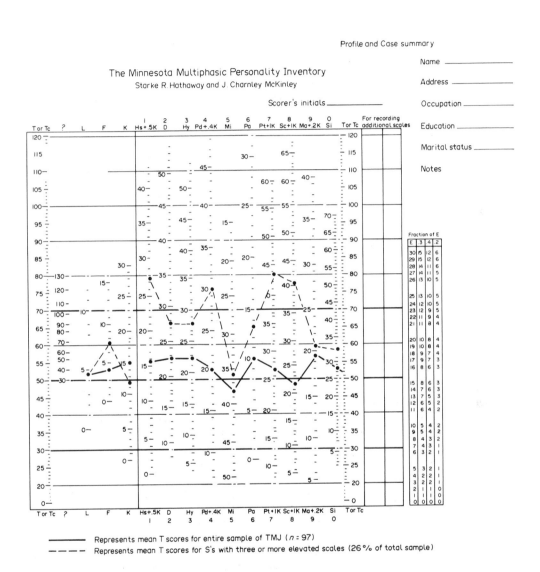

FIGURE 9.1. The Minnesota Multiphasic Personality Inventory
_____ Represents mean T scores for entire sample of TMJ patients (*n* = 97)
- - - Represents mean T scores for Ss with three or more elevated scales (26%of total sample)

patient has come to believe through experience that nothing practical can be done, and this results in increased frustration. Muscle tension follows, making the fear a self-fulfilling and self-reinforcing prophecy. This habitual somatic preoccupation is pivotal to maintaining the pain–stress–pain cycle, because it continually regenerates the physiologic source of the pain (muscle hyperactivity). Moving patients cognitively away from their persistent focus on pain and other symptoms, giving them a sense that there are things to be done, is crucial to their recovery. Techniques of relaxation with biofeedback increase the sense of control, and hypnotherapy, as a method of reframing the patient's orientation to the symptoms, while at the same time providing a means of relaxation, can also be helpful.

Patients who are not able to make the mental shift from illness to health predominate the ranks of those who do not respond to conventional dental therapy (Speculund et al., 1983). The constant anxiety over their pain wears down their reserves. They feel helpless to control it, gradually lose hope, and become demoralized. Depression in TMJ patients is the major factor leading to failure in treatment (Gessel, 1975). Simple relaxation and biofeedback procedures are sufficient for patients with uncomplicated anxiety of a somatic nature, but patients who have developed a significant depression present a dysfunction of cognition that precludes improvement unless it is challenged. Before biofeedback, the family conference, and any form of behavioral treatment, the clinician's first task is to provide hope, not of cure or pain-free existence, but of an ability to resume control over life again.

Most of the other clinical phenomena observed in TMJ patients appear to be secondary effects of depression. Insomnia, weight loss, lack of energy, anhedonia, and decreased sexual desire are common. Even the episodes of anger and irritability appear to be related to the often described sense of helplessness. The emotional lability associated with depression can result in tearfulness, but, due to the underlying chronic anxiety in TMJ patients, it is just as likely to produce irritability or episodes of explosive anger. This lability might play itself out in the patient's fury at health care providers over the lack of available cure. It might also occur in the form of passive–aggressive manipulation, splitting the affections of professional care providers, or abuse of secondary gains. Some patients experience increased mistrust of others and feelings that no one cares because no one understands. The patient feels exempted from responsibilities, cannot function at work, withdraws socially, and sometimes abuses narcotics. Family problems can arise. The financial stress of doctor's bills, medications, and missed work puts additional pressure on the stress–management consultant to "produce." By the time this specialist is ready to discuss the stress–management program with the patient, the tension of mounting expectation and doubt is almost palpable.

TREATMENT

In discussion of the treatment of TMJ sufferers, many of the common stress-management techniques like biofeedback and relaxation training will be familiar. The particular approaches, attitudes, and focuses that have been helpful might be new, however, and these small and subtle shifts in thinking can make a difference. Before covering specific techniques, it will be useful to consider some pretreatment conditions that appear to play a role in the outcome of the stress-management program.

Because of the complex psychophysiologic nature of TMJ, a broad, multifaceted approach is generally best. This might not be necessary for all patients, especially those who have come in early and appear well adjusted. There should be an effort to be flexible. The majority, however, should be encouraged to engage in most of the available modes of treatment, physical, psychophysiologic, and emotional. To provide complete care for TMJ patients, it is necessary for the stress-management expert to develop relationships with ancillary care providers. The dentist, oral surgeon, rheumatologist (or specialist in the diagnosis and treatment of arthritis), neurologist (especially in cervical neck involvement), physical therapist, and nutritionist might all play a part in the patient's recovery.

Also necessary is a good working relationship with a psychiatrist familiar with the unique aspects of pain-related psychopathology. The use of tricylic antidepressants is frequently helpful for TMJ patients (Gessel, 1975), not only for depression but also because of the implications of increased endorphin production with the use of tricyclics. The common problem of drug addiction in TMJ patients sometimes requires psychiatric admission to a hospital or drug facility for withdrawal before other treatment can get under way. Although it is helpful to use relaxation or self-hypnosis training to help the patient through the discomfort of withdrawal, doing stress management with a patient addicted to narcotics is about as effective as carrying water in a sieve.

The importance of the role of the stress-management expert as liaison between the patient and other health professionals cannot be overstated. To begin with, the clinician might find herself or himself in the position of having to prove her or his worth to the patient. Most patients are distressed and overwhelmed by the complex nature of their problem. Contact with other providers creates in the patient a sense that the therapist "knows what's going on" and also increases chances that the other care providers will try to incorporate recommendations that are consistent with stress-management goals. A good example of the reasoning for this can be shown by a case in which it took several weeks to develop a tenuous relationship with a very disturbed woman. Shortly after she had been convinced to come for therapy, she called to terminate, because her physical therapist had told her she did not need a psychologist. Some educating of the physical therapist helped prevent recurrence of that problem, but not before this patient's chance was lost.

Treatment of the TMJ patient begins with setting up the conditions for a therapeutic alliance, a task complicated by the fact that many of these patients are resistent to the idea that they might need the help of a "shrink." Ideally, this preparatory work should start in the referring dentist's office, educating him or her in the kind of language to use when discussing stress-management referral. Dentists find it helpful to give their patients a page-long essay on psychological consultation with TMJ entitled "Stress and TMJ — MPD." Patients who come in after having read this seem to feel more prepared, less apprehensive, and not as concerned that they will be judged to be crazy. The first objective is to reassure them that their pain is real. Arguing with patients about the source or reality of their pain is pointless. It is more useful to accept their experience of pain at face value, allowing them to move beyond that issue and address points like how it has affected their social lives, work, marriages, and children and, more importantly, how they can begin to develop techniques and change mental approaches so that they are able to modify their pain experiences. Psychotherapy, in its more traditional forms, might be appropriate for many TMJ patients at some point, but this should be addressed only when the clinician is certain that the patient will be receptive to it and understand its purpose in a total treatment plan.

A good example involves Mrs. H., a woman in her late 20s who had bucked her family system to become a career woman, only to become paralyzed by fear of failure several years into her career. The stressful anxiety created tension and TMJ problems. When she came to the office, she had quit her job and was depressed, tearful, a motionless princess waiting for rescue. Interpreting this for her was only

theoretically helpful, however, because she conceptualized her problems as stemming from a poor career choice. She denied any possibility that it was more complex than this. She believed that, if someone would simply suggest the right career, she would happily move foward again. Taking what little she was willing to work on, she embarked on 6 weeks of fruitless vocational counseling and some biofeedback, until she was comfortable enough with the therapeutic relationship to consider the possibility that her anxiety was due to fear of the risks inherent in achieving. Because of a firmer therapeutic alliance, she reluctantly accepted the idea that she would find the "right" career only after overcoming this fear. After a year of therapy, she has resumed working, in a job that offers new opportunities but employs many of her old skills. She has not experienced TMJ symptoms for some time and speaks proudly of her newly developed ability to read her feelings, recognizing and dealing actively with anxiety before it develops into physical symptoms.

In a sense, stress management with TMJ patients begins with the intake interview, because that is where the patient's first experience of attitude change occurs. The interview is begun by asking the patient to talk about the pain. This communicates interest in the patient's difficulties, allows assessment of the accuracy of her or his perceptions of her or his condition and how and when she or he complains, and provides a vehicle for the therapist's concern and compassion. Next, the psychosocial history is taken, with a focus on establishing who the patient was before the pain began and how its onset has changed his or her life. This is an important shift from physical to sociopsychological experience, and, with luck, a return to discussing physical problems will not occur. Once treatment begins, every minute spent discussing symptoms (even improved symptoms) is one that could be used productively on skills training or stress-reducing psychotherapy. The patient's mind-set is gradually altered by following the therapist's lead, away from preoccupation with physical symptoms toward life improvement. The patient's unending chronicling of physical complaints functions as resistance to change and should be put aside as soon as possible. The repeated venting of frustration and grief only reinforces the patient's sense of being stuck and the nagging conviction that no one is doing anything to help. Like approaching other forms of resistance, this setting aside can be done subtly (e.g., "You've talked about that pain a lot. Let's talk about your husband for awhile.'') Sometimes it must be addressed more directly, however, by interpreting for the patient that she or he is avoiding solving other problems when focusing on the pain.

Once conditions have been set up and treatment begins, the bulk of what is done for patients in stress management can be classified into three distinct areas: (a) psychophysiologic control including relaxation training or self-hypnosis and biofeedback, (b) behavioral awareness for habit management, and (c) identification and reduction of stressors. Although it is not within the scope of this paper to teach the reader how to employ these techniques, it is possible to provide some rationale in support of the simultaneous use of these treatment modes and offer some tips on special problems that could arise when working with TMJ patients.

The logical time to begin the approach to relaxation-skills training and the introduction to hypnosis and biofeedback is at the end of the patient's interview. Biofeedback and self-hypnosis training have been found to be extremely helpful with TMJ patients (Funch & Gale, 1980), producing long-term changes in muscular activity, reducing anxiety and panic, and increasing sense of control over physical experience. Patients vary in their responses to these techniques. Some are highly hypnotic and experience reduction or removal of subjective pain for minutes or hours at a time. Others respond best to the dials and digits of the biofeedback machine, which gives them tangible proof of their amazing, new found ability to tell their bodies what to do. Prior to this experience, most patients have felt that the pain controlled them. During this treatment process, they learn some of the ways they can gain control over their physiologic reactions.

Control over mind and body is central to the successful change away from symptom-sustaining somatic preoccupation. For this reason self-hypnosis training is uniquely helpful. Thanks to Milton Erickson, modern hypnotherapy offers special insight into the patient's resistance to change, suggesting a variety of approaches to helping the patient reframe a dilemma into winning choices (Erickson, 1967; Haley, 1972). In addition to this as D. Spiegel (1980) pointed out, self-hypnosis training, where the therapist hands the reigns of control over to the patient, sends a clear message about who is to take ultimate responsibility. In other words, ''the very occasion when the patient most expects to be controlled (in a hypnotic trance) can be an opportunity to teach the patient how much control he can exert over his life'' (Spiegel, 1980, p. 250).

Because the hypnotic trance can be characterized as ''an attentive, receptive concentration,'' it can also be used productively in conjunction with biofeedback equipment to enhance the relaxation potential of the patient. Even for patients without a great capacity for hypnotic experience, a deep state of relaxation can be achieved, especially if aided by traditional autogenic or progressive relaxation techniques. One note of concern here, however: Patients with TMJ and other painful conditions involving muscle tension and spasm sometimes experience increased pain with progressive muscle-relaxation methods. The tensing of muscles in these exercises sometimes irritates inflamed tissue, adding insult to injury. Autogenic techniques of warming images are a better choice, because most TMJ patients already associate heat and warmth with a decrease in their pain.

Biofeedback is generally a pleasant experience for patients. Most patients see biofeedback as nonthreatening, which presents advantages in a practice where biofeedback and psychotherapy are provided as separate treatments in sequence or by different clinicians. For the patient who denies any connection between life stressors and symptomatic muscle tension, biofeedback provides an opportunity to develop a therapeutic relationship and to test the waters of self-disclosure without admitting the need for psychotherapy. The clinician, meanwhile, can identify stressors and formulate approaches to change, so that, when the patient is ready for it (like Mrs. H., who was in biofeedback training during her first 6 weeks), some interpretations of conflicts or problem areas can be made.

For the individual practitioner, biofeedback can be a natural lead-in to the more probing, subjectively dangerous business of looking at and manipulating life stress. For clinicians practicing with a separate biofeedback technician, the different roles each plays allows greater flexibility in approach. For example, one useful tactic is the ''Starsky and Hutch routine,'' in which one tough guy and one softy are apparently coming from separate viewpoints but are heading in the same direction. The patient also has the magical experience of deja vu, when carefully coordinated suggestions and interpretations seem to have fallen out of two mouths independently. It is worth making an effort to reflect on differences in the personalities of clinicians who are working as a team, so that these varied skills in forming alliances can be used, together with separate techniques, to create a more intense and broader experience than one individual could provide.

A nice example of this was the case of Mrs. R., a

27-year-old woman who injured her jaw and neck in a fall. Prior to her injury, she had gone through life reactively, never learning about the usefulness of self-reflection. Her preferred problem-solving approach was to use the Goldilock's Method, trying things out indiscriminantly, getting burned or disappointed, and stumbling onto solutions that were "just right" just often enough that she never needed to question the effectiveness of this approach. Her TMJ brought on stress that was beyond the capacity of the Goldilocks Method to resolve. Each failure brought increasing discomfort and discouragement, and her lack of occasional success resulted in eventual depression. Treatment for her consisted of biofeedback with self-hypnosis training, coupled with an effort to teach her to be reflective about the effects of her activities and interpersonal relationships on her pain experience and vice versa. She began gradually to recognize the connection between her symptoms and her physical and emotional stressors. A comment she made near the end of treatment suggests that she was able to learn this from two angles simultaneously: "When I'm with Mary (the biofeedback therapist) I'm good by myself, and when I'm with you, I'm good with myself." One therapist had taught her the value of self-control, to feel good by herself because she felt confident and self-assured. The other taught her the value of understanding her effect on the world around her, that seeing herself through active self-reflection, even when this is difficult, can result in more effective control over relationships and events.

Self reflection and self-observation are prerequisite skills for stress management. Most patients suffer under several misconceptions about the stress-related nature of their problems. Self-observation helps lead to the self-awareness essential to dispelling myths like these:

1. Stress might make other people sick, but it doesn't affect me.
2. Psychosomatic illness is all in your head; my pain is real, so it is not psychosomatic.
3. Symptoms are only stress-related if they develop immediately following a stressful event.
4. I understand how my body works (so there is nothing you can teach me about it).
5. I must have a definite diagnosis in order to improve.
6. I cannot control the pain without medication.
7. The only acceptable outcome is total cure.
8. I cannot (will not) learn to live with it.

9. I cannot change the way things are.

In reality, patients have often taken the first steps toward change before entering the office. Their very act of desperation in seeking psychological intervention can signal a momentary openness to doing or thinking about things differently. When this crack in the armor appears, it is important to point it out and to congratulate patients on an already demonstrated willingness to resume control over life. Nevertheless, they still present a depressive cognitive focus around their pain, like that described by Beck (1970). They cling to negative ideas such as those just listed and often present an unshakable belief that these subjective realities are unchangeable.

To help the patient test these false assumptions the stress manager has to be armed with life data, which can be redefined for the patient. This information comes from interviews, psychological testing, behavioral records kept by the patient, and information provided by family members. In accumulating these data, the clinician is looking not only for situations and behavior related to illness, but also for health-related skills, talents, and circumstances, which will support recovery efforts. It is necessary to collect evidence of the pain–stress–pain connection for each particular patient, so that, as the theory of stress-related tension is discussed with the patient, reference to specific instances can serve as support for the argument. Daily pain records are extremely useful for this, but unfortunately many patients will not comply with this request. When the patient fills out a pain record, failure to comply should not be reprimanded but should be interpreted for him or her as further proof of how helpless and hopeless he or she feels. Rather than accusing the patient of hiding information or being uncooperative, the therapist has a good opportunity to empathize, reflecting he is so discouraged as to not be able to find the motivation to spend even 15 minutes a day helping himself.

In the process of teaching the patient about his or her pain–stress–pain cycle, each bit of information about problem areas and the reality they represent can be used by the clinician to create an attention–getting, "aha" experience. For example, a simple question based on observation can provide insight for the patient and credibility for the therapist. "Does your husband ever help you around the house when you *don't* have pain? No? Well, how do you feel about that?'' The focus on observed psychopathology is best limited to gaining the patient's acceptance that your viewpoint is informed or meaningful. Focusing on past problems is most helpful when it is presented as, "This is the way things used to be for you; now how would you like to change that?"

The interpretation of psychological tests can be useful in the process of gaining credibility. Scores and graphs, like those on the MMPI, look impressive and are technically appealing. If, during the interpretation session, they also yield "proof" of problem areas that the patient can identify with, so much the better. Beginning with a blank graph, the patient is shown how groups of items are pulled together to reflect different qualities of experience, and she or he learns that the line at T Score 50 represents the average and T Score 70 is "the distress line." Then the patient looks at his or her own graph. If there are several elevations, which TMJ patients typically show on scales F, 1, 2, 3, 7, or 8, the patient sees that she or he is distressed and is usually anxious to know more about what caused this. This helps convince the patient he or she has stress. The rest of the interpretation is then a way of beginning to reframe the patient's definition of problems or distress into positive approaches. If Scale 1 (somatic preoccupation) is elevated, the patient is reassured that elevations here are expected, and these scores generally decline as the patient learns to focus away from physical problems and on to the more normal problems of everyday life. It is even possible to use suggestion, in a hypnotherapeutic sense, during this "interpretation." Using Scale 1, as an example, it can be suggested that those with unusual awareness of their physical experience have "better" mind–body connections and therefore can benefit more easily from hypnosis and biofeedback.

Family or couple sessions are helpful in the observational stage, when stressors are being identified by the therapist and accepted and incorporated by the patient. Family members can provide information from their own observations and sometimes help overcome the patient's determined denial of emotional distress. At other times, family interviews unveil collusions between spouses, between parent and child, or among entire families. These might develop around a sick family member whose illness serves as a reinforcing focus away from other issues that are perhaps more threatening to the family. The wife of one TMJ patient found pleasure in her caretaking role and, while he continued to be needy and subdued by his pain, conveniently ignored the fact that, prior to his injury, her husband had been rowdy and repeatedly unfaithful. She had little interest in seeing him improve, for that would not improve family life at all in her estimation. Without intervention to create greater intimacy between them and strengthen her belief in their marriage, she would have continued to sabotage his recovery.

The emotional needs or distress of a member of the patient's family can impinge on the patient's ability to progress, by causing continued stress or by setting up expectations that are impossible to overcome. The mother of an attractive teenage girl with TMJ pain due to arthritis was angry with her daughter's behavior, which was described as rebellious and aloof. The mother, a traditional, quiet, passive woman, had no role in her life that she eagerly embraced except that of mother. As the empty nest loomed in the near future, she could not empathize with her daughter's pain, she could only center her attention on the girl's avoidance of her mother during times when the headaches were most severe. This increased the mother's sense of rejection, which resulted in passive–aggressive behavior, first on the part of the mother, then joined in by the daughter, widening the rift between them even further. In this case, the mother's concern over her daughter's "psychological" disturbance did bring her in for some biofeedback and hypnotherapy, which was probably somewhat helpful to her in managing a difficult chronic pain condition. The daughter's psychotherapy, however, requested by the mother, turned rapidly in the direction of addressing the mother's developmental issues, in the hope that she would be able to see her daughter's behavior as part of a normal bid for independence, perhaps complicated by the stress of chronic pain.

The psychotherapeutic issues in working with TMJ patients nearly always center on this type of normal developmental crisis. Although some functionally disturbed or psychotic patients have TMJ, a large share of TMJ sufferers are functional, upper-middle-class people who are achievement oriented, with demanding career or family obligations. For these individuals, stress has become a way of life, and, generally speaking, they handle themselves and their responsibilities very well. The sense of failure they experience at being unable to control their TMJ is ego-alien. As one highly successful CPA said of his TMJ problems, "This just isn't me." These individuals become obsessed with their inability to defeat their problem through logic or knowledge. It seems to undermine their confidence in their ability to succeed. Creative thinkers in their own areas of expertise, they are remarkably inflexible when it comes to making even small changes in life-style to accommodate their physical problems. Most are resistant to giving time to relaxation exercises or self-hypnosis, despite tremendous discomfort, even after experiencing significant relief using the same techniques in the doctor's office.

Much of this rigidity of thought might stem from the common developmental crisis of overextension. Progressing through life, we finish college, go to graduate school, enter a career or profession, buy a car and a house, get married, have children, and so on, each step bringing with it more and more personal and financial responsibilities. At some stage, most of us reach the point of overcommitment. We have created such a rigid, binding set of restraints on our time and thought that there is nothing left over to allow for the need to change and grow. The upheaval associated with change of lifestyle or career goals is so terrifying that we persist in following outmoded approaches. If functional changes are not introduced, the tension can become unbearable. It is this kind of tension that sometimes results in stress-related disorders like TMJ.

Faced with someone in this situation, the clinician not only finds resistance to seeing a need for change but also struggles with the patient to get her or him to sacrifice precious time for this purpose. Change poses a threat, because the ecology of his life is balanced on such a fine thread. Following Erickson's dictum to "go with the resistance," these patients are encouraged *not* to change until they are ready. This removes the demand for results although not necessarily the anxiety of the treatment. Because none of us stands still in life, it is impossible not to change, especially for upwardly mobile, self-demanding individuals. Avoiding the attempt to change specific things, however, allows the patient to experiment with ideas for change without the threat of dissolving life as it currently exists. If a patient says, "I'd like to do this, but I can't" the best response is, "Then I don't want you to do it. But tell me, what would have to be different in order for you to be able to do it?"

The threat of change is almost as powerful as the drive toward it. Although the clinician has to believe in the ultimate triumph of the individual's need to grow, he or she must also respect the power of the threat. The anxiety that accompanies this threat is tremendous. When individuals are stuck in the growth process, it is usually because they have succumbed to the anxiety by becoming afraid of it. Phobias are an example of this. For individuals with chronic pain like TMJ, the pain can function as an avoidance mechanism that is more socially acceptable than fear. Substituted for irrational or unacceptable fear is the fear of the pain, its recurrence or exacerbation. As suggested by the literature, rarely do patients develop the pain in order to avoid pressing emotional issues, but the secondary emotional benefits derived from the pain experience keep the patient's attention riveted on the pain and conveniently away from those issues that are causing emotional conflict.

When TMJ occurs in someone who is in the midst of a life crisis, it can serve as an escape mechanism, partly because it is legitimized by the patient, the family, the friends, and even the medical professionals. Mrs. S. was a 38-year-old housewife who flew in from another city for treatment of her TMJ condition about once every 4 to 6 weeks. Each time she came, she stayed for about a week in a pleasant hotel not far from our offices. She often remarked on how nice it was to be by herself, because her husband and three girls took up all of her time when she was home. At home, she said, the only time they left her alone was when she was in such pain that she insisted on entering her bedroom to rest. She was asked if she had ever lied about being in pain in order to have some time to herself. When she said, "Of course not," it was recommended that she do so, unless she felt that she could ask for such time without using an excuse. Her view of life was that it was totally restricted by her family. Prior to marriage, Mrs. S. had had a good job with some responsibility and enjoyed making decisions and being independent. Over the course of 10 years of marriage, she had given up every vestige of independence, and her family had come to expect that she would be available 24 hours a day. She had even given up having lunch with friends when the children were in school, because she thought her husband would be upset if she came into town and did not eat with him. She was depressed, restless, and experiencing a sense of desperation over things that she could not quite identify. The TMJ became her outlet; when it flared up, she flew away and took time for herself that she could not take at home. Treatment consisted of getting her to look at the pattern of escapes and convincing her that, as soon as she felt up to it, she should address the problem at home. After she had accepted referral to a marriage counselor in her own city, she did not need to return for more treatment.

This kind of escape is not uncommon and can serve a constructive purpose so long as it is not prolonged. Mrs. S.'s need for distance from her family was real. The nonfunctional aspects of her escapes for treatment were twofold: (a) she was not addressing the origin of the problem, and (b) this was maintaining a cycle of stress and escape, in which her physical symptoms renewed themselves periodically. In this case, addressing the original stressor allowed her to break this cycle, and her episodes of muscle tension abated.

Secondary gain of this nature need not always be looked upon as pathology. Sometimes it provides an easily recognizable focus for change and, so, can be productive. For those who suffer from over-commitment, illness can provide motivation to avoid bad patterns and thus be a vehicle for change. A young, frantic businessman, forced by his TMJ pain to take a few weeks off from business, found this acceptable so long as this relief from responsibilities was seen as enforced because of illness. For him it was helpful to recommend a lengthy period of recovery ("stay out of work as long as you can bear to"). Before his return to work, effort was made to help the patient let others know that special arrangements might be necessary and to teach him the benefits of acknowledging his limitations. Because the direction of flow is that significant others are already making accommodations, this is the time when the therapist can find more flexibility in the system, and permanent changes in situation and attitude can be more easily maneuvered. With the psychologically healthy patient, secondary gain can be addressed directly as a welcome but temporary side of the problem: "This is a tough way to get a vacation, but at least you got one." Encouraging patients to enjoy the benefits generally assures that they will not let that go on too long, because it is not legitimate to enjoy it. Despite the fact that Mrs. S. believed her trips for treatment were justified, there was a great deal of guilt associated with these hiatuses, along with regret for having abandoned her duties. It took several trips before she accepted the cause of her exacerbations, but, once she began to see the pain–stress–pain link, her illness no longer seemed quite legitimate. It was then that she was ready to consider other alternatives.

There is a different group of patients, however, for whom pain and illness are a primary source of identity. For them TMJ can be the most recent in a series of maladies and misfortunes, all of which support their sense of victimization. It is common to find mental and physical abuse in the family histories of these patients: a parent who was alcoholic or abused another parent, divorce, parental death, or just general turmoil during childhood. Life is not a series of purposeful actions for these patients but a matter of survival by doing as little as possible to attract attention. Some were placed in a parental role with other siblings, drawn into the parental dyad between parents inappropriately. Illness for these children was the only time they could ask for help without being expected to give anything back. Many report a parent with a chronic illness or pain problem, and more than a few have reported that they stayed home sick from school as children to "keep Mother company." Anger, mistrust, and self-serving resentment motivate their choices. For them secondary gains like Workman's Compensation, narcotics, and free treatment are part of what they deserve, because they "got a raw deal in life." For these individuals, life means pain, misery, and dysfunction. If you were successful in removing the illness, it could expose an emptiness that the patient would be poorly equipped to manage. In cases where a psychotic break is possible, approaches like hypnotherapy must be evaluated carefully and used guardedly, because such patients can be easily overwhelmed. Their defenses are brittle, and their ability to relate to others with consistency has never been developed.

These patients do not appear often, but when they do, they might present borderline personality profiles. Their ability to measure reality is thin, their description of physical problems is obsessive and has delusional qualities. They are socially alienated, depressive, periodically hostile, and frequently have a history of suicidal thinking or behavior. Referred to as help-rejecting complainers, some make an alliance too quickly with unrealistic expectations. The clinician's positive approach is then used against her or him, when she or he fails to achieve the results these patients wanted. Making a true therapeutic alliance is extremely difficult with such patients, because most have never experienced a trusting, helpful relationship before.

Unfortunately, identification of this kind of patient is often done in retrospect, after he or she is lost to treatment. When recognized early, the formation of an alliance becomes temporarily the only goal in treatment. It is possible for the clinician to espouse aspects of a stress-management program (for example, drug withdrawal) while still accepting the patient's unwillingness to comply initially with treatment. The soft sell suggests to the patient that the therapist is ready to work in the future, as well as being willing to stick out the tough times. As the relationship progresses, the patient can be encouraged to set a date when change can be considered. For someone who is bereft of all ability to relate to others, believing that someone else cares does not come naturally. With such a patient, the therapist works hard to earn her or his trust, a task made more difficult because failure is frequent.

Because of the hurtful nature of pain, chronic pain serves a unique purpose for patients like this. They see themselves as victims, and their pain reestablishes this familiar identity. It gives them an acceptable reason for being so unhappy and explains why their relationships are so poor. It is reassuring in that sense. In psychodynamic terms, the pain provides primary gain, reinforcement of internal beliefs based on low self-worth that shores up the patients' sense of who they are. It provides continuity, which might be the only stability they know.

CASE STUDY

Mrs. R. was a 27-year-old woman with a history of severe TMJ pain and migraines for 15 years. Her painful story included several blows to her jaw by her father. She had experienced constant verbal abuse from her mother, who reportedly had tried to make her stronger by hurling epithets at her to see if she could "learn to take it." Her mother, overweight and insecure, had smothered her development and kept her from escaping by repeatedly convincing her that she was incapable of succeeding in the outside world. Mrs. R.'s pain had become her fortress, a distraction from the emotional and physical hurt inflicted by her parents. She learned to wrap herself inside it, and there, although she could not escape, no one else could get in to harm her. It was in such a fashion that pain came to serve as a defense for her. By tensing every muscle in her body, she entered her "mental mode," and so she voluntarily created a "torture chamber" for herself to which she could retreat to "work through the bad feelings." She reported that, when her pain lessened, she became depressed. When she was able to become relaxed, she would develop "euphoria migraines," which relieved the anxiety of relaxation.

For a patient like Mrs. R. biofeedback and relaxation training are meaningless. Her pain was real (physiologically and anatomically), but it was so wrapped up in positive, protective ideation, that

removing it threatened to overwhelm her. An experience with hypnosis early in the treatment made her feel like she was "going to die," and persistence with this could have pushed her into psychosis. Yet she went to work every day and functioned. She was not technically crazy.

Treatment consisted of psychotherapy around social issues. We ignored the pain, although over half of the early sessions were filled with accounts of past and present misery. She decided to trust me and what we were doing, even though she did not fully understand the goals of treatment, which were (a) to provide an unconditionally safe relationship within which to examine her belief system in preparation for change, and (b) to encourage her, within this relationship, to take risks outside the fortress wall, so that love and trust could begin to replace her need to surround herself with pain. Gradually she let go of the pain long enough to explore and talk about her emotional life, including her feelings about her early years. Today she is married, and, although she still has pain because of permanent damage to her jaw, she controls it reasonably well with self-hypnosis. She has also made major strides toward enjoying a newfound independence from her family.

CONCLUSION

These complex cases can be the most exciting, if somewhat bewildering, for the meaning of pain is very personal and unique to each individual. Coming to understand the patients' own language of pain and learning to engage them within that private world constitutes a challenge that makes the work worthwhile. With these and other TMJ sufferers, perseverence is generally rewarded. Confused, alone, and unhappy, these patients desperately need support and care. Nearly everyone around them thinks that they have gone crazy, and often they have begun to believe it themselves. A kind, sensible approach to relaxation, regained self-control, and the solving of pressing life problems can result in changes so substantial that it is hard to believe that these people are the sames ones who walked through the door seeking care.

REFERENCES

Beck, A. (1970). The core problem in depression: The cognitive triad. *Science Psychoanalysis, 17,* 47, 1970.

Dell, W. (1969). Nonsurgical management of the pain dysfunction syndrome. *Journal of the American Dental Association, 79,*161.

Diddel, R. (1985, March). Uses of the MMPI in dentistry: Psychological consultation with temporomandibular syndrome (TMJ). Paper presented at the 20th Annual Symposium on Recent Developments in the Use of MMPI, Hawaii, March.

Dowling, C. (1974). *The Cinderella Complex.* New York: Dell.

Erickson, M. (1967). In Haley, J. (Ed.), *Advanced techniques of hypnosis and therapy.* New York: Grune & Stratton.

Funch, D. P., & Gale, E. N. (1980). Factors associated with nocturnal bruxism and its treatment. *Journal of Behavioral Medicine, 3,* (4), 385.

Gale, E. N. (1978). Psychological characteristics of long-term female temporomandibular joint pain patients. *Journal of Dental Research 57,* (3), 481.

Gessel, A. H. (1975). Electromyographic biofeedback and tricylic antidepressants in myofascial pain–dysfunction syndrome: Psychological predictors of outcome. *Journal of the American Dental Association, 91,* 1048.

Haley, J. (1972). *Uncommon Therapy.* New York: Penguin.

Heloe, B., & Heiberg, A. (1980). A multiprofessional study of patients with myofascial pain dysfunction syndrome, 2. *Acta Odontdonica Scandinavia, 38,* 109.

Johnson, D. L. Shipman, W. G., & Laskin, D. M. (1972). Physiologic responses to stressful stimuli in patients with myofascial pain dysfunction (MPD) syndrome. *Journal of Dental Research, 50,* 510, No.191.

Lupton, D. E. (1966). A preliminary investigation of the personality of female temporomandibular joint dysfunction patients. *Psychotherapy and Psychosomatics, 14,* 199.

Marbach, J. J., Lipton, J. A., Lund, P. B., Delahanty, F., &

Blank, R. T. (1978). Facial pains and anxiety levels: Considerations for treatment. *Journal of Prosthetic Dentistry, 40,* 434.

Perry, H., Lammie, G. A., Main, J., & Teuscher, G. W. (1960). Occlusion in a stress situation. *Journal of American Dental Association, 60,* 626.

Rothwell, P. S. (1972). Personality and temporomandibular joint dysfunction. *Oral Surgery, 34,* 734.

Rugh, J. (1983). Psychological factors in the etiology of masticatory pain and dysfunction. In D. Laskin,W. Greenfield, E. Gale, J. Rugh, P. Neff, C. Alling, & W. Ayer, (Eds.), *The President's Conference on the Examination, Diagnosis and Management of Temporomandibular Disorders* (Ch. 11, pp. 85–94). Chicago: *American Dental Association.*

Speculand, B., Goss, A., Hughes, A., Spence, N., & Pilowsky, I. (1983). Temporomandibular joint dysfunction: Pain and illness behavior. *Pain, 17,* 139.

Spiegel, D. (1980). Trance as metaphor. In H. Wain (Ed.), *Clinical hypnosis in medicine.* Chicago: Year Book Medical.

Sternbach, R. (1974). *Pain patient's traits and treatment.* New York: Academic Press.

Thomas, L. H., Tiber, N., & Shireson, S. (1973). The effects of anxiety and frustration on muscular tension related to the temporomandibular joint syndrome. *Oral Surgery, 37,* 763.

Yemm, R. (1979). *Impact on oral conditions and dental treatment.* Causes and effects of hyperactivity of jaw muscles. In Oral motor behavior: P. Bryant, E. Gale, & J. Rugh (Eds.), NIH Publication No. 79-1845. pp 138–156.

Chapter 10

Stress Management with Headaches

Gleb G. Bourianoff
Eva S. Stubits

INTRODUCTION

Biopsychosocial Model of Illness

In recent years there has been a resurgence of interest in the area of psychosomatic medicine. In a comprehensive overview of the field, Lipowski (1977) dismissed a dualistic approach to the mind–body problem as anachronistic. Engel (1977) argued for a *biopsychosocial* model of health and disease that would encompass the interactive effects among social environment, psychological factors, and physiological functioning. Other authors (D. T. Graham, 1972; Weiner, 1977) have contended that all medical and psychiatric illnesses are psychosomatic and, have recommended a holistic approach to patient care.

Despite general acceptance of the role of psychological factors and life events in the development and maintenance of all illnesses, major diagnostic systems (American Psychiatric Association, 1980) differentiate between physical symptoms with a primary psychological etiology and those with an organic etiology. There are no clear diagnostic provisions for psychophysiological disorders, which involve actual physiological defects that are precipitated or exacerbated by emotional factors. However, Sternbach (1966) provided a model for the development of psychophysiological disorders. His diasthesis–stress model proposes that individuals have a unique constitutional pattern of responding to environmental stimuli, with a

consistent activation of specific organs or physiological systems. Susceptible persons might have inadequate homeostatic mechanisms due to genetic predisposition, sustained stress, or previous illness or injury. Persistent exposure to either environmental or psychological activating events might combine with the first two factors to produce a psychosomatic episode.

Headaches as Psychophysiological Disorders

Bakal (1975,) in an extensive review of the migraine and muscle-contraction-headache literature, proposed that headache episodes are related to endogenous-specific responses to stressful stimuli. Bakal and Kaganov (1977) suggested that differences in reported symptomatology between migraine and tension headache patients appear to be more quantitative than qualitative and that their etiology consists of similar underlying psychobiological processes that become increasingly involved as the headache problem becomes more severe. This psychobiological schema of head pain is consistent with Sternbach's diasthesis–stress model of psychophysiological disorders. The model has important implications for the diagnosis and treatment of headache disorders because it proposed that genetic factors, environmental influences, and psychosocial stimuli interact to produce a headache episode. Consequently, a multimodal treatment approach is most likely to be efficacious.

Headache might very well be the most common medical symptom with which we are afflicted (A. P. Friedman & Merritt 1959). Most headaches are amenable to self-treatment or to simple measures like lying down for a few minutes. Not all headaches are that mild, however. It has been estimated that between 6% and 8% of the practice of a primary physician is comprised of patients who are coming in with the chief complaint of headache (Cypress, 1981). These people have already tried over-the-counter medications and home remedies, to no avail.

THE INITIAL APPROACH: PRACTICAL CONSIDERATIONS

When a patient comes to the office with a chief complaint of headache, adequate time must be allowed for evaluating the problem fully and carefully in the context of his or her entire medical history. It's unsuccessful and, in fact, dangerous to simply approach these people as one would approach someone with a cold. Sympton removal is not the goal, and a good deal of thought needs to go into the diagnostic process before entering the treatment phase (Gunderson, 1986). In practical terms, this means scheduling the patient with an initial visit of 45 minutes or an hour. This is not always easily done. And because the physician must charge for that time, the patient might resist. It's also quite common to find a patient who is "too busy to be sick" and is simply there to pick up some pain pills. She or he doesn't really care about the diagnosis, but is simply seeking a quick fix and might not be receptive to a more leisurely and thorough approach. Such a patient can usually be educated, if the physician is willing to make the effort.

Regarding psychological treatment approaches, it is important to remember that many headache patients initially resist psychological or behavioral interpretations of their head pain. It is common for headache patients to have seen numerous physicians, some of whom could have implied that their pain is all in their head or that they must want to be sick. Consequently, many patients are on the defensive during the initial visit and look for reasons to abort treatment. Development of a good therapeutic relationship is essential. Rapport is best achieved by an empathic discussion of the patients' prior treatment attempts and their own theories regarding etiology. The adjunctive role of stress, personality factors, and social interactions in the development and maintenance of headache episodes should be explained early in the assessment process. It is crucial for patients to feel themselves part of an information-gathering team, rather than "bad" patients who just want attention. The headache pain is very real.

Following the assessment process, it is necessary to delineate a structured, directive treatment approach. Although some headache patients do need long-term therapy, many are uncomfortable with ambiguous situations and drop out of nondirective psychotherapy approaches. In addition, many of them can be described as alexythymic such that they lack psychological insight and have repressed and disowned their feelings to such an extent that they are poor candidates for more traditional therapies. It is essential to involve the patients, the patients' families, and their referring physicians by outlining the treatment plan and explaining the rationale for each component of the treatment process. The patients' physicians and families are important therapeutic allies.

THE DIAGNOSTIC PROCESS: PHYSICAL ASPECTS

History

The history is all-important (Diamond & Dalessio, 1982). One needs to know when the headaches first began. Was it around the time of puberty? How often do they occur? How long do they last? How bad are they? It's difficult to assess the severity of the pain problem by simply asking. Indirect questions such as, Do they make you go home from work? or Do they prevent your doing activities you otherwise enjoy? can be helpful.

The location of the pain is an important item. Some types of headache, however, start in one portion of the head and travel to others as they develop. It's important, therefore, to refine a basic question like, Where does your head hurt? It might start hurting on one side alone, but, after an hour or two, the whole head might hurt. What is the character of the pain? Is it pounding, is it squeezing, is it stabbing, is it burning? Here again, verbal skills are important to clear communication. Is the headache preceded by an aura? Are there any premonitory or warning signs? These can be visual, auditory, or olfactory. Sometimes there is simply a vague feeling that something is wrong. Sometimes this aura takes the form of a mood change, either depression and lethargy or elation and hypomanic energy. Are there any associated symptoms in other organ systems? The most common of these are gastrointestinal, such as nausea, vomiting, or diarrhea.

The physician also needs to inquire about the general medical history. It's important to know if the patient has had any injuries to the head or neck. It's important to know if the patient has had any major surgical procedures or serious illnesses. Questions of this sort can give insight into how the patient has handled previous medical problems and can give one a clue as to how she or he views illness. Is there a positive family history for headache? This is not only of use in determining biological inheritance patterns but also valuable in getting an idea of whether role modeling has played a part in the patient's choice of symptoms (Ziegler, Hassnein, & Couch, 1977). What medications have been tried in the past? How have they worked? Is the patient taking any other medicines or drugs. Certain medicines can make headaches worse. Nitroglycerin is a well-known culprit. Certain blood pressure medications such as Apresoline can worsen headaches. Certain hormone preparations such as the birth control pill can occasionally worsen headaches (Diamond, Praeger, & Freitag, 1986). One needs to inquire about other medical problems such as heart trouble, respiratory problems, and digestive problems.

Musculoskeletal problems are particularly germane. This is especially true when the problems are related to neck and back pain. What is the patient's sleeping pattern? Does he or she have a sleep disorder suggestive of depression, such as early morning awakening. One needs to get a grasp of the personal history, occupational history, family setting, and general life-style. It's common to see patients with headaches who have very packed lives, who have too many things going on in too many spheres at the same time.

Accepting the patient's self-diagnosis can indeed be misleading. It's quite common for a person to come in and tell you she or he has migraine, whereas, in fact, what the patient means by "migraine" is simply a severe headache. He or she doesn't mean migraine headache in any technical sense, just that his or her head hurts a lot. "Sinus" is a similar frequent erroneous self-diagnosis.

The Physical Examination

The physical examination needs to be as comprehensive as was the history. One must not only do a good neurological assessment but also get an idea of whether the patient has concomitant

unrelated medical disorders that might complicate therapy of the headache problem (Bernat & Vincent 1986). Examples of this are asthma or diabetes, which might make it hazardous to use beta blocker drugs in the treatment of migraine. A patient with chronic constipation might be a poor candidate for treatment with a tricyclic antidepressant because this drug often makes constipation worse. Special provisions can be made to offset this side effect by means of stool softeners, bulk agents, and dietary modification.

It's also important to examine the head. The patient, after all, has come in for a chief complaint of headache. If you just listen to the heart and lungs and do a general exam, the patient might feel that you missed the point. Careful examination of the head is quite important. Auscultation of the cranium, the carotid arteries, and even the eyes for bruits might occasionally be useful. Examination of the dentition and temporomandibular joints is crucial (Saper, 1978). Signs of crepitation or internal pterygoid spasm are clues that malocclusion could be a contributing factor. Exploration for myofascial trigger points in the suboccipital musculature is a productive maneuver. Assessment of the state of muscle tension and spasm in the trapezius group and subscapular areas is also highly valuable in making the diagnosis and planning therapy. People with trouble along this axis frequently benefit from physical therapy as an adjunct to whatever else is being done for them (Blanchard, Andrasik, & Arena, 1983).

Diagnostic Studies

Rather than giving everyone the same tests, the diagnostic workup needs to be based on what is found in the history and physical (Lance, 1982). Certain basic things need to be done for everyone, to assess their general health and also to get an idea of whether there might be hazards or precautions involved in prescribing certain therapies. Basic blood count and chemistry profile and urinalysis are in this category. A chest X ray and an electrocardiogram are also basic studies to help in ruling out metabolic and organic causes of headaches.

A thyroid assay is also useful. If certain "red flags" have been present in the history, one should be more vigorous with the diagnostic workup. For example, if a 50-year-old person began having headaches that sounded like migraine, it would be suspicious, because migraines usually start in the teenage years. The index of suspicion for an organic cause such as a brain tumor would therefore be high, and one would go without delay to some of the more sophisticated tests such as the Cat-scan, which is a computerized 3-dimensional X ray of the brain. Similarly, in the physical exam, if focal neurological signs were found, one would proceed with the appropriate neuroradiologic tests, perhaps including angiography (Dukes & Vieth, 1964). If the patient had a fever and a stiff neck, one would think of infectious etiologies, and a lumbar puncture with examination of the cerebrospinal fluid would be necessary to rule out meningitis.

The Major Diagnostic Categories

Headaches are traditionally categorized as being functional 90% of the time and organic 10% of the time in a general clinic population (Speed, 1986). The lines between functional and organic headache are actually somewhat unclear, and there is a large area of overlap. It's common, for example, to find a patient with an organic problem and a functional overlay and resultant headaches. The primary organic causes of headaches are tumors, vascular accidents, and infectious conditions such as meningitis. These should always be thought of and carefully ruled out.

The most common functional group is the muscle-contraction headache (Saper, 1983). There are no gross structural alterations that accompany the pain, and therefore such headaches are called functional. Vascular headaches, by the same token, can be thought of as functional rather than structural. Vascular and muscle-contraction headaches can be mixed, providing a third group of functional headaches. They can occur simultaneously or sequentially.

Vascular headaches are further subdivided into migraine, cluster, and temporal arteritis (Ad Hoc Committee on Classification of Headache, 1962). Migraine is the most common of these. It can be either classic migraine, in which the pain is preceded by a definite aura, or common migraine, which does not have such a clear-cut prodrome. There are other types of migraine that are less frequent, such as ophthalmoplegic and hemiplegic migraine. Other characteristics of migraine headache include a) one-sided pain, b) scalp tenderness, and c) gastrointestinal symptoms frequently accompanying the pain (nausea and vomiting are the most common of these whenever migraine headaches are episodic). Although symptoms are not present every day, they can occur with a good deal of severity. They typically start at puberty or in the early teenage years.

The family history is frequently positive in that one or more other family members have also had migraine (Ziegler, 1985). More women than men have migraine. A hormonal connection is strongly suspected because they are frequently worse during or just before the menstrual period (Solbach, Sargent, & Kennedy, 1986). They also usually get better after menopause. The pain is usually described as pounding in character, rather than squeezing or stabbing.

Cluster headaches in contrast, are more common in men than in women (J. R. Graham, 1972). They are severe and frequently described as being located behind one eye. They are often characterized as stabbing. They are very intense, and the patient with cluster usually must stand or walk around, as contrasted with the migraine patient, who is most comfortable lying in a dark, quiet room. The cluster attack is often accompanied by lacrimation or nasal stuffiness on the same side as the pain.

Temporal arteritis primarily afflicts elderly people (Wolf, 1980). The pain itself can be rather vague, and it can involve the neck and shoulder as well as the head. The temporal arter might be tender to palpation, but this is not a universally reliable sign. The diagnostic lines between migraine and chronic muscle-contraction headaches are not always clinically as clear as their classical descriptions would lead one to believe. It's not uncommon for a patient to change from one type of headache to another or to have more than one type of headache at different times. For example, patients with chronic muscle-contraction headache frequently have superimposed migraines (Saper, 1982).

THE DIAGNOSTIC PROCESS: PSYCHOLOGICAL, SOCIAL, AND ENVIRONMENTAL ASPECTS

Following completion of the physiological aspects of the diagnostic process, the clinician must determine if psychological or environmental processes are contributing to the development, maintenance, or exacerbation of the headache disorder. This information can be obtained through a detailed personal history, interviews with family members and friends, and utilization of psychological testing. Frequently used tests include the MMPI, The Beck Depression Inventory, and the Social Readjustment Rating Scale. Projective psychological testing using the Rorschach Projective Technique or the Thematic Apperception Test can be administered if psychogenic disturbance is suspected. Pain questionnaires such as the Psychosocial Pain Inventory are also given. In addition, patients are asked to keep headache diaries. Information recorded includes daily ratings of the number of headaches, intensity of the head pain, antecedents and consequences of the headache episodes, and medication usage. The collected data are interpreted, to determine if environmental stressors, stressors related to personal coping styles, reinforcement contingencies, or cognitive factors are contributing to the patient's experience of pain.

Environmental Stressors and Life Events

The biopsychosocial model of health suggests that all types of headaches are affected by life stress. However, clinical experience and known physiological data indicate those most likely to be aggravated by emotional stress, are the "classic" migraine; the "common" migraine; the muscle-contraction headache; the mixed headache, headaches associated with delusional, conversional, or hypochondriocal states; and headaches caused by upper respiratory disease that are secondary to vasomotor reaction (Sargent, 1982). Stress can be defined as a nonspecific result of a demand upon the body (Selye, 1966). Selye discovered that every demand, physical or mental, produces a nonspecific, uniform stress response. This general adaptation syndrome consists of specific hormonal and neuronal changes, in addition to task-specific physiological responses. This stress response is generally adaptive, but prolonged or very intense stress can result in emotional distress or in the development or exacerbation of a disease process.

Environmental events that involve significant loss, such as bereavement, divorce, termination of employment, or loss of health, are very stressful for most people and can either contribute to the psychological reasons behind a headache episode or intensify an individual's experience of pain. Catastrophic events, including fires, wars, industrial accidents, and natural disasters, can also strain an individual's adaptive resources. It is not uncommon for a patient to report that her or his headaches began during or immediately following one of these difficult experiences. Emotional disturbances such as depression, anxiety, recurrent nightmares, intense anger, and other reactions associated with

posttraumatic-stress syndromes might also be present. Knowledge regarding the events surrounding the onset of the headaches is important for treatment planning.

Although traumatic events are stressful for nearly everyone, a series of significant life changes, positive or negative, during a relatively short period of time can have cumulative effects on bodily resistance and disease. The Social Readjustment Rating Scale (SRRS) developed by Holmes and Rahe (1967) is comprised of a series of common life experiences that are weighted using a ratio scale to estimate the degree of readjustment required on the part of the individual experiencing the event. The sum of these weighted events, or life change units, is considered to be an estimate of the amount of stress experienced by an individual within a specified period of time (usually 6 to 24 months). A host of research literature indicates a significant relationship between the experience of stress as assessed by life event scales and a plethora of adverse physical and emotional conditions (Holmes & Masuda, 1974; Rahe & Arthur, 1978). Consequently, this variable needs to be considered when treating headache patients.

Personal Coping Styles

Although the SRRS is a good gauge of life stress, life does not act on passive individuals. A person's appraisal of a situation, coping responses, social supports, and nature of life-style changes can significantly influence his or her physiological and emotional responses. For example, a major promotion can be seen as a challenging and joyful experience for a self-confident person with appropriate job skills. Another individual might feel threatened by the increased responsibility, fear failure, respond with increased anxiety, and begin drinking heavily to deal with the anxiety. Given an identical physiological predisposition for headaches, the second person would probably experience an increase in headache episodes.

Habitual ways of viewing the world, as well as appraisals of individual events, can affect the magnitude of the stress response. A hypervigilant individual who continually looks for potential threats might find it difficult to relax and let go, because at any moment something terrible could happen. Dealing with negative events through repression, or blocking out of conscious awareness, can lead to an accumulation of unexpressed feelings and subsequent anxiety. Such persons also avoid dealing with problems at an earlier, more easily resolvable, stage and might be setting themselves up for future trauma.

Personality characteristics or recurring behavior patterns can also contribute to an increase in headache episodes. Historically, migraine patients had been characterized by a constellation of obsessive traits including rigidity, perfectionism, and moral characteristics (A. P. Friedman, von Storch, & Merritt, 1954). However, subsequent research questions the validity of a migraine personality type (A. P. Friedman, 1958; Harrison, 1975), and clinical experience suggests an individualized assessment of coping styles. For example, persons who have an excessive need for order or expect everything to be just so can be expected to experience undue stress, because in this world nothing goes just as it is supposed to. Lack of assertiveness can result in excessive demands and feelings of guilt. Shy persons might experience intense anxiety in certain social situations. People with Type-A personality constellations tend to be hurried, driven, and extremely time conscious (Mitt Friedman & Rosenman, 1974). Type-A behavior patterns have been associated with an increased incidence of coronary problems (Rosenman, Brand, Sholtz, & Friedman, 1976) and tension and vascular headaches (Woods, Morgan, Day, Jefferson, & Harris, 1984). These examples of maladaptive coping styles can increase tension levels, lead to headache episodes, and intensify the experience of pain.

Operant Conditioning of Pain Behaviors

A third major concept in the psychological assessment of headache patients involves the conditioning of physiological processes, pain behaviors, and the experience of pain. Fordyce (1976) proposed that acute illness or pain episodes that persist for months or years become subject to the laws of learning such that a person can be inadvertently reinforced for pain experiences and behaviors. Consequently, these pain experiences increase in frequency and intensity over time, unless the behavioral patterns change. Research results indicate that reinforcement contingencies can play an important role in increasing the frequency of headache episodes (Blanchard et al., 1984). These reinforcers can be direct or indirect. Additionally, wellness behaviors might lack reinforcers or be punished.

Examples of direct reinforcers include attention and nurturance, rest, gratification of dependency needs, and physiological reinforcement from pain medication. Punishment of a spouse can also be reinforcing. For example, a headache patient resides in Colorado with her airline pilot husband. When his base of operations was transferred to Florida, the couple kept their home in Colorado. However, the patient was angry about the time her husband spent away from home. She was unable to express these feelings directly but developed frequent and severe headaches that coincided with the husband's time off. Once she learned to express her feelings directly, the incidence of headaches decreased dramatically.

In contrast with direct reinforcement, indirect reinforcement involves avoidance of an aversive or potentially aversive situation. Shy headache patients might find that their head pain gives them a socially acceptable reason to avoid anxiety-producing social encounters. Nonassertive patients have an acceptable reason for saying no. Children with school-related problems can stay home and avoid unpleasant school situations. The experiencing of pain can also justify time off from work and job-related responsibilities.

For example, a male mixed-headache patient developed increasingly frequent headaches over a period of years. He was raised by an extremely strict, critical father, who continually pushed him to work hard. As a man, the patient worked excessively long hours, had few friends, and had developed no hobbies. He found it hard to say no to his gregarious wife's requests to attend social functions, and he usually had a miserable time. While hospitalized for treatment of headaches, he discovered that he enjoyed being taken care of and not working. Because the experiencing of headaches was his only way to avoid continual activity and aversive social situations, the stage was set for development of a chronic pain syndrome.

Non-reinforcement or punishment of wellness behaviors can also maintain headache episodes. An overly concerned spouse or family member might actively discourage resumption of normal activities under the mistaken assumption that the patient needs rest to improve. A spouse with an excessive need to dominate or control might continually reinforce the headache patient's perception of inadequacy and discourage wellness behaviors. Assessment of these factors can frequently be made through family interviews.

Cognitive Influences on Pain Perception

Although excessive life stress and operant-conditioning factors play a major role in headache patients' experiences of pain, cognitive factors such as beliefs, expectations, and perceived degrees of control over the pain can also have a significant impact (Turk, Meichenbaum, & Genest, 1983). For some patients, their pain or the fear that their pain might increase in intensity becomes the central focus of their lives. Such individuals might avoid making plans, even simple ones like going to friends' houses for dinner, because they might have headaches. Restriction of activities and excessive focus on bodily cues is likely to engender anxiety, negative self-statements, and subsequent anxiety. This feedback loop could eventually precipitate a headache attack.

Patients might also learn to feel hopeless and ineffectual. By the time typical headache patients have been seen by a mental health professional, they have visited numerous physicians and tried many medications, to little or no avail. Having been disappointed so many times, patients might think that there is little or nothing they can do about their pain. These experiences of hopelessness and powerlessness can account for much of the depression frequently found in headache patients. A vicious cycle occurs in which the resultant depression leads to restriction of activities, more negative thinking, and increased focus on the pain. Awareness of these issues has led to the development of several cognitive-behavioral treatment approaches for headache patients (Bakal, Demjen, & Kaganov, 1981; Holroyd, Andrasik, & Westbrook, 1977; Knapp & Florin, 1981; Kremsdorf, Kochanowicz, & Costell, 1981; Mitchell & Mitchell, 1971; Mitchell & White, 1976a, 1976b, 1977; Reeves, 1976).

MEDICAL TREATMENT APPROACHES

Medications For Specific Headache Disorders

The pharmacologic therapy of migraine headache has two aspects: prophylactic and abortive. If the headaches are frequent and severe, prophylactic treatment must be considered (Saper, 1978). If a person is unable to carry on her or his normal daily activities because of migraine three or four times a month, she or he should be considered for treatment with a medication that will reduce the frequency and severity of the headache attacks even though that medication must be taken every day. Propranolol (Inderal) is the primary medicine used in this fashion (Kunkel, 1984). Other beta blockers are also effective (Dalessio, 1984). The acute attacks are usually treated with ergotamine preparations (The Medical Letter, 1976). There are many of these on the market such as Cafergot, Wygraine, and Ergomar. They are taken at the first sign of a migraine attack. They come in several dosage forms including sublingual tablets and rectal suppositories. The nausea and vomiting that often accompany migraine might make it difficult to take oral medication (Blau, 1982). Injectible forms of ergotamine are also available.

Chronic severe muscle-contraction headache responds quite well to amitryptaline (Elavil). It can be given in a single dose at bedtime. Fifty milligrams a day might be sufficient, although many patients require two or three times that amount. This is a prophylactic treatment approach, and it requires that the medication be taken every day. Acute treatment of muscle-contraction headache episodes with analgesics is unrewarding and not recommended. One runs the risk of addiction even to such nonopiate compounds as Fiorinal (Kunkel, 1982).

If temporal arteritis is suspected, corticosteroids such as Prednisone are the treatment of choice (Henderson & Raskin, 1972). One usually cannot make a definite diagnosis of temporal arteritis without biopsy of the temporal artery. This is a procedure that cannot always be arranged on short notice. When in doubt, Prednisone therapy can be started to prevent potentially serious sequelae such as blindness while the diagnosis is being confirmed. The sedimentation rate is a rapid laboratory test that is usually helpful when temporal arteritis is suspected.

Cluster headache usually responds well to methysergide (Sansert) (Solomon, Steel, & Spaccavento, 1983). Sansert has the drawback, however, of occasionally causing severe retroperitoneal fibrosis and, by constricting the ureters, kidney failure. It could also damage the heart valves. It must be used only intermittently and is reserved for severe cases. Lithium has proven useful for cluster headache when refractory to Sansert or when the clusters are very close together or unremitting. Blood levels must be monitored to determine the proper dosage and avoid toxicity.

The calcium channel blockers such as Verapamil and Nifedipine are the newest items in the therapeutic armamentarium (Solomon et al., 1983).

They promise relief of cluster headache with a more benign side-effect profile than either Sansert or Lithium (Hardenberg, 1983).

Physical Modalities

Physical therapy is often useful in treating headaches that have a muscle-contraction component. Suboccipital muscle spasm and myofascial trigger spots can be directly addressed with heat and cold. Ultrasound, diathermy, and related electrical modalities including transcutaneous electrical stimulation can be useful adjuncts. Injection with local anesthetics and steroids is occasionally required. Massage and range-of-motion exercises are essential. Aerobic training and a generally improved level of physical fitness might also help. This could be simply by virtue of altering endorphin levels (Appenzeller, 1976).

Dietary Considerations

Approximately 10% of migraine sufferers are sensitive to specific food components (Diamond et al., 1986). The most common offenders are chocolate and nitrates such as one might find in hot dogs or lunch meat (Henderson & Raskin, 1972). Red wine might produce migraine in someone who is prone to migraine, even if only a small amount is drunk. It appears to be not just the alcohol, but also the effect of vasoactive amines contained in the wine. Monosodium glutamate such as is frequently found in Chinese restaurant food can produce headache in migraine sufferers.

PSYCHOLOGICAL TREATMENT APPROACHES

Following medical and psychological assessment of headache patients and determination of appropriate medical regimes, various psychological treatment strategies can be employed. Frequently used procedures with headache patients include biofeedback, individual psychotherapy, and inclusion in stress-management or assertiveness-training groups. Appropriate treatment planning is dependent upon accurate assessment of the patients' degree of life stress, coping skills, reinforcement for pain episodes, and cognitive appraisals.

Biofeedback

Thermal and electromyographic biofeedback training procedures have emerged as one of the primary nonpharmacological treatment techniques for the headache patient. The strategy is to help the patient learn relaxation skills, increase body awareness, and gain control over the physiological processes hypothesized to play a major role in the development of the head pain. Although some reviewers have questioned the differential efficacy of biofeedback training versus general relaxation training (Silver & Blanchard, 1978), results of a fairly recent study indicate that biofeedback training led to a significant reduction in headache episodes for a patient group who did not show substantial improvement following a 10-session relaxation-training program (Blanchard et al., 1982). Success experiences with biofeedback could also lead to positive cognitive changes such as enhanced feelings of self-efficacy (Holroyd et al., 1984).

A substantial body of literature suggests that tension headaches, which are thought to result from sustained muscle contractions in the shoulder, back, and neck muscles, can be effectively treated by frontal electromyographic biofeedback, in which patients learn to lower muscle-tension levels in the frontalis muscle of the forehead (Beaty & Haynes, 1979; Blanchard & Andrasik, 1982). Peripheral thermal biofeedback procedures have been successful in the treatment of migraine headaches (Blanchard & Young, 1974; Sargent, Green, & Walters, 1973; Turk, Meichenbaum, & Berman, 1979), which are thought to result from prolonged constriction of the intracranial and extracranial arteries, followed by a rebound dilation that results in the experience of pain. Peripheral thermal training is thought to decrease blood flow to the cranial region (Sargent et al., 1973) and has been associated with a generalized decrease in sympathetic nervous system activity (Dalessio, Kunzel, Sternbach, & Sovak, 1979). More recently, the distinction between migraine and tension headaches has waned, with some researchers suggesting that excessive muscle contraction occurs in all headaches, with an increasing vascular component as the headaches become more severe (Bakal, 1975; Bakal & Kaganov, 1977); Philips, 1977), 1978). However, the Biofeedback Society of America currently recognizes EMG feedback from the forehead setting as the standard biofeedback procedure for tension headache, and finger-placement thermal biofeedback as the standard treatment for migraine patients (Diamond, Medina Diamond-Falk, & DeVeno, 1979). Mixed-headache patients are generally treated with a combination of thermal and EMG biofeedback approaches.

Because successful completion of a biofeedback training program often results in a reduction of headache episodes, most headache patients are referred for biofeedback treatment following completion of the assessment process. Patients who report the best results tend to be younger and more willing to acknowledge the role of psychosocial factors in their head pain. Seriously depressed headache patients are less likely to report reductions in head pain than other patients (Jacob, Turner, Szekely, & Erdelman, 1983), suggesting that the depression needs to be treated first. Patients who are receiving a great deal of reinforcement for their pain might also be less likely to benefit from biofeedback training. Consequently, these patients need to be seen for psychotherapy first or concomitantly with biofeedback.

If the patient is accepted for biofeedback training, the treatment rationale needs to be thoroughly explained during the first session. The patient should also be given an opportunity to "play" with the machine and increase body awareness. The next few sessions are often spent teaching various relaxation techniques (see Chapter 5), and home practice of relaxation exercises is stressed. As learning progresses, the patient is asked to consciously use these skills to help abort headache attacks or decrease anxiety levels (see Budzynski, 1979, for an in-depth discussion of biofeedback procedures). The length of training depends on the individual, but most patients do well with a 10-session format.

Individual Psychotherapy

Patients are usually seen for brief individual psychotherapy following completion of the biofeedback program. Patients who are seriously depressed, exhibit significant psychopathology, are in the midst of a personal crisis (such as marital problems), or are receiving a great deal of reinforcement for their experience of pain are seen for psychotherapy first or concomitantly with biofeedback. Long-term psychotherapy is recommended for some patients, but most headache patients are seen for 8 to 12 sessions. The treatment focus is on helping the patients' become aware of the multifaceted etiology of their headaches and use this knowledge to change emotional and behavioral patterns that intensify the head pain. Patients are asked to continue their headache diaries while in treatment. This information is used to fine-tune the treatment program. One or more sessions are also held with spouses or other family members to obtain information and set up behavioral programs to change reinforcement contingencies (see Fordyce, 1976, for more detail). Cognitive-behavioral techniques are used to decrease anticipatory anxiety and excessive focus on the pain, enhance feelings of self-efficacy, and change negative thought patterns that can lead to increased anxiety and depression (see Turk et al., 1983, for more detail). Hypnotherapeutic procedures and marital or family therapy sessions are added when applicable. Patients with an assertiveness problem might also be referred to an assertiveness-training group.

Group Techniques

Group techniques can be a powerful therapeutic adjunct in the nonpharmaceutical treatment of the headache patient. Group experiences help the headache patient realize that others have similar problems and can provide helpful social support. It is important for the patient to be ready for the group experience. Very shy, defensive, alexythymic, or seriously disturbed patients don't do well in these kinds of short-term group settings.

Stress-Management Groups

Appropriately referred headache patients experiencing a significant degree of life stress can benefit from inclusion in a stress-management group. The group runs for eight 90-minute sessions and consists of 6 to 10 members. The first few sessions are primarily didactic and educate patients regarding the effects of stress, the types of stressors, the typical maladaptive responses to stress, and alternative coping styles. Members are asked to keep stress diaries in which they list perceived stressors, their beliefs regarding the stressors, and their subsequent emotional reactions. The group discusses these episodes, and they help each other develop more appropriate coping styles. Problem situations are frequently role-played. The group is also taught several relaxation and movement techniques. Home practice is encouraged.

Assertiveness Groups

Headache patients with assertion problems are often asked to attend a six-session, 90-minute assertiveness-training group, as increased assertiveness skills can decrease anxiety levels and eliminate indirect reinforcement for pain behaviors. Assertiveness principles are explained in the first two sessions, and members discuss the results of their self-report assertiveness questionnaire (Rathus, 1973). The next four sessions are spent role-playing difficult situations. The role of headaches as avoidance maneuvers is also discussed.

CASE HISTORIES

Migraine Headache Patient

Following a medical assessment, Lee was referred for psychological evaluation and treatment. She was apprehensive during the initial interview and feared her physician and her therapist might think her headaches were all in her head. Consequently, it was very important to establish good rapport. Lee was informed that headaches, as well as many other physical disorders, were stress related in that stress frequently contributed to the development, increase in frequency, and exacerbation of her head pain. She was told that both her physician and her therapist believed her pain was very real and that the purpose of her visits was to determine if psychological or stress-related factors were contributing to her pain. Lee agreed to the assessment procedures and took a series of psychological tests including the MMPI, the Beck Depression Inventory, and various pain questionnaires. Lee's husband was also seen for an information-gathering interview.

Lee's case was selected because of its complexity. Results of interview and assessment procedures were suggestive of moderate to severe depression and anxiety, a significant level of life stress in the past year, stress-inducing coping styles, the presence of operant-conditioning factors, and maladaptive beliefs regarding herself and her pain. During the past 12 months, Lee had experienced marital problems that included a brief separation and reconciliation, changed jobs twice, and bought a new home. Maladaptive coping styles included repression of traumatic childhood experiences, perfectionism, low frustration tolerance, inadequate parenting skills, and lack of appropriate assertiveness skills. Sources of reinforcement for Lee's headaches included increased affection and attention from her husband and gratification of unmet dependency needs. In the cognitive area, Lee felt she had little or no control over her pain, saw herself as helpless and ineffectual, and frequently canceled social outings because she might have a headache.

Due to the complexity of her problems and the intense degree of psychological distress, long-term individual psychotherapy was recommended. Lee was seen on a once weekly basis for a 15-month period. The treatment technique was primarily cognitive-behavioral, with some utilization of hypnotherapeutic procedures. Lee and her husband were seen for several marital therapy sessions, and her son was seen for a psychological evaluation. She also attended a 10-session thermal biofeedback program and a 6-week assertiveness-training group following the first few months of individual psychotherapy. Due to the painful nature of much of the therapeutic material, Lee almost terminated treatment several times. However, her physician and her husband were good therapeutic allies and reinforced Lee's continued attendance.

By the end of treatment, Lee had made good progress in a variety of areas. She changed to a less stressful life-style, developed better parenting and assertiveness skills, increased her frustration tolerance, and reported decreased anxiety and depression. This reduction in tension helped decrease headache frequency.

Lee was also able to work through trauma associated with sexual abuse as a child. Lee's headaches had helped her repress this material, as her primary mode of dealing with head pain had been to take narcotic medications. Prior to resolving this conflict, Lee developed a headache every time she had a dream or association that reminded her of the sexual abuse. She then took medications that knocked her out and allowed her to avoid facing the memories. When she was able to deal with the memories, one source of reinforcement for her headaches was eliminated.

Another reinforcement of Lee's headaches was the fact that they prevented her from reaching her career goals and from dealing with her underlying fear of success. The headaches also brought a great deal of attention and affection from her husband. Dealing with these issues and altering the reinforcement contingencies led to further reduction in the frequency of Lee's headaches.

In sum, Lee became aware of the multifaceted role her headaches played in her life and her personality development. Although she continued to have occasional pain, she had developed increased awareness of the circumstances that exacerbated her pain and learned appropriate coping skills for dealing with these situations. Consequently, she felt increasingly in control of her life. Lee terminated treatment a year ago and has been seen for two follow-up sessions. She continues to report a 90% reduction in the frequency of her pain experiences.

Cluster Headache Patient

C. L. was a 50-year-old white male flight operations director whose case illustrates some of the complex interactions involved in chronic headache problems. He was first seen in consultation 5 years ago, when his headaches had begun interfering with his work. He described severe retro-orbited pain associated with tearing of the ipsilateral eye and stuffiness of the nostril on that side. He was unable to sit still or lie down during the attacks, finding that he had to pace the floor. The attacks occurred with maximum intensity at night, usually about 1 a.m., lasting 30 to 40 minutes. He related having had the first episode in his late 30s, but he had been free of them for almost 2 years. The presenting attack was in the spring of the year, often his worst time. It also coincided with a major increase in stress at work, because he was overseeing a space shuttle launch at NASA replete with deadlines and time pressures.

Family history was negative for headaches. His past history included surgery for a bleeding duodenal ulcer. He smoked two packs of cigarettes a day. He described himself as having been a heavy drinker in his 20s and 30s. He still drank 2 to 4 drinks a day during headache-free months. When he was having headaches, however, he could not consume even the smallest amount of alcohol without triggering sudden and severe head pain. Physical examination showed him to be thin and gray haired, with prominent facial creases and lines. The facial skin appeared thick and leathery. A well-healed abdominal surgical scar was noted. The remainder of the physical exam was unremarkable, as was the neurological exam.

He was usually accompanied by his wife, who was a registered nurse. She was no longer working outside the home. She usually allowed him to "give his report," which he did with the aid of a detailed notebook and a calendar marked with pens in several colors. She then supplemented his account, using more formal medical terminology and emphasizing how much he suffered. Prior to his coming to me, she had been giving him injectable ergotamines and analgesics during severe attacks.

The diagnosis of cluster headache was made, and he was begun on Methysergide tablets, with good response. He was very leery of taking medication that might affect his alertness and concentration. He felt it crucial to be in complete control at all times. As the primary cluster headaches improved, he began complaining more about a bandlike, squeezing headache accompanied by tight and tender suboccipital muscles. Amitryptiline was added to his medication program. He was referred for psychological counseling and biofeedback, in an effort to enable him to cope more effectively and to reduce his stress.

SUMMARY AND CONCLUSIONS

In sum, headaches can be conceptualized as complex psychophysiological disorders. Factors that might influence the development of a headache episode include physiological predispositions, diet, physical injuries, life stress, operant-conditioning factors, and cognitive coping strategies. Effective treatment planning needs to be based on comprehensive assessment of both the physiological and the psychosocial components involved in the headache process. Treatment planning might consist of prescription of prophylactic medications, dietary planning, physical therapy, psychotherapy, biofeedback or hypnosis, and conjoint therapy. Brief group therapy might also be indicated. Treatment is most likely to be successful if it follows a multimodal, multidisciplinary format.

REFERENCES

Ad Hoc Committee on Classification of Headache, (1962), *Journal of the American Medical Association, 179,* 717–718.

American Psychiatric Association. (1980), *Diagnostic and statistical manual of mental disorders* (3rd ed.), Washington, DC: Author.

Appenzeller, O. (1976). *Pathogenesis and treatment of headache.* Simon & Schuster, Spectrum.

Bakal, D. A. (1975). Headache: a biopsychosocial perspective. *Psychological Bulletin, 82,* 369–382.

Bakal, D. A., Demjen, S., & Kaganov, J. (1981), Cognitive behavioral treatment of chronic headache. *Headache, 21,* 81–86.

Bakal, D. A., & Kaganov, J. A. (1977), Muscle contraction and migraine headache: Psychophysiologic comparison. *Headache, 17,* 208–215.

Beaty, E. T., & Haynes, S. N. (1979), Behavioral intervention with muscle contraction headache: A review. *Psychosomatic Medicine, 41,* 165-180.

Bernat, J. L., & Vincent, F. M. (1986), Comprehensive neurologic exam: Clues from the history and mental status test. *Diagnosis, 3(8),* 61–64.

Blanchard, E. B., & Andrasik, F. (1982), Psychological assessment and treatment of headache: Recent developments and emerging issues. *Journal of Consulting and Clinical Psychology, 50,* 859–879.

Blanchard, E. B., Andrasik, F., & Arena, J. G. (1983), Non-pharmacological treatment of chronic headache. *Neurology, 33,* 1596–1603.

Blanchard, E. B., Andrasik, F., Arena, J. G., Neff, D., Jurish, S. E., Teders, S. J., Saunders, N. L.,

Pallmeyer, T. P., Dudek, B. C., & Rodichok, L. D. (1984), A bio-psycho-social investigation of headache activity in a chronic headache population. *Headache, 24,* 79–87.

Blanchard, E. B., Andrasik, F., Neff, D. F., Teders, S. J., Pallmeyer, T. P., Arena, J. G., Jurish, S. E., Saunders, N. L., Ahles, T. A., & Rodichok, L. D. (1982), Sequential comparisons of relaxation training and biofeedback in the treatment of three kinds of chronic headache, or the machines may be necessary some of the time. *Behaviour Research and Therapy, 20,* 469–481.

Blanchard, E. B., & Young, L. D. (1974), Clinical application of biofeedback training: A review of evidence. *Archives of General Psychiatry, 30,* 573–589.

Blau, J. N. (1982), A plain man's guide to the management of migraine, *British Medical Journal, 284,* 1095–1097.

Budzynski, T. H. (1979), Biofeedback strategies in headache treatment. In John V. Bajmajian (Ed.), *Biofeedback: Principles and Practice for Clinicians* (2nd ed.), 192–210. Baltimore: Williams & Wilkins.

Charlesworth, E. (1977), Relaxation procedures. In M. Russell (Ed.), *Stress management for chronic disease,* Elmsford, NY: Pergamon Press.

Cypress, B. K. (1981), Patient's reasons for visiting physicians: National Ambulatory Medical Care Survey. United States, 1977–78. *Vital Health Statistics, 13*(56), 1–128.

Dalessio, D. J. (1984), Beta blockers and migraine. *Journal of The American Medical Association, 252,* 1–2614.

Dalessio, D. J., Kunzel, M., Sternbach, R., & Sovak, M. Conditioned adaptation–relaxation reflex in migraine therapy. (1979), *Journal of the American Medical Association, 242,* 2102–2104.

Diamond, S., Dalessio, D. J. (1982), *The practicing physician's approach to headache* (3rd ed.). Baltimore: Williams & Wilkins.

Diamond S., Medina, J., Diamond-Falk, J., & DeVeno, T. (1979), The value of biofeedback in the treatment of chronic headache: A five-year retrospective study. *Headache, 19,* 90–96.

Diamond, S., Prager, J., & Freitag, F. (1986), Diet and headache. *Postgraduate Medicine, 79*(4), 279–286.

Dukes, H. T., & Vieth, R. G. (1969), Cerebral arteriography during migraine. *Neurology, 14,* 636–639.

Edelson, R. N. (1985), Menstrual migraine and other hormonal aspects of migraine. *Headache, 23,* 376–379.

Engel, G. L. (1977), The need for a new medical model: A challenge for biomedicine. *Science, 196,* 129–136.

Fordyce, W. E. (1976), *Behavioral methods for chronic pain and illness.* St. Louis: C. V. Mosby.

Friedman, A. P. (1958), The mechanism and treatment of migraine and tension headache. *Mississippi Valley Medical Journal, 80,* 141–146.

Friedman, A. P. & Merritt, H. H. (1959), *Headache, diagnosis and treatment, pp. 218–219.* Philadelphia: F. A. Davis.

Friedman, A. P., von Storch, T. J. C., & Merritt, H. H. (1954), Migraine and tension headaches: A clinical study of two thousand cases. *Neurology, 13,* 27–33.

Friedman, M., & Rosenman, R. H. (1974), Type A behavior and your heart. New York: Alfred A. Knopf.

Graham, D. T. (1972), Psychosomatic medicine. In N. S. Greenfield & R. S. Sternbach (Eds.), *Handbook of psychophysiology.* New York: Holt, Reinhart and Winston.

Graham, J. R. (1972), Cluster headache. *Headache, 11,* 175–185.

Gunderson, C. H. (1986, January), Management of the migraine patient. *American Family Physician,* 137–143.

Hardenberg, J., (1983), Clinical effectiveness of calcium entry blockers in prophylactic treatment of migraine and cluster headache. *Headache, 23,* 266–277.

Harrison, R. (1975), Psychological testing in headache: A review. *Headache, 15,* 177–185.

Henderson, W., & Raskin, N. J. (1972), Hot dog headache: Individual succeptibility to nitrite, *Lancet 2* (7788), 1162–1163.

Holmes, T., & Masuda, M. (1974), Life change and illness succeptability. In B. S. Dohrenwend & B. P. Dohrenwend (Eds.), *Stressful life events: Their nature effects.* New York: John & Sons, Wiley.

Holmes, T., & Rahe, R. (1967), The social readjustment rating scale. *Journal of Psychosomatic Research, 11,* 213–218.

Holroyd, K. A., Andrasik, F., & Westbrook, T. (1977), Cognitive control of tension headache. *Cognitive Therapy and Research, 1,* 121–133.

Holroyd, K. A., Penzien, D. B., Hersey, K. G., Tobin, D. L., Rogers, L., Holm, J., & Marcille, P. J. (1984), Change mechanisms in EMG biofeedback training: Cognitive changes underlying improvements in tension headache. *Journal of Consulting and Clinical Psychology, 52*(6), 1039–1053.

Jacob, R. G., Turner, S. M., Szekely, B. C., & Erdelman, B. H. (1983), Predicting outcome of relaxation therapy in headaches: The role of "depression." *Behavior Therapy, 14,* 457–465.

Knapp, T. W., & Florin, I. (1981), The treatment of migraine headache by training in vasoconstriction of the temporal artery and a cognitive stress-coping training. *Behavioral Analysis and Modification, 4,* 267–274.

Kremsdorf, R. B., Kochanowicz, N. A., & Costell, S. (1981), Cognitive skills training versus EMG biofeedback in the treatment of tension headaches. *Biofeedback and Self-Regulation, 6,* 93–102.

Kunkel, R. S., (1982), Migraine headache: Clinical and therapeutic aspects. *Panminerva Medicine, 24,* 41–44.

Kunkel, R. S. (1984), Clinical rationale for propanolol in migraine prophylaxis. The office practice series: Beta Blockade in Clinical Medicine. Wilton: Medical Education Programs.

Lance, J. W. (1982), *Mechanisms and management of migraine* (4th ed)., 122–123. London: Butterworths.

Lipowski, Z. J. (1977), Psychosomatic medicine in the seventies. An overview. *American Journal of Psychiatry, 134,* 233–244.

The Medical Letter, Drugs for Migraine, June 18, 1976.

Mitchell, K. R., & Mitchell, D. M. (1971), Migraine: An exploratory treatment application of programmed behavior therapy techniques. *Journal of Psychosomatic Research, 15,* 137–157.

Mitchell, K. R., & White, R. G. (1976a), The control of migraine headache by behavioral self-management: A controlled case study. *Headache, 16,* 178–184.

Mitchell, K. R., & White, R. G. (1976b), Self-management

of tension headaches: A case study. *Journal of Behavior Therapy and Experimental Psychiatry, 7,* 387–389.

Mitchell, K. R., & White, R. G. (1977), Behavioral self-managment: An application to the problem of migraine headaches. *Behavior Therapy, 8,* 213–222.

Philips, C. (1977), A psychological analysis of tension headache. In S. Rachman (Ed.), *Contributions to medical psychology* (Vol. 1). Oxford, England: Pergamon Press.

Philips, C. (1978), Tension headache: Theoretical problems. *Behavior Research and Therapy, 16,* 249–261.

Rahe, R. H., & Arthur, R. J. (1978), Life change and illness studies: Past history and future directions. *Journal of Human Stress, 4,* 3–15.

Rathus, S. A. (1973), A 30-item schedule for assessing assertive behavior. *Behavior Therapy, 4,* 396–406.

Reeves, J. (1976), EMG-biofeedback reduction of tension headache. *Biofeedback and Self-Regulation, 1,* 217–225.

Rosenman, R. H., Brand, R. J., Sholtz, R. I., & Friedman, M. (1976), Multivariate prediction of coronary heart disease during 8.5 year follow-up in the western collaborative group study. *American Journal of Cardiology, 37,* 903–910.

Saper, J. R. (1978, June), Migraine. *Journal of the American Medical Association, 239,* 22–23.

Saper, J. R. (1982), The mixed headache syndrome: A new perspective. *Headache, 22,* 284–286.

Saper, J. R. (1983), *Headache disorders: current concepts and treatment strategies.* John Wright Inc., 1983/PSG.

Saper, J. R., & Magee, K. R. (1978), *Freedom from headaches.* New York: Simon & Schuster.

Sargent, J. D. (1982), Stress and headaches. In L. Goldberger & S. Brezwitz (Eds.), *Handbook of Stress.* New York: Free Press.

Sargent, J. D., Green, E. E., & Walters, E. D. (1973), Preliminary report on the use of autogenic feedback training in the treatment of migraine and tension headaches. *Psychosomatic Medicine, 35,* 129–135.

Seyle, H. (1966), *The Stress of Life.* New York: McGraw-Hill.

Silver, B. V., & Blanchard, E. B. (1978), Biofeedback and relaxation training in the treatment of psychophysiologic disorders: Or, are the machines really necessary? *Journal of Behavioral Medicine, 1,* 217–239.

Solbach, P., Sargent, J. D., & Kennedy, K. M. (1986, June), Migraine associated with menstruation. *Internal Medicine, 7(6),* 93–103.

Solomon, G. D., Steel, J. G., & Spaccavento, L. J. (1983), Verapamil prophylaxis of migraine. *Journal of the American Medical Association, 250,* 2500–2502.

Speed, W. G. (1986), Headache classification. *Internal Medicine, 7(2),* 62–77.

Sternbach, R. A. (1966), *Principles of psychophysiology.* New York: Academic Press.

Turk, D. C., Meichenbaum, D. H., & Berman, W. H. (1979), Application of biofeedback for the regulation of pain: A critical review. *Psychological Bulletin, 86,* 1322–1338.

Turk, D. C., Meichenbaum, D., & Genest, M. (1983), *Pain and behavioral medicine: A cognitive-behavioral perspective.* New York: Guilford Press.

Weiner, H. (1977), *Psychobiology and human disease.* New York: Elsevier North-Holland.

Wolf, H. G. (1980), *Headache and other head pain* (4th ed.). Revised by D. J. Dalessio. New York: Oxford University Press.

Woods, P. J., Morgan, B. T., Day, B. W., Jefferson, T., & Harris, C. (1984), Findings on a relationship between type A behavior and headaches. *Journal of Behavioral Medicine, 7(3),* 277–286.

Ziegler, D. K. (1985), The epidemiology of migraine. *Keeping current in the treatment of headache, 4(5),* 3–11.

Ziegler, D. K., Hassnein, R. J., & Couch, J. R. (1977), Characteristics of life headache histories in a non-clinic population. *Neurology, 27,* 265–269.

Chapter 11

Stress Management and Hypertension

Gene Stainbrook

BACKGROUND

After World War II, cerebrovascular and cardiovascular heart disease emerged as the leading causes of morbidity and mortality in the United States and in other industrialized and urbanized Western countries. Hypertension also has become very common in the West and is strongly associated with cerebrovascular disease and stroke.

Hypertension is the third most common chronic disorder in U.S. adults and affects up to 60 million persons. Approximately 90% to 95% of all hypertensives have primary or essential hypertension. Of these, about 50%, or 25 million, have borderline essential hypertension, blood pressure in the range of 90–95 diastolic and 140–159 systolic. Persons with borderline hypertension are at greater risk for cardiovascular morbidity and mortality than those with lower pressure (European Working Party, 1985; Hypertension Detection and Follow-up Program Cooperative Group, 1979; Management Committee, 1980; Multiple Risk Factor Intervention Trial Research Group, 1982).

Hypertension is now the most common cause of office visits to physicians and a frequent cause of absenteeism at work. The cost of managing patients on antihypertensive drugs often averages over $50 per month. Thus, hypertension is an economic burden for many individuals and a source of escalating costs to the U.S. government.

The diagnosis and treatment of diastolic pressures between 90 and 95 in adults have significant therapeutic benefits. Aggressive step-care pharmacologic treatment reduces both morbidity and mortality in older adults (European Working Party, 1985; HDFP, 1979; Management Committee, 1980).

Although the lowering of diagnostic cutoff points and aggressive pharmacologic treatment of borderline hypertension can reduce morbidity and mortality, they also create new problems. Misdiagnosis and mislabeling become more common and can have negative mental and physical effects. Also, inappropriate drug therapy can lead to serious side effects (Haynes, Sackett, & Taylor, 1978; Guttmacher, Teitelman, Chapin, Garbowski, & Scnall, 1981). Careful analysis shows that as many as 50% of patients diagnosed as borderline hypertensives might be at relatively low risk for complications and either do not need drug treatment or can be managed effectively with behavioral techniques (James, 1973; Management Committee, 1980). Better differential diagnosis and wider use of behavioral therapies can reduce iatrogenic effects and long-term medical costs.

As mentioned briefly, in the United States approximately 90% to 95% of all persons with hypertension have essential hypertension or hypertension of unknown etiology that is without organic signs secondary to the elevated blood pressure. Thus, despite the expenditure of millions of dollars on biomedical research, there is still no consensus among experts as to the cause of 90% to 95% of all cases of hypertension. This results from the fact that hypertension is a disease with a complex, multifactorial etiology, which has both biologic and social bases that are highly interactive. Typical of most medical research, a narrow, reductionistic, strategy has been used to try to identify specific organic–structural and biochemical causes of hypertension. This approach has contributed to a much improved understanding of hypertension and to a wide range of relatively effective antihypertensive drugs. Overall, the successful lowering of high blood pressure with drugs has led to neglect of the careful examination and modification of social and behavioral factors that contribute to hypertension.

Many scientists now acknowledge that the etiology of hypertension is multifactorial and that social factors such as urban crowding, sedentary Lifestyles, and social stress play important roles. The social bases of hypertension and cardiovascular disease have received much study in the United States and other Western countries since World War II. It appears that industrialization and urbanization in most Western countries have contributed to the increased rates of hypertension, stroke, and cardiovascular disease. The major risk factors for hypertension are smoking, high-salt diets, high cholesterol levels, obesity, lack of physical exercise, and social stress. There is some evidence for the role of all of these factors in hypertension, but the focus of the following discussion will be solely on the role of stress in hypertension.

STRESS AND BLOOD PRESSURE

Psychosocial variables such as stress, psychological–behavioral response patterns, and emotional–psychophysiologic patterns have been implicated as either contributory or independent risk factors in hypertension and cardiovascular morbidity and mortality (Harlan, 1981; Rose, Jenkins, & Hurst, 1978; Rosenman et al., 1975; Weiner, 1979). However, problems of definition and measurement have impeded the full understanding of the role of phychosocial stress and psychophysiologic reactivity in hypertension and cardiovascular disease. Nevertheless, it can be argued that psychosocial factors should be analyzed as part of a good diagnostic workup for essential hypertension.

Stress: Acute Physiologic Effects

There is now conclusive evidence that stress produced by naturally occurring events; physical, mental, and emotional challenges; and experimental challenges can have pervasive short-term and sometimes more extended physiologic effects (Cannon, 1914; Levi, 1975; Selye, 1936). The effects of anger and rage, as typified by the classic fight-or-flight response (Cannon, 1929; Selye, 1956), and anxiety and fear, as demonstrated by Pavlovian unconditioned and conditioned reactions to aversive stimuli, on cardiovascular responses have long been known and are widely accepted (Gantt, 1960; Low & DeSilva, 1978; Pavlov, 1960). Equally well documented are the effects on pituitary–adrenal functioning of general alerting and arousal in anticipation of and during physical, mental, and emotional challenges (Levine, 1972; Mason, 1968). The effects of challenging and aversive events on neurotransmitters that regulate sympathetic nervous system function have also been clearly demonstrated (Dimsdale & Moss, 1980; Frankenhauser, 1975).

It is widely accepted that large pressor reactions can be elicited in response to both physically painful and conditioned aversive stimuli in animals and humans (Altschule, 1953; Brod, 1961; Cobb, 1950; Wolf & Wolff 1951). Some conditioned responses persist for very long periods of time (Gantt, 1960). Also, if experimental stimuli are presented on a schedule that requires continuous behavioral adjustments, blood pressure remains elevated indefinitely (Benson, Shapiro, Tursky, & Schwartz, 1971). Both short-term and long-term pressor responses to stressful stimuli are largely mediated through the sympathetic nervous system (Abboud, 1982; Frolich, 1977; Hess, 1957). Fairly recent work has demonstrated that sympathetic nervous system lability or overreactivity might be important in hypertension, especially borderline hypertension (Chobanian et al., 1978; Julius & Esler, 1975; Kaplan, 1977).

Sources and Mechanisms of Stress Response

There is considerable evidence that challenging tasks and aversive encounters have pervasive short-term effects on pituitary–adrenal and sympathetic nervous system activity (Levi, 1975; Levine, 1972). The anticipation of such events is typically associated with some degree of anxiety and the experiences generally described as stressful. Self-reports of increased anxiety, anger and hostility, and stress are frequently reflective of significant increases in the levels of pituitary–adrenal, sympathetic nervous system, and cardiovascular system functions (Levi, 1975). Furthermore, anxiety- and anger-producing situations and stressful exposures are often associated with transient, and sometimes more persistent, elevations in blood pressure (Weiner, 1979; Weiss, Matthews, Detre, & Graeff, 1984). Therefore, physiologic mechanisms clearly exist through which the effects of acute, intermittent, or more chronic stress, either external and physical such as noise or heat or more internal and psychological such as anxiety, anger, and self-imposed time pressure can directly influence blood pressure levels (Abboud, 1982; Harlan, 1981).

PERSONALITY FACTORS AND HYPERTENSION

As one moves from the laboratory into the clinic and the real world, it becomes difficult to establish firm linkages or causal connections between specific personality characteristics and high blood pressure.

Personality characteristics have long been implicated in the etiology and maintenance of hypertension (Schwartz et al., 1979; Weiner, 1979). Alexander (1939) suggested that hypertension be viewed as a psychosomatic illness. He felt that it was related to excessive inhibition of emotional responses to daily challenges. This position assumed a hydraulic type model in which internal forces would build up unless released, consistent with early Freudian theory. This largely unconscious mechanism was assumed to lead to an accumulation of anxiety and tension. According to this psychodynamic view, therapy should assist patients in developing more appropriate responses to emotional challenges and conflicts. The importance of anxiety and tension has remained central to most psychiatric and psychological theories of hypertension (Jacobson, 1939, 1967; Schwartz et al., 1979; Weiner, 1979).

Jacobson (1939), like Alexander, also linked anxiety and tension to the development and maintenance of hypertension. However, for purposes of clarity and measurement, he operationally defined anxiety in terms of skeletal-muscle tension and electromyographic activity. His view was based in part on the hypothesis that the tension of skeletal muscle and of smooth-muscle fibers in arterial vascular beds was involved in the regulation of blood pressure. Jacobson (1939)

suggested that increases and decreases in skeletal-muscle tension were associated with constriction and dilation of arteries and arterioles and thus with changes of peripheral resistance and blood pressure.

Subsequent attempts to establish associations between personality characteristics and high blood pressure have not been highly successful. Of the large number of psychological variables that have been tested for associations with high blood pressure, only anxiety, anger, and repressed hostility have consistently shown modest relationships in some studies. It also should be noted that increased levels of anxiety, anger, and repressed hostility can only be identified in a small subset of all patients with essential hypertension.

It has been assumed that the Type-A personality, previously linked to an increased incidence of cardiovascular heart disease, is also associated with high blood pressure. However, this hypothesis has not been consistently supported. In fact, in one of the major tests of this proposed relationship, it was found that Type-B personality was more predictive of hypertensive status than was Type-A personality (Rose et al., 1978). In the Air Traffic Controller Health Change Study, individuals who developed hypertension over the course of the study scored higher on Type-B than on Type-A characteristics. They also reported being less hard driving than those who remained normotensive. This finding is of interest because it suggests that care should be taken to examine sources of strong biases that might exist in responses to the questionnaire items.

The failure to find a relationship between Type-A behavior, especially the hostility, time-urgency, and hard-driving characteristics, and high blood pressure could have been due to several factors. One factor might have been that many individuals, aware of the direction of safe or socially desirable scores on the test, biased their responses in the direction of the most socially desirable behavior.

As noted previously, Alexander (1939) suggested that hypertensives would be more likely to suppress or inhibit emotional responses than nonhypertensives. Sapira, Scheib, Moriarty, and Shapiro (1971) have suggested that hypertensives often use denial as a defense mechanism against cardiovascular reactivity. They have suggested that the denial of existing conflicts blocks emotional involvement, so there is less anxiety and a greater sense of control. The findings of Pilowsky, Spalding, Shaw, and Korner (1973) also support this general position. They found that hypertensives generally tended to suppress anger, give a superficial appearance of being agreeable, and vent anger inappropriately, after which they showed intense guilt for being out of control.

Likewise, Linden and Feuerstein (1981) have described a behavioral pattern in hypertensives of passive–submissive tendencies, suppression of affect, overadjustment, and conflict avoidance. In a more recent paper, Linden and Feuerstein (1983) suggested that hypertensive individuals might bias their self-reports to give the appearance of being in control and well adjusted. Thus, on self-report tests they would have a tendency to respond with statements that approximated optimal psychological and social norms rather than giving unbiased statements of their actual psychological and social functioning.

Thus, at present there is support that some hypertensives tend to suppress emotions and overuse denial as a defense mechanism in order to deal with emotional conflicts and maintain a strong sense of control. These characteristics, plus a possible tendency to bias or positively skew responses on psychological and social rating scales, could contribute to the difficulty in establishing clear-cut differences in personality between hypertensives and normotensives. Thus, many hypertensives score higher on Type-B than on Type-A characteristics, due to the use of denial and positive self-statements. However, in contrast with these scores, they might exhibit Type A characteristics in their daily behavior.

At present, the relationship between scores derived from psychological and behavioral assessment instruments and hypertension is not very strong. However, some modest correlations and suggestive linkages have been found. The use of instruments to measure anxiety and anger in hypertensives patients might be useful. Also, the assessment of Type A and Type B behavioral profiles could be useful for general counseling purposes with many hypertensive patients. The assessment of repressed hostility or suppressed anger is a more difficult characteristic to test and is perhaps best detected through careful clinical interviews.

DIAGNOSIS OF HYPERTENSION

Before a clinician begins to develop a stress-management or relaxation-training program for a patient, it is important to recognize that many patients with a diagnosis of essential hypertension might have their blood pressure elevated only a small percentage of time each day. Thus, they might be at very low risk and not need treatment. Clinicians and behavioral therapists should be aware that there are critical limitations in the way that most blood pressure measurements are being made and in the criteria on which many diagnostic decisions are being based.

Problems of measurement.

Several problems exist in the way that blood pressure is being measured and that diagnostic decisions about hypertension are being made. Accurate differential diagnosis of essential hypertension is difficult. The extent of problems in obtaining representative blood pressure readings is not widely appreciated. Thus, systematic procedures have not been used to correct them. A factor that complicates good differential diagnosis is that blood pressure is a dynamic variable that constantly changes in response to different environmental and psychosocial demands.

In 1940, Ayman and Goldshine clearly showed that blood pressures recorded in a clinic are much higher than those taken by patients at home. This finding has been verified many times. Often, clinic systolic pressures are 15–20mm Hg, and diastolic pressures 10–12mm Hg, higher than blood pressures taken by individuals in their homes. In fairly recent, large, clinical trials in several countries, from 30% to 60% of individuals with initially elevated blood pressures reverted to normal over varying periods of time without medication (Management Committee, 1980). This observation has been termed *regression to the mean* and is considered a statistical artifact (James, 1973; Shepard, 1981). However, in individuals the tendency of blood pressure to rise in response to situational factors and fall as a result of repeated measurements is not artifactual. It reflects the dynamics of psychophysiological processes. Thus, rather than being dismissed as artifact, blood pressure reactivity and habituation should be carefully studied.

Habituation and sensitization.

Habituation and sensitization are basic physiological processes that have been carefully studied in both animals and humans. Habituation refers to the tendency of behavioral and physiological responses to decrease in frequency and magnitude to a stimulus that is presented repeatedly. In contrast, sensitization describes the tendency of behavioral and physiological responses to increase in frequency and magnitude to a previously neutral stimulus after the presentation of a strong aversive stimulus or "emotional shock" (Thompson, 1967).

The effects of sensitization on pressor responses to previously neutral stimuli is well documented in animal studies. Pressor responses represent defense reactions that reduce the aversiveness of painful or anxiety-producing stimuli. The reactivity and habituation of individuals' pressor responses are highly idiosyncratic and are of biological and medical importance. A tendency to exhibit exaggerated pressor responses to anxiety-provoking situations increases the likelihood that individuals will be incorrectly diagnosed and labeled hypertensive. Therefore, pressor responses to psychosocial demands could be major contributors to the establishment of more permanent hypertension.

Medical labeling.

Incorrectly telling persons that they have hypertension and giving them a disease label can sensitize them, which makes them overly concerned about their blood pressures. Thus, pressor responses to subsequent measurements might not habituate but might actually increase. A self-perpetuating cycle can be set up that maintains or increases the pressor response to measurement relatively permanently.

The confounding effects of sensitization on the measurement of blood pressure and on the diagnosis of hypertension are not well understood or appreciated. Therefore, satisfactory precautions are not taken to rule out this factor when screening is done. For example, a variety of persons, many with little experience or medical training, take blood pressures and are responsible for initial case findings. They usually rely solely on simplified guidelines to take blood pressures and to make preliminary diagnostic decisions. Inexperienced screeners rarely consider carefully the situational factors that elevate blood pressure. Thus, they can easily initiate an incorrect diagnosis that could lead to unnecessary treatment. Unfortunately, this results in economic, social, and individual human costs.

Differential diagnosis.

Treatment decisions are based on whether blood pressures taken in clinics are above or below the established normative value. The blood pressure values used in epidemiological studies to establish relationships with morbidity and mortality have been collected almost exclusively in clinics or physicians

offices. Although these casual measurements have some predictive power, basal blood pressure, measured when a person is relaxed at home can be more predictive of future morbidity and mortality (Perloff & Sokolow, 1978: Sokolow, Perloff, & Cowan, 1980). Nevertheless, most diagnostic and treatment decisions are made on the basis of pressures taken in clinics. When hypertension is severe, the difference between clinic pressures and basal or home pressures would rarely influence the decision to start treatment. In contrast, in persons with mild hypertension, diagnostic and treatment decisions could be greatly influenced by the set of measurements used. The exclusive use of clinic-based pressures creates a strong bias toward finding false positives. Thus, many persons are placed in treatment who are at very low risk and will not benefit substantially from treatment. However, in some cases, as will be discussed, blood pressure levels are higher and more variable in nonclinical settings (Devereau, et al., 1983; Pickering, Harshfield, Kleinert, & Laragh, 1982). To avoid this problem, systematic efforts should be made to obtain representative blood pressure readings in different settings for each individual before making diagnostic and treatment decisions.

Blood pressures in work settings.

Blood pressures measured in work settings may be of more diagnostic value than basal, home, or clinic pressures. They are more variable and higher than those at home and are often higher than clinic pressures (Devereu, et al., 1983). Both physical factors such as posture and physical activity and psychological factors such as time pressure, mental work overload, anxiety, and anger are associated with pressor responses. The simultaneous recording of blood pressure and type of activity indicates that pressor responses are associated more with mental stress than physical work. Common activities like public speaking are often sources of anxiety and are associated with large pressor responses.

In management and sales personnel, telephone conversations and oral presentations at business meetings may be associated with pressor responses. Telephone switchboard operators who must constantly interact verbally with many impatient and impolite strangers may exhibit prolonged elevations of blood pressure while on the job. The blood pressure of air traffic controllers, who generally have stressful jobs, is highest when the pace and mental demands of the work are greatest (Rose et al.,

1978). Those controllers who show the largest pressor responses to work demands are most likely to be diagnosed later as hypertensive. Thus, psychosocial factors and stress in many occupations are common causes of acute pressor responses.

The importance of the study of pressor responses to stressful work situations is now becoming clearer. Recent studies show that blood pressures taken at work are strongly associated with target organ damage. Findings show that left ventricular hypertrophy is correlated more closely with average blood pressure on a working day than on a nonworking day (Devereu et al., 1983). Also, patients with higher blood pressures at work have greater left ventricular dysfunction and exhibit more ventricular premature contractions. Thus, a detailed analysis of individuals' pressor response patterns at work should be an integral part of a high-quality diagnosis.

A poor differential diagnosis increases the likelihood of misdiagnosis, which can have serious consequences, as pointed out earlier. Misdiagnosis is most likely in young adults who show large pressor responses to threatening stimuli such as medical clinics. This might commit them to a permanent sick role and a requirement to take expensive and potentially harmful drugs. The achievement motivation and productive capacity of these individuals might be greatly diminished. Presently, there is a great need to improve the differential diagnosis of hypertension. This can be achieved by obtaining more representative blood pressure measurements.

Automated blood pressure measurement.

Taking multiple, manual, blood pressure measurements in home and work settings improves the representativeness of the measurement. However, it is time consuming and it precludes sampling during many daily activities and during sleep, which could be important in the assessment of the severity of hypertension. It is therefore essential to consider use of methods that circumvent or overcome this problem.

Noninvasive sphygmomanometric devices are now available that permit relatively continuous measurement of systolic and diastolic blood pressure and heart rate in outpatient settings. This equipment greatly extends capabilities for patient monitoring. Some models allow blood pressure and heart rate measurements to be made every 7.5, 15, or 30 minutes over a 24-hour period. These techniques have been shown to be reliable and valid in clinical field tests (Harshfield, Pickering, & Laragh, 1979; Kennedy, Padgett, & Horan, 1979; Sheps, Elveback, Close, Kleven & Bissen 1981).

Although these automatic monitoring devices require a fairly high initial investment, over time they can be a source of great cost savings. The 24-hour profiling of blood pressures allows persons to be placed in more precise diagnostic groupings. These categories represent different probabilities for the risk of complications. Recent findings indicate that the use of 24-hour profiles, along with consideration of other behavioral risk factors, can eliminate the need to treat with drugs nearly 50% of persons who would normally be so treated (McCall & McCall, 1981).

STRESS MANAGEMENT FOR HYPERTENSION

Relaxation and short-term physiologic responses.

A substantial body of basic research suggests that relaxation training can reduce short-term physiologic responses to stressors.

Relaxation procedures have been shown to reduce acute, largely sympathetically medicated, physiologic responses to physical, mental, and emotional challenges. Blood pressure, heart rate, and galvanic skin responses to acute challenges have all been found to be reduced after relaxation training (Lehrer, 1980; Orme-Johnson, 1973; Patel, Marmot, & Terry 1981; Stoyva, Anderson, Vaughn, Budzynski, & MacDonald, 1980). Also, training in relaxation has been associated with reductions in levels of sympathetic transmitters (Matthew et al., 1980) and with decreased sympathetic responsivity to plasma norepinephrine (Hoffman et al., 1982). Finally, relaxation training has been shown to reduce cortisol responses to acute stress (Michaels, McCann, & Vander, 1979) and resting levels of cortisol (Jevning, Wilson, & Davidson, 1978; McGrady, Yonker, Tan, Fine, & Woerner, 1981; Patel, et al., 1981). Therefore, the regular practice of relaxation procedures can decrease both sympathetic nervous system and pituitary–adrenal activity to acute, experimentally manipulated physical, mental, and emotional challenges. Given the critical metabolic mediating roles of the hormones and transmitters of the pituitary–adrenal and sympathetic nervous systems, it might be expected that decreases in their level of activity would be reflected in lower blood pressure.

Relaxation and psychosomatic conditions.

Relaxation and stress-management training have often been associated with reductions in self-reported levels of anxiety, anger, and other stress-related disorders such as headaches, gastric upset, and mild insomnia (Silver & Blanchard, 1978). All of these conditions are importantly influenced by excessive pituitary–adrenal and sympathetic activity.

Considerable evidence now supports the effectiveness of relaxation and stress-management procedures in lowering blood pressure in both normotensives and hypertensives (Stainbrook & Green, 1983). Although many of the early studies were poorly controlled and followed up participants only for short intervals, more recent studies have shown significant longer term reductions in blood pressure. The fact that relaxation training is often associated with concomitant reductions in anxiety, anger, and blood pressure, strengthens the link between them suggested by correlational studies Stainbrook & Green (1983). Finally, the observation that cessation of relaxation practice is sometimes associated with returns to pretreatment levels of both anxiety, anger, and blood pressure provides further evidence for their association.

Relaxation and high blood pressure

A number of stress-management and relaxation-training interventions have been utilized in the treatment of essential hypertension. Prominent among these are supportive psychotherapy, biofeedback training, and relaxation and meditation techniques. In addition, sodium restriction, weight management, smoking cessation, and exercise training have been advocated. This brief review, or synopsis, will focus upon only those techniques oriented specifically to stress management, namely, supportive psychotherapy, biofeedback, and relaxation and meditation training.

It appears that these three types of behavioral interventions are successful to the extent that they elicit the relaxation response. Thus, a brief review of this response should be instructive.

The relaxation response is associated with hypometabolic physiologic changes that are similar to those described by Hess (1957) in the cat as part of what he termed a trophotropic or restorative process. Changes observed in people have included decreased oxygen consumption, carbon dioxide elimination, respiratory rate, heart rate, arterial blood lactate, and arterial blood pressure, as well as increased skin resistance and frequency of alpha and theta activity on the electroencephalogram (Benson, 1977; Wallace, 1970; Wallace & Benson, 1972). These physiologic changes are consistent with decreased sympathetic nervous system activity (Benson, 1977; Wallace, Benson & Wilson, 1971). The techniques associated with the elicitation of the relaxation response contain several elements in common: (a) a passive attitude (b) a mental device, (c) a quiet environment, (d) a decrease in muscle tonus (Benson, 1975; Benson, Beary & Carol, 1974). Based on these four elements, Beary & Benson (1974) presented instructions for a simple, noncultic technique that elicits the relaxation response. However, it must be emphasized that this technique is only one of many such procedures. It should not be confused with the physiologic changes of the response itself.

Supportive psychotherapy, biofeedback, and relaxation and meditation techniques have all been used in the therapy of hypertension. Each has been based on a somewhat different view of the etiology and pathogenesis of this disease. As noted earlier, each of these techniques will be briefly discussed in the following section, and representative studies using the methods will be reviewed.

Supportive psychotherapy.

The use of supportive psychotherapy to lower blood pressure is based on the assumption that blood pressure can be lowered indirectly by reducing anxiety, by generating optimism about the treatment, and by improving the cooperation of patients with other aspects of their medical management. Small, transient reductions in blood pressure have been associated with supportive psychotherapy (Bali, 1979; Brauer, Horlick, Nelson, Farquhar, & Agras, 1979; Roskies, Sperack, Surkis, Cohen, & Gilman, 1978; Taylor, Farquhar, Nelson, & Agras, 1977). Given the nonspecificity of this approach, positive outcomes cannot be clearly attributed to a particular technique or mechanism. Thus, although anxiety reduction might mediate blood pressure changes (Bali, 1979; Roskies et al., 1978; Taylor et al., 1977), a clear distinction cannot be made between the reduction of anxiety and the positive demand or expectancy effects that might also facilitate blood pressure reductions.

Biofeedback.

In contrast with supportive therapy, biofeedback is a narrowly focused, specific approach to the treatment of hypertension. Based largely on operant-conditioning principles, it involves training the self-regulation of typically involuntary processes (Benson & Greenwood, 1976; Miller, 1969; Schwartz & Shapiro, 1973). Electronic instrumentation allows blood pressure responses to be monitored and relayed to patients in the form of auditory or visual signals. Often patients are told merely to raise or lower blood pressure by using the feedback signals as discriminative cues. Although knowledge of correct performance has often been a sufficient motivator, rewards in the form of verbal praise or money are also used (Frumkin, Nathan, Prout, & Cohen, 1978; Schwartz & Shapiro, 1973; Silver & Blanchard, 1978).

Direct blood pressure biofeedback was believed to have promise as a treatment for hypertension (Benson, Shapiro, Tursky, & Schivartz, 1971; Elder, Ruiz, Deabler, & Dillenkoffer, 1973; Goldman, Kleinmann, Snow, Bidus, & Kovol, 1975; Kristt & Engel, 1975; Miller, 1969). However, subsequent findings have dampened this initial optimism (Blanchard, Miller, Abel, Haynes, & Wicker, 1979; Elder & Eustis, 1975; Miller, 1975; Schwartz & Shapiro, 1973). Furthermore, when biofeedback has been compared directly with the methods of progressive muscle relaxation and those of relaxation and meditation, it has not been proven to be superior (Blanchard et al., 1979; Hager & Surwit, 1978; Surwit, Shapiro, & Good, 1978). Biofeedback is also dependent upon instrumentation that is costly and sometimes cumbersome.

There is now increased support for the view expressed by Benson and Greenwood (1976) that biofeedback was likely to be only an elaborate and largely unnecessary way of eliciting the relaxation response (Blanchard & Epstein, 1978; Frumkin et al., 1978; Schwartz et al., 1979). Hence, Silver and Blanchard (1978) have suggested that relaxation might be conceived of as a final common pathway in the biofeedback treatment of many psycho-physiologic disorders. The feasibility of using direct blood pressure biofeedback alone as a mode of therapy in the treatment of hypertension is, therefore, now in question (Agras & Jacob, 1979; Frumkin et al., 1978; Schwartz et al., 1979; Shapiro, Schwartz, Ferguson, Redmond, & Weiss, 1977).

However, biofeedback can be a useful teaching tool and adjunct to other forms of relaxation training.

Relaxation and meditation techniques.

Progressive muscle relaxation was perhaps the first formalized behavioral method used to treat hypertension (Jacobson, 1939). Its objective was to help patients detect muscle tension and reduce this tension by systematically tensing and relaxing major muscle groups. Reduced muscle tension was thought to lead to lower levels of emotional and physiologic arousal and, thus, to lower blood pressure.

The effects of progressive muscle relaxation have been examined by a number of investigators (Brady, Luborsky, & Kron, 1974; Deabler, Fidel, Dillenkofer, & Elder, 1973; Jacobson, 1939; Roskies et al., 1978; Shoemaker & Tasto, 1975). Both reliable within-session changes (Jacobson, 1939; Deabler et al., 1973) and between-session changes in blood pressure (Brady et al., 1974; Roskies et al., 1978; Shoemaker & Tasto, 1975) have been reported. When compared with other forms of behavioral therapy, the results are equivalent to supportive therapy (Roskies et al., 1978) and sometimes superior to biofeedback (Blanchard et al., 1979; Hager & Surwit, 1978; Shoemaker & Tasto, 1975). Over the years, significant changes have occurred in the manner in which progressive muscle relaxation is being taught. The duration of muscle tensing and relaxing exercises has been reduced. Also, the tensing and relaxing component is being supplemented by the addition of other components such as controlled breathing, constant auditory stimuli, and visual imagery (Bernstein & Borkovic, 1973; Bali, 1979; Brauer et al., 1979; Patel & North, 1975; Taylor et al., 1977). Progressive muscle relaxation has been widely accepted and relatively successful in the treatment of hypertension, as it is easily understood by most patients and can be learned quite readily. Relaxation and meditation techniques that elicit the relaxation response also have been used in the treatment of hypertension by a number of investigators (Benson, Rosner, Marzetta, & Klemchuck, 1974a, 1974b; Blackwell et al., 1976; Datey, Deshmukh, Dalvi, & Vinekar, 1969; Seer & Raeburn, 1980; Stone & DeLeo, 1976).

In a fairly recent study, Seer and Raeburn (1980) obtained reliable treatment effects using a relaxation procedure patterned after transcendental meditation. Participants received five weekly sessions. Three groups (self-relaxation with mantra, self-relaxation without mantra, and waiting-list control) were followed for 3 months. The two treatment groups showed equivalent blood pressure reductions that were significantly greater than those of the control group. Overall, these outcomes suggest that relaxation and meditation techniques can effect significant blood pressure reductions in patients who have essential hypertension.

Mixed behavioral therapies.

Although reliable treatment effects have been reported in many studies in which relaxation and meditation procedures have been used, some subjects in these studies do not show significant blood pressure reductions. Also, the reductions are sometimes not maintained after the training and clinical contacts are terminated. Such considerations have prompted an increase in the use of mixed or eclectic relaxation protocols, which allows tailoring of the procedure to better fit the preferences and abilities of individual patients.

Patel and her associates (Patel, 1973, 1975a,b,c; Patel & Caruthers, 1977; Patel & North, 1975; Patel et al., 1981) have consistently demonstrated blood pressure reductions in patients using eclectic relaxation proocols. Their procedures include progressive muscle relaxation, breathing exercises, visual imagery, and supplemental biofeedback. They also emphasized homework and record keeping, and the patients were taught to use environmental cues as prompts for brief relaxation pauses.

Using a yogic exercise and supplemental biofeedback, Patel (1973) demonstrated reliable blood pressure reductions in hypertensive patients. Training consisted of approximately 18 hours of contact over a 3-month period. Later, Patel (1975b) strengthened the outcomes of the earlier study by extending the follow-up of the treatment group by 12 months and by adding a control group. Patients in the treatment group were not given additional training but were encouraged to continue to regularly practice their technique. The treatment group maintained previously established lower blood pressure over the additional 12-month period, whereas the control group showed negligible changes. As a number of patients reported problems in practicing relaxation daily for 15 to 20 minutes, they were taught to incorporate very brief relaxation exercises into their daily routines.

In a controlled, prospective investigation, Patel and North (1975) more clearly demonstrated the efficacy of a relaxation and meditation technique with supportive biofeedback. Patients in the treatment group were given two 30-minute training sessions

per week for 6 weeks, a total of about 6 hours of instruction. They were also encouraged to regularly practice their meditative technique and to incorporate brief relaxation pauses into their daily routines. Both experimental and control patients showed reliable blood pressure reductions at 6 months but those of the experimental group were significantly greater. In the Patel studies, the contribution of regular practice of a daily relaxation and meditation technique cannot be isolated from that of supplemental biofeedback and the use of brief relaxation breaks. In most subsequent studies, the authors have tended to follow Patel's practice of including brief progressive muscle relaxation exercises and supplementing them with other procedures such as controlled breathing, constant auditory stimuli, and visual imagery. To improve compliance and transfer of training, they have also taught participants to take brief relaxation pauses in addition to longer (10- to 20-minute) relaxation and meditation sessions.

Comparisons of the use of biofeedback by Patel and North (1975) and Bali (1979) with that of Frankel, Patel, Horowitz, Freidenwold, & Gardner (1978) indicate that the greatest reductions in blood pressure result when the training places minimal demands on patients. Biofeedback was most effective in a supportive role that reinforced relaxation (Bali, 1979; Patel, 1975a; Patel & North, 1975). When the biofeedback training was rigorous and required considerable time and effort, it seemed to adversely affect the lowering of blood pressure (Frankel et al., 1978; Hager & Surwit, 1978).

Taylor et al. (1977) found relaxation training to be superior in lowering the blood pressure of patients with essential hypertension to a control group that received supportive therapy. Patients given the relaxation training received a mean of six 30-minute sessions. They were also requested to practice their techniques at least once daily, to keep records, and to report periodically on their practice. Both after training and at a 6 month follow-up the patients in the relaxation group showed reliable blood pressure reductions that were significantly larger than those of the control group. Agras, Southham, and Taylor (1983) and Agras, Taylor, Kraemer, Allen, and Schneider (1980) also demonstrated the effectiveness of similar relaxation training in lowering the blood pressure to levels below their own baselines of essential hypertensive patients when their blood pressure was monitored continuously over 24-hour periods. The effects of relaxation training and supportive therapy were also compared by Bali (1979). Participants in the relaxation group received 6–10 structured sessions, were encouraged to practice the technique at home at least once daily for approximately 20 minutes, and were advised to use the technique a few minutes every hour. They were also asked to record their practice daily and to submit the practice records monthly. Supportive-therapy patients were given an equivalent number of brief therapy sessions. Six months after treatment, the relaxation group showed significant blood pressure reductions, whereas the supportive-therapy control group showed little change. Finally, Brauer et al. (1979) compared the effects of therapist-guided relaxation training with a tape-recorded relaxation protocol and individual supportive therapy. Subjects in the guided-relaxation group were given a total of ten 30-minute sessions. Differences were not found among the groups immediately following therapy, but at 6-month follow-up the therapist-conducted relaxation groups showed a greater decrease in systolic blood pressure than the two other groups. [These outcomes replicated the findings of Taylor et al., 1977, and strengthened the position that relaxation training had greater effects than supportive therapy.]

Summary

Supportive psychotherapy, biofeedback, and relaxation and meditation training have all been shown to have utility in the treatment of hypertension. At the present, the greatest amount of support for clinical efficacy exists for eclectic relaxation and meditation techniques that tailor procedures to individual needs. In terms of treatment outcome, durability, and cost effectiveness, relaxation and meditation training appears preferable to both supportive psychotherapy and biofeedback as a general strategy (Agras & Jacob, 1979; Frumkin et al., 1978; Schwartz et al., 1979; Shapiro et al., 1977). However, biofeedback might be useful in some patients, if it is employed along with relaxation and meditation training (Bali, 1979; Patel, 1975a; Patel & North, 1975).

The regular practice of relaxation techniques lowers blood pressure in both medicated and nonmedicated patients. It is unlikely that relaxation practice alone will prove sufficient as a therapy for severe or moderate hypertension (Benson, 1977; Schwartz et al., 1979; Silver & Blanchard, 1978), but it is probably valuable as an adjunctive therapy in

these cases. Furthermore, in mild borderline and labile hypertension, it offers a potential alternative to pharmacotherapy. It could be particularly useful in the therapy of hypertension that appears early in life.

Broader utilization and improved clinical outcomes with relaxation and meditation strategies now depend on several factors. *First*, it is necessary to establish a better understanding of the mechanism(s) through which blood pressure is reduced. *Second*, it is critical to develop guidelines for tailoring approaches to the needs and abilities of individuals to increase initial acceptance and to assure long-term compliance.

RELEVANT ASSESSMENT MEASURES

General Discussion

On the basis of previous research, the use of standard personality tests has limited utility with hypertensive patients. The correlations between personality characteristics and high blood pressure typically have been quite low, and findings have not been consistent between studies. Therefore, in the absence of specific complaints or presenting psychological symptomatology their value in clinical work would be quite limited with the average hypertensive patient.

Although standard personality assessments are not likely to be of much use with hypertensive patients, instruments that assess general well-being, mood, and range and frequency of psychosomatic symptoms can be helpful. A number of different self-report instruments are available. The following are suggested because they have been used frequently and are appropriate for use with an essentially normal population.

Structured Questionnaires

For a measure of general adjustment and psychological well-being, the General Well Being Scale (Fazio, 1977) is useful. It is a frequently used instrument, nonthreatening, and standardized, with norms established on a generally healthy population through national surveys.

A standard instrument for the measurement of mood is the Profile of Mood States (McNair, Lorr, & Droppleman, 1971). This self-report checklist provides information on a broad range of moods that patients might experience. It includes items for anxiety and anger that have been most strongly correlated with blood pressure elevations. In addition to providing a general assessment of mood states, it could be useful in evaluating more carefully the frequency and extent of anxiety and anger. For this purpose, the Spielberger State-Trait Anxiety Scale (Spielberger, Gorsuch, & Lushene, 1970) and a recently developed anger scale (Spielberger, Jacobs, Russel, & Crane, 1983; Spielberger, 1983) can be used. The State-Trait Anxiety Scale has been used frequently in studies with hypertensive patients, and scores on this scale have been correlated with hypertensive status. This instrument has been used widely and has established norms and good reliablilty and validity. Less information is available on the anger scale.

Assessment of the type and frequency of psychosomatic symptoms can also be helpful. Essential hypertension is not typically associated with particular symptoms, but it might be part of a more general sympathetic nervous system overreactivity that includes associated psycho-somatic complaints. Two instruments frequently used to assess psychosomatic symptoms are the Hopkins Symptom Checklist (Derogatis, Lipman, Rickels, Uhlenhuth, & Covi, 1974) and the Symptom Checklist-90 or SCL-90 (Derogatis, 1975). Both of these inventories have normative data and established reliabililty and validity. The Hopkins has 58 items and the SCL-90 has 90 items. The SCL-90 is a more recent and expanded version of the Hopkins and for these reasons might be preferable.

With most hypertensive patients it might be useful both for diagnostic and counseling purposes to collect information on overall levels of life stress and specific sources of life stress in home and work settings. Assessment of levels of stress in nonwork and work settings is useful in evaluating the mental and emotional load that a patient is under. One of the most widely used self-report questionnaires for evaluating life stress is the Schedule of Recent Experiences, (Holmes & Rahe, 1967). A newer instrument is the Life Experiences Survey (LES), which allows respondents to give positive or negative weightings to items (Sarason, Johnson, & Siegel, 1978). For purely clinical purposes, both of these scales would be satisfactory. However, if a clinician were also interested in research, the LES provides more information and therefore might be more useful. These tools help patients become more aware of particular situations and personal interactions that pose problems for them. Regardless of which of these scales or other instruments of this type is used, the primary purpose

should be to provide background or context and not specific diagnostic values for hypertension.

Because many of the events listed in these instruments either do not occur or occur infrequently in the lives of patients, it is helpful to supplement them with a questionnaire that samples more frequently occuring events. Use of less formal data-collection instruments such as lists of daily hassles (Kanner, Coyne, Schaefer, & Lazarus, 1981) can provide helpful information of this type. The psychometric properties of this scale are not well developed, but it can be a useful tool for clinical purposes.

For employed patients, it is also important to obtain information about sources of stress at work. Neither the general life-events scales nor the daily-hassles inventories have many items related to specific sources of stress at work. It does not appear that a general questionnaire on work stressors is readily available.

The work setting could be a source of both acute and more chronic stress for many persons. It could also be the setting in which blood pressure is most persistently elevated. Thus, it is important to collect as much information as possible on specific sources of stress at work. This can be done with more informal, semistructured methods.

Semistructured or Informal Methods

Very selective use of standardized instruments is recommended with hypertensive patients. Usually, they should be used as adjuncts to good clinical interviews and less formal, semistructured information-collecting procedures. For example, having patients keep a daily stress record or log helps target specific sources of stress in nonwork and work environments. It also gets the patient more involved in the diagnosis and treatment process. Record keeping helps patients develop awareness of specific stressful situations. In addition to the logging in of events that cause stress reactions, it is also helpful to have patients briefly describe their reactions to those situations and log in how long it takes them to recover or calm down afterward.

Having the patient monitor his or her breathing rate and pulse or heart rate before and after anticipated stressful events can provide useful diagnostic information. Also, the use of a thermally sensitive band that can be worn around a finger or a wallet-sized biofeedback card with a temperature-sensitive area that allows the patient to check on finger temperature can help her or him identify stressful situations and become more aware of physiologic responses to the situations.

Blood Pressure Recording

As was pointed out in the background section, a complete stress assessment of hypertensive patients should include getting representative blood pressure readings outside of the clinic. Ideally, blood pressures should be measured in both work and home settings. This might require that patients learn to take their own blood pressures and record the measurements. As is the case with keeping daily stress logs, self-monitoring of blood pressure gets patients more actively involved in the diagnostic and treatment process. Comparisons between blood pressures taken at different times of day, and in a variety of settings, can help target high-risk times and situations and provide a necessary baseline against which to measure treatment effects.

The use of automated, ambulatory, blood pressure monitoring devices can be highly useful in defining event- or situation-specific elevations in blood pressure. Although this equipment is usually available only in special hypertension clinics, efforts should be made to have this type of monitoring done whenever possible. In addition, having patients keep a diary or log of details of their posture, level of activity, level of tension, personal interactions, and so on, concomitant with the blood pressure readings can provide information on relationships between real-world events and blood pressure that are not otherwise obtainable. Frequent sampling of blood pressure, for example, at 5- to 10-minute intervals, also allows estimates to be made of how long blood pressure stays elevated after situations that cause physical or emotional arousal. In general, the more complete the information obtained about the conditions under which blood pressure is elevated, the more specific and effective the treatment plan can be.

Psychophysiologic Stress Tests

Considerable work has been done on psychophysiologic stress testing with hypertensive persons. Persons with hypertension often have been found to be more reactive in terms of pressor responses and other autonomic variables to sources of mental and emotional challenges. Simple tests of blood pressure reactivity can be carried out in the clinic at low cost. For example, a series of blood pressure measurements can be taken before and

after a patient becomes comfortable and relaxed. When the blood pressure reaches a low plateau, the patient can be asked some fairly complex questions and be placed under time pressure to come up with answers. Blood pressure measurements should be taken both during and after completion of the task, until it again reaches its lowest level. A similar type of test can be run to measure emotional reactivity by having a patient answer very personal questions on a written form or in an interview. Talking about personal problems in a clinical interview is particularly stressful for many patients and is often associated with pressor responses (Lown, DeSilva, Reich, & Murawski, 1980; Lynch, Long, Thomas, Malinow, & Katcher, 1981). The analysis of the blood pressure responses to specific challenges provides useful diagnostic information and can help identify specific problem areas and coping deficits.

General Health Habits

In addition to obtaining details on blood pressure levels under both nonstressed and stressed conditions, it is also important to get information on the general health habits of patients. This can be done with structured or semistructured questionnaires. Several relatively brief, computer-scorable, health-hazard or risk-appraisal instruments are available that provide a good way to establish a profile on the preventive health habits of patients (National Health Information Clearinghouse, 1981). This information is useful in general patient counseling and in setting up stress-management programs for the patients.

COMPONENTS OF A CLINICAL STRESS-MANAGEMENT PROGRAM FOR HYPERTENSIVE PATIENTS

Diagnosis

The first component of a stress-management program for hypertensive patients, as should be the case in any good treatment program, is a good medical background, or history, and a careful clinical interview.

Before a provider of psychological or behavioral services begins to work with a patient with hypertension it is important that the patient have a careful medical history taken. It is also important that a careful diagnostic workup be done, specifically on the hypertension, to rule out specific organic factors in its etiology and signs of organic damage secondary to the hypertension.

Once it has been established that the hypertension exists independent of definable organic dysfunction, it is important to do a behavioral analysis of the blood pressure. This allows a better determination of the relative risk that the blood pressure poses for the patient. It also permits the specification of when and where blood pressure is highest and whether pressor responses are related to specific situations or interactions.

The preferred procedure for the behavioral diagnosis of hypertension is to use automatic, 24-hour monitoring devices. Along with this, it is important to have patients keep a log of stressful events during waking hours and to record their locations and behaviors at the times that the blood pressures are being taken. At present, this is the best procedure for linking pressor responses to specific behaviors and mental or emotional states to environmental events and situations.

If it is not possible to get a continuous, 24-hour blood pressure profile on a patient, then it is necessary to get representative blood pressure readings in home and clinical settings to establish a reasonable working baseline. Reliance upon clinic-based blood pressure readings only should be a last resort.

To provide a working knowledge of the patients' stress levels, it is recommended that they be given a standard life-events inventory and a less formal daily-hassles checklist. This should often be supplemented with a mood checklist, to assess the type and frequency of moods. Finally, if it is suggested by patient reports in daily logs or by clinical impressions, brief tests to measure anxiety and anger could be given.

The information derived from patient logs, formal and information questionnaires, and clinical impressions should all be synthesized and related as specifically as possible to the high blood pressure of the patient. If is is determined that stress clearly plays a contributory role in the hypertension, the next step is to develop a treatment plan.

Treatment Plan

Taken together, the results of prior clinical studies suggest that the critical component of a stress-management program directed at lowering blood pressure in patients with essential hypertension is relaxation training that elicits the relaxation response. Most commonly used relaxation techniques can be used to lower blood pressure. Possible methods include hypnosis-induced relaxation, autogenic training, progressive muscle relaxation, meditative relaxation, and biofeedback-aided relaxation. The choice of methods depends on several factors. One is the patients' knowledge and preference for particular techniques. For example, many patients have heard about biofeedback and specifically request this form of treatment. In this case, the patients' views should be carefully considered and weighed against other factors. The results of prior studies should also be considered. They suggest that an approach that combines several different relaxation methods is most effective.

Prior to introduction of any of the relaxation techniques, at least one session should be spent reviewing the patients' logs of stressful events and their descriptions of their reactions. If records of breathing rate, heart rate, or finger temperature have been kept, these should be discussed with the patients. It is important that patients clearly understand the relationship between events and interactions that they perceive as stressful and their physiologic reactions, particularly pressor responses to the situations.

If patients have had no experience with monitoring their physiologic responses, it is helpful to give them some experience with biofeedback equipment. It is not necessary to use expensive equipment, as the primary purpose of this exposure is orientation and education. Use of inexpensive EMG or electrodermal feedback devices is satisfactory for most teaching purposes. After patients have a clear understanding of the relationship between sources of stress and reactions or stress responses, the concept of relaxation and the relaxation response should be introduced. Patients should understand that there is an innate, biologic response, the relaxation response, that can prevent or reduce the stress response.

After the basic concepts of the stress response and the relaxation response are understood, patients should be taught some simple muscle-tensing and relaxing exercises. This gives them some practical experience with, and a feel for, the concepts of tension and relaxation. Next, it is useful to have patients monitor their breathing. They should be instructed to breathe through their noses only and to attend to each inspiration and expiration. Breathing rates should be monitored and recorded. Patients should then be taught simple deep breathing exercises. Emphasis should be placed on consciously slowing down the breathing and taking deep, full breaths; or diaphragmatic breathing, rather than rapid, shallow breaths, or thoracic breathing. In addition to the slow, deep breaths, it is also important for patients to keep their attention focused on a single point, preferably the point at which air is felt to enter and leave the nostrils. Learning to keep attention focused at one point while maintaining relaxed posture and slow deep breathing is critical. It is a key element that distinguishes meditative techniques from more purely physical techniques such as exercise. For many patients, attention focusing is difficult. However, the development of improved facility in this skill is important to long-term therapeutic benefits. After patients have had an opportunity to practice and get feedback on this basic relaxation skill, relaxation practice schedules for home and work should be developed.

It is important that patients initially set particular times and places for relaxation practice each day. Prior studies and clinical experience suggest that it is best to get patients to set a time early in the morning, soon after they have gotten up and before they have eaten or begun to get distracted by things and events. They should be asked to keep records of the times and places of practice. Also, they should be asked to keep diaries of their sources of stress and their reactions throughout the week. Pulse rate and finger temperature during the day, particularly before and after known stressors, should continue to be collected. Patients should be kept on this schedule for about 4 weeks and be seen on a weekly basis to check on their skill development, stress records, and blood pressure levels. Blood pressure should be taken at each clinic visit, and, whenever possible, patients should routinely be taking blood pressures at work and at home.

After the first week of practice, it has been found useful to discuss carefully with patients those sources of stress they feel still give them the most trouble and cause the greatest physiologic responses. These sources of stress should be roughly prioritized on the basis of their frequency and the extent of the reactions they cause.

One technique that can be a useful supplement to regular, daily, relaxation practice is cue-controlled relaxation. For example, if phone conversations are a frequent cause of stress, the patient might put a little red sticker on the receiver. This can be a cue to slow down, relax, and take a few deep breaths before making or taking calls.

Modalities other than relaxation can, and often should, be incorporated into a stress-management program for hypertensive patients. However, these should only be adjuncts or supports to the routine relaxation practice and not substitutes for it.

When sources of stress are persistent, and patients feel that they compromise other efforts, specific work should be done on these problems. Often, training in time management, decision making, and communication and assertiveness skills can be useful. When skill building and corrective feedback are not satisfactory, more in-depth work could be required.

Relaxation training for hypertension has been conducted successfully in individual and group formats. If possible, patients should be given a choice of individual or group therapy. In early training sessions, when general principles and skills are discussed, the group format might be preferable.

Unfortunately, many patients are not willing to practice relaxation on a regular basis. Sometimes this is due to psychological problems that interfere with their ability to organize their lives and to concentrate their attention. If serious interfering problems are identified in therapy, attention must be given to their resolution. Often, major problems cannot be identified, but patients simply will not exercise sufficient discipline to practice regularly. This problem deserves immediate attention. If early in treatment, good habits are not developed, it is unlikely that bad habits will spontaneously improve. General guidelines have been developed to facilitate the health behaviors of patients (Marlatt & Gordon 1980). These guidelines, combined with good therapist–patient rapport, can often improve the patient's practice regime. If after 4 weeks, patients have shown little effort to keep records of sources of stress and most important to practice relaxation on a regular basis, they should be given a choice of improving the regularity of their practice or seeking purely pharmacological control of the hypertension. Clearly, not all patients, even those who show high initial interest, are good candidates for controlling high blood pressure through stress-management and relaxation training.

In general, if a patient has maintained a daily relaxation routine for about 1 month, most of the impact on blood pressure lowering should have been achieved. At this time, if possible, another continuous 24-hour profile of blood pressure should be obtained. If this is not possible, it is necessary to get representative blood pressures in work and home settings with manual measurement techniques. For the therapy to be considered successful, blood pressures in the clinic and home settings should be below 140mm Hg systolic and

90mm Hg diastolic most of the time. If blood pressure has been brought successfully under control, the patient can be placed on a less frequent monitoring schedule. It is suggested that the patient be requested to come back about one time per month over the next year to check on the regularity of relaxation practice, success in coping with specific sources of stress, and, most important, the control of blood pressure.

CASE STUDY

The following case illustrates the use of behavioral diagnosis and stress-management training for a patient who was referred with a diagnosis of borderline, essential hypertension. The patient was a 19-year-old male with no preexisting medical or psychological conditions. On a recent routine physical examination, he had been found to have systolic blood pressure in the mid-150s and diastolic pressures in the mid-90s. This was the first time that the patient had been diagnosed with hypertension, and there were no secondary signs associated with the diagnosis. He was referred for a more detailed examination of the blood pressure and for behavioral counseling. Prior to the first interview, several blood pressure readings were taken while the patient was in a sitting position. Although the initial readings were close to those from the prior physical exam, after several measurements, the systolic pressure dropped down to the mid-140s and the diastolic to the low 90s.

During the initial interview, it was found that the patient considered himself to be under a great deal of tension. He had been a full-time college student until his father had passed away not long before. At this point, it was necessary for him to drop down to part-time study and to help out with the management of a family-owned restaurant under the supervision of his mother. He said he disliked the work very much, because he did not like working for his mother and also had problems with the supervision of some of the restaurant employees. He also reported that he was not doing well in his school work, which he was very unhappy about. His general health habits were only fair. He did not smoke and reported drinking only occasionally. However, his dietary habits were irregular, he was not getting regular exercise, and his sleep habits were irregular.

Because automatic 24-hour blood pressure monitoring equipment was readily available, the patient was asked to wear the monitoring equipment during one of his regular working days, to get a comprehensive blood pressure profile. He was also asked to log in the situations and events that were occurring around the times that blood pressures were being recorded during normal waking hours.

After habituation to the novelty of the equipment, his blood pressure stabilized, with most readings in the low 140s and low 90s. The only situations during the day in which blood pressure was greatly elevated were during driving in heavy inner-city traffic and while at work at the restaurant. The average blood pressures were highest at work, and several sharp peaks occurred after exchanges with one of the employees. Blood pressure dropped down close to 140/90 when he was at home and was generally much lower during sleep.

The 24-hour blood pressure profile was shown to the patient and was discussed in relation to his stress log. He had indicated that driving in heavy traffic was a major hassle and that supervising employees at the restaurant was his biggest problem. Because the patient reported being nervous and tense quite often, he was asked to fill out the Spielberger State-Trait Anxiety Scale. He scored above average on the state but not on the trait scale. Given this particular profile, it was felt that the patient could benefit from relaxation training and also needed some counseling to help resolve the problem of work at the restaurant. The patient agreed to this plan and was started on a relaxation-training program similar to the one discussed in the prior methods section. He proved to be relatively consistent in his record keeping and relaxation practice and was seen for 6 weekly sessions. After this time, another 24-hour blood pressure profile was taken, and the patient was again asked to keep a concomitant log of stressful events. By this time, the average blood pressure during nonstress periods was below 140 systolic and 90 diastolic. Blood pressure levels still became elevated during driving, at work, and in other emotionally arousing situations but were generally lower than at the initial baseline. Whereas blood pressure initially had been elevated over 50% of the time at work, at the 6-week follow-up it was elevated less than 20% of the time. Although this was not a complete success, it was an improvement. The patient felt that he had made progress and had things under better control. Therefore, it was decided, in consultation with the referring physician, that his blood pressure could continue to be managed without drugs. It was suggested that the patient come back on a regular monthly basis to discuss his status and have his blood pressure checked. The patient was also encouraged to purchase his own manual blood pressure monitoring equipment and to take blood pressures at work two or three times per week.

REFERENCES

Abboud, F. (1982). The sympathetic nervous system in hypertension: State-of-the-art-reviews. *Hypertension, 4*, suppll, II, 208–225.

Agras, S. and Jacob, R. (1979). Hypertension in O. F. Pomerleau & J. P. Brady (Eds.), *Behavioral Medicine: Theory and Practice*. Baltimore: Williams and Wilkins.

Agras, W. S., Southam, M. A., & Taylor, C. B. (1983). Long-term persistence of relaxation-induced blood pressure lowering during the working day. *Journal of Consulting and Clinical Psychology, 51*(5), 792–794.

Agras, S., Taylor, C. B., Kraemer, H., Allen, R. A., and Schneider, M. S. (1980). Relaxation training: twenty-four hour blood pressure reductions. *Archives of General Psychiatry, 37*, 859–863.

Alexander, F. (1939). Emotional factors in hypertension, *Psychosomatic Medicine, 1*, 173–179.

Altschule, M. D. (1953). *Bodily Physiology in Mental and Emotional Disorders*. New York: Grune & Stratton.

Ayman, D., Goldshine, A. D. (1940). Blood pressure determinations by patients with essential hypertension: 1. The difference between clinical and home readings before treatment. *American Journal of Medical Science, 200*, 465–474.

Bali, C. R. (1979). Long-term effect of relaxation on blood pressure and anxiety levels of essential hypertensive males: A controlled study. *Journal of Psychosomatic Medicine, 41*(8), 637–646.

Beary, J. F., & Benson, H. (1974). A simple psychophysiologic technique which elicits the hypometabolic changes of the relaxation response. *Psychosomatic Medicine, 36*, 115–120.

Benson, H. (1975). *The Relaxation Response*. New York: Avon Books.

Benson, H. (1977), Systemic hypertension and the relaxation response. *New England Journal of Medicine, 296*(20), 1152–1156.

Benson, H., Beary, J. F., & Carol, M. P. (1974). The relaxation response, *Psychiatry, 37*, 37–46.

Benson, H., & Greenwood, M. M. (1976). Behavioral modifications of blood pressure in man. In G. Olsi, M. Fernandes, & K. Kim (Eds.). *Regulation of Blood Pressure by the Central Nervous System*. New York: Grune & Stratton.

Benson, H. B., Rosner, B. A., Marzetta, B. R., & Klemchuk, H. M. (1974a). Decreased blood pressure in borderline hypertensive subjects who practiced meditation, *Journal of Chronic Diseases, 27*, 163–169.

Benson, H. B., Rosner, B. A., Marzetta, B. R., & Klemchuk, H. M. (1974b). Decreased blood pressure in pharmacologically treated hypertensive patients who regularly elicited the relaxation response. *Lancet, i*, 289–291.

Benson, H., Shapiro, D., Tursky, B., & Schwartz, G. (1971). Decreased systolic blood pressure through operant conditioning techniques in patients with essential hypertension. *Science, 173*, 740–742.

Bernstein, D. & Borkovic, T. (1973). *Progressive relaxation training: A manual for the helping professions*. Champaign, Illinois: Research Press.

Blackwell, B., Bloomfield, S., Gartside, P., Robinson, A., Hanenson, I., Magenheim, H., Nidich, S., & Ziegler, R. (1976). Transcendental meditation in hypertension: Individual response patterns. *Lancet, i*, 223–226.

Blanchard, E. B., & Epstein, L. H. (1978). *A Biofeedback Primer*. Reading, MA: Addison-Wesley.

Blanchard, E. B., Miller, S. T., Abel, G. G., Haynes, M. R., & Wicker, R. (1979). Evaluation of biofeedback in the treatment of border-line essential hypertension. *Journal of Applied Behavior Analysis, 12*(1), 99–109.

Brady, J. P., Luborsky, L., & Kron, R. E. (1974). Blood pressure reduction in patients with essential hypertension through metronome conditioned relaxation: A preliminary report. *Behavior Therapy, 5*, 203–209.

Brauer, A. P., Horlick, L., Nelson, E. Farquhar, J. W., & Agras, W. S. (1979). Relaxation therapy for essential hypertension: A Veterans Administration outpatient study. *Journal of Behavioral Medicine, 2*(1), 21–29.

Brod, J. (1961). Hemodynamic response to stress and its bearing on the hemodynamic basis of essential hypertension. In J. H. Court (Ed.), *The Pathogenesis of Hypertension: Proceedings of the Prague Symposium*. Prague: State Publishing House, 256–264.

Cannon, W. B. (1914). The emergency function of the adrenal medulla in pain and in the major emotions. *American Journal of Physiology, 33*, 356–372.

Cannon, W. B. (1929). *Bodily Changes in Pain, Hunger, Fear, and Rage*. New York: Appleton.

Cobb, S. (1950). *Emotions and Clinical Medicine*. New York: W. W. Norton.

Chobanian, A. V., Gravas, H., Gravas, I., Bresnahan, M., Sullivan, P., & Melby, J. C. (1978, September). Studies on the activity of the sympathetic nervous system in essential hypertension. *Journal of Human Stress*, 22–28.

Datey, K. K., Deshmukh, S. N., Dalvi, C. P., & Vinekar, M. D. (1969). "Shavasan": A yogic exercise in the management of hypertension. *Angiology, 20*, 325–333.

Deabler, H. L., Fidel, E., Dillkenoffer, R. L., & Elder, S. T. (1973). The use of relaxation and hypnosis in lowering high blood pressure. *American Journal of Clinical Hypnosis, 16*(2), 75–83.

Derogatis, L. R. (1975). *The Symptom Checklist 90-R (SCL-90-R)*. Baltimore: Clinical Psychometrics Research.

Derogatis, L. R., Lipman, R. S., Rickels, K., Uhlenhuth, E. H., & Covi, L. (1974). The Hopkins Symptom Checklist (HSCL): A measure of primary symptom dimensions, In P. Pichot (Ed.), *Psychological Measurements in Psychopharmacology: Modern Problems in Pharmacopsychiatry*, (Vol. 7). Basel, Switzerland: S. Karger, 79–110.

Devereux, R. B. et al. (1983). Left ventricular hypertrophy in patients with hypertension: Importance of blood pressure response to regularly recurring stress. *Circulation, 68*, 470–476.

Dimsdale, J. E., & Moss, J. (1980). Plasma catecholamines in stress and exercise. *Journal of the American Medical Association, 68*, 340–342.

Elder, S. T., & Eustis, N. K. (1975). Instrumental blood pressure conditioning in out-patient hypertensives. *Behaviour Research and Therapy, 1975, 13*, 185–188.

Elder, S. T., Ruiz, Z. R., Deabler, H. L., & Dillenkoffer, R.

L. (1973). Instrumental conditioning of diastolic blood pressure in essential hypertensive patients. *Journal of Applied Behavioral Analysis, 6,* 377–382.

European Working Party on High Blood Pressure in the Elderly (EWPHE). (1985, June 15). Mortality and morbidity results from the European Working Party on high blood pressure in the elderly trial. *Lancet,* 1350–1354.

Fazio, A. F. (1977). *A Concurrent Validation Study of the NCHS General Well-Being Scale.* Washington, DC: U. S. Government Printing Office (SN 017-022-0591-3).

Frankel, B. L., Patel, D. J., Horowitz, D., Friedenwald, W. T., & Gardner, K. R. (1978). The treatment of hypertension with biofeedback and relaxation techniques. *Psychosomatic Medicine, 40,* 276–293.

Frankenhauser, M. (1975). Experimental approaches to the study of cataecholamines and emotion, In L. Levi (Ed.). *Emotions: Their Parameters and Measurement.* New York: Raven Press, 209–234.

Frolich, E. D. (1977). The adrenergic nervous system and hypertension: State-of-the-art, *52,* 361–368.

Frumkin, K., Nathan, R. J., Prout, M. F., & Cohen, M. C. (1978). Nonpharmacologic control of essential hypertension in man: A critical review of the experimental literature. *Psychosomatic Medicine, 40* 294–319.

Gantt, W. H. (1960). The cardiovascular component of the conditional reflex to pain, food, and other stimuli. *Physiological Reviews, 291,* 266–291.

Goldman, H., Kleinman, K. M., Snow, M. V., Bidus, D. R., & Korol, B. (1975). Relationships between essential hypertension and cognitive functioning: Effects of biofeedback. *Psychophysiology, 12,* 569–573.

Guttmacher, S., Teitelman, M., Chapin, G., Garbowski, G., Schnall, P. (1981), February 12-20). Ethics and preventive medicine: The case of borderline hypertension. Hastings-on-Hudson, NY: *Hastings Center Report.*

Hager, J. L., & Surwit, R. S. (1978). Hypertension self-control with a portable feedback unit or meditation-relaxation. *Biofeedback and Self Regulation, 3*(3), 269–276.

Harlan, W. R. (1981). Physical and psychosocial stress and the cardiovascular system. *Circulation, 63,* suppl., 266a–271a.

Harshfield, G. A., Pickering, T. G., & Laragh, J. H. (1979). A validation study of the Del Mar Avionics Ambulatory Blood Pressure System. *Ambulatory Electrocardiography, 1,* 7-12.

Haynes, R. B., Sackett, D.C. & Taylor, D. W. (1978). Increased absenteeism from work after detection and labeling of hypertension patients. *New England Journal of Medicine, 299,* 741–744.

Hess, W. R. (1957). *The Functional Organization of the Diencephalon.* New York: Grune & Stratton.

Hoffman, J. W., Benson, H., Stainbrook, G. L., Arns, P. A., Landsberg, L. L., Young, J. P., & Gill, A. (1982), Reduced sympathetic nervous system responsivity associated with the relaxation response. *Science, 215,* 190–192.

Holmes, T. H., & Rahe, R. H. (1967). The Social Readjustment Rating Scale. *Journal of Psychosomatic Research, 11,* 213–218.

Hypertension Detection and Follow-up Program Cooperative Group. (1979). Five-year findings of the hypertension detection and follow-up program. I. *Journal of the American Medical Association, 242,* 2562–257.

Jacobson, E. (1938). *Progressive Relaxation.* Chicago: University of Chicago Press.

Jacobson, E. (1939). Variation of blood pressure with skeletal muscle tension and relaxation. *Annals of Internal Medicine, 12,* 1194–1212.

Jacobson, E. (1967). *Biology of Emotions.* Springfield, IL: Charles C. Thomas.

James, K. E. (1973). Regression toward the mean in uncontrolled clinical studies. *Biometrics, 19,* 121–130.

Jevning, R., Wilson, A. F., & Davidson, J. M., Adrenocortical activity during meditation. *Hormones and Behavior, 10,* 54–60.

Julius, S., & Esler, M. (1975). Autonomic nervous cardiovascular regulation in borderline hypertension. *American Journal of Cardiology, 36,* 685–696.

Kanner, A. D., Coyne, J. C., Schaefer, C., & Lazaras, R. S. (1981). Comparison of two models of stress measurement: Daily hassles and uplifts versus major life events. *Journal of Behavioral Medicine, 4,* 1–39.

Kaplan, N. M. (1977, September). Stress, the sympathetic nervous system and hypertension. *Journal of Human Stress,* 29–34.

Kennedy, H. L., Padgett, N. E., & Horan, M. J. (1979). Performance reliability of the Del Mar Avionics non-invasive ambulatory blood pressure instrument in clinical use. *Ambulatory Electrocardiography, 1,* 13–17.

Kristt, D. A., & Engel, B. T. (1975). Learned control of blood pressure in patients with high blood pressure. *Circulation, 51,* 370–378.

Lehrer, P. (1980). Effects of progressive relaxation and autogenic training on anxiety and physiological measures, with some data on hypnotizability. In F. J. McGuigan, W. E. Sime, & J. McDonald Wallace (Eds.), *Stress and Tension Control* (pp. 171–184). New York: Plenum.

Levi, L. (1975). *Emotions: Their Parameters and Measurement.* New York: Raven Press.

Levine, S. (1972) *Hormones and Behavior.* New York: Academic Press.

Linden, W., & Feuerstein, M. (1981). Essential hypertension and social coping behavior. *Journal of Human Stress, 7,* 28–34.

Linden, W., & Feuerstein, M. (1983). Essential hypertension and social coping behavior: Experimental findings. *Journal of Human Stress, 9*(3), 22–31.

Lown, B. & DeSilva, R. A. (1978). Roles of psychologic stress and autonomic nervous system changes in provocation of ventricular premature complexes, *American Journal of Cardiology, 41,* 979–985.

Lown, B., DeSilva, R., Reich, P., & Murawski, B. (1980). Psychophysiologic factors in sudden cardiac death. *American Journal of Psychiatry, 137,* 1325–1335.

Lynch, J. J., Long, J., Thomas S., Malinow, K., & Katcher, A. (1981). The effects of talking on the blood pressure of hypertensive and normotensive individuals. *Psychosomatic Medicine, 43,* 25–33.

Management Committee. (1980). The Australian

therapeutic trial in mild hypertension. *Lancet (1)*, 1261–1267.

Marlatt, G. A., & Gordon, J. R. (1980). Determinants of relapse: Implications for the maintenance of behavior change. In P. O. Davidson & S. M. Davidson (Eds.), *Behavioral medicine: Changing health lifestyles*. New York: Guilford.

Mason, J. A. (1968). A review of psychoendocrine research on the pituitary-adrenal cortical system. *Psychosomatic Medicine, 30*, 323–333.

Matthew, R. J., Beng, H. T., Kralik, P., Taylor, D., Hsu, L., & Claghorn, J. L. (1980). Adrenergic and cholinergic mechanisms in anxiety and relaxation. *Proceedings of the Biofeedback Society of America* Colorado, (pp. 96–99).

McCall, W. C., & McCall, V. R. (1981). Diagnostic use of ambulatory blood pressure monitoring in medical practice. *Journal of Family Practice, 13*, 25–30.

McGrady, A. V., Yonker, R., Tan, S. Y., Fine, T. H., & Woerner, M. (1981). The effect of biofeedback-assisted relaxation on blood pressure and selected biochemical parameters in patients with essential hypertension. *Biofeedback and Self-regulation, 6*, 343–353.

McNair, M., Lorr, M., & Droppleman, L. F. (1971). *EITS Manual for the Profile of Mood States (POMS)*. San Diego, CA: Educational and Industrial Testing Service.

Michaels, R., McCann, D., & Vander, A. J. (1979). Renin, cortisol, and aldosterone during transcendental meditation. *Psychosomatic Medicine, 41*, 50–54.

Miller, N. E. (1969). Learning of visceral and glandular responses. *Science, 163*, 434–445.

Miller, N. E. (1975). Clinical applications of biofeedback: Voluntary control of heart rate rythym and blood pressure. In H. I. Russek (Ed.), *New Horizons in Cardiovascular Practice* (pp. 239–249). Baltimore: University Park Press.

Multiple Risk Factor Intervention Trial Research Group (1982). Multiple Risk Factor Intervention Trial: Risk factor changes and mortality results. *Journal of the American Medical Association, 248*, 1465–1477.

National Health Information Clearinghouse. (1981). *Health risk appraisals: An inventory*. Washington DC: Department of Health and Human Services.

Orme-Johnson, D. W. (1973). Autonomic stability and transcendental meditation. *Psychosomatic Medicine, 35*, 341–349.

Patel, C. (1973). Yoga and biofeedback in the management of hypertension. *Lancet*, 1053–1055.

Patel, C. (1975a). 12-month follow-up of yoga and biofeedback in the management of hypertension. *Lancet, i*, 62–64.

Patel, C. (1975b). Yoga and biofeedback in the management of hypertension. *Journal of Psychosomatic Research, 19*(5–6), 355–360.

Patel, C. (1975c). Yoga and biofeedback in the management of "stress" in hypertensive patients. *Clinical Science and Molecular Medicine, 48*, Suppl. 2, 171–174.

Patel, C. and Caruthers, M. (1977). Coronary risk factor reduction through biofeedback aided relaxation and meditation. *Journal of the Royal College of General Practitioners, 27*, 401–405.

Patel, C., Marmot, M. G., & Terry, D. J. (1981). Controlled trial of biofeedback-aided methods (behavioral) in reducing mild hypertension. *British Medical Journal, 282*(6281), 2005–2008.

Patel, C., & North, W. R. (1975). Randomized controlled trial of yoga and biofeedback in the management of hypertension. *Lancet, ii*, 93–95.

Pavlov, I. (1960). *Conditioned Reflexes* (G. V. Anrep, Trans.). London: Oxford University Press. (Original work published 1927)

Perloff, D., & Sokolow, M. (1978). The representative blood pressure: Usefulness of office, basal, home, and ambulatory readings. *Cardiovascular medicine*, 655–668.

Pilowsky, M. D., Spalding, B. A., Shaw, H. J., & Korner, P. I. (1973). Hypertension and personality. *Psychosomatic Medicine, 35*, 50–56.

Rose, R. M., Jenkins, C. D., & Hurst, M. W. (1978). *Air Traffic Controller Health change Study* Galveston, TX: University of Texas Press.

Rosenman, R. H., Brand, R. J., Jenkins, C. D., Friedman, M., Strauss, R. & Warum, M. (1975). Coronary heart disease in the Western Collaborative Group Study: Final follow-up experience of 8½ years. *Journal of the American Medical Association, 233*, 872–877.

Roskies, E., Spevack, M., Surkis, A., Cohen, C., & Gilman, S. (1978). Changing the cornary-prone (Type A) behavior pattern in a non-clinical population. *Journal of Behavioral Medicine, 1*, 201–216.

Sapira, J. D., Scheib, E. T., Moriarty, M. D., & Shapiro, A. P. (1971). Differences in perception between hypertensive and normotensive patients. *Psychosomatic Medicine, 33*, 239–250.

Sarason, I. G., Johnson, J. H., & Siegel, J. M., (1978). Assessing the impact of life changes: Development of the Life Experiences Survey. *Journal of Consulting and Clinical Psychology, 46*, 932–946.

Schork, M. A. (1973). Socio-ecological stress, suppressed hostility, skin color, and black-white male blood pressure: Detroit. *Psychosomatic Medicine, 35*, 276–296.

Schwartz, G. E., & Shapiro, D. (1973). Biofeedback and essential hypertension: Current findings and theoretical concerns. *Seminars in Psychiatry, 5*, 493–503.

Schwartz, G. E., Shapiro, A. P., Redmond, D. P., Ferguson, D. C. E., Ragland, D. R., & Weiss, S. M. (1979). Behavioral medicine approaches to hypertension: An integrative analysis of theory and research. *Journal of Behavioral Medicine, 2*, 311–363.

Seer, P., & Raeburn, J. M. (1980). Meditation training and essential hypertension: A methodological study. *Journal of Behavioral Medicine, 1980, 3*(1), 59–71.

Selye, H. (1936). A syndrome produced by diverse nocuous agents. *Nature* (London), *138*, 32.

Selye, H. (1956). *The Stress of Life*. New York: McGraw-Hill.

Shapiro, A. P., Schwartz, G. E., Ferguson, D. C. E., Redmond, D. P., & Weiss, S. M. (1977). Behavioral methods in the treatment of hypertension: A review of their clinical status. *Annals of Internal Medicine, 86*, 626–636.

Shepard, D. S. (1981). Reliability of blood pressure measurements: Implications for designing and evaluating programs to control hypertension. *Journal of Chronic Diseases, 34*, 191–209.

Sheps, S. G., Elveback, L. R., Close, E. L., Kleven, M.

K., & Bissen, C. (1981). Evaluation of the Del Mar Avionics Automatic Ambulatory Blood Pressure-recording Device. *Mayo Clinic Proceedings, 56*, 740-743.

Shoemaker, J. E., & Tasto, D. L. (1975). The effects of muscle relaxation on blood pressure in essential hypertensives. *Behaviour Research and Therapy, 13*, 29-43.

Silver, B. V., & Blanchard, E. B. (1978). Biofeedback and relaxation training in the treatment of psychophysiological disorders: Or, are the machines really necessary? *Journal of Behavioral Medicine, 1*, 217-239.

Spielberger, C. D. (1983). Manual for the State-Trait Anxiety Inventory (Revised Ed.). Palo Alto, CA: Consulting Psychologists Press.

Spielberger, C. S., Jacobs, G. A., Russel, S., & Crane, R. S. (1983). Assessment of anger: The State-Trait Anger Scale. In J. W. Butcher & C. D. Spielberger (Eds.), *Advances in Personality Assessment, Vol 2*. Hillsdale, NJ: Lawrence Erlbaum.

Spielberger, C. D., Gorsuch, R. L., & Lushene, R. E. (1970). *State-Trait Anxiety Inventory*. Palo Alto, CA: Consulting Psychologists Press.

Sokolow, M., Perloff, D., & Cowan, R. (1980). Contribution of ambulatory blood pressure to the assessment of patients with mild to moderate elevation of office blood pressure. *Cardiovascular Reviews and Reports, 1*, 295-303.

Stainbrook, G. L., & Green, L. W. (1983). Role of psychosocial stress in cardiovascular disease. *Houston Heart Bulletin. 3*, 1-8.

Stone, R. A., & DeLeo, J. (1976), Psychotherapeutic control of hypertension. *New England Journal of Medicine, 294*(2), 80-84.

Stoyva, J., Anderson, C., Vaughn, L., Budzynski, T., & MacDonald, K. (1980). Relaxation training in mild to moderate essential hypertension. *Proceedings of the Biofeedback Society of America* (pp. 162-164).

Surwit, R. S., Shapiro, D., & Good, M. I. (1978). Comparison of cardiovascular biofeedback, neuromuscular biofeedback, and meditation in the treatment of borderline essential hypertension. *Journal of Consulting and Clinical Psychology, 46*, 252-263.

Thompson, R. F. (1967) *Foundations of physiological psychology*. New York: Harper & Row.

Taylor, C. B., Farquhar, J. W., Nelson, E., & Agras, S. (1977). Relaxation therapy and high blood pressure. *Archives of General Psychiatry, 34*, 339-342.

Wallace, R. K., Benson, H., & Wilson, A. F. (1971). A wakeful hypometabolic physiologic state. *American Journal of Physiology, 221* 795-799.

Weiner, H. (1979). *Psychobiology of Essential Hypertension*. New York: Elsevier Science.

Weiss, S. M., Matthews, K. A., Detre, T., & Graeff, J. A. (Eds.) (1984). *Stress, Reactivity, and Cardiovascular Disease: Proceedings of the Working Conference* (NIH Publication No. 84-2698). Washington, D.C.: U.S. Government Printing Office.

Wolf, S., & Wolff, H. G. (1951). A summary of experimental evidence relating life stress to the pathogenesis of essential hypertension in man. In E. T. Bell (Ed.), *Essential Hypertension*. Minneapolis: University of Minnesota Press.

Chapter 12

Stress Management in Cardiovascular Disease: Postmyocardial Infarction Patients

Keith F. Revel
Paul E. Baer
Sidney E. Cleveland

PSYCHOLOGICAL COMPLICATIONS AFTER MYOCARDIAL INFARCTION

The experience of a myocardial infarction (MI) involves both physical pain and an immediate threat to life. Psychological complications resulting from the MI are typically distressing and can at times be as debilitating as the primary illness (Doehrman, 1977). Most frequently, the individual feels bombarded by a multitude of ambiguous sensory events, separated from normal support systems, and thrust into an unfamiliar medical environment for survival. Beyond the psychological complications resulting from MI, this chapter addresses assessment and treatment issues. Relevant medical and psychological measures and treatment attempts are reviewed. Development of a cardiac stress-management program, from theoretical orientation to specific procedures, is presented along with a case study.

The extensive body of literature reviewing the psychological experience of the post-MI individual provides evidence of commonly employed coping behavior and affective reactions (Doehrman, 1977; Gentry & Williams, 1975). Anxiety and depression seem to best represent the emotional experience of this person. Presence of these affective reactions is commonly viewed as evidence of ineffective coping (Gentry, Foster, & Haney, 1972). Further supportive evidence of ineffective coping is the presence of Type-A behavior. Individuals recovering from an MI frequently deny its the occurrence or severity (Croog, Shapiro, Levine, 1971). The use of denial as a defense mechanism appears to be the most common coping strategy in this health population. A significant number of patients perceive themselves as lacking adequate defenses to cope and often become depressed and hopeless about the future (Gentry & Williams, 1975). Postmyocardial depression has been identified as a prime prognostic indicator of cardiac morbidity (Mayou, Forester, & Williams, 1978).

Denial as a Coping Strategy

The use of denial as a defense mechanism has long been recognized as a primary way an individual can cope with threatening situations. The consequences of denial in hospitalized patients have been described in a variety of populations (Pomerleau & Brady, 1979). In MI patients, denial has been described by clinicians as leading to serious disregard of significant symptoms that affect both the seeking of medical care and the level of treatment compliance (Gentry et al., 1972). For example, denial can lead a patient to postpone seeking medical care. If care is provided, the patient might refuse to accept medical recommendations, which could cause exacerbation of the illness and perhaps even death. Hackett & Cassem (1975) concluded that MI patients who deny their illness might be using a defense mechanism that aids in short-term psychological coping with a stressful condition, but could well have an effect on their future status.

Croog et al. (1971) reported an investigation that attempted to determine the extent of denial in post-MI patients. Denial was defined as the expression of either ''No'' or ''Don't Know'' in response to the question of whether the patient believed he or she had had a heart attack.

In terms of medical compliance, a higher proportion of deniers indicated noncompliance than nondeniers. Deniers more often did not comply with physicians recommendations to reduce smoking and to return to work at a certain date or advice on rest, weight control, and physical activity.

Croog et al. (1971) concluded that their results were consistent with the clinical reports of denial in post-MI patients. Fully 20% of study participants denied their medical status 18 days and at a 1-year follow-up. As Croog et al. (1971) pointed out, a patient who has not admitted that a problem exists can hardly be expected to show motivation to cope with that problem.

Type-A Behavior

It is becoming increasingly evident that the Type-A behavior pattern is probably related not only to prevalence but also to complication in recovering from an MI. Kenigsberg, Zyanski, Jenkins, Wardwell, & Lucciardello (1974) provided evidence that the Type-A behavior pattern is more highly represented in hospitalized coronary patients than in patients hospitalized for surgery or traumatic injury. A previous report by Roseman, Friedman, & Strauss (1970) demonstrated this relationship using the Type A structured interview.

The major finding in this investigation was that the coronary patient group was significantly higher than the surgery and traumatic injury group on the general Type A and Hard Driving factors. Both the Job-Involvement and Speed/Impatience group differences were in the expected direction but not significantly different.

For the survivors of an MI, the role of Type-A behavior in their disease process could be important to their future health status. Prospective evidence appears to link Type A-behavior with the reoccurrence of coronary heart disease. When Type-A behavior is elevated at a coronary-related hospitalization it could place an individual at higher risk for subsequent coronary heart disease events (Kenigsberg et al., 1974).

Depression

Bruhn, Chandler, and Wolf (1969) provided evidence that level of depression could be a reliable discriminator between survivors and nonsurvivors of an MI. Patients participated in a longitudinal study of coronary heart disease during which they received extensive physical examination, laboratory tests, and psychological and psychiatric interviews at 4- to 8-week intervals over a 7-year period. The survivor group consisted of 30 patients who had survived at least one well-documented MI. The nonsurvivor group was composed of 17 patients who survived at least one-well documented MI and died during the course of the investigation.

The main comparison between the groups was on the MMPI completed on entry to the study. A significant difference between the groups was found on the Depression subscale. The nonsurvivors had a significantly higher group mean than the survivors. MMPI results obtained at the end of the project showed that the survivors of MI had become more depressed since entry into the project.

Bruhn et al. concluded that the study results were consistent with earlier findings that depression is significantly elevated in post-MI patients. This finding is even more pronounced in nonsurvivors of an MI during follow-up evaluation. The 7-year follow-up profile of the survivors closely approximated the initial profile of the nonsurvivors. Bruhn et al. speculated that the survivors' elevated level of depression could possibly be an indication of impending death among survivors of MI.

Anxiety

As Wrzeniewski (1977) pointed out, an exhaustive number of clinical accounts have documented the fact of elevated anxiety in the post-MI population. Many of these reports show a considerable delay between the occurrence of the MI and the self-report of anxiety. It has been suggested that elevated anxiety in post-MI patients could represent a long-term effect of the illness, life-event changes, difficulty with attempts at risk-factor modification or all three.

Wrzesniewski (1977), after conducting an extensive evaluation of post-MI patients, concluded that anxiety, or fear, is one of the most important psychological effects of the illness. In this investigation, the post-MI group consisted of 105 males, age 28 to 60 years, who had experienced their first MI within 15–121 days of study participation. Two groups, one of 63 normal males with no coronary heart disease and one of 34 rheumatic patients, served as comparison groups.

Procedures involved all subjects' completing self-report measures for cardiac anxiety and general anxiety. Results showed that the post-MI group was significantly higher than either control group on general anxiety and cardiac anxiety about the occurrence and complications of the MI.

With a decrease in MI mortality over the past decade, there has been a natural increase in demand for post-MI rehabilitation. During this same time, there has been increased awareness of the complex process involved in recovery from an MI. Currently, clinicians view an MI as one of the most serious life-threatening events an individual can experience. Successful recovery from this event ought to involve treatment for both the physiological and psychological effects of the disease. (Gentry & Williams, 1975). It is evident that many individuals are ill-prepared psychologically to cope effectively with the life-threatening event of an MI.

ASSESSMENT OF POST-MI PATIENTS

Medical Assessment

Determination of cardiac status in a clinical setting might best be determined by the primary-care cardiologist. Cardiac status evaluation can follow guidelines reported by other cardiologists (Norris, 1970). The major symptoms included persistent angina, signs of congestive heart failure, and recurrent arrhythmias. The presence of any one of these three major symptoms can warrant classifying a patient's condition as complicated. With an absence of symptoms, her or his condition can be considered uncomplicated. A daily review of the patient's medical records for vital signs, progress notes, and medications yields information required for determining cardiac status. Consultation with a patient's cardiologist is required should cardiac status become complicated.

Physical complaints specific to the post-MI patient's recovery can be collected on a self-report symptom checklist. Specific to cardiac functioning are such symptoms as heart racing, shortness of breath, and heart skipping. Other symptoms that signal medically significant events include dizziness, nausea, somatic pain, faintness, and rapid breathing. These symptoms are typically considered in the routine management of the post-MI patient during rehabilitation (Gentry & Williams, 1975).

Psychological Status

Self-report by the post-MI patient is relevant to assessment and treatment during rehabilitation. The measures described are representative of the psychological variables most frequently assessed by clinicians.

The Hopelessness Scale is a useful measure of depression with post-MI patients (Beck, Weissman, Lester, & Trexler, 1974). This measure of depression taps an individual's expectations about his or her future. Specifically, the scale attempts to assess an individual's negative expectations concerning herself or himself and her or his future life.

A common component of hopelessness is loss of motivation, expressed as a decision to give up or to not try to improve life. The depressed individual frequently experiences not only a sense of hopelessness but also a loss of control in coping with what concerns him or her most now and in the future. This experience of depression is consistent with the concept of learned helplessness.

The State Anxiety Inventory, as a measure of state anxiety, addresses a patient's current concerns or fears (Spielberger, Gorsuch, & Lushene, 1970). State anxiety is conceptualized as a transitory emotional state of an individual that is characterized by subjective, consciously perceived feelings of tension and apprehension and heightened autonomic nervous system activity. It is assumed that state anxiety varies in intensity and fluctuates over time. Such an anxiety measure appears particularly useful for the highly changeable and stressful conditions a post-MI patient faces.

A self-report Type-A behavior measure, the Behavior Pattern Activity Scale (BPAS), as described by MacDougall and Dembrowski (1979), can be used in a psychological battery. like other Type A measures, the BPAS is constructed primarily along the speed and impatience and hard-driving dimensions lines. Unlike the Jenkins Activity Survey (Jenkins, Zyzanski, & Rosenman, 1971), the BPAS can be administered as a state measure. The assumption in its use is that it might reflect state Type-A behavior. Although not an ideal measure of state changes, it appears to be the best measure available.

The Profile of Mood States (POMS) developed by McNair, Lorr, and Droppleman (1971) can be used to measure psychological mood states. McNair et al. offer the POMS as a multidimensional measure of subjective feelings or affect that includes tension, depression, anger, vigor, fatigue, and confusion. The POMS is constructed as a state measure of these subjective feelings.

The assessment during cardiac rehabilitation of the 65-item POMS might be too lengthy to have post-MI patients complete on alternate days. On the basis of a POMS normative data study involving male Veterans Administration patients (McNair, et al., 1971), 32 items were selected to represent the scale. The criteria for selecting an item was that it loaded on a factor with a value greater than .30.

The Moos Coping Scale (Billings & Moos, 1981) is a measure of coping style involving active attempts to cope with stressful events: cognitive, behavioral, or avoidance. Active cognitive coping includes attempts to manage self-perception or appraisal of a situation. Active behavior includes overt behavioral attempts to cope directly with a situation. Avoidance includes attempts to escape or deny the stressful event. Most clinicians agree that coping strategies can be effective in reducing the stress associated with a variety of situations. Self-reported coping strategies can parallel the impact of a stressful situation in both mood and symptom levels. Billings and Moos (1981) further describe coping as either problem or emotion focused. Problem-focused coping includes attempts to modify stress through one's own behavior. Emotion-focused coping represents attempts to manage emotional consequences of stress. For the post-MI patient, assessment of coping style could help discriminate successful from nonsuccessful patients during the rehabilitation process.

Based on prior experiences, an individual develops expectancies about her or his capability to regulate future behavior. Rotter (1975) has pointed out that a major shortcoming in locus-of-control research is the use of a cross-situational measure. According to locus-of-control theory, when the aim is to predict behavior in a specific situation, the expectancy measure needs to be specific to that situation.

The Wallston, Wallston, Kaplan, and Maides (1976) measure of Health Locus of Control addresses an individual's perception of control of health status. The Wallston et al. work is based on the assumption that a health-related locus of control would provide a more sensitive prediction of the relationship between internality and health behavior. With an increase in health locus-of-control, the post-MI patient could be expressing a greater sense of compliance with medical treatment recommendations. Baer et al. (1985) reported the use of a Staff Observation Scale (SOS) as a measure of post-MI psychological adjustment. This 35-item rating scale was developed to measure specific maladaptive behavior and denial of medical status for inpatients recovering from a recent MI. The SOS has been reported to differentiate between a post-MI treatment and a post-MI control group (Baer et al., 1985). At hospital discharge, the treatment group showed better overall psychological adjustment, which includes less depression, anxiety, low energy, and cardiac-invalid role, when compared with the control group. These results were based on a comparison between the two groups on an earlier factor analysis. Significant factors from the SOS include Treatment Compliance, Depression-Anxiety, Irritability, Low Energy, Cardiac Anxiety, and Invalid Role. For each item, a minimum factor loading was set an eigen value of .30. Results from the factor analysis were interpreted as a step in establishing construct validity for the SOS. Further development of this scale is needed. However, it does appear to be a useful step in specifically assessing the psychological status of the post-MI patient during rehabilitation.

INTERVENTIONS WITH POST-MI PATIENTS

Psychotherapy Interventions

Many early psychological interventions involving post-MI patients employed group psychotherapy.

The results of these studies provide limited support for the therapeutic benefit of such therapy (Blanchard & Miller, 1977).

Unlike prior attempts, Gruen (1975) provided individual psychotherapy to the treatment patients. Daily sessions were held for a half hour during the 11 days the patient was hospitalized after his MI. Providing of the intervention during the acute phase was also a unique aspect of the study. During treatment, both cognitive and affective control were left up to the patients. Thus, if a patient preferred the use of denial as a defense, this was allowed, providing it did not interfere with medical treatment. The treatment program included 10 major components designed to foster self-awareness, feedback, and positive reinforcement. These components included development of a genuine interest in the patient, reassurance to the patient that negative reactions to an MI were normal reactions, clarification of the patient's positive coping strategies, feedback of feelings and conclusions the patient appeared to be experiencing, feedback of the therapist's faith in the patient's capacity to cope, and constant reinforcement of coping strategies and other resources used by the patient.

Gruen (1975) found promising results for the use of psychotherapy with post-MI patients. On self-report measures, the treatment group was significantly different from the control group on variables of surgency, affection, sadness, and anxiety. Physicians' notes revealed less depression, and nurses' notes revealed less weakness in the treatment group. Physiological data indicated significant differences in favor of the treatment group: days in the hospital, days in intensive care, days on the cardiac monitor, and number of patients with congestive heart failure.

In this investigator's view, treatment appeared to instill a feeling of hope that aided patients in coping. He concluded that the patient who realistically evaluates his or her illness and future feels a new sense of coping and even optimism about the future. Critical to treatment success was the provision to the patient of adequate feedback on a cognitive level. With the support and assistance of the therapist, patients were able to make rational and calm choices and try new coping strategies.

Behavioral-Therapy Interventions

From a behavioral perspective, Suinn (1974) reported the use of stress management as a psychological intervention for post-MI patients. More specifically, this investigation was interested in providing an effective intervention for Type A post-MI patients.

The treatment program consisted of five 1-hour sessions. Patients were trained in coping strategies for stress situations and stress arousal. The program was a combination of two behavior-modification programs developed by the investigator (Suinn, 1974). Anxiety-management training involves procedures that train patients in the identification of physical signs of stress and management through relaxation techniques. These procedures are reported to have been successful with chronically anxious patients (Edie, 1972; Nicoletti, 1972). Visuomotor-behavior rehearsal involves training individuals to acquire new adaptive behavior through controlled imagery conditions. On a posttreatment self-report questionnare, 83% of the treatment patients reported substantial reduction of daily tension. A replication of this study with similar results was reported in a single-group outcome study (Suinn, 1975). Suinn (1974) concluded that, as a pilot study, the results appear promising that the Type A behavior pattern can be modified by stress-management techniques.

Previous intervention attempts also have in common a considerable delay after MI before treatment is initiated. Treatment might be most effective when introduced as soon as the patient is physically stable. Of primary consideration is that an MI is an immediate threat with which the patient might be ill-prepared to cope. Aiding the individual in gaining control and developing competence in handling her or his condition could circumvent the often dysfunctional affective reactions and ineffective means of coping (Gentry & Williams, 1975).

Stress management as an effective inhospital treatment intervention for post-MI patients has received support (Baer et al., 1985). With a control group pretest–posttest design, 81 post-MI subjects were assigned to either the attention–placebo control group or the stress-management treatment group. The stress-management program was based on relaxation training, self-awareness, self-reinforcement, practice, and behavioral rehearsal as major procedural components.

More recently, psychological interventions in coronary artery disease have been reviewed (Kolman, 1983; Razin, 1982). Although methodological problems remain, there is agreement that psychological interventions can be beneficial with consistent psychological gains and less consistent but clinically significant physiological gains. Representative studies (Langosch et al., 1982; Rahe, Ward, & Hayes 1979) have shown that patients who had group therapy as a behavioral intervention showed reduced anxiety, depression, or Type-A behavior, with effects evident during a follow-up period.

THEORETICAL ORIENTATION: STRESS MANAGEMENT AS A SELF-CONTROL STRATEGY

The use of stress management as a psychological intervention is integrally related to the cognitive-behavioral theoretical framework. More specifically, within this structure the construct of self-control is of primary importance to stress management in both its early development and its current format. The phenomenon of self-control has long interested the scientific community. Prior to the 1960s, it was common practice to equate such concepts as *willpower* and *ego strength* with self-control.

With a shift in theory to a cognitive–behavioral perspective, it became necessary to reformulate self-control. Current conceptualization of self-control includes primary regulation by cognitive factors. Perhaps the clearest definition of self-control from this perspective is offered by Thoresen and Mahoney (1974). They define self-control as ''the display of behavior when in the relative absence of immediate external constraints a behavior is engaged in, where previous probability has been less than alternative behavior'' (324). This type of response pattern is often characterized by delayed rewards, greater exertion, and overcome aversive factors.

In determining the primary source of self-control, theorists have argued from both external and internal perspectives (Bandura, 1976; Skinner, 1953). Most agree that such a dichotomy over controlling influences is virtually meaningless. Aware that external and internal forces are highly interactive, the cognitive–behavioral approach has offered a number of potential mediators that are in essence internally oriented. Within the theoretical framework, both positive and negative incentives have been suggested as mediators of self-control (Bellack, 1976; Dunbar & Agras, 1977; Meichenbaum, 1977). Self-monitoring, or self-awareness, is also recognized as a potential change agent (Kanfer, 1970; Kazdin, 1974). Although there are other hypothesized mediators of self-control, goal specification, cuing strategies, and rehearsal,

the primary ones have focused on awareness and reinforcement.

These theories and hypotheses led applied reseachers to develop and test the effects of self-reward in client populations. In general, investigations (Meichenbaum, 1977) provide substantial support for the use of self-reward procedures. Particularly impressive is the quality of the empirical evidence that is dominated by treatment-outcome studies. Dunbar and Agras (1977) suggested that this effectiveness might be further enhanced by combining self-control strategies. The reason for this suggestion comes from their successful clinical use of self-monitoring and self-reinforcement instruction. For essential hypertensive clients, these researchers found the combination to be more effective than the single use in gaining adherence to medical treatment.

The importance of self-awareness, or self-monitoring, has been stressed as an important element of the self-control model. Thoresen and Mahoney (1974) have offered tentative guidelines for this component of self-control. They believe that self-awareness is quite similar to skill development. In skill development, whether it is learning how to play the piano or observing one's self, the desired behavior needs to be carefully explained and demonstrated. A person can then carry out practice of this behavior. It is generally accepted that overt or covert practice is required for improvement in skill performance (Mahoney & Arnkoff, 1979). Skill adquisition might be enhanced by modeling, immediate and accurate feedback, systematic reinforcement, and a gradual transfer of monitoring responsibilities to the client.

Self-reward, the self-presentation of reward contingencies on performance of some desired behavior, is by far the most frequently researched area in self-control. According to Bandura (1976), self-reward can actually refer to two processes; self-presentation of the reinforcement and self-selection of the contingencies. In some cases, it is more desirable for the client to be able to self-reward and the therapist to set the criteria for the reinforcement. The assumption is that, for self-reward to be an effective procedure, persons who impose severely strict contingencies on reinforcement might first need to learn to set realistic criteria. Because of this characteristic, unintentional sabotage of the procedures might occur. Depressed individuals and persons displaying the Type A behavior pattern have often been characterized as being extremely strict and rigid in judging themselves (Beck, Weismann, Lester, & Trexler, 1979).

Mahoney and Arnkoff (1978) suggested that any given instance of self-reinforcement can be further broken down into a number of important components. These include beliefs or expectancies regarding the process of the procedure, self-deprivation of freely available rewards, evaluation of performance in relation to goals, and cognitive and affective self-reactions. However, the act of presenting oneself with a reward is still considered by most to be perhaps the most crucial. A self-reward can be in the form of positive self-statements, tangible rewards, and manipulation of social support. From a cognitive–behavioral perspective, Mahoney (1977) believes that positive self-statements are probably the most reliable, transituational, cheapest, and effective way to change behavior.

Researchers investigating self-awareness (Kanfer, 1970; Kazdin, 1974) soon recognized that this assessment technique often had an impact of its own on the target behavior. In early use of self-monitoring, it was common to send a client home to gather baseline information on the target behavior. Instead of simply setting the stage for the "real treatment," clients would often return with glowing reports of improvement of the target behavior. This phenomena, often referred to as the *reactive effects of self-monitoring*, has been tested to determine the extent of its treatment effects.

Some studies investigating the long-term effects of self-monitoring (Nelson, 1976; Nelson, Lupinski, & Black, 1976) have shown only limited support for its use as a treatment strategy. In general, these investigations indicate that, during the first few weeks, significant changes often occur with this procedure. Moreover, a further consistent finding is that self-monitoring loses its effectiveness if not supported by other strategies. Mahoney and Arnkoff (1978) believe that, although self-monitoring might be insufficient to produce long term-effects, its importance as an assessment device and possible use as a component of a more comprehensive treatment program overshadow this limitation.

Integral to the understanding of self-awareness is the classification of cuing strategies in self-control. These strategies are designed to help focus on the important factors regulating one's behavior. Such factors should be the primary focus on natural objects of self-awareness. These factors have been conceptualized as varying across three general areas; social, physical, and private. Inanimate objects that surround a person make up the physical domain, and the social domain consists of other persons. The physiological and psychological, both cognitive and affective, compromise the private domain. These three domains are often judged in terms of antecedents, behavioral mediation, and consequences.

More recent conceptualization of self-control has focused on a person's internal behavior, cognitions, images, and affect as sources of behavioral control. Although this has obviously been accepted in other treatment approaches, self-control and cognitive–behavioral strategies are the first behavioral approaches to respect these human qualities. The determination of antecedents and consequences is not where primary importance is placed in this approach; rather, the importance is placed on the cognitive processes as mediators. Whether a stimulus precedes or follows a cognitive event is not as critical as the cuing quality of this stimulus on an appropriate coping strategy (Bandura, 1977). This concession is necessary when one considers our current limitations in determining causality. Often it is beyond our capabilities to determine with confidence what caused a specific behavior, thought, or feeling, beyond the theoretical and experimental levels, specific interventions have been developed that facilitate the development of self-control. The cognitive restructuring approach is represented best by Ellis's (1962) rational–emotive therapy (RET) and Meichenbaum's (1974) self-instruction therapy.

Meichenbaum's (1974) self-instruction approach has much in common with, but differs significantly from, RET. Both agree that self-statements are critical in the development and maintenance of maladaptive behavior. However, where Ellis focused on "irrational ideas," Meichenbaum emphasized idiosyncratic thought patterns. The self-instructional approach focuses on the development of specific coping skills for dealing with the problematic behavior. The treatment program contains elements of desensitization, modeling, and behavior rehearsal. Where RET attempts to negate self-punitive cognitions, Meichenbaum's approach contains a constructive skill-development phase. In other words, where RET focuses on rationality as being synonymous with adaptation, self-instructional training places more emphasis on constructive alternatives. In both cognitive-restructuring approaches, the fundamental treatment goal is to discover more appropriate and adaptive cognitive patterns.

Suinn and Bloom's (1978) anxiety-management

training (AMT) and Meichenbaum's (1975) stress inoculation represent the foundation for the development of the coping-skills approach of stress management. Suinn and Bloom (1978) used anxiety-management training in the successful modification of the Type-A behavior pattern. AMT is typically conducted in three stages. In the first stage, clients are taught deep-muscle relaxation. In the second stage, anxiety-provoking images are aroused through imagery. At this time, clients are taught to identify the physiological cues accompanying these images. In the third stage, clients gain practice in learning to recognize physical cues and engage in relaxation as a coping response. These researchers' major contention, that stress is an integral part of Type A behavior and that stress-management techniques would be an effective treatment, is supported by their initial investigation.

A CARDIAC STRESS-MANAGEMENT TREATMENT PROGRAM

Baer et al. (1985) have developed a stress-management program for post-MI patients that attempts to utilize a number of the self-control mediators in a more comprehensive treatment package. Based on earlier interventions (Meichenbaum, 1975; Suinn & Bloom, 1978), this treatment program includes components of self-awareness, cuing strategies, self-reinforcement, practice, and rehearsal. Overall treatment goals were to increase awareness of stress, to develop stress-coping skills, to practice successful management of stress, to provide acute management of stress, and to develop generalizable ability to manage stress after the termination of treatment.

The cardiac stress-management program involves one introductory individual session, followed by eight group-training sessions. Throughout training, all patients are expected to attend daily 45-minute group sessions. In addition, 20 minutes of morning and evening relaxation practice are assigned. The group-treatment session consists of four relaxation-training sessions, followed by four stress-management sessions. However, the individual patient's progression from relaxation training to stress management is dependent on the ability to demonstrate deep relaxation.

During the introductory individual session, patients are informed that the primary goal of the rehabilitation program is to promote cardiovascular health that will aid in preventing future com-

plications. A general introduction to risk factors, including stress, is conducted. Stress is described as an experience that all of us share in today's world. Specifically, stress is defined as the psychological and physiological state of a person facing demands that require coping. The identification of stress can be made on either a physical or a psychological state level, by specific situations, or by a combination of these indicators. Part of the rehabilitation program is explained to aid each patient in the development of skills to handle stress. Primary importance is placed on the skill that is applicable to physical tension, deep-muscle relaxation. The rationale for relaxation training is explained. Emphasis is placed on the requirement of practice and the potential application of this self-control procedure.

For deep-muscle-relaxation training, the standard exercises are modified by replacing tension with focused awareness and muscle movement in the relaxation cycle. Verbal descriptions of the relaxation experience are encouraged. From these descriptions and observations, made during the guided exercise, the therapist can assess each patient's ability to obtain deep relaxation.

Session one is held on the same day as the introductory session. The group session begins with a review of the rationale for relaxation training. Emphasis is placed on required relaxation for skill development. Patients are informed that relaxation training involves "allowing" oneself to follow instructions and the "letting go" of tension to experience relaxation. A step-by-step explanation of the 16-muscle-group procedures is conducted. After all questions are answered, the group participates in the guided exercise.

Session two begins with a discussion of each patient's compliance, difficulties, and success during individual practice. The rationale and progressive nature of relaxation are reviewed prior to the guided exercise. After the 16-muscle-group exercise, patients are encouraged to describe verbally their experiences and are reminded of the practice assignment.

In session three, after the evaluation of individual practice, the seven-muscle group exercise is conducted. The goal of this session is to start the reduction in the exercise procedure necessary to obtain deep-muscle relaxation. Following discussion of the relaxation experience, patients are instructed in several short relaxation exercises. Relaxation by recall, a slow in-and-out breathing cycle, counting backward from 10 to 1 and feeling progressively more relaxed are the new exercises. Patients are instructed to practice these in addition to the regular assignment.

The evaluation of individual practice, including that of the shorter exercises, opens the fourth group session. The seven-muscle-group exercise is then repeated. At the end of this session, if a patient is judged capable of obtaining deep-muscle relaxation, a transfer to the stress-management group is initiated. The patient is informed of his or her success at physical relaxation and that further development of coping skills would be possible in the stress-management group.

Sessions five through eight represent the stress-management stage of the program. All sessions begin and end with 10 minutes of deep relaxation. During stress management, patients are exposed to procedures that aid in the identification of stress, the use of appropriate coping skills, the labeling of self-control attempts, and the behavioral rehearsal of the entire process.

Initially, the therapist encourages patients to identify signs, or indicators, of stress. If patients are unable to provide examples, the therapist has at her or his disposal a number that are frequently reported. Care is taken to provide examples that evoke the least reaction. Thus, identification of stress is focused on a level at which patients would be most receptive. Once an indication of stress is offered, the emphasis is shifted to the thoughts and feelings associated with it. With the therapist taking the coping-model role, alternative ways of responding to stress are discussed. Specifically, relaxation and cognitive coping skills are suggested as alternative ways of coping with stress. Patients are instructed to use these stress-reduction skills when stress is identified. They are encouraged to label attempts at skills application as examples of self-control. At this point patients participate in a behavioral rehearsal involving the discrimination of stress, the application of coping skills, and the labeling of this as a self-control attempt.

In session five, the concept of stress management is introduced by having patients identify physiological indicators of stress. They are encouraged to provide recent examples of stress experienced while in the hospital. If facilitation is necessary, the therapist has at his or her disposal indicators such as tense muscles, rapid breathing, and heart pounding, that are often reported by patients. From a coping-skills perspective, a discussion follows on alternative ways of handling the stress experience. Emphasis is placed on using physiological indicators as cues to begin applying relaxation or cognitive coping skills.

Patients are further instructed to label the use of coping skills as examples of self-control. A behavioral rehearsal of this process follows. In addition to the daily individual practice, self-monitoring for physiological indicators of stress during routine activities is encouraged. If stress is identified while watching TV, walking, shaving, and so on, patients are instructed to complete the process using appropriate coping skills and labeling the self-control attempt.

Following the group relaxation exercise, individual practice attempts are reviewed in session six. Care is taken to assure continued deep relaxation and to analyze any difficulties patients experienced while applying stress-reduction skills. In this session, situational stress indicators asssociated with the ward are identified. Examples available to the therapist include schedule delays and environmental disturbances. Primary importance is placed on having patients identify personally relevant stress indicators. With the therapist taking the coping-model role, the discussion focuses on alternative ways of responding to stress. The use of situational indicators as cues to apply coping skills is explained as being essential in stress reduction. Once the relaxation and cognitive skills are applied to the stress experience, the labeling of the self-control attempt completes the process. Practice of stress management is accomplished by behavioral rehearsal. An additional practice suggestion is to use the situational indicators as cues to employ coping responses on the ward.

In session seven attention is focused on patients' attempts at coping with stress during individual practice. Any difficulties are resolved before the continuation of stress management. Content of this session shifts to include both on- and off-ward indicators of stress. The therapist can provide examples of discharge delay, activity reduction, undetermined medical status, and so on. The use of deep relaxation and cognitive coping skills is discussed in terms of its being more functional than negative thoughts and feelings experienced during stress. Afterward, the behavioral rehearsal of stress identification, the application of coping skills, and the labeling of the self-control attempt are conducted. Patients are encouraged to practice the process, which is cued by indicators relevant to them. The therapist also provides examples that demonstrate how this self-control procedure could be utilized after hospital discharge.

As in all previous training sessions, the final session begins with the assessment and resolution of difficulties encountered during individual practice. Identification of stress outside the hospital is the focal point of this group session. Financial problems, family conflict, and uncertainty about the future are common examples. Feelings and thoughts associated with these stress indicators are discussed. Emphasis is placed on using alternative coping skills in response to these stress indicators. After the behavioral rehearsal, the treatment program is reviewed. All patients are reminded that identification of and coping with stress is an ongoing process. It is suggested to all patients that they use their coping skills to reduce stress in their daily lives after discharge.

CASE STUDY

We briefly describe a study testing this intervention in a sample of 40 male post-MI patients. All post-MI patients were admitted to the cardiac rehabilitation program from the coronary intensive care unit at the Houston Veterans Administration Medical Center.

The sample was divided equally into the stress-management treatment group ($N = 20$) and the patient education-control group ($N = 20$). The average length of participation in the cardiac rehabilitation program was 9.5 days for the treatment group and 10.8 days for the control group. The majority, 13 control and 13 treatment patients, were hospitalized for their first MIs. Cardiac-risk factors of family history, hypertension, obesity, smoking, lack of exercise, and stress were assessed for all patients by the rehabilitation program's chief cardiologist. On the average, three risk factors were identified for each participant.

The average age for the treatment group and the control group was 58.8 years and 56.6 years, respectively. Most of the patients had the equivalent of a high school education and were from a predominately lower socioeconomic background. A majority of the patients were Caucasian, with only 7 control and 5 treatment patients from other ethnic groups. Prior to hospitalization, 13 control and 19 treatment patients were employed on a full-time basis. Fourteen control and 13 treatment patients were married.

No unusual problems were encountered in recruiting patients to participate in the study. Only two potential candidates refused to participate, because they were seeking early discharge from the rehabilitation program.

Procedures

Forty hospitalized patients in the cardiac rehabilitation program were equally assigned to the patient-education control group and the stress-management treatment group. All patients participated in an individual introductory session and eight group sessions.

On alternating days of participation patients completed the Daily Experience Record (DER), a self-report measure of physical complaints, and the POMS. The POMS is a self-report measure of tension, depression, anger, vigor, fatigue, and confusion mood states. In addition, all patients were asked to complete five psychological self-report questionnaires on the first and final days of participation. The following questionnaires were completed in random order: State Anxiety Inventory, Health Locus of Control, Hopelessness Scale, Moos Coping Scale and Behavior Pattern Activity Scale.

Beginning on the first day of rehabilitation, behavior ratings were made on all patients. After the first assessment, all were then rated on alternating days throughout participation. The Staff Observation Scale, designed to be sensitive to post-MI psychological adjustment, was used as the behavioral rating scale. Two raters conducted assessment of each patient until discharge.

Physiological evidence of cardiac status was obtained from each patient's medical records on a daily basis. Specific indicators of cardiac status recorded were signs of congestive heart failure, persistent angina, and cardiac arrhythmias. Patients' medication and dosage were also used in determining if daily physiological functioning was uncomplicated or complicated.

A 6-month follow-up evaluation included the psychological questionnaire administered pre and post discharge. Telephone interviews provided information on return to work, sexual adjustment, and compliance with relaxation and other stress-management strategies.

Treatment

The Patient Education Control Program consisted of one introductory session and eight group sessions. All sessions were 45 minutes in length. The major focus of this program was to provide patients with education material relevant to their cardiovascular health. Major areas covered during sessions were cardiovascular system functioning, factors related to posthospital rehabilitation, and risk factors

TABLE 12.1. Patient education program during hospitalization for myocardial infarction (MI)

SESSION	TOPICS
Individual, day 1	Introduction to cardiac rehabilitation; focus on risk factor for MI
Group, day 1	Focus on physical effects of MI; cardiovascular system function
Group, day 2	Physical adjustment to MI. Angina and sexual function
Group, day 3	Review of risk-factor modification for MI
Group, day 4	Hypertension as risk factor for MI; treatment compliance
Group, day 5	Smoking as risk factor for MI; common strategies for stopping smoking
Group, day 6	Exercise, diet, obesity as risk factors for MI; recommendations for changing habits
Group, day 7	Stress role in MI recovery
Group, day 8	Review of risk factors for MI

TABLE 12.2 Relaxation and stress–management program during hospitalization for myocardial infarction (MI)

SESSION	TOPICS
Individual, Day 1	Introduction to stress, coping, and risks in rehabilitation after MI; rationale for relaxation training and practice; preparation for group program
Group, level 1 day1	16-muscle-group technique taught, using movement to focus awareness; twice daily 20-minute practice
Group, level 1 day 2	Compliance, review of practice, and guided relaxation exercise
Group, level 1 day 3	7-muscle-group exercise; relaxation by recall, respiratory control, and counting to progressive relaxation
Group, level 1 day 4	Evaluation of practice, assessment for achievement of deep-muscle relaxation
Group, level 1 day 5	All level-2 sessions begin and end with 10-minute deep relaxation; introduction to physiologic indexes of stress and cues for labeling, coping and rehearsal; self-monitoring for stress
Group, level 2 day 6	Review of experience with stress-reduction skills; identification of ward-based stress, modeling of coping
Group, level 2 day 7	Off-ward stressors; replacement of negative ideation with relaxation and coping skills; self-control after discharge from hospital
Group, level 2 day 8	Postdischarge stress; review of behavioral rehearsal, emphasis on coping with stress as an ongoing process in daily life

associated with cardiovascular disease. The first 30 minutes of all group sessions were devoted to instruction. The final 15 minutes were reserved for a question-and-answer period on the material presented. Table 12.1 summarizes the sessions.

The subjects for the stress-management group consisted of the first 20 individuals who agreed to participate after the control procedures were completed. The stress-management program has been previously described and is summarized in Table 12.2.

Research Design

A nonrandomized control group pretest-posttest design was utilized in this investigation. This design is consistent with a level of investigation attempting to test for group differences in a clinical population. Because of the use of a nonrandomized design, it was critical to test for initial differences between groups that could confound study findings.

The independent variables in this investigation were the patient-education control group and the stress-management treatment group. The dependent variables included locus of control, state anxiety, hopelessness as a dimension, depression, coping style, Type-A behavior, psychological mood states, physical symptoms, and post-MI psychological adjustment.

Results

Data analysis procedures for the psychological test variables of state anxiety, health locus of control, active cognition, active behavior, avoidance, depression, and Type A behavior addressed five of the research hypotheses. The pretest multivariate analysis of variance (MANOVA) on these variables demonstrated no significant differences between the control and the stress-management groups (F 7,32 -

2.01; $p < .08$) prior to the experimental manipulation. Posttest MANOVA on the psychological test variables yielded significant differences between the groups ($F\ 7,32 - 4.07$; $p < .01$). Post hoc analysis of univariate F and standard discriminant analysis were performed. Post hoc analysis showed nonsignificant differences on the state anxiety, avoidance, and Type A behavior variables. However, the control and stress-management groups were significantly different on variables of health locus of control ($F\ 7,32 - 6.57$; $p < .05$), active behavior ($F\ 7,32 - 4.27$; $p < .05$), and depression ($F\ 7,32 -10.14$; $p < .01$).

Posttest MANOVA on the POMS variables yielded significant differences between the groups. Post hoc analysis of univariate F and standard discriminate analysis were performed to detect the specific POMS variables the groups differed on. No significant differences were detected on the depression, anger, or fatigue variables. The control and stress-management groups were significantly different on the tension ($F\ 7,32 - 12.14$; $p < .01$), vigor ($F\ 7,32 - 8.02$; $p < .01$), and confusion variables ($F\ 7,32 - 6.46$; $p < .05$).

A significant posttest MANOVA ($F\ 7,32 - 2.17$; $p < .05$) demonstrated that the groups were different on the DER variables during the final days of participation. Post hoc analysis of univariate F and standard discriminate analysis detected no single variable the groups significantly differed on.

Pretest MANOVA on the SOS variables yielded significant differences between the two groups ($F\ 7,32 - 3.35$; $p < .01$). To determine the specific variables on which the groups differed, univariate F and standard discriminant analysis were performed. These analyses detected a pretest difference on the treatment compliance and invalid-role variables. To remove this pretest bias, a posttest analysis of covariance (ANCOVA) was performed with covariates of pretest treatment compliance and invalid role. The significant ANCOVA ($F\ 7,32 - 2.71$; $p < .05$) was followed by post hoc analysis of univariate F and standard discriminate analysis. From these analyses it was demonstrated that the stress-management group, compared with the control group, was significantly different on variables of low energy, anxiety and depression and invalid role. No significant differences were detected on the treatment compliance, irritability, or cardiac anxiety variables. The findings that the stress-management group exhibited less anxiety and depression, fewer signs of low energy, and less acceptance of an individual role are interpreted as supporting a higher level of post-MI adjustment.

The posttest ANCOVA yielded nonsignificant results for the group X rater interaction ($F\ 7,32 - .16$; $p\ .99$) and rater effect ($F\ 7, 32 - .24$; $p\ .96$). Thus, it appears the raters were consistent in their observations and not biased by the groups they were rating.

Cardiac status as reflected by persistent angina, cardiac arrhythmia, and congestive heart failure yielded nonsignificant results in separate two-dimension chi-squares. The results were persistent angina ($x^2 = .84$; $p > .05$), cardiac arrhythmias ($x^2 = 1.64$; $p > .05$), and congestive heart failure ($x^2 = 2.28$; $p > .05$).

Discussion

Results from this investigation demonstrate support for the use of stress management with post-MI patients. At discharge, stress-management patients' lower anxiety self-report did not reach statistical significance. However, on a related measure, the POMS tension scale, the group did report less tension and anxiety. In addition, the behavioral observation data detected a significant difference in anxiety between the groups. Both raters agreed that the stress-management patients appeared less anxious than the control patients. The trained observers were probably more capable of assessing anxiety than the study participants. This conclusion appears warranted, because in behavioral assessment, trained raters consistently provide more accurate observational data.

The scale used to measure a dimension of depression, hopelessness, reflects an individual's negative expectancies concerning herself or himself and the future. The stress-management patients appear to have avoided the negative experience of hopelessness to a greater extent than the control patients. The stress-management patients appeared to be looking forward to the future with more hope and enthusiasm. Throughout stress-management training, patients were encouraged to establish their cardiovascular health as a top priority. It is possible that the stress-management patient has heightened expectations of success in participating in the control of his or her cardiovascular health. In part, this expectation might reflect a greater sense of self-efficacy over the stress of post-MI rehabilitattion. Therefore, this positive expectancy could result in more effective coping both on a psychological level and in compliance with treatment recommendations.

This study employed a health locus-of-control measure (Wallston et al., 1976). This measure is based on the assumption that a health locus-of-control scale would be more sensitive to the relationships between internality and health behavior. By reporting a more internal locus of control, the stress-management patients appeared to communicate an expectation of greater control over their future health status than the control patients. Successful post-MI rehabilitation requires professional medical care. However, most clinicians agree that an integral part of successful recovery is a patient's active participation in her or his own health care. Modification of risk factors and maintenance of prescribed medical care at home are but two components of health care over which an individual has virtually complete control. Beyond treatment compliance, the greater sense of control over health status is consistent with the decreased feelings of helplessness or hopelessness that the stress-management patients experienced.

The stress-management patients made more active cognitive and behavioral attempts during the immediate post-MI hospitalization. Discriminative evidence for a more active coping style by the stress-management patients was the nonsignificant difference between groups in the use of avoidant strategies. Active coping includes strategies to decrease the impact of a stressful event. Active cognitive attempts to cope include the assessment of the stressful event such as "tried to step back from the situation and be more objective." Active behavioral coping refers to overt behavioral attempts to successfully manage stress. Examples are "took some positive action" and "talked with a professional person about the situation." This intervention was designed to facilitate the development of both cognitive and behavioral coping skills. It appears that the stress-management patients were employing a more active coping style, which could in part be attributed to the treatment procedures. The effectiveness of a more active coping style is given support by the positive changes in mood the stress-management patients experienced.

A possible explanation for the nonsignificant results is that the Type-A measure used in the study was not sensitive to change during the rehabilitation period. The BPAS scale was adapted with special instructions to assess state Type-A behavior. In the study, patients completed the scale during the first and final days of participation. Because patients were hospitalized throughout participation, there was a low probability of change on specific scale items. It appears that, to detect Type-A behavior change, either a more sensitive state or a situational measure is needed.

Behavioral observation data indicated that stress-management patients demonstrated fewer signs of low energy, showed less anxiety and depression, and were less accepting of a cardiac or invalid role. As reported, anxiety and depression are common affective reactions of the post-MI patients. Low energy level is frequently interpreted as a component of depression. Although post-MI energy level is certainly effected by cardiac status, the stress-management patients' exhibition of a higher energy level is also consistent with feeling less depressed.

The invalid role is well recognized by clinicians treating post-MI patients. Often referred to as a *cardiac cripple*, this individual views himself or herself as being unable to take care of himself or herself and defers this care to others. Although a certain amount of dependency on others is appropriate, an excessive lack of responsibility can create complications during and following hospitalization. The fact that stress-management patients were less accepting of this role, compliments the findings of a higher level of control over health status and more active coping style. Within medical guidelines, the stress-management patients appear to be more effectively coping with post-MI rehabilitation.

Stress management patients, compared with control patients, did not report significantly fewer physical complaints. The nonsignificant results could be attributable to the relatively few physical complaints reported by both groups. With few complaints being made, detection of a group difference is highly unlikely. It could have been predicted that few complaints would be reported, because all patients were stable and undergoing routine cardiac rehabilitation.

Cardiac status, determined by persistent angina, cardiac arrhythmias, and congestive heart failure, was assessed for all patients. Given the nature of the sample, it was unlikely that a psychological intervention, in this case, stress management, would have a significant impact on cardiac status. However, stress management might facilitate future improvements in cardiac status. After hospital discharge, a patient's condition is determined more by voluntary treatment compliance and risk-factor modification. In addition to more effective psychological adjustment, the active coping style demonstrated by the stress-management patient might transfer to other health-related behavior and result in future improvements in cardiac status.

Based on a cognitive–behavioral theoretical framework, the stress-management patients employed a more active coping style than the control patients. Stress-management patients reported using more active cognitive and behavioral attempts to cope with the stress of post-MI rehabilitation. This more active coping style appears as clear evidence that stress-management patients were developing stress-coping skills. Further, the stress-management patients perceived a greater sense of control over their health status than the control patients. Perceived controllability has been proposed as perhaps the most important cognitive process following an MI (Krantz, 1980). This interpretation is consistent with the self-control model for stress management. It could well be that, by becoming active participants in their own health care, stress-management patients perceived a greater sense of mastery over stress.

The fact of stress-management patients being less accepting of an invalid role complements the findings of a more active coping style and greater perceived controllability. The invalid role, or cardiac cripple, is characterized by a sense of helplessness and excessive dependence on others. These characteristics are both inconsistent with successful coping according to the self-control model of stress management.

Successful coping with stress should result in a decrease of negative stress reactions. The study results support the contention that the stress-management patients were more successful in coping with stress. Stress-management patients reported feeling less depressed, tense, fatigued, and confused. Further, the stress-management patients were observed to be less anxious, to exhibit less depression, and to show fewer signs of low energy. Such a decrease in negative stress reactions by the stress-management patients also supports the cognitive–behavioral mediational model of self-control.

Particularly impressive is the finding of less depression in the stress-management patients. In this study, depression was conceptualized as an individual's negative expectations about herself or himself and the future. Associated with these negative expectations are feelings of helplessness and hopelessness in controlling one's life. It appears that, because stress-management patients are employing a more active coping style and feeling more in control of their health, one result has been not feeling so helpless in coping and hopeless about the future.

Prior to this study, there was evidence supporting the use of stress management with post-MI patients. Suinn (1974, 1975) reported two pilot studies using stress management as the intervention. Both single-group outcome studies detected marked behavioral change and physiological evidence that supported the use of the treatment procedures. These results were replicated by Suinn (1975), but Baer et al. (1985) reported the first control-group outcome study using stress management with post-MI patients.

The current study was an attempt to both replicate and extend the Baer et al. (1985) study. It was successful in replicating the behavioral observation results. The consistent finding in both studies was that stress-management patients, compared with control patients, appeared significantly less depressed, were less anxious, showed fewer signs of low energy, and were less accepting of an invalid role. Beyond the behavioral observation data, this study obtained self-report and physiological data. Self-report data was viewed as critical to testing the effectiveness of the intervention. Stress management is based on an individual's increased self-awareness and an active cognitive and behavioral coping style. If an individual is successful in coping with stress, this should be detected by self report of anxiety, depression, and other psychological experiences.

In general, prior psychological interventions involving post-MI patients have in common a considerable delay between the MI and treatment procedures. In a recent review, Razin (1982) concluded that there are virtually no reports on the use of a psychological intervention for post-MI patients during the acute phase. Consistent with the Baer et al. (1985) work, this study provided treatment immediately after patients were transfered from the intensive care unit. Both studies appear to offer a unique contribution to the acute management of post-MI patients.

RECOMMENDATIONS

Research in the psychological management of post-MI patients is at an early stage of development. Although a multiple-measurement approach was utilized in this study, the assessment of change did have important shortcomings. A major limitation was the lack of input from a significant other. With a majority of patients married, spouse assessment could have provided valuable collateral information. Input from the spouse could have focused on both patient behavior and marital discord. Spouse rating of marital discord could have provided an index of both existing marital difficulties at the onset and those following the patient's MI.

Denial was not assessed during this study. With the available evidence that denial is common in the post-MI population, the lack of its assessment limits this study. Currently, the only recognized measure of denial is a behavioral rating scale (Hackett & Cassem, 1975). Although not widely used, this measure could have provided an index of denial. It will be important for future research to develop a valid measure of denial.

Type-A behavior results might have been different with a Type-A structured interview. The structured interview is designed to elicit an individual's characteristic way of responding to a variety of situations. These situations are ones that should elicit impatience, hostility, and competiveness from a Type-A individual. Providing post-MI patients with an opportunity to respond to the interview questions would appear to be a more sensitive and objective measure of Type-A behavior. The interview would provide both a self-report and the interviewer's rating.

This study relied on routine physiological measures obtained during cardiac rehabilitation. These measures are critical to the patient's medical care, but they might be too insensitive to detect possible changes resulting from the stress-management procedures. During stress management, patients are trained to reduce both psychological and physiological reactions to stressful events. A variety of self-report measures was used to detect possible psychological changes during stress. Similar assessments of possible physiological changes would have enhanced the evaluation of stress management. A psychophysiological assessment under mildly stressful conditions would have provided a valuable index of patients' physiological responsivity under stress.

Beyond this study, future opportunities can be divided into investigations with other subject groups, therapists, and treatment strategies. This classification closely follows an alternative to traditional psychotherapy evaluation (Gottman & Markman, 1978).

This study's sample consisted of male post-MI patients from a VA hospital setting. Most of the sample were from a lower socioeconomic background, married, middle-aged, and with prior cardiovascular histories. This sample is viewed as representative of only a portion of the total post-MI population. One of the most obvious limitations is the lack of female post-MI patients in the sample. By including in future research other post-MI patients not represented in this study sample, it might be possible to generalize the results to a greater portion of the population. In addition, by including other post-MI patients, it would be possible to check for differential response to treatment. For example, one could test whether males or females respond more positively to stress-management procedures. The role of prior cardiovascular health warrants a similar test.

Stress management is representative of psychological interventions that focus on the individual and not on the therapist. The orientation is one of understanding how the individual is functioning and how to produce change. One implication is to develop a cost-effective program that is not so heavily dependent on the therapist's skills for change to occur. In this study, stress-management sessions were conducted by a therapist with doctoral training in psychology. Because few psychologists are avaliable to cardiac rehabilitation programs, it becomes a very practical question as to what skills are required to successfully conduct a stress-management program. Because the procedures are designed to deemphasize the therapist, it is possible that medical health professionals could develop the required skills in a relatively short time. Future research could address questions of therapist skills necessary for conducting a successful stress-management program.

Earlier investigations produced minimal support for the effectiveness of a psychological intervention for post-MI patients. These investigations have in common numerous methodological limitations. They also share in considerable delay from the occurrence of the MI to the administration of treatment procedures (Razin, 1982). The evidence supporting the effectiveness of stress management needs to be replicated with other psychological interventions under similarly stringent conditions. It is quite possible that the methodological limitations contributed to the negative results of earlier investigations. The delay in providing treatment could also be an important confounding variable. One unique aspect of this study was the provision of treatment approximately 3 days after the MI, while the patient was still hospitalized. At a time when an individual feels particularly overwhelmed, he or she might be more receptive to the support of a psychological intervention. Therefore, future research could address the issue of whether there are unique characteristics of stress management as a psychological intervention or whether timing of the intervention is a critical factor.

REFERENCES

Baer, P. E., Cleveland, S. E., Montero, A. C., Revel, K. F., Clancy, C. & Bower, R. (1985). Improving post-myocardial infarction recovery status by stress management training during hospitilization. *Journal of Cardiac Rehabilitation*, 5, 191–196.

Bandura, A. (1976). Self-reinforcement: Theoretical and methodological consideration. *Behaviorism*, 4, 135–155.

Bandura, A. (1977). Self-efficacy: Toward a unifying theory of behavioral change. *Psychological Review*, 84, 191–215.

Beck, A. T., Rush, A. J., Shaw, B. F., & Emery, G. D. (1979). *Cognitive therapy for depression.* New York: Guilford Press.

Beck, A., Weismann, R., Lester, D., & Trexler, L. (1974). The measurement of pessimism: The hopelessness scale. *Journal of Consulting and Clinical Psychology*, 42(6), 861–865.

Bellack, A. S. (1976). A comparison of self-reinforcement and self-monitoring in a weight reduction program. *Behavior Therapy*, 7, 68–75.

Billings, A. G., & Moos, R. H. (1981). The role of coping responses and social resources in attenuating the stress of life events. *Journal of Behavioral Medicine*, 42, 139–155.

Blanchard, E. B., & Miller, S. T. (1977). Psychological treatment of cardiovascular disease. *Archives of General Psychiatry*, 34, 1402–1413.

Bruhn, J. G., Chandler, B., & Wolf, S. (1969). A psychological study of survivors and nonsurvivors of myocardial infarction. *Psychosomatic Medicine*, 31, 8–19.

Croog, S. H., Shapiro, D. S., & Levine, S. (1971) Denial among male heart patients. *Psychosomatic Medicine*, 33, 385–397.

Doehrman, S. R. (1977), Psychosocial aspects of recovery from coronary heart disease: A review. *Social Science and Medicine*, 18, 199–218.

Dunbar, J., & Agras, W. S. (1977). *A behavioral strategy for improving adherence to medication.* Paper presented at the annual meeting of the Association for the Advancement of Behavior Therapy, Atlanta.

Edie, C. (1972). *Uses of AMT in treating trait anxiety.* Unpublished doctoral dissertation, Colorado State University, Ft. Collins.

Ellis, A. (1962). *Reason and emotion in psychotherapy.* New York: Lyle Stuart.

Gentry, W. D., Foster, S., & Haney, T. (1972). Denial as a determinant of anxiety and perceived health status in the coronary care unit. *Psychosomatic Medicine*, 34, 39–44.

Gentry, W. D., & Williams, R. B., Jr. (Eds.) (1975). *Psychological aspects of myocardial infarction and coronary care.* St. Louis: C. V. Mosby.

Gottman, J., & Markman, H. (1978). Experimental designs in psychotherapy research. In A. E. Bergin & S. L. Garfield (Eds.), *Handbook of Psychotherapy and Behavior Change.* New York: John Wiley & Sons.

Gruen, W. (1975). Effects of brief psychotherapy during the hospitalization period on the recovery process in heart attacks. *Journal of Consulting and Clinical Psychology*, 43, 232–233.

Hackett, T., & Cassem, N. II. (1975). Psychological management of the myocardial infarction patient. *Journal of Human Stress*, 1, 25–38.

Jenkins, C. D., Zyzanski, S. J., & Rosenman, R. H. (1971). Progress toward validation of a computer-scored test for the type-A coronary-prone behavior pattern. *Psychosomatic Medicine*, 33, 193–202.

Kanfer, F. II. (1970). Self-monitoring: Methodological limitations and clinical application. *Journal of Consulting and Clinical Psychology*, 35, 148–152.

Kazdin, A. E. (1974). Self-monitoring and behavior change. In M. J. Mahoney & C. E. Thoresen (Eds.), *Self-control: Power to the person.* Monterey, CA: Brooks/Cole.

Kenigsberg, D., Zyzanski, S. J., Jenkins, C. D., Wardwell, W. I., & Licciardello, A. T. (1974), The coronary prone behavior pattern in hospitalized patients with and without coronary heart disease. *Psychosomatic Medicine*, 36, 344–351.

Kolman, P. B., (1983). The value of group psychotherapy after myocardial infarction: A critical review. *Journal of Cardiac Rehabilitative Medicine*, 3, 360–366.

Krantz, D. S. (1980). Cognitive processes and recovery from heart attack: A review and theoretical analysis. *Journal of Human Stress*, 5, 29–38.

Langosch, W., Seer, P., Brodner, G., Kalinke, D., Kulick, B., Heim, F. (1982). Behavior therapy with coronary heart disease patients: Results of a comparative study. *Journal of Psychosomatic Research*, 26, 475–484.

MacDougall, J. M., & Dembrowski, T. (1979). The structured interview and questionnaire methods of assessing coronary-prone behavior in male and female college students. *Journal of Behavioral Medicine*, 2(1), 71–83.

Mahoney, J. J. (1977). Reflections on the cognitive learning trend in psychotherapy. *American Psychologist*, 32, 5–13.

Mahoney, M. J., & Arnkoff, D. B. (1978). Cognitive and self-control therapies. In A. E. Bergin & S. L. Garfield (Eds.). *Handbook of Psychotherapy and behavior Change.* New York: John Wiley & Sons.

Mahoney, M. J. & Arnkoff, D. B. (1979). Self management. In O. F. Pomerleau & J. P. Brady (Eds.), *Behavioral Medicine: Theory and Practice* (pp. 75–96). Baltimore: Williams & Wilkins.

Mayou, R., Forester, A., Williamson, R. (1978). Psychosocial adjustment in patients one year after myocardial infarction. *Journal of Psychosomatic Research*, 22, 447–453.

McNair, D. M., Lorr, M., & Droppleman, L. T. (1971).

Profile of mood states. San Diego: Educational and Industrial Testing Services.

Meichenbaum, D. (1974). *Cognitive behavior modification.* Morristown, NJ: General Learning Press.

Meichenbaum, D. (1975). A self-instructional approach to stress management: A proposal for stress inoculation training. In C. Spielberger & I. Sarason (Eds.), *Stress & Anxiety: Vol. I* (pp. 238–263). NY: Wiley.

Meichenbaum, D. (1977). *Cognitive behavior modification.* New York: Plenum.

Nelson, R. O. (1976). Self-monitoring: procedures and methodological issues. In J. O. Cone & R. P. Hawkins (Eds.), *Behavioral assessment: New directions in clinical psychology.* New York: Brunner/Mazel.

Nelson, R. O., Lupinski, D. P., & Black, J. L. (1976). The relative reactivity of external observations and self monitoring. *Behavior Therapy, 7,* 314–321.

Nicoletti, J. (1972). *Anxiety management training.* Unpublished doctoral dissertation, Colorado State University.

Norris, R. M. (1970). Coronary prognostic index for predicting survival after recovery from acute myocardial infarction. *Lancet, 140,* 485–487.

Pomerleau, O. V., & Brady, J. P. (1979). *Behavioral medicine: Theory and practice.* Baltimore: Williams & Wilkins.

Rahe, R. H., Ward, H. W., & Hayes, V. H. (1979). Brief group therapy in myocardial infarction rehabilitation: three to four-year follow-up of a controlled trial. *Psychosomatic Medicine, 41,* 229–241.

Razin, A. M. (1982). Psychosocial intervention in coronary artery disease: A review. *Psychosomatic Medicine, 44,* 363–387.

Rosenman, R. H., Friedman, M., & Strauss, R. (1970). Coronary heart disease in the western collaborative group study. *Journal of Chronic Disease, 23,* 173–190.

Rotter, J. B. (1975). Some problems and misconceptions related to the construct of internal versus external control of reinforcement. *Journal of Consulting and Clinical Psychology, 43*(1), 56–67.

Skinner, B. F. (1953). *Science and human behavior.* New York: Macmillan.

Spielberger, C. D., Gorsuch, R. L., & Lushene, R. E. (1970). *State-trait anxiety inventory.* Palo Alto CA: Consulting Psychologists Press.

Suinn, R. M. (1974). Behavior therapy for cardiac patients. *Behavior Therapy, 5,* 569–571.

Suinn, R. M. (1975). The cardiac stress management program for type-A patients. *Cardiac Rehabilitation, 5,* 13–15.

Suinn, R. M., & Bloom, L. J. (1978). Anxiety management training for pattern A behavior. *Journal of Behavioral Medicine, 1,* 25–35.

Thoresen, C. E., & Mahoney, M. J. (1974). *Behavioral self-control.* New York: Holt, Rinehart and Winston.

Wallston, B. S., Wallston, K. A., Kaplan, G. D., & Maides, S. A. (1976). Development and validation of the health locus of control scale. *Journal of Consulting and Clinical Psychology, 44*(4), 580–585.

Wrzesniewski, K. (1977). Anxiety and rehabilitation after myocardial infarction. *Psychosomatics, 27,* 41–46.

Chapter 13

Stress Management in Obstetrics and Gynecology

Christine T. Bradshaw

The role of stress in the etiology and maintenance of obstetrical and gynecological disorders and conditions has only recently begun to receive attention, and few firm conclusions have been reached. Even more foreign to this particular field are attempts at managing the stress associated with pregnancy, menstrual disorders, and other ob-gyn related problems, despite the fact that numerous practitioners and researchers have cited the need to do so and have suggested the positive impact it would have on the treatment of these conditions. Because the state of the art of stress management in obstetrics and gynecology is still in such an early stage of development, this chapter will, of necessity, focus more on what needs to be done than on what has been done. This approach might prove frustrating to those practitioners looking for tried-and-true methods to employ with their own patient population, but it offers an exciting challenge to those who would like to place themselves in the forefront of developing and testing the efficacy of new treatment modalities within their specialty.

The practice of obstetrics and gynecology is unique among medical specialities in the degree to which it is interwoven with the emotional life of its patients. Practitioners find themselves dealing with many of the most important milestones in a woman's life, including menarche, sexuality, family planning, pregnancy, pelvic operations, and menopause, and the practitioner is frequently looked upon as a "trusted significant other" (Burchell, 1978, p. 165). Obstetrical medicine, in particular, is not so much designed to treat complications as it is to enable the obstetrician to foresee potential problems and avert them (Crandon, 1979). Because stress interacts with the physiological functioning of the patient and can contribute to the development and maintenance of such conditions as menstrual disorders, sexual dysfunction, infertility, complications of pregnancy, and menopausal symptomatology, it is critical that the obstetrician–gynecologist be familiar with the assessment and treatment of stress as it relates to conditions falling within her or his specialty. Individuals in other fields such as psychology, psychiatry, clinical social work, and nursing who find their interactions with women patients centering around these concerns should also be aware of the contribution they can make to the well-being of these patients when they present themselves for treatment of stress-related ob–gyn conditions or disorders.

In conceptualizing the role of stress in ob–gyn related conditions, it is critical to note that stress is

192

not a unidirectional construct. One might initially think in terms of external, environmental factors that act as stressors, impact on the physiological and psychological functioning of the individual, and contribute to the development of ob–gyn complications and disorders, but one might overlook the role of the complications and disorders themselves as producers of stress that could contribute to the exacerbation or maintenance of symptoms. Thus, stress must be considered in terms of its circularity, as both a source and a product, both contributing to and resulting from the immediate medical condition presented by the patient (Patterson & Wilner, 1981; Reichlin et al., 1979).

THE ROLE OF STRESS IN PREGNANCY

Pregnancy has been described as a normal developmental or maturational crisis involving changes that challenge the adaptive capacity of the woman physiologically, psychologically, and socially (Carlson & Labarba, 1979; Ching, Gordon, & O'Mahoney, 1981). Thus, pregnancy itself constitutes a stressor, but one that is not perceived as uniformly stressful among women or for the same woman at different times in her life (Norbeck & Tilden, 1983). Women's reactions to pregnancy are individually determined by their life experiences and their characteristic modes of reacting (Chalmers, 1982), as well as by the overall balance between stresses and supports in their lives (Cohen, 1979).

Considerable attention has been paid to the role of maternal emotions in pregnancy, particularly as they relate to various complications of the pregnancy. Carlson and Labarba (1979) reviewed the literature on the role of maternal emotionality as a risk factor in infertility, habitual abortion, hyperemesis gravidarum, toxemia, labor difficulties, multiple complications, prematurity, stillbirth, and early infant behavior, and they concluded that the more methodologically sound studies supported the idea that "increased emotionality during pregnancy may predispose the expectant mother to various pregnancy and birth complications" (p. 368). These investigators identified the woman's anxiety as the single most discriminating factor for predicting complications, with intensity and duration of the emotional state being critical variables (McDonald, 1968). They suggested that continuation of the stress over a period of time affects reproduction via chronic overactivity of the adrenocortical system.

Other explorations of the role of emotional factors in pregnancy have focused on the specific impact of life-stress events. Gutnik and Moore (1983) pointed out that, using Holmes and Rahe's (1967) stress-rating data, the cumulative stress value of the changes likely to be associated with pregnancy represents a life-change value which predicts that 48% of individuals will undergo a major change in health. Fagley, Miller, and Sullivan (1982) noted that each successive month of pregnancy showed an increasingly greater number of life changes, with a small exception in the fourth month. Their overall stress coefficient was highest in the eighth month, and they suggested that stresses during this month should be carefully managed by the pregnant woman. Several researchers have sought to demonstrate a direct, positive relationship between the number of life-stress events experienced by women just before or during pregnancy and various complications of pregnancy, with mixed results. Hetzel, Breur, and Poidevin (1961) found a higher incidence of stressful life experiences for patients with prolonged vomiting and toxemia, but not prolonged labor, whereas Gorsuch and Key (1974) found that increased life stress in the second and third trimesters, but not the first, was associated with a variety of obstetrical complications. Georgas, Giakoumaki, Georgoulias, Koumandakis, and Kaskarelis (1984) also found high psychosocial stress during the 6 months prior to delivery to be positively related to obstetrical complications among a sample of Greek women.

Examining the relationship between stress and a single complication of pregnancy, Picone, Allen, Schramm, and Olsen (1982) found stress to be associated with low weight gain but not decreased caloric intake, and they suggested that stress might contribute to low weight gain by reducing the body's utilization of calories. The results of a study by Williams, Williams, Griswold, and Holmes (1975) indicated that the timing of delivery was not affected by the degree of life change during pregnancy or the 2 years prior to conception, but a study by Newton, Webster, Binu, Mabrey, and Phillips (1979) found that levels of psychosocial stress were particularly high in women who delivered prematurely. Thus, measures of the frequency of life-stress events have shown some relationship, albeit an inconsistent one, to various complications of pregnancy.

Some researchers have suggested that the impact of life-change events on the woman, or the subjective distress they create, is a better predictor than a simple measure of their frequency, but again the evidence is inconclusive. For example, the discovery by Rizzardo et al. (1982) that women with pregnancy complications reported not only more life events but also significantly more uncontrolled events led them to the conclusion that the quality of the events, or the women's perceptions of them, should be examined. However, when Newton and Hunt (1984) examined both the objective and the self-rated occurrence of major life events, they found that only the former was significantly associated with low birth weight and prematurity. Exposure to stress in the last trimester was especially likely to be related to low birth weight as the result of premature delivery.

The role of psychosocial assets (psychological or social factors that contribute to a woman's ability to adapt to her pregnancy) as mediators between the occurrence of stressful events and pregnancy complications has also been examined. Nuckolls, Cassell, and Kaplan (1972) found that women who had high life stress before and during pregnancy but possessed favorable psychosocial assets had only one-third the complication rate of women who were similarly stressed but who had poor psychosocial assets, and thus concluded that the expectant mother's perception of interpersonal support appeared to buffer the potential effects of numerous life changes. Norbeck and Tilden (1983) focused on the occurrence of negative life events in the 12 months preceding the mid-trimester of pregnancy and found that high life stress and low social support were significantly related to a wide variety of pregnancy complications and infant conditions.

In summary, it appears that a relationship between stress and pregnancy complications does exist, although the precise nature of the relationship is not fully understood, due to conflicting results from studies that differ in terms of construct definition, time and method of stress and pregnancy outcome measurement, and differences among samples studied. Although the pregnancy itself constitutes a stressor, the mother's experience of anxiety and the occurrence of external stressful life events also appear to have a negative impact on pregnancy outcome. The manner in which these factors interact is, at this time, however, inconclusive.

Research on Stress Management During Pregnancy and Childbirth

The rationale for psychological intervention during pregnancy and childbirth is succinctly stated by Gutnik and Moore: "As is the case with all illnesses, prevention or attentuation of problems is more effective and efficient for the physician, and in the patient's best interests. Pregnancy and child-birth offer . . . a unique opportunity to intervene before related life-events and changes can result in emotional and physical illness" (1983, p. 10). Unfortunately, many writers and practitioners have stated the need for such intervention, but few have specifically indicated how such intervention should be carried out. One of those who has is Bassoff (1983), who outlined a model for counseling the pregnant woman that has three foci: (a) facilitating personal reorganization, (b) promoting appropriate relationships, and (c) decreasing unwarranted stress. The first goal of the counselor is to encourage the woman's growth by helping her to experience and incorporate fully the natural processes of emotional and psychological reorganization and change that accompany pregnancy. The second goal is to strengthen the relationship of the expectant couple and the relationship of the mother-to-be to her own mother and to help her develop the skills needed to gain support from other relatives, friends, and community resources. The third goal is to assist her in avoiding unnecessary external stress and in handling those stresses that do occur. Bassoff recommended a multimodal treatment approach aimed at achieving these goals, including brief relationship therapy, building of communication skills, dreamwork, education, and social intervention, including referral to support groups as needed.

The vast majority of material related to intervention during pregnancy has focused specifically on the relief of the anxiety, stress, and pain associated with childbirth. The finding that stressful stimuli disrupt the electromyographic activity of the uterus suggests that intervention designed to reduce stress could have a positive effect on the birth process (Lederman, Lederman, Work, & McCann, 1978). In addition, psychological intervention could impact positively on the well-being of the child by decreasing the woman's need for medication during labor and delivery (Standley, Soule, & Copans, 1979).

Such intervention, termed *psychoprophylaxis,* or prepared childbirth, is not new (Dick-Read, 1944; Lamaze, 1958; Velvovsky, Platanov, Ploticher, & Shugom, 1960). Although the emphasis of intervention varies from method to method, four components are unusually included: (a) education regarding the processes of pregnancy, labor, and delivery; (b) training in muscle relaxation; (c) use of focused attention and breathing techniques; and (d) involvement of the husband as "coach" during labor and delivery (N. C. Beck, Geden, & Brouder, 1979, N. C. Beck & Siegel, 1980). Such procedures have been widely incorporated into obstetrical practice, and have been associated with decreased anxiety, improved attitudes, shorter labors, decreased use of medication and other obstetric interventions, decreased perception of pain, and better condition of the infant at birth (N. C. Beck & Hall, 1978). However, a comprehensive review of the literature by Beck and Siegel (1980) concerning the effectiveness of such procedures led the authors to conclude that the lack of internal validity evidenced by studies of the therapeutic effectiveness of these methods made cause-and-effect statements regarding treatment and outcome impossible. They suggested that the components be examined individually and in combination to determine their effects.

The idea of incorporating psychosomatic research relating to pain, anxiety, and stress reduction into the current approaches to preparing women for childbirth has been advocated by both Stevens (1976) and Beck and Siegel (1980). Stevens reviewed the use of systematic relaxation, cognitive control via dissociation and interference strategies, cognitive rehearsal, systematic desensitization, and the Hawthorne effect in reducing pain perception in controlled laboratory settings and encouraged the application of these findings to programs in prepared childbirth. Beck and Siegel (1980) viewed as particularly promising the use of various stress-inoculation techniques, particularly those developed by Meichenbaum and Turk (Meichenbaum, 1977; Meichenbaum & Turk, 1976; Turk, 1975, 1976) that involve the use of multiple cognitive strategies coupled with relaxation training to reduce stress and pain. They also recommended that the distraction technique currently utilized in psychoprophylactic training (breathing exercises or use of a focal point) be replaced by the more effective technique of restructuring the sensory experience of pain (Blitz & Dinnerstein, 1971; Chaves & Barber, 1974; Spanos, Horton, & Chaves, 1975). Finally, they suggested that treatment approaches demonstrated to be effective in the reduction of anxiety in other situations, such as systematic desensitization (Paul, 1966), modeling (Bandura, 1969), flooding (Boulougouris, Marks, & Marset, 1971), and reinforced practice (Leitenberg & Callahan, 1973), should be examined within the context of labor and delivery.

Only a few studies have been published that examine the use of these techniques as applied to the childbirth experience. Motivated by the finding that both the duration of labor and the perception of pain increased significantly with increasing levels of anxiety, Kondas and Scetnicka (1972) compared systematic desensitization with the psycho-prophylactic method and found systematic desensitization to be more powerful in reducing anxiety for pregnant women with high levels of situational fear. The duration of labor and the intensity of pain experienced were also significantly less in the systematic-desensitization group.

The effective use of biofeedback-assisted relaxation training for the relief of pain during childbirth was reported anecdotally by Frazier (1974), whose wife reported finding her delivery "very easy and almost a pleasant sensation as the waves of the labor passed over her" (p. 17). Gregg, Nesbit, and Frazier (1979) compared a group of women who had received biofeedback training with a group who had not (90% of all the women had received prepared childbirth training) and found that the biofeedback-trained patients used 4 to 10 times less medication than the untrained group and that the average duration of the first stage of labor for biofeedback-trained multiparous women was significantly shorter than for the untrained group. Although statistical comparison was not possible for the primigravidas, due to small sample size, the first stage of labor for the biofeedback group lasted only 4.9 hours, compared with 10.5 hours for the untrained patients. Gregg (1979) used biophysical monitoring with 10 women who had had previous premature deliveries and found evidence of maladaptive organ responses and tension. They were trained for 6 weeks or more in biofeedback techniques and all carried their babies to term. Conclusions drawn from this study are tentative, because no control group was involved, but results do suggest better than chance results worthy of additional investigation.

THE ROLE OF STRESS IN POSTPARTUM DEPRESSION

A pregnancy-related disorder that deserves attention because of the frequency with which it occurs is postpartum depression, which ranges from mild, transitory postpartum "blues," through nonpsychotic postpartum depression, to postpartum psychoses. Cutrona (1982), who has provided an excellent review of symptomatology and etiology, described postpartum psychoses as rare, affecting only one to two women per thousand deliveries, but highly disabling, often requiring hospitalization. Postpartum blues, on the other hand, which involve transitory symptoms of depression during the first week or so following delivery, affect 50% to 70% of women. Nonpsychotic postpartum depression is characterized by symptoms of anxiety and depression that persist from 2 weeks to a year postpartum and interfere to some extent with the woman's ability to function effectively. Between 3% and 33% of woman are affected, depending on the diagnostic criteria used.

Because it is not possible to refer individually to the wide range of studies relating to the etiology of these disorders within the limitations of this chapter, the reader is referred to the aforementioned review by Cutrona (1982) and to one by True-Soderstrom, Buckwalter, and Kerfoot (1983). Based on a review of four categories of causal factors—precipitating stressful events, causal social support, psychological predisposition, and physiological factors—Cutrona (1982) concluded that experimental studies supported the role of stressful events around the time of pregnancy and delivery, marital dissatisfaction and inadequate social support outside the marriage, and a history of prior psychiatric symptoms as all being of etiological significance in increasing the probability of nonpsychotic postpartum depression. Her suggestion that various cognitive characteristics of the woman might also predispose her to postpartum depression is supported by O'Hara, Rehm, and Campbell's (1983) finding that cognitive–behavioral measures that reflect depression proneness were significantly related to postpartum depression over and above the variance they shared with prepartum depression. Both Cutrona (1982) and True-Soderstrom et al. (1983), who reviewed psychosocial predicators, psychiatric history predictors, obstetrical factors, and hormonal and genetic factors, emphasized that single-factor models are too simplistic to explain the etiology of this disorder and that more complex multiple-causation hypotheses that take into account the interaction of environmental, psychological, and physiological variables need to be explored.

Research on Stress Management in Postpartum Depression

Braverman and Roux found that seven questions taken from their study questionnaire would have accurately predicted 85% of the women who developed postpartum depression, and they suggested that these questions be included as part of a routine written prenatal history to be completed by the patient. The questions are:

1. Do you feel often that your husband (boyfriend) does not love you?
2. Can you honestly say at this time that you really do not desire to have a child?
3. Do you have marital problems?
4. Was your pregnancy unplanned (accidental)?
5. Did you become very depressed or extremely nervous in the period following the birth of your last child?
6. Are you single or separated?
7. Do you more or less regret that you are pregnant? (1978, p. 732).

Cutrona's (1982) conclusions regarding the etiology of postpartum depression indicate that the patient should also be questioned regarding stressful events in her life during pregnancy and delivery, the adequacy of her support systems inside and outside of the home, and any history of previous psychiatric symptoms. Based on their finding that level of depression during pregnancy was the best predictor of postpartum depression level, O'Hara, Rehm, and Campbell (1982) suggested that patients be screened periodically during pregnancy with the Beck Depression Inventory (A. T. Beck, Ward, Mendelson, Mock, & Erbaugh, 1961) or a similar measure. Garvey and Tollefson (1984) recommended that patients identified as at risk be counseled about the signs and symptoms of depression and be scheduled for biweekly visits between the 2nd and 6th postpartum weeks for evaluation of depression.

Several preventive measures for high-risk patients have been outlined by Braverman and Roux (1978). *First,* professionals (obstetrician, nurses, family physician, social work staff, etc.) should provide maximal emotional and physical support throughout pregnancy, delivery, and postpartum. *Second,* they should encourage and assist the patient to obtain maximal support from family, friends, and other members of her support network. *Third,* those patients who regret their pregnancies should discuss the possibility of abortion, and psychological consultation should be provided if it is indicated. *Fourth,* the professional should discuss with the husband, when it is needed, the importance of the wife's feeling loved and secure. Meetings with both husband and wife might also be needed to clarify feelings and improve communication and attitudes. *Fifth,* referrals for marriage counseling or psychotherapy during pregnancy should be made when the need is indicated. O'Hara et al. (1983) suggested that support groups for new mothers at high risk for depression might be helpful, and Gutnik and Moore (1983) recommended that the physician provide a monthly discussion period for all patients due to deliver in the following month so that he or she can provide them with information regarding the feelings and stresses that accompany the arrival of the baby and so that the patients can receive peer confirmation and support from the group.

MENSTRUAL CYCLE DISORDERS

The menstrual cycle itself has traditionally been viewed as a stressful event in the lives of women, involving physiological, affective, cognitive, and behavioral changes that include over 150 associated symptoms, although an alternate view holds that the effects of the menstrual cycle have been overrated and that supposed cyclic changes are attributable to menstrual folklore, mythology, and cultural stereotype (Dalton, 1964, 1969, 1977; Jensen, 1982; Paige, 1971, 1973; Parlee, 1974). In an effort to understand the basis of reported changes associated with the menstrual cycle, a wide range of causative factors has been explored including hormonal changes; the influence of historical and developmental factors such as cultural expectations; personality factors, including acceptance of the female role; external environmental factors such as life-change events; psychiatric illness; and poor diet, vitamin or mineral deficiencies, incorrect posture, lack of exercise, and other general health problems. A precise relationship between any particular set of symptoms and causative factors has not been defined, and it seems likely that differing variables play different roles in particular groups of symptoms (Sommer, 1978). The symptom groups to be reviewed in this chapter include functional amenorrhea, or the absence of menstruation not due to organic causes; primary dysmenorrhea, or painful menstruation not due to organic causes; and premenstrual syndrome, (PMS), which has received the preponderance of attention and study in the past few years.

Functional Amenorrhea

The diagnosis of functional amenorrhea is made when organic conditions such as hypopituitarism, ovarian agenesis, intrauterine synechiae, vilifying

tumors, or other known causes such as weight loss have been ruled out (Osofsky & Fisher, 1967; Yaginuma, 1979). Attempts to relate various psychological variables to the occurrence of amenorrhea have been inconclusive. After reviewing a number of these studies (Loftus, 1962; Menz, 1953; Piotrowski, 1962; Rakoff, 1962; Reifenstein, 1946; Sturgis et al. 1962), Osofky and Fisher concluded that "even when possible psychological relationships have been reported, it has been difficult to rule out the possibility that the already present menstrual disturbance preceded or at least intensified the reported 'causative' factors". (1967, p. 16). Yaginuma (1979) examined the relationship between external stressors such as final examinations, change of dwelling or occupation, and death of a close relative and suggested that the stress initially led to anovulatory cycles that were amenable to treatment with ovulation-inducing drugs such as Clomid, but that, if the anovulation were allowed to continue for more than a year or so, the amenorrhea became more refractory to treatment because of declining ovarian function and reduced estrogen secretion. He advocated, therefore, that stress amenorrhea be diagnosed and treated as early as possible.

Primary Dysmenorrhea

The diagnosis of primary dysmenorrhea or painful menstruation, which can involve either short episodes of acute cramplike pains or prolonged dull aching pains throughout the body, sometimes accompanied by nausea, headache, irritability, and gastrointestinal disturbances, is made in the absence of gross pathological conditions in the pelvic organs (Chesney & Tasto, 1975). Dalton (1969) proposed a distinction between two types of dysmenorrhea, spasmodic and congestive. Spasmodic dysmenorrhea, related to an excess of progesterone over estrogen, begins during the first day or two of the menstrual period, involves acute pain limited to the back, inner sides of the thighs, and lower abdomen, and can be accompanied by nausea, diarrhea, vomiting, and fainting. Congestive dysmenorrhea, a variation of the premenstrual syndrome related to a relative excess of estrogen over progesterone, occurs for several days preceding menstruation and is characterized by feelings of increasing heaviness; dull, aching pains in the lower abdomen; edema; stiffness in muscles and joints; constipation; irritability; depression; and lethargy. Nelson, Sigmon, Amodei, and Jarrett

(1984) contended, however, that this distinction has not been substantiated by etiological factors (Webster, 1978) or differential response to treatments, although evidence is divided on the latter point (Chesney & Tasto, 1975; Cox, 1977; Quillen & Denney, 1982).

Dysmenorrhea is the most common gynecologic disorder, with reports of menstrual pain ranging between 10% and 90% of women in differing populations. This condition has traditionally been viewed as being of psychogenic origin, although cervical factors, lesions within the sacral nerves, endocrine factors, hypercontractility and uterine blood flow, the role of prostaglandins, and various psychosocial factors have also been examined as to their etiological significance (Brown, 1982). Paulson and Wood (1966) suggested that a combined psychological and physiological explanation was the most appropriate.

Aberger, Denney, and Hutchings (1983) tested the commonly accepted view that dysmenorrheic women are more sensitive to pain and less adequate in coping with pain than nondysmenorrheic women, using response to a muscle ischemia procedure as their measure of pain responsivity. They found no differences between the two groups of women on pain threshold, pain tolerance, or self-reported pain, or in their use of cognitive or behavioral coping strategies. Examining the hypothesis of greater stress responsivity among dymenorrheic women who are menstruating, Plante and Denney (1984) found that they differed from nondysmenorrheic women on only one physiological measure, that of showing a higher pulse rate during a stressful laboratory task. In addition, dysmenorrheic status was not associated with retrospective self-reports of anxiety, depression, or hostility during confrontation with the stressful laboratory tasks. Extending the study of external stressors to dysmenorrhea outside the laboratory, Jordan and Meckler (1982) examined the relationship of dysmenorrhea to life-change events and social support, predicting a positive relationship between levels of life change and the severity of dysmenorrhea experienced by college women when the level of social supports was low but no relationship between life change and dysmenorrhea when the level of social supports was high. They found small but significant correlations between life change and dysmenorrhea; however, social support did not consistently act as an intervening variable in the relationship between life change and dysmenorrhea, except for the presence of a confidant within an individual's support network.

A review of treatments for dysmenorrhea by Brown (1982) includes various surgical and pharmacologic approaches, as well as recommendations regarding use of heat, exercise, hygiene, nutrition, simple reassurance, and change in environment, although none of these has been demonstrated as completely effective. Psychophysiologic approaches to treatment have included the use of biofeedback, autogenic training, progressive muscle relaxation, systematic desensitization, and psychotherapy. Cerutti, Foresti, Ferraro, Crema, and Grazioli (1979) used autogenic training (a form of relaxation training) for the relief of dysmenorrhea in girls between 15 and 16 years of age. They found that 36% of the girls with severe menstrual pain showed a total remission and 61% had a definite improvement, while 90% of those with light dysmenorrhea demonstrated total remission. In a controlled study that combined autogenics and biofeedback from a vaginal thermometer, a significant reduction in dysmenorrhea was obtained (Heczey, 1977). Fleischauer (1977) reported decreased menstrual pain in college women who used Lamaze techniques designed for the first stage of labor. Mullen (1968, 1971) reported successfully treating a 37-year-old woman who had experienced severe menstrual cramping for 21 years, as well as a group of five college students who had suffered from dysmenorrhea for 7-10 years, using systematic desensitization involving anxiety hierarchies related to the subjects' menstrual cycles. Tasto and Chesney (1974) obtained a significant reduction in dysmenorrhea with seven college students trained to use muscle relaxation accompanied by the imagining of scenes associated with the reduction of menstrual pain. In a subsequent study, Chesney and Tasto (1975) differentiated women experiencing congestive dysmenorrhea from those experiencing spasmodic dysmenorrhea. They found that treatment involving deep-muscle relaxation in conjunction with scenes associated with the onset of menstruation was highly effective in reducing reported symptomatology with the spasmodic, but not with the congestive, form of dysmenorrhea. However, differential treatment effects were not replicated by Cox (1977) or Quillen and Denney (1982).

THE PREMENSTRUAL SYNDROME

Reports regarding the prevalence of PMS vary widely. Hargrove and Abraham (1983) identified

50% of 1,395 American gynecologic patients not using hormonal contraception as experiencing PMS. Of, 1,083 Swedish women screened for PMS, 2% to 3% reported severe or distressing premenstrual symptoms, 70% reported mild or moderate emotional and physical changes, and 92% reported at least one premenstrual change (Andersch, 1980; Sanders, Warner, Backstrom, & Bancroft, 1983). Chakmakjian (1983) reported a prevalence rate of 20% to 40%, with 5% to 10% of women experiencing symptoms severe enough to disrupt their lives. Reid and Yen (1981) felt the incidence was unclear because of the fact that women with PMS are more likely than those without it to enter studies.

Probably the major reason for difficulty in identifying PMS sufferers, however, is the fact that there is no generally agreed upon definition of the premenstrual syndrome. Sampson and Prescott defined PMS as "a global term which implies changes in mood, behavior, and physical symptoms in relation to the menstrual cycle, usually with an increase in the intensity of symptoms premenstrually and a diminution in intensity with the onset of menstruation" (1981, p. 399). The most commonly reported emotional symptoms are tension, anxiety, depression, irritability, and hostility. Included among the somatic complaints are backache, headache, edema, breast tenderness, and abdominal bloating. Frequently reported behavioral changes include crying spells, avoidance of social contact, change in work habits, and increased tendency to pick fights, particularly with a spouse or children (Abplanalp, 1983b). The frequency, severity, and range of symptoms vary not only among women, but also within the same woman from cycle to cycle, and the factors that influence this variability are not clear (Abplanalp, 1983a, 1983b). Sampson and Prescott (1981) suggested that the diagnosis of PMS could actually encompass several different subgroups of women, each with a different cluster of symptoms that show a differential response to treatment approaches.

Abplanalp (1983b) raised the question whether the severe, disabling symptoms reported by a small percentage of women represent one end of a continuum that includes the milder forms of the same symptoms that many women report. Attempting to address this issue, Sanders et al. (1983) compared women who had sought treatment for PMS with two groups of volunteers, those reporting PMS symptoms and those not reporting them. Self-ratings of "well-being" for all three groups reached their

maximum in the late follicular phase of the menstrual cycle (the time near ovulation), declining throughout the luteal, or second half, of the cycle. "Physical distress" increased for all three groups during the second half, reaching a maximum in the late luteal phase. The two PMS groups showed similar patterns of symptomatology, although women undergoing treatment reported more intense symptoms that began earlier in the cycle (during the early luteal phase). Volunteers with no PMS symptoms demonstrated a very slight and nonsignificant pattern of well-being across cycle phases and a significant but mild pattern of physical symptoms, particularly breast tenderness. Based on their findings, these researchers were unable to reach a conclusion as to whether physical and emotional symptoms of PMS acted separately or were interdependent with each other and perhaps with other unidentified cyclical patterns, nor could they determine whether those women who experience cyclical mood change represent one extremity of a continuum of PMS symptomatology or whether their hormonal cycles are physiologically abnormal.

Despite the fact that the cause or causes of PMS have been the focus of considerable study, its etiology remains elusive, in part because of the broad range of symptoms associated with it. Because PMS is characterized by both physical and psychological symptomatology, both physical and psychological factors have been implicated in its etiology (Osborn, 1981). Following an extensive review of biochemical factors posited as contributing to the pathophysiology of PMS, including estrogen excess or progesterone deficiency, vitamin deficiency, hypoglycemia, endogenous hormone allergy, fluid retention, and neurointermediate lobe peptides, Reid and Yen (1981) concluded that no single hypothesis had adequately explained the range of symptoms composing the premenstrual syndrome. Focusing on the emotional symptomatology of PMS, Clare (1983) concluded that a multifactorial model of causation was required. Such a model "assumes an interaction between hormonal and hormonally related changes in the premenstruum, the basic personality, including perhaps the woman's basic attitude to and threshold for pain and other discomforts, and social dissatisfactions, adverse life circumstances, and interpersonal stresses" (p. 134). Abplanalp (1983b) noted, however, that the multifactorial approach to PMS is still in its infancy.

Considerable attention has been paid to the role of attribution and social expectations as they relate to the manifestation of PMS symptomatology

(Abplanalp, 1983a; Brattesani & Silverthorne, 1978; Osborn, 1981; Parlee, 1973; Ruble, 1977; Sommer, 1973; Vila & Beech, 1980). Osborn (1981) suggested that a woman might report PMS symptoms during the premenstruum either because she expects to be in distress or because she attributes physical and mental discomforts occurring during that time to the menstrual cycle. Sommer (1973) and Parlee (1974) posited a social-expectations theory of menstrual symptomatology based on discrepancies between women's retrospective self-reports and concurrent assessment of their symptoms.

To test these ideas, Vila and Beech (1980) compared women's self assessments of mood during the intermenstrual and premenstrual phases of their cycles and found that they reported clear mood changes during the two phases of their cycle when reporting retrospectively but not when concurrent assessment was made during these phases under conditions that disguised the purpose of the study. They agreed with Koeske and Koeske (1975) that mood changes associated with the menstrual cycle result from an interaction between biological changes and attributional processes, and that both are necessary to produce such change. Ruble (1977) studied a group of women at 1 week prior to the onset of their menstrual periods and led some to believe, based on various physiological tests, that menstruation would begin in 1 or 2 days, while convincing others that their periods were not due for 7 to 10 days. They found that women who believed they were premenstrual reported experiencing a significantly higher degree of several physical symptoms, including water retention, pain, and change in eating habits. Interestingly, ratings of negative affect did not approach significance. Other studies using objective measures of cognitive and perceptual motor behavior have frequently not identified the types of menstrual cycle fluctuations found in studies using women's self-reports (Sommer, 1973).

The role of stressful life events in PMS has also been explored. Wilcoxon, Schraeder, and Sherif (1976) found the experience of stressful events to be related to the psychological symptom of negative mood but not to the physical symptoms of pain and water retention. Measuring both desirable and undesirable life changes, however, Siegel, Johnson, and Sarason (1979) found that undesirable life changes significantly predicted menstrual discomfort, including pain and water retention. Speculating on the nature of this relationship, they

suggested that stress might break down the woman's ability to cope physically and psychologically with menstruation. Women undergoing the stress of life changes might experience a deteriorated physical condition leading to the experience of greater discomfort during menstruation, or the stress of adapting to life changes might cause women to be less psychologically capable of coping with discomfort, so that symptoms are perceived as especially troublesome. Woods, Dery, and Most (1982) focused on stressful life events related to reproductive and general health status in an effort to determine whether they were responsible for more of the variance in PMS than other life events. They found that, when health-related events were controlled, other stressful events had a diminished effect on symptoms. Summarizing the role of psychological factors in the development of PMS, Reid and Yen (1981) concluded that, although it seems likely that they modulate an individual's interpretation or experience of premenstrual symptoms, there is little evidence to support psychological factors as being solely responsible for the range of PMS symptomatology. Both biological and psychosocial factors appear to be significant contributors to the premenstrual syndrome, although the precise nature of their interaction is still not clearly understood.

Assessment of PMS

Because of the frequency with which patients experiencing symptoms of PMS are encountered in gynecologic practice (Hargrove & Abraham, 1982) and the possibility that PMS reflects abnormal luteal function (Abraham, Elsner, & Lucas, 1978; Backstrom & Carstensen, 1974; Hargrove & Abraham, 1979), Hargrove and Abraham (1983) recommended that every premenopausal gynecologic patient be screened for PMS. The instrument most widely used in the assessment of menstrual symptomatology has been the Menstrual Distress Questionnaire (Moos, 1977), a self-rating scale that lists 47 symptoms, each rated on a 6-point scale. A separate score is obtained for each of eight symptom clusters reflecting empirically correlated symptoms: pain, concentration, behavioral change, autonomic reaction, water retention, negative affect, arousal, and control. A modified version of this questionnaire has been developed by Clare and Wiggins (1979) for those desiring a briefer assessment tool to provide similar information. The

Premenstrual Mood Index (O'Brien, Craven, Selby, & Symonds, 1979) allows assessment of symptom severity along a 10-cm line.

Once the initial assessment has taken place and potential PMS patients have been identified, Abplanalp (1983a) recommended a careful psychologic and, if indicated, physical, diagnostic workup including a complete menstrual history and a history of premenstrual problems. Careful descriptions of symptoms and analyses of their severity, timing, and effect on the patient's daily life are important. The patient should be asked to keep a daily diary of symptoms for at least one complete cycle, with separate ratings of different symptom groups, as differing patterns of symptoms could require differing treatments. In addition, the patient should note daily stresses and strains that might cause fluctuations in symptomatology that are not directly related to the menstrual cycle (Sampson & Prescott, 1981).

Treatment of PMS

It has been suggested that the assessment process itself can be therapeutic for the PMS sufferer because it helps her to realize that her complaints are being taken seriously (Abplanalp, 1983a). Unfortunately, the clinician has little firm guidance in the treatment of PMS beyond that point, as the various therapies applied to the treatment of this disorder have yielded conflicting results in terms of their efficacy. This is true, in part, because "treatments have by and large been indiscriminately applied to a heterogeneous collection of premenstrual symptoms despite the growing evidence that the premenstrual syndrome is not uniform but is composed of a number of distinct, though related symptom clusters or complexes" (Clare, 1979, p. 578). In addition, treatments have been based on an underlying idea of the etiology of PMS, and, because its etiology is still uncertain, it is reasonable to expect that no single treatment would be universally effective (Chakmakjian, 1983; Osborn, 1981).

Treatments for PMS have included the use of sex steroid hormones (natural and synthetic progesterones, estrogens, androgens, and oral contraceptives), a prolactin inhibitor (bromocriptine), pyridoxine, nutritional supplements (especially vitamin B_6), diruretics, antianxiety agents, antidepressants, dietary changes, (less refined sugar, table salt, and processed foods), exercise, relaxation, and psychotherapy (Abplanalp,

1983a; Chakmakjian, 1983). These are often applied on a trial-and-error basis, because it is not known which symptoms in which patient will respond to which treatments. This individualized approach to treatment is necessary, in part, because no treatment has unequivocally withstood the test of double-blind controlled trials (Abplanalp, 1983a; Steiner & Carroll, 1977). Reported successes in treatment have often been the result of uncontrolled studies or the high rate of placebo response encountered in this disorder (Jordheim, 1972; Mattson & Schoultz, 1974; Sampson, 1979; Sampson & Prescott, 1981). Abplanalp (1983a) noted that clinicians have, in general, been more successful in treating the symptoms that appear to be directly related to fluid retention than in treating the affective components such as severe depression, uncontrollable irritability, and extreme hostility that characterize severe PMS.

Chakmakjian (1983) outlined a treatment regimen for PMS that includes counseling the patient and her family and giving them support; and prescribing vitamin B_6 for patients with moderate to severe symptoms, progesterone suppositories for those who complain primarily of irritability, small doses of estrogen during the luteal phase of the cycle to treat depression, bromocriptine for breast tenderness, and diruretics for edema. Dunlavy (1983) suggested several nonpharmacologic therapies, including encouraging the minimization of stress during the premenstruum; use of general health measures such as increased exercise, reduction of alcohol and smoking, loss of excess weight, and regular meals with less refined sugar; and biofeedback and relaxation techniques for premenstrual headaches, tension, and irritability. Brattesani and Silverthorne (1978) suggested that relatively permanent changes in attitude toward menstruation would bring about changes in the experiences of menstrual symptoms. In light of the role of expectation and attribution in the manifestation of PMS symptomatology, it also seems reasonable that the cognitive therapies could prove useful as treatment modalities, and their effectiveness should be tested in future research.

A PROPOSED PROGRAM FOR ASSESSMENT OF STRESS IN OB–GYN PATIENTS

The role of stress in the development and maintenance of the obstetrical complications and gynecologic disorders reviewed here has been shown to be twofold; that is, stressogenic events contribute to these problems, and the problems themselves create stress within the lives of the patients attempting to deal with them. The literature has demonstrated that professionals who deal with ob–gyn patients endorse the importance of prospectively identifying the patient experiencing stress that might contribute to the development of complications of pregnancy, labor, delivery, postpartum depression, or various menstrual disorders and of identifying the patient who is experiencing increased stress in her life as a result of her conditions, with the goal of designing interventions to help the patient alleviate the stress and thus avoid its negative effects on her health or the health of her unborn child. Unfortunately, the assessment and management of stress is rarely carried out in any systematic fashion with ob-gyn patients. The proposed ''package'' of assessment and treatment modalities suggested here is one that could be integrated into any group practice, and, with some minor modifications, could also be utilized by the individual practitioner.

The first issue that needs to be addressed is: Who should be assessed? Patients who have been determined, on the basis of medical examination, to be at risk for the development of pregnancy or menstrual-related disorders might receive additional attention in terms of their psychological needs as related to these conditions, but Jones (1978) recommended that screening should also include patients identified by medical exam as free of obvious medical symptomatology, to allow the detection of potential problems in patients otherwise presumed to be free of risk. Because many patients do not spontaneously volunteer information about anxieties and stressful events in their lives that might affect health, it becomes the responsibility of the practitioner to provide the opportunity for such information to be made known in an open and accepting atmosphere. Therefore, each patient should receive, at minimum, a brief initial assessment of the existence and role of stress in her life, as it might relate to her obstetrical or gynecological health. This can be handled simply and matter-of-factly as part of the history-taking procedure by explaining that worries and stressful events can play a part in the development of many health-related problems and asking the patient whether there is anything going on in her life, at home or at work, within herself or her relationships with others, that might be causing her any concern. If the patient is being seen for a particular physical problem, rather than for a routine checkup, the

professional should also ask whether the condition itself presents any worries or problems in her daily living and explain that the stress of having the condition can create problems that tend to maintain or even worsen the condition. It is critical during these discussions that the interdependence of stress and physical health be emphasized and that any implication that the physical condition is not real or is ''all in her head'' be avoided.

The second issue that the practitioner needs to determine is: Who conducts the assessment? This depends on the size of the practice; the training, abilities, and inclinations of the staff; and the extent to which the patient is assessed. In most cases, the initial assessment question just described should preferably be asked by the physician. The patient views the physician as the primary caregiver and often has considerable investment in this relationship. If the initial questioning about the role of stress in the patient's life is relegated to adjunctive personnel, the patient might feel that the matter is of little importance or that the physician is not concerned about such psychological matters in the same way she or he is about purely physical concerns. On the other hand, if history taking is routinely handled by a nurse or other personnel, this individual might also inquire about stress factors in the patient's life. However, the physician should then follow up this information in the same way he or she would follow up on physical concerns reported by the patient.

Once the physician has identified the fact that stress factors are operating in the patient's life that might be related to her health, or that a presenting condition is creating undue stress for the patient, she or he must determine whether to follow up personally with a more intensive assessment or to refer the patient to a mental health professional for additional assessment and, if indicated, treatment. Many physicians feel they have neither the time nor the training to pursue such assessment and treatment further, and they prefer to refer the patient to a psychologist, a psychiatrist, a clinical social worker, or a psychiatric nurse. Again, such referral should be presented to the patient matter-of-factly as part of the physician's routine practice so that the patient is less likely to feel she is being shunted aside and will be forgotten by the physician. It is imperative that it be clear to the patient that the physician and the professional who is handling assessment and treatment of stress are working in close cooperation with each other. The patient should understand that the assessment and treatment, if needed, that are provided by the mental health professional are a part of the total health care being provided for her. The message to the patient should be that the stress factors operating in her life are viewed as being on a par with purely physiological factors, and they deserve equal attention from a professional qualified to deal with them.

Ideally, the mental health professional to whom referral is made should function as a member of a multidisciplinary team within a particular practice. The mental health professional may be a full-time partner in a large group practice or may be hired to come to the office on a part-time basis for small-group or individual practices. Such an arrangement emphasizes to the patient that assessment and treatment of stress are, indeed, a regular part of the physician's treatment goals, and it makes it less likely that the patient who is wary of psychologically oriented treatment will feel she has a ''serious mental disorder.'' If such an arrangement is not possible and referral to a source outside the practice must be made, regular consultation between the physician and the mental health provider should take place, and the patient should be made aware that such a collaborative relationship exists. (Horsley, 1972; Pion, Wetzel, Montgomery, & Pion, 1978; Tourkow, 1979).

The third issue to be considered is: When should assessment of stress factors take place? Ideally, it should begin during the initial contact with the patient, as part of the routine medical assessment, and should continue as an ongoing part of treatment and follow-up. Again, the patient should perceive that this is a regular part of routine care and that she is not being singled out because the physician feels her physical condition is simply a reflection of some type of emotional problem. If such assessment has not occurred at the beginning of the physician–patient contact, it should be carried out when the patient presents a particular complaint, such as amenorrhea, in which the role of stress has been demonstrated or, in the case of pregnancy, at the first prenatal visit (Chalmers, 1982; Horsley, 1972).

Once the need for more intensive assessment of stress factors has been determined, the final issue that must be addressed is: What is to be assessed, and how should the assessment be carried out? At the most basic level, the clinician must identify the kinds, severity, and timing of current and recent stresses, together with the resources at the patient's disposal, either personal or interpersonal, for coping with such stresses, and her ability to make use of such resources in dealing with stress (Cohen, 1979; Edlund, 1982; Williamson & English, 1981).

A primary area of focus is the assessment of stressful events in the life of the patient, as the presence of recent and current stressful events has been found to be associated with a broad range of obstetrical complications and gynecological disorders (see, for example, Barnett, Hanna & Parker, 1983; Cutrona, 1982; Gorsuch and Key, 1974; Paykel, Emms, Fletcher, & Rassaby, 1980). Such events could involve dramatic upheavals in the patient's life, such as the death of a close relative or friend, divorce, loss of a job, or a move to a new location. They could be of a more chronic nature such as inadequate housing, ongoing financial difficulties, or a chronic health problem in the patient or a family member. Or they could reflect the accumulation of daily hassles, minor events that seem to be of little consequence but that can create significant stress (Kanner, Coyne, Schaefer, & Lazarus, 1981; Monroe, 1983). The literature suggests that it is important to determine not only the objective occurrence of these events but also the patient's perception of their stressfulness, as individuals vary in the way they perceive various stressors and in their ability to cope with them.

Because cognitive factors can play a significant role in the patient's perception and handling of stressful events, assessment of such factors as the patient's attributional style and locus of control should be included. The role of attribution and social expectations in the manifestation of PMS symptomatology has been reviewed previously in this chapter. In addition, Cutrona (1982) and O'Hara (1980) found that women who made depressive causal attributions before delivery were more likely to become depressed following the stress of childbirth. Hayworth et al., (1980) reported that patients with an external locus of control were more likely to develop postpartum depression. Scott-Palmer and Skevington (1981) found that women who believed themselves to be in personal control of their lives experienced significantly shorter labors than those believing in the uncontrollability of events. Thus, it appears that both the attributions patients make about various experiences in their lives and the degree to which they feel in control of their lives have an impact on the way they respond to significant obstetrical and gynecological events and are therefore important foci of a total assessment.

The patient's ability to cope with stress has been shown to depend, in part, on the strength of her supportive relationships. Accordingly, her perceived need for support from others and the availability of support from those around her, including her ability to elicit and make use of available support, should be addressed during the assessment. Of particular concern is her relationship with her husband, if she is married. Barnett, Hanna, and Parker (1983) indicated that serious marital disharmony has a negative effect on the woman's ability to adapt to pregnancy and the maternal role, and Horsley (1972) emphasized the critical role of the total economic, emotional, and physical support given the wife by her husband during pregnancy. Cutrona (1982) suggested that the woman in a tumultuous or nonsupportive marriage appears to be at especially high risk for postpartum depression, whereas an exceptionally good relationship could prevent depressive reactions, even when circumstances might otherwise predispose her to its development. Horsley (1972) suggested that the relationship between the patient and her mother was an important area for exploration during pregnancy, and Jordan and Meckler (1982) found the existence of a confidant to be important in determining whether college-age women experienced dysmenorrhea.

Finally, some assessment of previous psychiatric symptomatology should be included. Cutrona (1982) noted that a history of affective symptoms was an especially good predictor of postpartum depression. Paykel et al., (1980) reported that women with a history of psychiatric symptoms were at increased risk for postpartum depression whether or not they experienced stressful events around the time of childbirth, although women who had previous psychiatric symptoms and experienced stress during pregnancy were the most likely to become depressed. Women with a previous history of depression, especially postpartum depression following an earlier pregnancy, were found by Garvey and Tollefson (1984) to have a much greater incidence of postpartum depression.

Assessment Instruments

Assessment of the areas described may be covered in a verbal interview, although such a procedure might prove very time consuming. A number of written instruments used in ob–gyn stress research may be used as part of the assessment process. These can be given to the patient to complete, with a thorough explanation of their purpose. Much of the scoring can be done by a nonprofessional, allowing the professional to make use of his or her time to interpret the findings and verbally follow up identified trouble spots with the patient. A variety of assessment instruments will be reviewed, so that those best meeting the needs of a particular patient and the needs of the individual conducting the assessment can be chosen. As it is not possible to describe each instrument in detail in this chapter, the reader is referred to cited references for more in-depth descriptions.

Several instruments have been developed for the assessment of stressful life events. One of the most frequently used has been the Social Readjustment Rating Scale (Holmes & Rahe, 1967; Rahe, Ryman, & Ward, 1980), which measures the occurrence of stressful events and assigns them a point value based on the amount of life change and readjustment required for an individual to cope with each of the 42 life-change events. The Life Experiences Survey developed by Sarason, Johnson, & Siegel (1978) allows for the separate assessment of positive and negative life experiences, as well as individualized ratings of the impact of events, thus taking into account the patient's own perception of the event. The Impact of Event Scale (Horowitz, Wilner, & Alvarez (1979) provides a subjective measure of the stressfulness of a current specific event and might prove useful in assessing the impact of a stressful obstetrical or gynecological condition on the patient's life, and in measuring the impact of other events possibly related to the patient's condition. Barnett et al. (1983) developed separate life-events scales for primiparous and multiparous women, using high-ranking items from existing general life-event scales and items relevant only to pregnant women. Both the frequency of each life event and the degree of resultant distress are assessed with this scale. The developers of this scale found which approximately one-third of the high-rating items on the scales were pregnancy related, a result that suggests that this scale would be useful for assessing the perceived stressfulness of the pregnancy itself, as well as the stressfulness of more general life events.

In addition to assessing the impact of major life events, the clinician might also wish to examine the role of accumulated minor events occurring in daily life by examining daily hassles (negative events) and uplifts (positive events) in the patient's life (Kanner et al., 1981; Monroe, 1983). Because social supports appear to play a mediating role in the patient's reaction to stressful events, the assessor might want to make use of the Social Adjustment Scale (Weissmann & Bothwell, 1976), which examines role functioning in the areas of work, social and leisure time, the extended family, marital and parental relationships, and the family unit. The patient's skill in eliciting social reinforcers can be assessed via the Interpersonal Events Schedule (Youngren & Lewinsohn, 1980).

Measurement of certain aspects of the patient's cognitive style might also be appropriate. The Locus of Control scale (Rotter, 1966) measures the patient's belief in the degree to which she controls what happens to her, versus the degree to which she perceives her life to be controlled by external forces beyond her control. The Attributional Style Questionnaire (Seligman, Abramson, Semmel, & Von Baeyer, 1979) measures attributional constructs related to the reformulated learned-helplessness model of depression. Finally, as depression and anxiety are frequently related to the occurrence of stressogenic events, the Beck Depression Inventory (A. T. Beck et al., 1961) and the State-Trait Anxiety Inventory (Spielberger, Gorsuch, & Lushene, 1970) can prove simple and useful assessment tools.

As stated previously, pregnancy and menstruation can, in and of themselves, create stress in the woman's life. To assess the stressfulness of pregnancy, Standley et al. (1979) developed a structured interview that, when rated, provides seven prenatal anxiety measures related to general pregnancy concerns, physical aspects of pregnancy, the fetus, childbirth, child care, infant feeding, and psychiatric symptoms such as unexplained insomnia, fearfulness, strange ideas, and racing thoughts. The Adaptive Potential for Pregnancy questionnaire, or TAPP (Nuckolls et al., 1972) measures the women's psychosocial assets in relationship to pregnancy and thus can provide useful information about her ability to cope with its stresses. The questionnaire measures her feelings or perceptions about herself, her pregnancy, and her overall life situation, including her relationship with her husband, her extended family, and her community. A third measure that has been developed to uncover stress factors related to pregnancy is Horsley's (1972) Pregnancy Assessment Record.

The most frequently used measure of menstrual symptomatology is the Menstrual Distress Questionnaire (Moos, 1968), described previously in this chapter. This measure elicits information about an entire cycle and indicates which symptoms are experienced at various times during the cycle, so that cyclical profiles of reported symptomatology can be graphed and used as baseline information for planning treatment and as an ongoing check on

treatment effectiveness. Clare and Wiggins (1979) have also developed a modified version of the Menstrual Distress Questionnaire that they feel provides a simplified scoring system yet also supplies equivalent information.

MANAGEMENT OF STRESS IN PREGNANCY-RELATED CONDITIONS AND MENSTRUAL–CYCLE DISORDERS

The management of stress-related factors should be incorporated as an integral, rather than merely adjunctive, part of routine ob–gyn care. Only in this way can such factors be handled in both a preventive and postventive manner. Given the negative impact of stress on the health of the woman and her unborn child, its management deserves far more attention than it has been given in the past.

Burchell (1978) has provided a basic outline for counseling patients in an ob–gyn practice that can be readily applied in the case of stress management. He points out that the patient's initial request for psychological help is likely to be more subtle, indirect, and easily discouraged, compared with her more usual direct, open request for physical care. The patient might complain of signs and symptoms that seem unwarranted on the basis of physiological findings, or she might make an appointment for a vague complaint and then "test" the physician to see how much time and attention she or he is willing to make available. Thus, it is important that the physician create a comfortable environment in which the patient can feel free to make such requests for help with "nonmedical" concerns and that he or she take the request seriously and let the patient know that all possible help will be given. Burchell makes the practical suggestion that the individual taking appointments should ask the patient if she has any problems to discuss and would like a longer appointment, so that extra time will be available to deal with that patient's concerns and so that the patient will be committed to discussing the problem during the specific visit. He also indicates that, although many physicians are reluctant to do so, they have a right to charge for the time they spend counseling the patient and that not to do so cheats the patient of her right to buy "listening time" just as she would any other medical service.

In some instances, it might not be enough to be receptive to the patient's request for help when she asks for it. Tourkow (1979) defined the physician's responsibility as, *first,* being alert and sensitive enough to know that a patient is under stress; *second,* finding out how she is attempting to cope and how successful these coping mechanisms have been; and *third,* what price her attempts at coping are extracting from her emotional comfort. If it is determined that the patient needs and wants help in coping with her stress, the physician must decide whether to work with her personally, the advantage of this approach being the fact that she or he might already have a strong working relationship with the patient, or whether to refer her to a mental health professional.

Although it is important that the physician be alert to the existence of psychological factors such as anxiety and stress in the treatment of all patients, certain groups of patients need special attention, because they are even more likely than the average patient to be at risk in terms of the role stress plays in their lives. Among these are patients experiencing infertility, high-risk pregnancy, pregnancy loss or the death of a newborn, and treatment for gynecologic malignancies. Caplan (1960), addressing the problems patients face when premature birth occurs, emphasized the critical nature of such an experience with this statement:

> The relatively short periods of crisis when individuals and groups are struggling to cope with the danger and frustration of stressful events are apparently of special significance for their mental health. During such periods there is a temporary disorganization of personality functioning, and, during the subsequent reorganization phase, new, lasting, and sometimes drastically changed personality patterns are possible. The responses to the stress have, therefore, more enduring significance for mental health than merely the immediate relief from frustration or escape from danger. The discontinuity and imbalance of the customary patterns of behavior and feeling during the crisis period are associated with an increased susceptibility to change, which may be in the direction either of improved mental health or mental illness. (p.365)

Given the demonstrated effect of stress on the physical well-being of the parents and expected or newborn infant, the experience of a crisis such as premature birth is likely to precipitate a similar upheaval of physiological functioning, with prospects for either improved or deteriorated physiological well-being determined by the effectiveness of interventions designed to enable the parents to improve their abilities to cope with the crisis experience.

Another of these groups is made up of the 20% of obstetrical patients having a high-risk pregnancy, in which there is a significant possibility of fetal demise or anomaly or of life-threatening illness in the newborn infant (Warrick, 1974). When expectant parents become aware of the possible threat to their unborn child, it becomes very difficult for them to go through the normal process of psychological adaptation to the pregnancy, and the uncertainty typically experienced in the first trimester of a "normal" pregnancy continues until the threat to the fetus is resolved. This creates a highly stressful situation for both parents and sometimes precipitates underlying difficulties that could separate the couple (Lederman, 1980; Penticuff, 1982). Similar difficulties in accepting the pregnancy and attaching to the fetus or newborn infant could be experienced by women who have a health problem, such as renal or heart disease, which is exacerbated by pregnancy or childbirth.

Penticuff (1982) applied a stress-adaptation and learned-helplessness conceptual framework to explain parental reactions to high-risk pregnancy, and she utilized it to identify families at greatest risk for failure to adapt to pregnancy and parenthood and to formulate supportive intervention. She identified the following as factors influencing successful adaptation to high-risk perinatal experiences: (a) the degree to which family members communicate with each other and with resource persons such as perinatal staff their perceptions of the medical condition, and their concerns, feelings, and needs; (b) how realistically they understand the medical condition, its treatment and prognosis; (c) the prior experiences of the family and the adequacy of their coping in terms of ultimate psychologic outcome; (d) the support available to them in the current stress situation; and (e) the extent to which they realistically comprehend the threats they face and the extent to which they use reality-distorting defenses such as denial. The degree of effective, versus ineffective, functioning in these various spheres can then be evaluated on the cognitive, emotional, and behavioral levels. If the couple attempts behaviors designed to minimize risk to the fetus, only to have such efforts fail, they can develop a sense of helplessness, which is likely to lead to a decrease in voluntary efforts such as seeking information, solving problems, and persistence. Their cognitive difficulty in seeing that certain responses do work is accompanied on the emotional level by an overwhelming sense of vulnerability, passivity, fatalism, and depression. Because the ultimate impact of high-risk pregnancy on the parents' ability to cope with the associated uncertainties and fears is determined by their ability to comprehend their problems realistically and to change their behavior and the environment in such a way as to produce solutions and to minimize the stress, Penticuff considered it critical that appropriate support be given these families and that they be taught specific coping strategies such as which kinds of voluntary efforts reduce the threat to themselves and their unborn child, to prevent a sense of helplessness from enveloping them.

Women who are hospitalized as the result of high-risk pregnancies face the stresses associated with hospitalization at the same time that they are attempting to deal with the emotional, physiological, and social changes inherent in pregnancy. White and Ritchie (1984) attempted to identify those experiences that antepartum hospitalized women found to be the most stressful, to provide a starting point for interventions designed to reduce their stress. Stressors identified in their study fell into three groups. Most stressful were separation from home and family and disturbing emotions that the patients experienced during hospitalization. Moderately disturbing were changing family circumstances, health concerns, and changing self-image; communications with health professionals and the hospital environment itself were the least stressful. The last finding contrasts with Weil's report that "high-risk pregnancy patients felt a lack of empathy from almost every health care professional they came in contact with" (1981, p. 2047).

The various ob–gyn conditions and disorders reviewed in this chapter have all appeared to be multidetermined, resulting from combinations of physiological and psychosocial factors, including both internal and external stress factors. It is not within the scope of this chapter to present a separate paradigm for the management of the stress associated with each condition or disorder, but the fact that, in each, stress has demonstrated some degree of responsiveness to a similar range of treatment modalities suggests that these should be incorporated into a general approach to stress management for ob–gyn patients. Such interventions may be incorporated into the medical practice of obstetrics–gynecology, as well as the practices of other health care professionals who come into contact with women seeking treatment for stress in association with obstetrical and gynecological conditions.

The logistics of providing for the assessment and treatment of stress have been addressed in earlier sections of this chapter, but a brief review seems in order here. Physicians who are so inclined and have received appropriate training might wish to take advantage of the relationship they have already established with the patient by providing treatment themselves, especially for patients who might benefit primarily from the opportunity to ventilate their concerns and receive basic emotional support. Such attempts require some alteration of the regular office routine, with longer appointment times being set aside for counseling. In some situations, such as helping patients deal with the "normal" stresses associated with pregnancy and becoming new parents, or providing explanations concerning the role of stress in menstrual disorders, physicians might find it more efficient to schedule group sessions for patients with similar concerns. This format not only allows the professional to provide information in a manner that makes better use of her or his time than repeating it individually to each patient, but also provides an opportunity for the patient to learn that she is not alone or unusual in terms of the stress she is experiencing in relation to her medical condition and to receive information from others about their successful and unsuccessful attempts to cope with the problem and their emotional support.

Many physicians, however, might prefer to involve other professionals in the treatment of these patients. Referral to someone who has no direct association with the ob–gyn practice could be perceived by the patient as an attempt on the physician's part to wash his or her hands of the problem (and perhaps the patient as well), or it might suggest to her that she has some sort of serious "mental disorder" rather than a "problem of everyday living." Therefore it is preferable to engage a psychologist, a psychiatrist, a clinical social worker, or a psychiatric nurse with expertise in stress management and some knowledge of and interest in ob–gyn concerns to work within the practice on a part- or full-time basis. This arrangement emphasizes to the patient that management of the stress she is experiencing is an integral part of her total medical care. It also makes frequent consultation between the physician and the mental health professional easier and more efficient and allows the physician, when appropriate, to act as cocounselor. From a very practical standpoint, such an arrangement could benefit the patient in terms of having to make fewer individual trips to the doctor's office, thus requiring less time off from work or away from children. At least one practice that utilized such an arrangement has reported it was so well received by patients that the volume of the practice increased considerably (Pion, Wetzel, Montgomery, & Pion, 1978).

A PROPOSED PROGRAM FOR STRESS MANAGEMENT IN OBSTETRICAL AND GYNECOLOGICAL PATIENTS

Patients will, of course, vary in terms of the types and focus of intervention required to manage the particular stresses each is experiencing. The intervention components suggested here cover the broad range of needs that might be found among the patients in any practice, and it is therefore suggested that all components be available. Clinicians may, of course, select those interventions that meet the needs of the individual patient, as based on a thorough assessment of the effects of stress on her medical condition.

Focus 1: Stress Prevention

Although the exact nature of the relationship between stress and ob–gyn complications and disorders is not yet clearly understood, a fairly strong relationship between the two does appear to exist. Stress can be related to and stem from the condition itself, as is the case with women who have suffered severe menstrual pain for many years, those who find themselves unprepared for the physical and psychological changes required by pregnancy, or those who must deal with the continued uncertainties inherent in a high-risk pregnancy. Or the stress might impinge on them externally as the result of various life events or changes requiring a considerable degree of adaption on their part. Having become aware of the negative impact of stress on their patients, professionals have a responsibility to attempt to limit such stress as much as possible. Stress stemming from the condition itself often responds to the educating of patients about their condition, encouraging them to speak openly about their fears and anxieties, and providing them with reassurance and emotional support (Gutnik & Moore, 1983; Horsley, 1972; Williamson & English, 1981). The effects of external stressors can sometimes be avoided by advising patients of the impact on their condition of the increased stress resulting from major life changes and encouraging them to avoid such voluntary changes as moving and changing jobs. Such advice

can be particularly appropriate in helping women planning to become pregnant to arrange for a relatively stable, orderly, prenatal period. If they can be helped to avoid unnecessary external stress, their chances of coping well with the necessary, endogenous stress of pregnancy can be improved (Bassoff, 1983).

Focus 2: The Patient's Need to Know: Providing Her with Information Regarding Her Condition and Treatment

When a patient seeks medical help, whether for a "normal" condition such as pregnancy or for treatment of a particular problem such as PMS, she is basically entering an unknown sphere. She might have little information about her own body and the changes or symptoms she is experiencing, and she might be exposed to tests and procedures whose purpose she does not understand and that could be painful or, at the least, anxiety provoking. Research regarding the results of providing information about stressful medical procedures in other fields has shown that patient distress is decreased by such activities as description of the objective events and subjective sensations to be experienced, and by exposure to videotaped presentation of the procedures (Egbert, Battit, Welch, & Bartlett, 1964; Johnson, 1973, 1975; Johnson & Levanthal, 1974; Johnson, Rice, Fuller, & Endress, 1978; Shipley, Butt, Horwitz, & Farbry, 1978; Staub & Kellett, 1972).

It therefore seems reasonable that such activities would also prove helpful in reducing the stress of the ob–gyn patient. A study that supports this idea was carried out by Berne-Frommell and Kjessler (1984), who found that women involved in an antenatal serum alpha-fetoprotein screening program, which provides the expectant patient with information about the possibility of congenital birth defects in the unborn child, had a decreased level of anxiety in mid and late pregnancy, whereas the anxiety levels of women not involved in the screening program increased during that time. Indeed, one rationale for prepared childbirth training is to provide information about pregnancy and childbirth in an effort to combat the anxiety and stress associated with them (Chalmers, 1982; Standley et al., 1979). Gutnik and Moore (1983) suggested that the physician help pregnant patients identify the emotions they will probably feel during pregnancy and as new parents and acknowledge them as being normal and acceptable. Brown (1982) encouraged clinicians to explain to dysmennorheic patients how years of suffering menstrual pain would reasonably cause them to be anxious and negative in anticipation of their periods and how such anxiety can actually increase the experience of pain. Information provided to patients should be concise and understandable, specific to the needs and concerns of each patient, and consistent (Welch, 1979).

Focus 3: The Patient's Need for Control: Involving Her in Self-Care

Closely related to the patient's need for information about her condition and its treatment is her need to feel at least some degree of self-involvement with and control over them. It has been demonstrated that events are most stress producing when they are perceived as being out of the individual's control (Miller, 1979), and studies have found that beliefs about the controllability of events influence the reporting of pain in such conditions as chronic rheumatoid arthritis and chronic back pain (Skevington, 1979). Interestingly, Scott-Palmer and Skevington (1981) found that women with an internal locus of control experienced both shorter menstrual periods and shorter childbirth labors than women with an external locus of control, suggesting that beliefs might regulate and influence the duration of some physiological processes.

Several researchers have suggested that the amount of control a woman feels she has over her childbirth experience is a central factor in the degree of satisfaction she feels about the experience and that childbirth preparation training helps to increase her feelings of being in control. (Davenport-Slack, 1975; Humenick, 1981; Humenick & Bugen, 1981; Nadelson, Notman, & Ellis, 1983). For example, one study (Willmuth, 1975) showed that the major factor associated with a positive rating of childbirth was the woman's perception of having control during the birth; that is, she felt she was able to influence the decisions made during her labor and maintain a working alliance with professional staff. Humenick (1981) proposed a mastery model of childbirth, suggesting that a sense of mastery over the experience, rather than simple pain management, is the key factor to achieving a satisfactory childbirth experience. In the mastery model, the woman is encouraged to become informed about childbirth, set realistic childbirth goals, learn coping skills for pain management, prepare for active participation in decision making, and develop an adequate support

system of significant others and health care providers.

Not only do women who initially have a sense of internal control seem to handle labor and delivery in a more satisfying manner, but also there are indications that preparing the women for a more satisfying or masterful birth experience can lead to an increased sense of internal control. Felton and Segelman (1978) found that Lamaze training led to a significant increase in new mothers' seeing themselves as origins of control. They suggested that learning to perceive an internal origin for responsibility helps women to implement new and more effective behaviors, and they pointed out that such an orientation can be taught systematically through individual or group psychotherapy.

Focus 4: Making the Most of Relationships: Strengthening the Patient's Social Support Network

The relationship of social support to pregnancy complications, postpartum depression, and menstrual disorders has been reviewed in previous sections of this chapter. The emphasis here will be on the importance of intervention designed to help the patient make use of her existing support network or to strengthen a weak support system. Tilden (1983) pointed out that although many stressful life events are beyond the control of health care providers, social support systems can be responsive to manipulations designed to meet the patient's needs. Jordan and Meckler (1982) emphasized the need to facilitate the strengthening of the patient's support system, as an adjunct to other interventions, through individual counseling, referral to support groups, or encouraging her involvement in work, social, or religious activities.

The nature of expectant women's relationships with significant others was also found to be of critical significance to the emerging mother–child relationship (Richardson, 1981). Women's descriptions of their important relationships indicated that pregnancy was a time of major social change, with every relationship changing at some point during pregnancy. Relationships with husbands and other children changed more than those with parental figures and peers, and the relationship with the husband was the most critical in the reorganization process. Women's basic expectations of their relationships with parents and peers were to be supported, nurtured, and cared for, and they were likely to detach themselves from relationships that did not provide the support they needed, seeking other relationships that provided them with more support. Richardson concluded that an adequately functioning support system provides emotional refueling that enables women to deal with the stresses of pregnancy, whereas an inadequately functioning system could place them at higher risk for developing complications of pregnancy. She noted that each of the women in her study who demonstrated a medical complication during pregnancy was dealing with multiple problematic relationships at the time the complication developed.

The support of the woman's husband is especially important, particularly for the pregnant woman but also for the woman reporting other medical problems (N. C. Beck & Siegel, 1980; Braverman & Roux, 1978; Campbell & Worthington, et al., 1981; Cronenwett & Kunst-Wilson, 1981; O'Hara et al., 1983). Thus it is critical that attention be directed toward assessing the strengths and weaknesses of this relationship and that efforts be made to improve the supportive quality of it. In the case of a woman suffering from PMS, Chakmakjian (1983) recommended that the patient and her family be counseled together and suggested that apprising them of the physiological basis of the disorder can help the family to cope better with its symptomatology. During pregnancy, the husband should be included in prenatal visits, so that he can both be helped to understand the changes his wife is experiencing and give her the support she needs and to make known his own needs, because his wife's pregnancy is likely to be a stressful time for him, too. Efforts aimed at improving communication skills between the two are particularly important (Bassoff, 1983), not only because these skills are needed to weather the demands of pregnancy, but also because they are necessary to their role as parents. The role of the husband's participation in and support during labor and delivery has been shown to be a critical one. One study demonstrated that women whose husbands were present during labor and delivery reported less pain and received less medication than patients whose husbands were absent (Henneborn & Cogan, 1975).

Involvement of patients in various kinds of groups, both informational and supportive, has been utilized successfully with patients experiencing various conditions and disorders. Such groups provide the opportunity for patients to learn that they are not alone in the problems and anxieties they may be experiencing and to receive the support of others in like circumstances. Support groups can be particularly helpful for patients whose natural support system is weak. Aranoff and Lewis (1978) developed a program of lecture and discussion for small groups of expectant parents that focused on their changing roles. Horsley (1972) recommended weekly support groups for selected groups of expectant mothers, to give them an opportunity to discuss jointly with the physician any changes of feeling, appetite, anxiety, or mood. Gutnik and Moore (1983) suggested that monthly discussion groups involving the physician and patients due to deliver that month be held to discuss the patients' feelings about childbirth and parenthood. Noting the important role of social support in protecting women against postpartum depressions, O'Hara et al. (1983) recommended support groups for new mothers determined to be at high risk for this disorder. A telephone hot-line between two or three patients undergoing a high-risk pregnancy, volunteer support of current high-risk patients by those who have successfully endured a difficult pregnancy, monthly support meetings for husbands, and continued follow-up and support after delivery were interventions suggested by Weil (1981). Support groups for patients suffering from dysmenorrhea have also been found to be helpful (Budoff, 1980; Heczey, 1977).

Focus 5: Specific Stress–management Techniques for Treatment of Anxiety and Pain of Pregnancy and Menstrual Disorders

A number of cognitive and behavioral therapies have been shown to be effective in the management of the anxiety and pain accompanying pregnancy and menstrual disorders, yet these strategies are not widely employed with ob–gyn patients, despite their accepted use in other medical fields. As reviews of the experimental use of these strategies have been covered previously, this section will focus on brief explanations of the procedures and suggestions for their clinical use.

Relaxation Training

The most commonly used procedure for training patients to relax is the progressive deep-muscle relaxation technique introduced by Jacobson (1938, 1967). The basic premise for its use is that muscle tension is related to anxiety, which can be reduced if tense muscles can be made to relax. Relaxation training does produce changes in the response of the autonomic nervous system, including response to anxiety-evoking stimuli. In addition, relaxation procedures provide patients with a coping response to use in dealing with anxiety and stress, helping them to feel there is something they can do about them. The basic procedure involves providing patients with an explanation of the relationship between muscle tension and anxiety and how the use of systematic deep-muscle relaxation can be used to help them control their anxiety, followed by instructions on the successive tensing and relaxing of voluntary muscles in an orderly sequence until all the main muscle groups of the body have been relaxed. Another relaxation procedure, autogenic training, involves teaching clients to engage in autosuggestion to the extent that their bodies feel heavy and warm. Presumably the heaviness leads to muscle flaccidity and the warmth to vasodilation, both of which are closely associated with subjective feelings of relaxation. Both procedures have demonstrated their effectiveness as treatment modalities for a variety of medical problems. A more recent advance in relaxation techniques involves the use of biofeedback, in which the individuals' physiological functioning is systematically monitored and fed back to them, usually in the form of an audio or visual signal. Individuals are trained to modify the signal in order to change the physiological function. Biofeedback-assisted relaxation training involves the use of EMG feedback, which monitors and amplifies muscular activity and provides sensory feedback to patients practicing some form of muscular control.

In obstetrics and gynecology, relaxation training is most widely used as one component of prepared childbirth training. Although relaxation alone does not generally provide sufficient relief from the pain and anxiety associated with childbirth, its use in conjunction with other treatment modalities provides sufficient relief to allow for decreased use of medications that might adversely affect the infant, can result in shorter labors, and might be useful in delaying what would have been a premature birth. The usefulness of relaxation techniques has also been demonstrated in relieving the pain of dysemorrhea and in treating the headaches, tension, and irritability associated with PMS.

Systematic Desensitization

Systematic desensitization (Wolpe, 1958, 1969, 1973) uses a counterconditioning approach that pairs an anxiety response with a response directly inhibitory or antagonistic to it, the relaxation response. The procedure involves, *first,* training the patient in systematic deep muscle relaxation as previously described. *Second,* the patient and therapist construct a list of situations that produce

anxiety for the patient, listing them in order from those eliciting the least anxiety to those eliciting the most. *Finally,* the patient is asked to imagine experiencing the least anxiety-producing situation on the hierarchy for a few seconds, followed by instructions to relax. Once the patient is successfully able to relax while thinking of that experience, she repeats the procedure with the next situation on the hierarchy, and so on, until she is able to remain relaxed while imagining the most anxiety-provoking situation. Once the anxiety-provoking situations have been mastered in imagination, in some cases a similar process can be carried out in vivo, that is in the actual situations in which the anxiety response occurs (Bandura, 1969; Garfield, Darwin, Singer, & McBreaty, 1967; Wolpe, 1969). In a variation of the process called Anxiety Management Training (Suinn & Richardson, 1971), anxiety hierarchies related to the problem areas are not used; instead, the patient is taught to recognize the initial cues of anxiety and to use these as discriminitive stimuli for competing responses such as relaxation.

Systematic desensitization has been effectively used to treat a broad spectrum of problems including a wide range of phobias, speech disorders (Walton & Mather, 1963), sexual dysfunction (Obler, 1973; Wincze & Caird, 1976), asthma attacks (Moore, 1965), and insomnia (Steinmarck & Borkovec, 1974). Applications of systematic desensitization to these and other disorders is based on the premise that the disorders arise from fear attached to specific external events and so are similar to phobic reactions. Stevens (1976) suggested that prepared childbirth classes provide an informal form of desensitization to the fear of the pain associated with childbirth, and Kondas and Scetnicka's (1972) formal use of the procedure to desensitize women to the anxiety associated with labor and delivery was based on the assumption that patients suffer from "labour phobia." In their study, systematic desensitization appeared to produce more powerful effects than traditional psychoprophylactic procedures. A greater decrease in anxiety was reported by the systematic desensitization group. They experienced shorter labors and were rated by their obstetricians as experiencing less pain and showing less restlessness. Systematic desensitization has also been used successfully in the treatment of dysmenorrhea (Chesney & Tasto, 1975; Mullen, 1968; Tasto & Chesney (1974).

There are several practical advantages to the use of systematic desensitization as a treatment modality. It can be used successfully with groups of patients experiencing similar problems, as the use of individually constructed hierarchies is not always necessary (Chesney & Tasto, 1975). Members of the group may construct a hierarchy together, or each patient may construct her own and write each item on a separate card. As the desensitization session is conducted, patients can be instructed to imagine the scene on card 1, then card 2, and so forth. Automated (audiotaped) desensitization instructions (Cotler, 1970) have also been used successfully (Evans & Kellam, 1973; Lang, Melamed, & Hart, 1970), thereby providing more efficient use of patient–therapist contact time. Finally, sessions are generally brief (15–30 minutes), and improvement is usually noted with only a small number of sessions.

Cognitive–Behavioral Treatment Modalities

Among the most promising of the treatment strategies for pregnancy and menstrual cycle disorders are various cognitive–behavioral techniques, which aim at modifying an individual's feelings and actions by influencing her or his patterns of thought. Although there has been little reported usage of these techniques in the treatment of ob–gyn patients, they have been hailed as promising by several researchers in the field, especially for cases in which the patient's attitude or attributions about particular body functions or events, such as labor and delivery, affect her perception and reaction to them. The role of cognitive factors as they relate to a woman's response to her menstrual cycle has been explored, and personal and cultural attitudes and beliefs do appear to play a role in PMS and dysmenorrhea (Abplanalp, 1983a; Brooks, Ruble, & Clarke, 1977; Koeske & Koeske, 1975; Osborn, 1981; Ruble, 1977; Vila & Beech, 1980). Noting that negative causal statements were related to postpartum depression, Cutrona (1982) suggested that cognitive therapies might be well suited for treatment of this disorder.

The cognitive therapies of A. T. Beck (1972, 1976) are aimed at systematically inducing fundamental attitude change through the use of a number of techniques designed to alter negative cognitive sets. Intended specifically for the treatment of depression, this approach teaches the patient that the way he or she feels is related to maladaptive thought patterns and trains him or her to identify and logically challenge the erroneous assumptions underlying these patterns by examining events from his or her life that disconfirm their validity. This approach would seem appropriate for the treatment of postpartum depression and the negative mood often accompanying menstrual disorders.

Cognitive strategies also hold promise for the amelioration of pain associated with childbirth and menstrual disorders. As the higher brain centers play a significant role in identifying, interpreting, and altering pain impulses before they enter consciousness, the perception of pain is related not only to the strength of the pain stimulus but also to the mental state of the individual (Stevens, 1976). Pain may be controlled cognitively by involving the mind in mental activities other than the awareness of the incoming pain stimuli. Stevens cited two major types of cognitive control, the dissociation strategy and interference strategies. Dissociation involves focusing attention on nonpainful characteristics of the pain stimulus or cognitively restructuring it in some way; for example, interpreting labor contractions as muscular contractions of the uterus rather than as labor pains, or imagining that the pelvic area is numb or insensitive to pain. Interference strategies involve the use of distraction, a passive process utilizing noise or other stimuli to distract one's attention from the pain, and attention focusing, a more active process of purposeful attention to nonpain stimuli. The latter can involve something as simple as attending to a particular visual focal point or can involve more complicated processes such as imagining oneself involved in a pleasant situation away from the pain or anxiety-producing stimulus. A third strategy that can be used to reduce the perceived level of pain is cognitive rehearsal, which provides the patient with the opportunity to utilize both objective and subjective information about the upcoming pain experience to prepare herself mentally for it and thereby decrease her anxiety about the event. All three of these strategies have been incorporated into training for prepared childbirth and could also be utilized on a regular basis by women experiencing menstrual pain.

The active ingredient accounting for the success of such cognitive strategies in managing pain is the fact that patients are provided with active coping skills they can use to manage their pain. A comprehensive approach that can be used for the self-management of the stress of both pain and anxiety is stress-inoculation training (Meichenbaum, 1977; Meichenbaum & Turk, 1976; Novaco, 1975). In the first phase of this training program, patients are taught that responses such as anxiety and the reaction to physical pain are modifiable through coping responses such as relaxation, changing the kinds of self-statements one makes about the event, and providing self-reinforcement statements. During the second phase, patients actually learn these responses and have an opportunity to practice them, and in the third phase they test their abilities by using them in actual pain or anxiety-producing situations. This procedure has not been utilized in the treatment of ob–gyn-related pain and anxiety, but its successful use in other areas suggests that its application in new arenas deserves attention. Such a procedure would provide women attempting to deal with the anxiety and pain associated with childbirth and menstrual disorders with multiple coping strategies they could use to alter both their attitudes toward and perceptions of these events.

REFERENCES

Aberger, E. A., Denney, D. R., & Hutchings, D. F. (1983). Pain sensitivity and coping strategies among dysmenorrheic women: Much ado about nothing. *Behaviour Research and Therapy, 21,* 119–127.

Abplanalp, J. M. (1983a). Premenstrual syndrome: A selective review. *Women & Health, 8,* 107–123.

Abplanalp, J. M. (1983b). Psychologic components of the premenstrual syndrome: Evaluating the research and choosing the treatment. *Journal of Reproductive Medicine, 28,* 517–524.

Abraham, G. E., Elsner, C. W., & Lucas, L. A. (1978). Hormonal and behavioral changes during the menstrual cycle. *Senologia, 3,* 33.

Andersch, B. (1980). *Epidemiological, hormonal, and water balance studies on premenstrual tension.* Unpublished thesis, University of Goteborg.

Aranoff, J. L., & Lewis, S. (1978). An innovative group experience for couples expecting their first child. *American Journal of Family Therapy, 7,* 51–55.

Backstrom, T., & Carstensen, H. (1974). Estrogen and progesterone in plasma in relation to premenstrual tension. *Journal of Steroid Biochemistry, 5,* 527.

Bandura, A. (1969). *Principles of behavior modification.* New York: Holt, Rinehart and Winston.

Barnett, B. E., Hanna, B., & Parker, G. (1983). Life event scales for obstetric groups. *Journal of Psychosomatic Research, 27,* 313–320.

Bassoff, E. S. (1983). The pregnant client: Understanding and counseling her. *Personnel and Guidance Journal, 62,* 20–23.

Beck, A. T. (1972) *Depression: Causes and treatment.* Philadelphia: University of Pennsylvania Press.

Beck, A. T. (1976). *Cognitive therapy and the emotional disorders.* New York: International Universities Press.

Beck, A. T., Ward, C. H., Mendelson, M., Mock, J., & Erbaugh, J. (1961). An inventory for measuring depression. *Archives of General Psychiatry, 4,* 561–571.

Beck, N. C., Geden, E., & Brouder, G. (1979). *Preparation for labor: A multidisciplinary approach to pain and anxiety reduction.* Paper presented at the 26th Annual Convention of the Academy of Psychosomatic Medicine, San Francisco.

Beck, N. C., & Hall, D. (1978). Natural childbirth: A review and analysis. *Obstetrics and Gynecology, 52,* 371–379.

Beck, N. C., & Siegel, L. J. (1980). Preparation for childbirth and contemporary research on pain, anxiety, and stress reduction: A review and critique. *Psychosomatic Medicine, 42,* 429–447.

Berne-Frommell, K., & Kjessler, B. (1984). Anxiety concerning fetal malformations in pregnant women exposed or not exposed to an antenatal serum alpha-fetoprotein screening program. *Gynecologic and Obstetrical Investigation, 17,* 36–39.

Blitz, D., & Dinnerstein, A. J. (1971). Role of attentional focus in pain perception: Manipulation of response to noxious situations by instructions. *Journal of Abnormal Psychology, 77,* 42–45.

Boulougouris, J. C., Marks, I. M., & Marset, P. (1971). Superiority of flooding to desensitization as a fear reducer. *Behaviour Research and Therapy, 9,* 7–16.

Brattesani, K., & Silverthorne, C. P. (1978). Social psychological factors of menstrual distress. *Journal of Social Psychology, 106,* 139–140.

Braverman, J., & Roux, J. F. (1978) Screening for the patient at risk for postpartum depression. *Obstetrics and Gynecology, 52,* 731–736.

Brooks, J., Ruble, D. N., & Clarke, A. E. (1977). College women's attitudes and expectations concerning menstrual-related changes. *Psychosomatic Medicine, 39,* 288.

Brown, M. A. (1982). Primary dysmenorrhea. *Nursing Clinics of North America, 17 (1),* 145–153.

Budoff, P. (1980). *No more menstrual cramps and other good news.* New York: G. P. Putnam's Sons.

Burchell, R. C. (1978). Counseling in gynecologic practice: An overview. *Clinical Obstetrics and Gynecology, 21,* 165–172.

Campbell, A., & Worthington, E. L. (1981). A comparison of two methods of training husbands to assist their wives with labor and delivery. *Journal of Psychosomatic Research, 25,* 557–563.

Caplan, G. (1960). Patterns of parental response to the crisis of premature birth: A preliminary approach to modifying the mental-health outcome. *Psychiatry, 23,* 365–374.

Carlson, D. B., & Labarba, R. C. (1979). Maternal emotionality during pregnancy and reproductive outcome: A review of the literature. *International Journal of Behavioral Development, 2,* 343–376.

Cerutti, R., Foresti, G., Ferraro, M., Crema, M. G., & Grazioli, E. A. (1979). Juvenile dysmenorrhea, personality profiles and therapeutic approach with autogenic training. In L. Carenza & L. Zichella (Eds.), *Emotion and Reproduction: 5th International Congress of Psychosomatic Obstetrics and Gynecology, 20A,* (pp. 165–167). London: Academic Press.

Chakmakjian, Z. H. (1983). A critical assessment of therapy for the premenstrual tension syndrome. *Journal of Reproductive Medicine, 28,* 532–538.

Chalmers, B. (1982). Psychological aspects of pregnancy: Some thoughts for the eighties. *Social Science in Medicine, 16,* 323–331.

Chaves, J. F., & Barber, T. X. (1974). Cognitive Strategies, experimental modeling, and expectation in the attenuation of pain. *Journal of Abnormal Psychology, 83,* 356–363.

Chesney, M. A., & Tasto, D. L. (1975). The effectiveness of behavior modification with spasmodic and congestive dysmenorrhea. *Behaviour Research and Therapy, 13,* 245–253.

Ching, J. W., Gordon, R., & O'Mahoney, M. T. (1981). Crisis following severe psychological trauma in late pregnancy. *Hospital and Community Psychiatry, 32,* 53–56.

Clare, A. W. (1979). The treatment of premenstrual tension. *British Journal of Psychiatry, 135,* 576–579.

Clare, A. W. (1983). The relationship between psychpathology and the menstrual cycle. *Women and Health, 8,* 125–136.

Clare, A. W., & Wiggins, R. D. (1979). The construction of a modified version of the Menstrual Distress Questionnaire for use in general practice populations. In L. Carenza & L. Zichella (Eds.). *Emotion and Reproduction: 5th International Congress of Psychosomatic Obstetrics and Gynecology, 20A,* (pp. 191–197). London Academic Press.

Cohen, R. L. (1979). Maladaption to pregnancy. *Seminars in Perinatology, 3(1),* 15–24.

Cotler, S. B. (1970). Sex differences and generalization of anxiety reduction with automated desensitization and minimalist therapist interaction. *Behaviour Research and Therapy, 8,* 273–285.

Cox, D. J. (1977). Menstrual Symptom Questionnaire: Further psychometric evaluation. *Behaviour Research and Therapy, 15,* 506–508.

Crandon, A. J. (1979). Maternal anxiety and obstetric complications. *Journal of Psychosomatic Research, 23,* 109–111.

Cronenwett, L. R., & Kunst-Wilson, W. (1981). Stress, social support, and the transition to fatherhood. *Nursing Research, 30,* 196–201.

Cutrona, C. E. (1982). Nonpsychotic postpartum depression: A review of recent research. *Clinical Psychology Review, 2,* 487–503.

Dalton, K. (1964). *The premenstrual syndrome.* Springfield, IL: Charles C. Thomas.

Dalton, K. (1969). *The menstrual cycle.* New York: Pantheon.

Dalton, K. (1977). *The premenstrual syndrome and progsterone therapy.* London: Heinemann.

Davenport-Slack, B. (1975). A comparative evaluation of obstetrical hypnosis and antenatal childbirth training. *International Journal of Clinical and Experimental Hypnosis, 23,* 266–281.

Dick-Read, G. (1944). *Childbirth without fear.* New York: Harper Bros.

Dunlavy, J. (1983). Premenstrual syndrome (clinical conference). *Journal of Family Practice, 17,* 29–30, 32, 41–42.

Edlund, B. J. (1982). The needs of women with gynecologic malignancies. *Nursing Clinics of North America, 17,* 165–177.

Egbert, L. D., Battit, G. E., Welch, C. E., & Bartlett, M. K. (1964). Reduction of post-operative pain by encouragement and instruction of patients: A study of doctor-patient rapport. *New England Journal of Medicine, 270,* 825–827.

Evans, P. D., & Kellam, A. M. P. (1973). Semi-automated desensitization: A controlled clinical trial. *Behaviour Research and Therapy, 11,* 641–646.

Fagley, N., Miller, P., & Sullivan, J. (1982). Stress, symptom, proneness, and general adaptational distress during pregnancy. *Journal of Human Stress, 8,* 15–22.

Felton, G. S., & Segelman, F. B. (1978). Lamaze childbirth training and changes in belief about personal control. *Birth and the Family Journal, 5,* 141–150.

Fleischauer, M. L. (1977). A modified Lamaze approach in the treatment of primary dysmenorrhea. *Journal of the American College Health Association, 25,* 273–275.

Frazier, L. M. (1974). Using biofeedback to aid relaxation during childbirth. *Birth and the Family Journal, 1,* 4–17.

Garfield, Z. H., Darwin, P. L., Singer, B. A., & McBreaty, J. F. (1967). Effect of "in vivo" training on experimental desensitization of a phobia. *Psychological Reports, 20,* 515–519.

Garvey, M. J., & Tollefson, G. D. (1984). Postpartum depression. *Journal of Reproductive Medicine, 29,* 113–115.

Georgas, J., Giakoumaki, E., Georgoulias, N., Koumandakis, E., & Kaskarelis, D. (1984). Psychosocial stress and its relation to obstetrical complications. *Psychotherapy and Psychosomatics, 41,* 200–206.

Gorsuch, R. L., & Key, M. K. (1974). Abnormalities of pregnancy as a function of anxiety and life stress. *Psychosomatic Medicine, 36,* 352–362.

Gregg, R. M. (1979). Biophysical monitoring of autonomic and neuromuscular systems during pregnancy. In L. Carenza & L. Zichella (Eds.). *Emotion and Reproduction: 5th International Congress of Psychosomatic Obstetrics and Gynecology, 20B,* (pp. 923–927). London: Academic Press.

Gregg, R. H., Nesbit, R. A., & Frazier, L. M. (1979). Biofeedback relaxation training effects in childbirth. In L. Carenza & L. Zichella (Eds.). *Emotion and Reproduction: 5th International Congress of Psychosomatic Obstetrics and Gynecology, 20B,* (pp. 937–941). London: Academic Press.

Gutnik, B. D., & Moore, S. L. (1983). Pre-emptive postpartum stress reduction. *Nebraska Medical Journal, 68,* 9–13.

Hargrove, J. T., & Abraham, G. E. (1979). Effect of vitamin B6 on infertility in women with the premenstrual tension syndrome. *Infertility, 2,* 315.

Hargrove, J. T., & Abraham, G. E. (1982). The incidence of premenstrual tension in a gynecologic clinic. *Journal of Reproductive Medicine, 27,* 721.

Hargrove, J. T., & Abraham, G. E. (1983). The ubiquitousness of premenstrual tension in gynecologic practice. *Journal of Reproductive Medicine, 28,* 435–437.

Hayworth, J., Little, B. C., Bonham-Carter, S., Ratopoulos, P., Priest, Z. G., & Sandler, M. (1980). A predictive study of postpartum depression: Some predisposing characteristics. *British Journal of Medical Psychology, 53,* 161–167.

Heczey, M. D. (1977). *Effects of biofeedback on dysmenorrhea.* Paper presented at the meeting of Menstrual Cycle Interdisciplinary Conference, Chicago.

Henneborn, W. J., & Cogan, R. (1975). The effect of husband participation on reported pain and probability of medication during labor and birth. *Journal of Psychosomatic Research, 19,* 215–222.

Hetzel, B. S., Breur, B., & Poidevin, L. O. S. (1961). A survey of the relation between common antenatal complications in primiparae and stressful life situations during pregnancy. *Journal of Psychosomatic Research, 5,* 175.

Holmes, T., & Rahe, R. (1967). The social readjustment rating scale. *Journal of Psychosomatic Research, 11,* 213–218.

Horowitz, M. J., Wilner, N., & Alvarez, W. (1979). Impact of event scale: A measure of subjective distress. *Psychosomatic Medicine, 41,* 209–218.

Horsley, S. (1972). Psychological management of the prenatal period. In J. G. Howells (Ed.), *Modern perspectives in psycho-obstetrics* (pp. 291-312). New York: Brunner/Mazel.

Humenick, S. S. (1981). Mastery: The key to childbirth satisfaction? A review. *Birth and the Family Journal, 8,* 79–83.

Humenick, S. S., & Bugen, L. A. (1981). Mastery: The key to childbirth satisfaction? A study. *Birth and the Family Journal, 8,* 84–90.

Jacobson, E. (1938). *Progressive relaxation.* Chicago: University of Chicago Press.

Jacobson, E. (Ed.). (1967). *Tension in medicine.* Springfield, IL: Charles C. Thomas.

Jensen, B. K. (1982). Menstrual cycle effects on task performance examined in the context of stress research. *Acta Psychologica (Amst), 50,* 159–178.

Johnson, J. (1973). Effects of accurate expectations about sensations on the sensory and distress components of pain. *Journal of Personality and Social Psychology, 27,* 261–275.

Johnson, J. E. (1975). Stress reduction through sensation information. In I. G. Sarason & C. D. Spielberger (Eds.) *Stress and anxiety: Vol. 2* (pp. 361–378). NY: Wiley.

Johnson, J. E., & Leventhal, H. (1974). Effects of accurate expectations and behavioral instructions during a noxious medical examination. *Journal of Personality and Social Psychology, 29,* 710–718.

Johnson, J. E., Rice, V. H., Fuller, S. S., & Endress, M. P. (1978). Sensory information, instruction in a coping strategy, and recovery from surgery. *Research in Nursing and Health, 1(1),* 4–17.

Jones, A. C. (1978). Life change and psychological distress as predictors of pregnancy outcome. *Psychosomatic Medicine, 40,* 402–412.

Jordan, J., & Meckler, J. R. (1982). The relationship between life change events, social supports, and dysmenorrhea. *Research in Nursing and Health, 5,* 73–79.

Jordheim, O. (1972). The premenstrual syndrome: Clinical trials of treatment with a progestogen combined with a diuretic compared with both a progestogen alone and with a placebo. *Acta Obstetrica Gynecologica Scandinavica, 51,* 77–80.

Kanner, A. D., Coyne, J. C., Schaefer, C., & Lazarus, R. S. (1981). Comparison of two modes of stress measurement: Daily hassles and uplifts versus major life events. *Journal of Behavioral Medicine, 4,* 1–39.

Koeske, R. K., & Koeske, G. F. (1975). An attributional approach to moods and the menstrual cycle. *Journal of Personality and Social Psychology, 31,* 473–478.

Kondas, O., & Scetnicka, B. (1972). Systematic

desensitization as a method of preparation for childbirth. *Journal of Behavior Therapy and Experimental Psychiatry, 3,* 51.

Lamaze, F. (1958). *Painless childbirth.* (L. R. Celestin, Trans.). London: Burke.

Lang, P. J., Melamed, B. G., & Hart, J. (1970). A psychophysiological analysis of fear modification using an automated desensitization procedure. *Journal of Abnormal Psychology, 76,* 220–234.

Lederman, R. P. (1980, June). *Developmental challenges and conflicts in pregnancy and childbirth.* Paper presented at the 52nd Convention of the American Nurses' Association, Houston.

Lederman, R. P., Lederman, E., Work, B. A., & McCann, D. S. (1978). Relationship of maternal anxiety, plasma catecholamines, and plasma cortisol to progress in labor. *American Journal of Obstetrics and Gynecology, 132,* 495–500.

Leitenberg, H., & Callahan, E. J. (1973). Reinforced practice and reduction of different kinds of fears in adults and children. *Behaviour Research and Therapy, 11,* 19–30.

Loftus, T. A. (1962). Psychogenic factors in anovulatory women. Vol. III, Behavioral and psychoanalytic aspects of anovulatory amenorrhea. *Fertility and Sterility, 13,* 20.

Mattson, R. H., & Schoultz, B. V. (1974). A comparison between lithium, placebo, and a diuretic in premenstrual tension. *Acta Psychiatrica Scandinavica Supplement, 255,* 75–84.

McDonald, R. L. (1968). The role of emotional factors in obstetric complications: A review. *Psychosomatic Medicine, 30,* 222–237.

Meichenbaum, D. H. (1977). *Cognitive–behavior modification.* New York: Plenum.

Meichenbaum, D. H., & Turk, D. (1976). The cognitive behavioral management of anxiety, anger, and pain. In P. Davidson (Ed.). *The behavioral management of anxiety, depression, and pain.* New York: Bruner/Mazel.

Menzer, D. (1953). Importance of psychological factors in gynecology. *New England Journal of Medicine, 249,* 519.

Miller, S. M. (1979). Controllability and human stress: Method, evidence, and theory. *Behavior Research and Therapy, 17,* 287–304.

Monroe, S. M. (1983). Major and minor life events as predictors of psychological distress: Further issues and findings. *Journal of Behavioral Medicine, 6,* 189–205.

Moore, M. (1965). Behavior therapy in bronchial asthma: A controlled study. *Journal of Psychosomatic Research, 9,* 257–276.

Moos, R. H. (1968). The development of a menstrual distress questionnaire. *Psychosomatic Medicine, 30,* 853-867.

Moos, R. H. (1977). *Menstrual distress questionnaire manual.* Stanford, CA: Standford University, Social Ecology Laboratory.

Mullen, F. G. (1968). The treatment of a case of dysmenorrhea by behavior therapy techniques. *Journal of Nervous and Mental Disorders, 147,* 371–376.

Mullen, F. G. (1971, September). *Treatment of dysmenorrhea by professional and student behavior therapists.* Paper presented at the Fifth Annual

Meeting of the Association for the Advancement of Behavior Therapy, Washington, D.C.

Nadelson, C. C., Notman, M. T., & Ellis, E. A. (1983). Psychosomatic aspects of obstetrics and gynecology. *Psychosomatics, 24,* 871–875, 878–880, 882–884.

Nelson, R. O., Sigmon, S., Amodei, N., & Jarrett, R. B. (1984). The menstrual symptom questionnaire: The validity of the distinction between spasmodic and congestive dysmenorrhea. *Behaviour Research and Therapy, 22,* 611–614.

Newton, R. W., & Hunt, L. P. (1984). Psychosocial stress in pregnancy and its relation to low birth weight. *British Medical Journal, 288,* 1191–1194.

Newton, R. W., Webster, P. A., Binu, P. S., Mabrey, N., & Phillips, A. B. (1979). Psychosocial stress in pregnancy and its relation to the onset of premature labour. *British Medical Journal, 2,* 411–413.

Norbeck, J. S., & Tilden, V. P. (1983). Life stress, social support, and emotional disequilibrium in complications of pregnancy: A prospective multivariate study. *Journal of Health and Social Behavior, 24,* 30–46.

Novaco, R. W. (1975). *Anger control: The development and evaluation of an experimental treatment.* Lexington, MA: D. C. Heath.

Nuckolls, K. B., Cassell, J., & Kaplan, B. H. (1972). Psychosocial assets, life crisis, and the prognosis of pregnancy. *American Journal of Epidemiology, 95,* 431–441.

Obler, M. (1973). Systematic desensitization in sexual disorders. *Journal of Behavior Therapy and Experimental Psychiatry, 4,* 93–101.

O'Brien, P. M., Craven, D., Selby, C., & Symonds, E. M. (1979). Treatment of premenstrual tension by spironolactone. *British Journal of Obstetrics and Gynecology, 86(2),* 142–147.

O'Hara, M. (1980). *A prospective study of postpartum depression: A test of cognitive and behavioral theories.* Unpublished doctoral dissertation, University of Pittsburgh.

O'Hara, M. W., Rehm, L. P., & Campbell, S. B. (1982). Predicting depressive symptomatology: Cognitive behavioral models and postpartum depression. *Journal of Abnormal Psychology, 91,* 457–461.

O'Hara, M. W., Rehm, L. P., & Campbell, S. B. (1983). Postpartum depression: A role for social network and life stress variables. *Journal of Nervous and Mental Disease, 171,* 336–341.

Osborn, M. (1981). Physical and psychological determinants of premenstrual tension: Research Issues and a proposed methodology. *Journal of Psychosomatic Research, 25,* 363–367.

Osofsky, H. F., & Fisher, S. (1967). Psychological correlates of the development of amenorrhea in a stress situation. *Psychosomatic Medicine, 29,* 15–23.

Paige, K. E. (1971). Effects of oral contraceptives on affective fluctuations associated with the menstrual cycle. *Psychosomatic Medicine, 33,* 515–538.

Paige, K. E. (1973). Women learn to sing the menstrual blues. *Psychology Today, 7,* 41–46.

Parlee, M. B. (1973). The premenstrual syndrome. *Psychological Bulletin, 80,* 454–465.

Parlee, M. B. (1974). Stereotypic beliefs about menstruation: A methodological note on the Moos Menstrual Distress Questionnaire and some new data. *Psychosomatic Medicine, 36,* 229–240.

Patterson, V., & Wilner, N. (1981). Scaling the stressfulness of gynecological complaints. *International Journal of Psychiatry in Medicine, 10,* 315–325.

Paul, G. L. (1966). *Insight versus desensitization in psychotherapy: An experiment in anxiety reduction.* Stanford, CA: Stanford University Press.

Paulson, M. J., & Wood, K. R. (1966). Perceptions of emotional correlates of dysemorrhea. *American Journal of Obstetrics and Gynecology, 95,* 668–672.

Paykel, E. S., Emms, E. M., Fletcher, J., & Rassaby, E. S. (1980). Life events and social support in puerperal depression. *British Journal of Psychiatry, 136,* 339–346.

Penticuff, J. H. (1982). Psychologic implications in high-risk pregnancy. *Nursing Clinics of North America, 17,* 69–78.

Picone, T. A., Allen, L. H., Schramm, M. M., & Olsen, P. N. (1982). Pregnancy outcome in North American women. I. Effects of diet, cigarette smoking, and psychological stress on maternal weight gain. *The American Journal of Clinical Nutrition, 36,* 1205-1213.

Pion, G. J., Wetzel, R. L., Montgomery, R. B., & Pion, R. J. (1978). Counseling couples: Enabling improved relationships. *Clinical Obstetrics and Gynecology, 21(1),* 249–258.

Piotrowski, Z. A. (1962). Psychogenic factors in anovulatory women. II. Psychological evaluation. *Fertility and Sterility, 13,* 11.

Plante, T. G., & Denney, D. R. (1984). Stress responsivity among dysmenorrheic women at different phases of their menstrual cycle: More ado about nothing, *Behaviour Research and Therapy, 22,* 249–258.

Quillen, M. A., & Denney, D. R. (1982). Self-control of dysmenorrheic symptoms through pain management training. *Journal of Behavior Therapy and Experimental Psychiatry, 13,* 123–130.

Rahe, R. H., Ryman, D. H., & Ward, H. W. (1980). Simplified scaling for life change events. *Journal of Human Stress, 6,* 22–26.

Rakoff, A. E. (1962). Psychogenic factors in anovulatory women. I. Hormonal patterns in women with ovarian dysfunctions of psychogenic origin. *Fertility and Sterility, 13,* 11.

Reichlin, S., Abplanalp, J. M., Labrum, A. H., Schwartz, N., Sommer, B., & Taynor, M. (1979). The role of stress in female reproductive dysfunction. *Journal of Human Stress, 5,* 38–45.

Reid, R. L., & Yen, S. S. C. (1981). Premenstrual syndrome. *American Journal of Obstetrics and Gynecology, 139,* 85–104.

Reifenstein, E. C., Jr. (1946). Psychogenic or "hypothalamic" amenorrhea. *Medical Clinics of North America, 30,* 234.

Richardson, P. (1981). Women's perceptions of their important dyadic relationships during pregnancy. *Maternal Child Nursing Journal, 10(3),* 159–174.

Rizzardo, R., Magni, G., Andreoli, C., Merlin, G., Andreoli, F., Cosentino, M., & Ziglio, R. (1982). Life events and obstetrical complications: A preliminary report. *Psychological Reports, 51,* 1035–1038.

Rotter, J. B. (1966). Generalized expectancies for internal

vs. external control of reinforcement. *Psychological Monographs, 80* (whole no. 609).

Ruble, D. (1977). Premenstrual symptoms: A reinterpretation. *Science, 197,* 291–292.

Sampson, G. (1979). Premenstrual syndrome: A double-blind controlled trial of progesterone and placebo. *British Journal of Psychiatry, 135,* 209–215.

Sampson, G. A., & Prescott, P. (1981). The assessment of the symptoms of the premenstrual syndrome and their response to therapy. *British Journal of Psychiatry, 138,* 399–405.

Sanders, D., Warner, P., Backstrom, T., & Bancroft, J. (1983). Mood, sexuality, hormones, and the menstrual cycle. I. Changes in mood and physical state: Description of subjects and method. *Psychosomatic Medicine, 45,* 487–501.

Sarason, I. G., Johnson, J. H., & Siegel, J. M. (1978). Assessing the impact of life change: Development of the Life Experiences Survey. *Journal of Consulting and Clinical Psychology, 46,* 932–946.

Scott-Palmer, J., & Skevington. S. M. (1981). Pain during childbirth and menstruation: A study of locus of control. *Journal of Psychosomatic Research, 25,* 151–155.

Seligman, M. E. P., Abramson, L. Y., Semmel, A., & von Baeyer, C. (1979). Depressive attributional style. *Journal of Abnormal Psychology, 88,* 242–247.

Shipley, R. H., Butt, J. H., Horwitz, B., & Farbry, J. E. (1978). Preparation for a stressful medical procedure: Effect of amount of stimulus preexposure and coping style. *Journal of Consulting and Clinical Psychology, 46,* 499–507.

Siegel, J. M., Johnson, J. H., & Sarason, I. G. (1979). Life changes and menstrual discomfort. *Journal of Human Stress,* 41–46.

Skevington, S. M. (1979). Pain and locus of control: A social approach. In D. J. Oborn, M. H. Grunenberg, & J. P. Eise (Eds.). *Research in Psychology and Medicine, (Vol. I).* London: Academic Press.

Sommer, B. (1973). The effect of menstruation on cognitive and perceptual-motor behavior: A review. *Psychosomatic Medicine, 35,* 515–534.

Somer, B. (1978). Stress and menstrual distress. *Journal of Human Stress, 4,* 5–10, 41–47.

Spanos, N., Horton, C., & Chaves, J. (1975). The effects of two cognitive strategies on pain threshold. *Journal of Abnormal Psychology, 84,* 677–681.

Spielberger, C. D., Gorsuch, R. L., & Lushene, R. E. (1970). *Manual for the State-Trait Anxiety Inventory,* Palo Alto, CA: Consulting Psychologists Press.

Standley, K., Soule, B., & Copans, S. (1979). Dimensions of prenatal anxiety and their influence on pregnancy outcome. *American Journal of Obstetrics and Gynecology, 135,* 22–26.

Staub, E., & Kellett, P. S. (1972). Increasing pain tolerance by information about aversive stimuli. *Journal of Personality and Social Psychology, 21,* 198–203.

Steiner, M., & Carroll, B. J. (1977). The psychobiology of premenstrual dysphoria: Review of theories and treatment. *Psychoneuro-endicrinology, 2,* 321.

Steinmark, S. W., & Borkovec, T. D. (1974). Active and placebo treatment effects on moderate insomnia under counterdemand and positive demand instructions. *Journal of Abnormal Psychology, 83,* 157–163.

Stevens, R. J. (1976). Psychological strategies for management of pain in prepared childbirth. I: A review of the research. *Birth and the Family Journal, 3,* 157–164.

Sturgis, S. H., et al. (1962). *The gynecological patient.* New York: Grune Statton.

Suinn, R. M., & Richardson, F. (1971). Anxiety management training: A nonspecific behavior therapy program for anxiety control. *Behavior Therapy, 2,* 498–510.

Tasto, D. L., & Chesney, M. A. (1974). Muscle relaxation treatment for primary dysmenorrhea. *Behavior Therapy, 5,* 668–672.

Tilden, V. P. (1983). The relation of life stress and social support to emotional disequilibrium during pregnancy. *Research in Nursing and Health, 6,* 167–174.

Tourkow, L. P. (1979). Psychiatric knowledge and skills: Integral parts of complete care. *Michigan Medicine, 78,* 562–563.

True-Soderstrom, B. A., Buckwalter, K. C., & Kerfoot, K. M. (1983). Postpartum depression. *Maternal-Child Nursing Journal, 12,* 109–118.

Turk, D. (1975). *Cognitive control of pain: A skills training approach for the treatment of pain.* Unpublished master's thesis, University of Waterloo.

Turk, D. (1976). *An expanded skills training approach for the treatment of experimentally induced pain.* Unpublished doctoral dissertation, University of Waterloo.

Velvovsky, I., Platanov, K., Ploticher, V., & Shugom, E. (Eds.). (1960). *Painless childbirth through psychoprophylaxis.* (D. A. Myshne, Trans.). Moscow: Foreign Languages Publishing House.

Vila, J., & Beech, H. R. (1980). Premenstrual symptomatology: An interaction hypothesis. *British Journal of Social and Clinical Psychology, 19,* 73–80.

Walton, D., & Mather, M. D. (1963). The relevance of generalization techniques to the treatment of stammering and phobic symptoms. *Behaviour Research and Therapy, 1,* 121–125.

Warrick, L. H. (1974). *An aspect of prenatal nursing: Support to the high risk mother.* Paper presented at the American Nurses' Association Clinical Sessions, San Francisco. NY: Appleton-Century-Crofts.

Webster, S. K. (1978). Problems for diagnosis of spasmodic and congestive dysmenorrhea. In A. Dan, E. Graham, & C. Beech (Eds.). *The Menstrual Cycle: A Synthesis of Interdisciplinary Research* (pp. 292–304). New York: Springer.

Weil, S. G. (1981). The unspoken needs of families during high-risk pregnancies. *American Journal of Nursing, 81,* 2047–2049.

Weissmann, M. M., & Bothwell, B. (1976). Assessment of social adjustment by patient self-report. *Archives of General Psychiatry, 33,* 1111–1115.

Welch, D. (1979). Assessing psychosocial needs involved in cancer patient care during treatment. *Oncology Nursing Forum, 6,* 12–18.

White, M., & Ritchie, J. (1984). Psychological stressors in antepartum hospitalization: Reports from pregnant women. *Maternal-Child Nursing Journal, 13,* 47–56.

Wilcoxon, L. A., Schraeder, S. L., & Sherif, C. W. (1976). Daily self-reports on activities, life events, moods, and somatic changes during the menstrual cycle. *Psychosomatic Medicine, 38,* 339–417.

Williams, C. C., Williams, R. A., Griswold, M. J., & Holmes, T. H. (1975). Pregnancy and life change. *Journal of Psychosomatic Research, 19,* 123–129.

Williamson, P., & English, E. C. (1981). Stress and coping in first pregnancy: Couple-family-physician interaction. *Journal of Family Practice, 13,* 629–635.

Willmuth, L. R. (1975). Prepared childbirth and the concept of control. *JOGN Nursing, 4,* 38.

Wincze, J. P., & Caird, W. K. (1976). The effects of systematic desensitization in the treatment of essential sexual dysfunction in women. *Behavior Therapy, 7,* 335–342.

Wolpe, J. (1958). *Psychotherapy by reciprocal inhibition.* Stanford, CA: Stanford University Press.

Wolpe, J. (1969). *The practice of behavior therapy.* Oxford: Pergamon Press.

Wolpe, J. (1973). *The practice of behavior therapy* (2nd ed.). Oxford: Pergamon Press.

Woods, N. F., Dery, G. K., & Most, A. (1982). Stressful life events and perimenstrual symptoms. *Journals of Human Stress, 8,* 23–31.

Yaginuma, T. (1979). Progress and therapy of stress amenorrhea. *Fertility and Sterility, 32,* 36–39.

Youngren, M. A., & Lewinsohn, P. M. (1980). The functional relationship between depression and problematic interpersonal behavior. *Journal of Abnormal Psychology, 89,* 333–341.

Chapter 14

Stress Management and the Eating Disorders

John P. Foreyt
Jill K. McGavin

This is a unique chapter in this volume in that disorders are frequently viewed by laypersons as being under the control of the "victim." Although it is widely recognized that many disorders including chronic pain, headaches, hypertension, emphysema, and cardiovascular disease have a behavioral component, there is at least some disagreement about the victim's responsibility. The victims of these disorders are not typically given the entire blame for contracting and maintaining the disorders in their lives. Although society, in its efforts to believe that the world is a fair and just place, might hold people with these medical disorders somewhat responsible for their development, such disorders typically call forth at least minimally sympathetic responses. Even if they "brought it on themselves," any feel that there is little or nothing they can do about it now. Certainly, no matter how drastically they modify their behavior, they cannot effect total cure. What they did in the past is in the past, and there is nothing than can be done to change the past. For the most part, all that can be expected of the afflicted is that

they follow the prescribed medical regimen, give up any bad habits that might worsen their prognosis, and fight their disability and not their doctors.

Few of these qualifications are seen to apply to the case of persons, usually women, with obesity, bulimia, or anorexia nervosa. Obesity elicits disgust, not sympathy. Obese people are blamed for their excess weight, and it is assumed that the problem can be gotten rid of by the efforts of those who have it. The solution is simple, the requisite behavior is obvious: eat sensibly, reduce caloric intake, and exercise in moderation. Binge eating and purging behaviors are considered shameful. The solution, again, seems simple: stop binging, stop purging, and eat sensibly. Anorexia nervosa, on the other hand, has captured the imagination of the popular media. Even so, those who treat it or watch a family member or friend waste away, find that it is a perplexing and infuriating condition. Who can understand why young women are bound and determined to starve themselves to death? The women with these disorders are viewed as being responsible for or

Preparation of this chapter was supported in part by Grant Number 1 RO1 HL 33954-01 from the National Heart, Lung, and Blood Institute, National Institutes of Health, Bethesda, Maryland.

having, at least theoretically, control over their eating behavior.

If only the obese person would not eat so much and would show a little self-control, if only the bulimic would stop binging and purging, and if only the anorexic would eat sensibly, . . . then all would be fine. What could be simpler? The sad fact of the matter is that it is not this simple. Furthermore, the view that it *is*, *should*, or *could* be simple could lead to further stress in the lives of the women who battle these problems.

THE ROLE OF STRESS

Stress might play a role in the development of obesity and the eating disorders, but it is likely only one component of a highly complex set of factors involving physiology, cognition, behavior, and affect. Stress, of course, has correlates in each of these domains, but cannot be reduced to any one correlate. Currently, obesity and the eating disorders are regarded as multiply determined (Garfinkel & Garner, 1982). With respect to the role of stress in their development, there are four major questions requiring answers.

1. Is there a relationship between stress and obesity, bulimia, and anorexia nervosa?
2. If so, what is the nature of that relationship?
3. How can the development of this relationship be avoided or changed?
4. What will be the consequences of such changes?

In asking the first question, one assumes that the concept of stress is understood. This, however, is not the case. The concept of stress has a notorious history of conceptual confusion. Stress has been variously defined and subsumes such concepts as anxiety, conflict, frustration, emotional disturbance, trauma, alienation, and anomie (Cofer & Appley, 1964). In attempting to operationalize stress, some have focused on changed situational factors (Holmes & Rahe, 1967), assuming that they account for the largest portion of the variance, whereas others have considered intrapersonal factors (a stress reaction) to be the hallmark of stress (Selye, 1956). The importance of the interplay between personal factors and situational factors and how they interact over time has only recently been recognized and accepted.

Lazarus and Folkman (1984) have argued for and elaborated upon this position. They assumed that (a) stress reactions and coping are contextual and change from one type of encounter to the next, (b) psychological stress and coping change as the encounter unfolds, and (c) stress is a product of the person's appraisals or interpretations of events and her or his values and goals.

Not all events are equally stressful to all persons. Differences among individuals are in large part due to differences in those individuals' cognitive appraisals or perceptions of events. One dimension of importance in the appraisal is the desirability or undesirability of an event. Obviously, the same event can be judged to be desirable by one individual and undesirable by another or desirable and undesirable by the same person at two different times. One must consequently be cautious in generalizing across individuals. Appraisals can be broken down into categories; situations can be seen as challenging, threatening, benign, irrelevant or positive for one's well-being. Events viewed as challenging and threatening are stressful. Individuals also appraise themselves and what the situation requires of them. They ascertain what type of action is called for in response to the particular situation or event and whether they have appropriate and adequate resources to cope with the situation or to meet the challenge. Thus, in order to understand stress, we must allow for it to be tailored to individuals and their environments *as the relationship between the two unfolds over time*. The research that has been done on stress and the eating disorders has not yet clearly evaluated the interactive nature of stressors, cognitive appraisal, and the changing nature of coping.

Obesity and Stress

There is a relatively long history of researchers, theoreticians, and clinicians attempting to show a relationship between obesity and stress or anxiety (Robbins & Fray, 1980). In the psychoanalytic tradition, obese individuals are thought to be fixated at or regressed to the oral stage of psychosexual development. Obesity is a symptom of an underlying psychological conflict resulting from unresolved dependency needs (Jones, 1953). Individuals become obese by overeating in response to nonspecific tensions, because eating is a source of gratification when other areas of life provide little satisfaction (because of a related, underlying emotional illness e.g., depression), or by eating in order to achieve sedation because of a learned association between food and security or well-being (Hamburger, 1951) or both. More recently, Bruch (1980, 1981) argued that developmental obesity (which begins in childhood and adolescence) is due to overeating in response to intrapsychic stress resulting from inappropriate nurturance in childhood and a learned inability to distinguish among various needs (e.g., emotional and bodily). These hypotheses are essentially untested, although various related formulations have been explored empirically. Although they fall into several different categories, most try to relate present stressors or the experience of arousal or negative affect with eating behavior. The significance of these relationships for the development of obesity is not known. To clarify, eating in response to stress might be a consequence and not a cause of obesity. Perhaps people indulge themselves in their favorite (forbidden) misbehavior whenever they feel sorry for themselves or perceive themselves to be under stress. For the obese, this behavior is probably eating. Nonobese people might indulge themselves in other, merely different, vices.

Eating as a response to stress.

One line of research has attempted to show an abnormal relationship between negative affect and eating in the obese, compared with the nonobese. Obese persons consistently report that they perceive themselves to eat more when they feel emotionally upset, guilty, depressed, or angry than when they do not (Atkinson & Ringuette, 1967; Castelnuovo-Tedesco & Schiebel, 1975; Freed, 1947; Kalucy & Crisp, 1974; Leon & Chamberlain, 1973b; Plutchik, 1976). Holland, Maslin, and Copley (1970) compared obese and normal-weight persons and found that the normal-weight persons were comparatively less likely to report that they ate when not hungry, when anxious, or when depressed than the obese subjects. Furthermore, eating in response to emotional arousal assessed by self-report techniques has been shown to predict a negative treatment outcome (Leon & Chamberlain, 1973a, 1973b; Leon & Rosenthal, 1984). These investigations were based upon the hypothesis that obese persons eat in response to anxiety, perhaps to reduce it, and are not appropriately responsive to interoceptive, internal cues regarding hunger and satiation.

This hypothesis has been tested in experimental situations in which the stressor could be manipulated. Schachter, Goldman, and Gordon (1968) found that normal-weight male college students reduced their intake when they were led to expect a painful electrical shock, compared with when they expected only a mild one, but that obese male college students did not respond differentially to these two conditions in terms of intake. Using irregular noise and insoluble puzzles, Meyer and Pudel (1972) were able to alter food intake of subjects 30% of the time; over two-thirds of these alterations occurred in the direction of increased intake. Moreover, increased intake occurred most frequently in the obese, whereas decreased intake was most likely in the underweight. McKenna (1972) threatened his subjects with physiological measurements requiring the collection of blood, urine, and stool samples and found that this threat decreased the consumption of normal-weight controls and increased the intake of obese subjects. Obese subjects were found to eat more than nonobese subjects under a variety of arousing conditions (sexual, humoral, or fearful) but did not differ from nonobese subjects in terms of intake after viewing a nonarousing film (travelogue) (White, 1973).

Reznick and Balch (1977) found that obese male and female college students ate similar amounts regardless of whether they were told that scores on an experimental task reflected intelligence and that they would be shocked for errors (high-anxiety condition) or given relaxation-inducing instructions (low-anxiety condition), but a larger number of obese subjects (compared to normal-weight subjects) ate in the low-anxiety condition than in the high-anxiety condition. Anxiety led to increased consumption among obese individuals, compared with nonobese individuals, when the source of their arousal was unclear but not when it was labeled for them (Slochower 1976, 1983). Specifically, when obese subjects were given false feedback about their heart rate (that it was abnormally fast) and told that the laboratory conditions generally caused subjects' hearts to beat faster, they ate less than when they were given the same feedback without such an explanation. Slochower and Kaplan (1980) found that a perceived inability to control the source of arousal and the absence of a label or explanation contributed independently and additively to increased eating in obese, but not in normal-weight subjects.

Experimental data also exist that qualify or contradict the findings just reviewed. Abramson and Wunderlich (1972) were unable to induce overeating in obese subjects. Obese persons did not react differently when they were exposed to *objective fear* (a shock) versus a type of *neurotic anxiety* (false feedback regarding interpersonal stability), as had been predicted on the basis of psychoanalytic thinking. Although Schachter et al. (1968) found obese and normal differences in intake, their findings did not support the view that the eating was done to manage anxiety. The obese subjects did not report any fear reduction following eating, and, consequently, this second hypothesis was not considered to have been supported. In the McKenna (1972) study, the interaction between intake and weight status was only observed when the food was high in palatability, not when it was low. Consequently, it was reasoned that anxiety reduction must not be the primary causal agent in overeating. Had anxiety reduction been the primary cause of overeating, McKenna argued, overeating should have occurred regardless of such a factor as palatability. And again, eating did not reduce reported anxiety in either group. Abramson and Stinson (1977) did not find any between-group differences comparing normal and overweight female college students. Both groups ate more when they were bored than when they were interested. Finally, Ruderman (1983) found that female obese individuals ate *less* when highly anxious than when mildly anxious, whereas normal-weight subjects ate about the same under both of these conditions. Ruderman suggested that this was due to an inverted U-shaped relationship between anxiety and eating in the obese persons. Consumption was thought to be lower at high levels of anxiety because anxiety interferes with response sequencing. Why this relationship between anxiety and response sequencing should be specific to obese persons is not clear.

In summary, tests of the hypothesis that eating is a general response to anxiety that functions to reduce anxiety in the obese have produced conflicting findings. Contributing to the problem has been a reliance on laboratory studies that have depended on manipulations that were contrived in terms of how arousal was induced, the responses available to subjects, and the range of coping processes and emotions studied (Leon & Roth, 1977; Lowe & Fisher, 1983). It is not clear how the findings generalize to the natural stressors and coping responses available in everyday life.

Fortunately, there have been several attempts to explore the relationship between naturally occurring stressors and eating or weight in obese and nonobese persons. Slochower, Kaplan, and Mann (1981) found emotional eating in response to a naturally occurring stressor. Slochower (1983) compared students' eating behavior in the laboratory just prior to taking a final exam to their eating after the exam period and found that obese college women ate more when under stress than did nonobese college women. Lowe and Fisher (1983) asked normal-weight and overweight female college students to monitor their moods prior to eating for a period of 13 days. They found that obese women experienced more intense negative emotional arousal prior to eating and that this arousal correlated with percentage of overweight. Intake during snacks in terms of calories was higher under conditions of negative mood and lower under conditions of positive mood in the obese, whereas the reverse was true of the normal-weight subjects.

In a similar line of research, relapse following successful weight-loss, treatment has been related to high levels of reported stress during the follow-up (Gormally, Rardin, & Black, 1980). Interestingly, there was not a significant difference (defined at the .05 level of probability) in overall life stressors between those who successfully maintained their weight loss and those who did not. But, those who were successful reported that stressful life events impacted on their weight status *positively*, whereas those who had not maintained their weight loss indicated that their stressful life experiences had influenced their weight status *negatively*. The successful and unsuccessful participants appeared to have interpreted the stressful life events differently, at least retrospectively. It is possible that those who were successful at maintaining their weight loss experienced more desirable or positive changes and that those unsuccessful at weight-loss maintenance experienced more undesirable, negative life changes. It is also possible, however, that those who were unsuccessful at maintaining their weight loss were motivated to find a reason (something to blame) for their lack of maintenance and chose to evaluate their life changes negatively or to selectively attend to the negative life changes as a way of justifying their failure. Answers to these questions await further research.

The Obese as hypersensitive to stressors.

Another major hypothesis regarding the relationship between stress and eating has postulated that the obese are more emotionally reactive in general and, consequently, experience higher levels of stress than the nonobese. Obese subjects have been repeatedly found to be more distressed, by self-report, by a variety of noxious experimental stimuli than normal-weight subjects (Abramson & Wunderlich, 1972; Pliner, Meyer, & Blankstein, 1974; Rodin, Elman, & Schachter, 1974). Rodin (1982) found that the threat and use of a painful electrical shock interfered with the performance of obese persons more than it interfered with the performance of nonobese persons on a complex maze task. She argued that arousal is a general activator and that, under conditions of arousal, an organism is likely to exhibit the most available, dominant, and reinforcing response (Rodin, 1977, 1982). For this reasoning to hold up as an explanation for obesity or its maintenance, it would have to be demonstrated or assumed that eating is a more available, dominant, or reinforcing response for obese than nonobese persons or that the obese are more aroused than the nonobese (and eating is an available, dominant, and reinforcing response for everyone). In a separate but related type of research program, Leon and Chamberlain (1973b) had current, formerly obese, and never-obese women monitor the occurrence of traumatic events and the level of tension for 3 days, and they found that the current and formerly obese women reported more traumatic events and higher levels of tension. Similarly, Doell and Hawkins (1982) found that overweight subjects reported less enjoyment of pleasant activities than did 211 normal control subjects. Jacobs and Wagner (1984) compared obese, previously obese, and never obese subjects in terms of time spent in various situations or activities and their enjoyment of those activities. Obese persons spent the least amount of time per week and never-obese spent the most time with friends; previously obese were in between the other two groups but closer to the obese than to the never obese. With respect to social activities, however, the obese reported spending more time than the obese and the never obese. Previously obese individuals rated social activities as much less reinforcing than either of the other two groups.

Dieting as a stressor.

Herman and Polivy (1975) have argued that the hyperresponsiveness to emotional cues that has been found in the obese is due to the consequences of obesity, in particular the effects of chronic dieting, and not the obesity per se. They measured the amount of ice cream subjects consumed in an ostensible taste test after the subjects were led to expect that they would be receiving either an electrical shock or a "mild tactile stimulation". Chronic dieters, also called restrained eaters, consumed more ice cream than unrestrained eaters in the electrical shock, or high-anxiety, condition. Restrained subjects became more anxious than unrestrained subjects in the high-anxiety condition. Herman and Mack (1975) also broke these dieters' "restraint" by giving them a forced, high-calorie preload, a milkshake. The restrained eaters who had had their restraint broken went on to consume larger amounts of ice cream in a taste test, whereas their unrestrained counterparts decreased the size of their intake following such a preload (this finding has been replicated by Hibscher & Herman, 1977, and Spencer & Fremouw, 1979). It is reasoned that restrained eaters consciously attempt to restrict their intake, in other words must exercise self-control, and that the exercise of restraint is stressful and leads to counter regulatory eating patterns. In other words, chronic dieters tend to be immoderate in both directions; they alternate between overeating and undereating. Furthermore, this effect appeared to be cognitively mediated. This counterregulatory pattern was not induced when subjects were led to believe that the preload was not high in calories (Polivy, 1976). The subjects apparently perceived, under the former condition, that they had blown their diets and felt that they might as well give up.

Animal studies.

A laboratory model of stress-induced eating has been developed using rats. Gross (1968) used unpredictable deprivation intervals, or scarcity, as a stressor. Compared to constant and regular deprivation and no deprivation, unpredictable scarcity for a period of 100 days led to a pattern of external control in rats. This pattern continued long after the scarcity had ceased, and it also applied to food cues that did not involve eating.

Another of the stressors investigated in rats has been a mild tail pinch. Antelman and Szechtman (1975) found that mild tail pinch induces eating in rats when administered acutely, and Rowland and Antelman (1976) reported that chronic applications could lead to substantial weight gains.

Anorexia, Bulimia, and Stress

Theoretical accounts of the etiology of anorexia nervosa have emphasized the role of stress or anxiety. The fact that stress plays a role, however, has been taken for granted, and little research exists that explores the nature of the relationship directly. For example, in its most popular conceptual form, anorexia norvosa is viewed as a pathological reaction or maturational crisis provoked by the "stress" of the onset of adolescence, in particular to changes associated with the emergence of sexuality, greater autonomy, and increased responsibility. This stress has been viewed psychoanalytically in terms of identification with a negative maternal introject, with the development of secondary sexual characteristics, and by social learning theorists in terms of the new social role, demands, and expectations associated with adolescence and approaching adulthood. Cognitive–behavioral theorists have discussed persons with anorexic and bulimic behaviors as having faulty cognitive assumptions and self-regulatory deficits (Garner, 1986). These deficits are believed to be the consequence of negative expectancies following repeated exposure to uncontrollable aversive events. Recent clinical attention (Johnson & Larson, 1982) given to the affective domain has led some to believe that the binge–purge cycle distracts attention away from negative affective states associated with feelings of low self-esteem and ineffectiveness. Family theorists have emphasized the difficulties that the families of bulimics and anorexics have in allowing them to grow up and apart. Each of these perspectives assumes that the dysfunction and its causes are related to stress or anxiety, interpersonal, intrapersonal, or environmental. It seems probable that anorexia nervosa and bulimic symptoms are the joint outcome of a combination of individual and environmental (familial, sociocultural, peer group) vulnerabilities or inadequacies and life stresses.

In one of the very few empirical studies of stress and anorexia, Strober (1984) compared bulimic and restrictive anorexics with respect to life stresses. He found that bulimic anorexics, anorexics who show a pattern of binging and purging, had experienced two and a half times the magnitude of life stress generally observed in normal adolescents over a comparable period (Coddington, 1972). Furthermore, comparing the bulimic anorexics to restrictive anorexics, anorexics who control their weight by strict dieting, the bulimic anorexics had also experienced significantly more life stress than the restrictive group in each of three 6-month periods preceding the onset of the illness. Specifically, the bulimic anorexics reported more changes in acceptance by peers, increases in arguments between and with parents, and more serious

illnesses of parents. There was also a significant correlation between the severity of the bulimia and the stress score and between the stress and depression scores. Restrictive and bulimic anorexics also differ in terms of chronic anxiety scores (Wold, 1983), although these studies rely upon self-report data and do not address whether the conflicts are actually greater or whether they are merely perceived of as greater.

Stress and Binge Eating

In a nonbulimic population, Kagan and Squires (1983) found compulsive eating and dieting to be related to stress in a college student population (423 subjects); the most salient stresses were related to grades, finances, self-confidence, and career. Wolf and Crowther (1983) investigated several personality and eating-habit variables as predictors of the severity of binge eating and weight deviation. The amount of stress experienced in the past year was a significant predictor of binge eating. Severity of binge eating was also related to anorexiclike eating attitudes, dissatisfaction with body image, and poor self-image. These findings warrant further study. *First*, these data rely upon self-report, which is subject to biased perceptions. It is not clear whether the amount of stress experienced by subjects with binge eating problems was actually different or whether they merely perceived it to be so. *Second*, daily activities and events generally considered to be of less importance, such as daily hassles, need to be included in such studies. Given that binges most often occur at times during the day when the person is alone in unstructured situations, usually during evening hours at home (Larson & Johnson, 1985; Pyle, Mitchell, & Eckert, 1981), Johnson (1985) has argued that binge eating is associated with "transition times." Gandour (1984) also emphasized transitions between home and school or work and added such events as returning to parents' home after time away, drinking alcohol, and going out with a member of the opposite sex.

Negative internal states can be considered stressful and have been targeted as precipitants of binge eating. Such states include feelings such as tension, boredom, and loneliness (Gandour, 1984). Leon, Carroll, Chernyk and Finn (1985) surveyed 213 male and female college students regarding their eating habits. Thirty-four percent of the female students and 30% of the male students admitted to binge eating defined as "gorging or eating excessive quantities of food, i.e., consuming 4,000 calories or more in a period of one to two hours or less" (p. 47). Anxiety feelings before a binge were reported by 57.1% of the females and 50% of the males. A significantly greater proportion of the females indicated that before and during a binge they were depressed, angry, and disgusted with themselves than did the males. Edelman (1981) investigated what she termed *emotion–distress related* eating in 49 men and 51 women aged 21 to 55 years and concluded that this was common among women and that motives for binge eating varied across subjects, but each subject would typically endorse only one or two reasons (e.g., anxiety, loneliness, frustration). Edelman suggested that binge eating might reduce stress for many people.

Summary of Research Studies.

Laboratory and experimental research into the area of stress, obesity, and the eating disorders is only in its infancy. Very little is actually known, and the evidence that exists seems to point in slightly varied directions. Clinically, however, there appears to be some consensus that a concept such as stress could be useful. Clearly, an overwhelming percentage of overweight and eating-disordered people, usually women, identify the fact that stress and negative emotions influence their eating behaviors negatively. Thus, for the purposes of this chapter, it will be assumed that *stress might have potentially detrimental effects in terms of mood, functioning, and interpersonal relationships in the psychological domain and in terms of compliance with respect to the initiation and continuance of adaptive, health-related behaviors in the medical area, whether or not stress plays a role in the development of the disorder.* The research studies examining the relationship between stress, obesity, and eating disorders have been limited by inadequate definitions of stress and eating disorders. Stress is either defined in terms of certain situations that are considered to be stressful by definition, such as university final examinations, or in terms of intrapersonal dispositions or events such as the experience of "anxiety." In order to adequately address the hypothesis, research would have to look at situational and intrapersonal factors in interaction. We suspect that, if this interactive nature of stress could be captured in an empirically rigorous manner, the hypothesis that stress, obesity, and eating disorders are related would be supported more clearly and productively.

The model of stress and coping of Lazarus and Folkman (1984) offered a framework within which such hypotheses could be tested on an individual level. As stated previously, this framework emphasizes the role of appraisal and coping and how these are mediated by a person's commitments, values, and resources. It is not the case that stress is "created equal." In particular, in order for any event to be stressful, it must tax individuals beyond their resources and threaten something of importance to them. "Vulnerability is not just a deficit in resources, but is defined by the relationship between the individual's patterns of commitments and his or her resources for warding off threats to these commitments" (Lazarus & Folkman, 1984, p. 51). Commitments include that which is important or has meaning to the person, in other words, is rewarding or reinforcing. Commitments are not absolutistic, and they vary by degree. Consequently, "potential for an encounter to be psychologically harmful or threatening, or for that matter, challenging, is directly related to the depth with which a commitment is held" (p. 58). Emotions are viewed as a by-product of appraisal; they can be used to indicate what is important to a person.

A second major concern is the person's appraisal of a situation in terms of what action is called for and whether he or she has the resources to carry out this action. Whether or not a person perceives a stressful situation as one which he or she can actually do something about, versus one he or she has to accept, is a potent predictor of whether the person uses emotion-focused coping or problem-focused coping (Folkman & Lazarus, 1980). It is also suggested that being able to believe that there is a "higher purpose" for the difficulties in one's life can make those hardships and losses less overwhelming.

It would, however, be a mistake to believe that people with similar problems necessarily appraise situations similarly or hold or share identical commitments, values, or environments, although there might be some commonalities. In each case, the relationship between stresses and their problematic eating behaviors needs to be analyzed in terms of its different aspects in the cognitive, behavioral, affective, and interpersonal realms. This information helps to guide decisions regarding where, when, and how to intervene. In this model, the goal of stress management is to stimulate new ways of appraising the situations that produce distress and of coping with them in more effective ways. Therapy should be built around the clients' particular areas of vulnerability and strength. People only seek therapy for distress that is overwhelming and disruptive and affects an area central to them.

STRESS MANAGEMENT

Person Factors

To explore the relationship of stress to the treatment of obesity, we must consider the specific relevancy to the disorder of various commitments, appraisals, meanings, and coping skills. Whether obese women are able to realign their commitments and values in terms of a thinner life-style, are able to appraise potentially threatening situations as challenges and cope effectively, or have control over their eating behaviors influences the amount of stress they experience regarding their weight and weight changes.

Commitments and Values.

In terms of obesity and attempts to reduce to a desirable weight, it is difficult at first glance to see anything more than the obvious. Significant obesity is a health risk and elicits very negative social evaluations. Obese people are discriminated against and criticized for having no willpower, self-respect, self-control, or all three. It is easy to argue that the positive health and social consequences of weight reduction represent commitment-worthy values. These are the slogans of laypersons, the media, and a large percentage of health professionals. Unfortunately, these types of values do not appear adequate to initiate and maintain adequate changes in eating behavior for some individuals, or the stress of not being able to live up to these socially lauded values might interfere with the obese person's ability to cope. Exploration of the individual's commitments and values regarding food, eating, and weight could result in productive paths to follow in terms of stress management.

For example, a woman who comes from a traditional Mexican–American family or culture that emphasizes the importance of a selfless, nurturing, all-giving, abundantly fertile mother figure might not be able to follow a reducing diet if it is framed as a self-improvement project, yet she might be able to change her eating habits if such a change is presented as something more that she must do to be a good mother, one who will live to help with her grandchildren's weddings (Cousins, 1985). Continuing with this same example, for a Mexican–American woman to establish herself as someone with a separate and independent identity could be very threatening to her kinship network. If the woman is asked to prepare a dinner for herself

separate from that which she serves to her family, the unity of the kinship network might be undermined. If the women in a community tend to put on 15 pounds with the birth of every child, a mother who does not do this might be seen as deviant, dangerous, or suspect. Strategies must be developed that are sensitive to such commitments. Beliefs regarding the importance of being attractive, about what it means if one diets and spends time on appearance and one's body, need to be explored. If the body is viewed as unimportant in a spiritual or existential way, it will be hard to convince people that they should deprive themselves or work hard to be attractive. Overweight clients who come to health professionals believing that they should lose weight and complaining that they cannot motivate themselves might in fact hold core values that work against their compliance with weight-loss procedures.

A dominant value in today's culture is that people, particularly women, should be loving and giving. Food can be one of the major vehicles for the expression of togetherness, love, caring, and nurturance. To be loving and approving, of oneself or others, one might feel the need to be involved in the giving and receiving of foodstuffs. The prototype is the mother who slaves over the hot stove all day to keep her family happy. Both she and her family benefit from this arrangement. She gains esteem by her perhaps extreme self-sacrifice, and the family eats well and is assured by her love. In the same or other settings, weight might be a symbol of power or greatness. It might be very important for a person to be large to effectively communicate greatness or powerfulness; if this person reduced in size, it could be necessary to develop quite different, possibly more difficult, ways of being powerful. In these and other cases, dieting might be viewed as a form of punishment or hard-hearted self-denial.

Each of these values or commitments, which might not be readily voiced or acknowledged, can make weight loss and dieting stressful and less successful. To prevent or alleviate such stress, we suggest that these values be addressed and that creative, alternative ways of expressing these commitments be explored. These are common and not-so-common core values that influence weight and eating. To understand particular clients, one must understand their core values and the role of stress in their lives. Discussions about what clients find stressful, what they find fearful or worrisome, and what they find desirable give clues to the role of stress in their lives and can hint at the relationship between stress and their eating problems. It is sometimes productive to have clients imagine what changes would occur in their daily stresses if they were able to rid themselves of their eating problems. Some overweight clients are surprised to discover that their fat insulates and protects them from some of the stresses of the world. Given that one's appraisal of a situation could be crucial in determining coping, helping clients to perceive situations in ways that are challenging, benign, or irrelevant, rather than dangerous or threatening, might help them cope effectively.

Coping.

Recently, attention has been given to the importance of problem-solving strategies in working with the obese (Marlatt & Gordon, 1980; Perri, Shapiro, Ludwig, Twentyman, & McAdoo, 1984). These emphasize the identification of situations that are likely to provoke a relapse and strategies to avoid and maintain one's resolve in the face of great risk. Lazarus and Folkman (1984) suggested that the appraisal of a situation, especially one's beliefs about control, determines whether a stressful encounter is viewed positively as a challenge or negatively as a threat. Stressful situations that are judged to be beyond one's control typically call forth emotion-focused coping strategies, whereas problem-solving strategies are utilized in situations one believes one can actually do something about. To enhance or encourage effective coping, the client's perceptions of events might need to be modified. There are three points relevant to this issue.

First, if food and weight are judged to cause stress and are viewed by the client as being beyond her or his control, it might be difficult to encourage the client to use problem-solving strategies without changing the belief that the task is beyond her or him. Such appraisals vary across situations and contexts and change over time. In particular, it has been argued that dieters and binge eaters lose control of their eating behavior after they perceive themselves to have overindulged. Because they have "blown it" already, they feel they might as well indulge further. To reduce the stressfulness of such situations and reduce the possibility that a slip will become a full-blown relapse, one can encourage more lenient standards such that the initial slip will not be judged so harshly. On the other hand, in speaking of addictions, Peele (1985) argued that, to take charge of a problem behavior, the client must develop an overwhelming desire to quit. The first step in developing this desire involves the accumulation of

enough unhappiness that one believes that the rewards of quitting will surpass the rewards gotten from the habit. This reasoning follows the philosophy that it has to get bad before it can get better. The stress of changing is always contrasted with or relative to the stress of *not* changing. This hypothesis has gone unexplored in the field of eating disorders. *Second,* "problematic" eating behavior might be an emotion-focused coping strategy. If eating or gaining weight is a way to pamper oneself, express anger, or accept oneself, the development of other ways to express these emotions or sentiments might be quite helpful. Thus, it is important to help the client develop or uncover alternative affect-regulation strategies. *Third,* as a therapist, one needs to be cautious in pushing for problem-solving strategies when the client is not receptive to them. Actively trying to take control of a problem might seem desirable to the therapist, but clients might not perceive themselves as capable of or motivated sufficiently to do so.

To move from emotion-focused coping to active problem solving or to add to their repertoire of active problem-solving without reducing the emotion-focused coping, clients might first need to prove that they have control over their eating behaviors. This could be applicable to obesity and the eating disorders, to some extent. It might not be enough to educate bulimic or obese people regarding effective problem-solving techniques. If they do not believe they can control their eating to begin with, they might never implement the techniques appropriately. In fact, overweight persons state that they have less control over eating than normal-weight persons, and females believe that they have less control over eating than males (Klesges, Beatty, & Berry, 1985). O'Leary (1985) argued that persons with eating disorders have low self-efficacy with respect to their management of food and body weight. She suggested that low self-efficacy might undermine the utilization of effective self-regulatory measures for weight control and that a major goal of treatment should be to enhance self-efficacy.

Outcome studies of weight-loss programs support the view that self-efficacy plays a role in weight loss, particularly in persons with an internal locus of control (Chambliss & Murray, 1979; Weinberg, Hughes, Critelli, England, & Jackson, 1984). Lazarus and Folkman (1984) pointed out that it is possible to give people more control than they will benefit from. In fact, in the work of Chambliss and Murray (1979), it was found that self-efficacy attributions did not increase ability to reduce weight in subjects who viewed their behavior as externally controlled. Obese persons might not wish to be given complete control over their eating behavior; instead, they might want to be *told* what to do, or they might prefer to believe that their weight is controlled by external events. At the same time, it is possible for the therapist to take too much control (Rozensky & Bellack, 1976). Highly self-reinforcing subjects, subjects highly disposed to deliver self-reinforcement, were hindered in their weight-loss efforts when the therapist had control over financial contingencies, whereas low self-reinforcing subjects' weight loss was unaffected by self- or therapist-control. It is also important to keep in mind that different forms of coping are appropriate at different times. Information seeking, one form of active coping, might be related to adaptive psychological functioning at one point and not at others. However "good," almost any form of coping can be misused. As with eating, one can exercise to excess. It is thus important to allow for some individualization and modification regarding the amount of control the client is led to experience and the type of coping employed.

To predict which situations will elicit stress and threatening emotions like anger, boredom, and guilt, there are two important questions to ask. *First,* How difficult is the situation for the person? *Second,* How much is at stake for the person in that situation? Lazarus and Folkman argued that the more difficult the situation and the more there is at stake in the situation or the greater the personal commitment the greater the potential threat or harm. For the obese person, no matter how stressful it is to be obese, efforts to change are likely to be very threatening because much might be at stake. He or she might perceive that weight status influences his or her interpersonal relationships, job, self-esteem, and health. These situations could be ones in which the person has experienced problems and failures. She or he might be wondering whether it is her or him or her or his "fat" that is responsible for the failures and might not want to risk finding out which it is. Thus, although there is much at stake in the way of positive outcomes for the obese person if he or she loses weight, there could be frightening possibilities in store as well.

Environmental Factors.

Much has been said about the individual and coping, but it is always important to remember that obese persons might have the requisite coping skills but fail to employ them because of contingencies in their environment. Social support has been targeted as a major moderator variable with respect to stress and health (Janis, 1983). Although social support was not found to be related to illness, there was a stronger relationship between negative life events and illness among people with low levels of social support than among those with high levels (Sarason, Sarason, Potter, & Antoni, 1985). Extrapolating from these findings, we realize it could be that the relationship between obesity and stress is only marked in persons lacking satisfactory levels of social support or in persons whose environment is actively nonsupportive. Furthermore, environments that support the overweight person might be less supportive of a normal-weight or thin person. Anecdotally, it is not uncommon to hear women who have lost significant amounts of weight complaining that their husbands have become jealous and accusatory. Their previously secure romantic relationships have now become riddled with conflicts and suspicions that the weight reducer is having an affair, is planning to end the relationship, or both. Other women might fear that they will become promiscuous or unfaithful if given the chance. They might expect that their environment would offer them that "chance" if they were thinner, and, for this reason, they are hindered in their attempts to reach a desirable body weight and maintain it. Again, however, this might not be a risk or a potential stress if the family or marital relationships and social environment are stable and supportive. Ironically, these situations might be stressful precisely because the marriage or relationship is valued and there is a commitment to it.

When values conflict, as they do in a situation where loyalty to a relationship is pitted against desire to be healthy or more attractive, the stress can be nearly intolerable. When the dieter actually wishes to sever a relationship or to make changes in his or her interpersonal environment, weight loss can represent a relatively nonstressful mechanism for doing so. The key is the individual's appraisal of the situation, both the dieter and the persons involved in relationships with the dieter, and the perceived consequences of changes in weight status or eating behavior. Environmental events can only be stressful if they are appraised as threatening. Thus, person factors determine whether an environmental event is or is not stressful. The environment, in contrast, determines how critical the person factors will be. The more ambiguous a situation, for example, the more person factors play a prominent role. According to the model developed by Lazarus and Folkman (1984), weight and dieting are situations with a mixture of both very ambiguous and very unambiguous factors. Thus, person and situation factors can both be presumed to influence eating and weight regulation, although in different ways and perhaps at different times.

Formal properties of situations.

Novelty.

If a situation is completely novel, then it is not previously connected with harm, danger, or mastery and cannot be threatening. People gain experience with dieting and the impact of weight both directly and vicariously. Dieting and weight regulation efforts are not all novel in today's society. Thus, they are potentially threatening. If these efforts are associated with mastery or gain, an appraisal of challenge is more likely. If they are associated with failure, the efforts are more likely to be threatening and therefore stressful. Most people who attempt to and do lose weight, tend to gain it back. The efforts are likely to end in failure. Thus, if the person who is interested in losing weight is aware that the outcome of weight-loss efforts is generally negative, the situation is likely to be stressful.

Less obviously, there are also some possibly novel interpersonal situations. Along with a new body come new reactions from friends, families, people in the workplace, and strangers on the street. Onlookers might feel rejected, criticized, inferior, angry, competitive, or, of course, jealous. Formerly obese persons could find themselves "promoted" to jobs that are highly visible. These positions might require interpersonal skills they don't have or that have grown rusty with disuse. Furthermore, they might perceive that the new "positive" reactions they get only underscore how "awful" they used to look or make them feel like they have joined the ranks of a very superficial, appearance-preoccupied group of people.

Predictability.

Event uncertainty refers to the probability of something's occurring. The more likely a negative event is to occur, the more stressful it is; the greater the uncertainty regarding an event's occurrence, the greater the arousal. With weight loss, more than 90% of those who lose weight regain it. Given such a high likelihood, relapse is presumably very stressful. The interpersonal reactions just discussed might be highly predictable.

Temporal imminence.

The closer a negative event is in time, the more stressful. This reminds us of the mad pushes people make to lose weight prior to a date or prior to a major, stressful engagement. In this case, it might be more appropriate to divert the stress-management efforts toward the event than toward the weight.

Temporal duration.

It is commonly believed that enduring, chronic events wear people down. Certainly, a lifelong need to restrict and restrain one's intake, fighting one's wants and desires, would appear to be stressful. No one can tell you how long it will take; after a time a dieter tends to feel she or he will be dieting "forever."

Temporal uncertainty.

Temporal uncertainty refers to a situation that is going to occur, but *when* it will occur is unknown. Interpersonal reactions, although highly probable, are not temporally fixed and can occur at almost any time.

Timing in the life cycle.

Events that usually occur at a certain developmental stage or time in life are hypothesized to cause stress when they occur too early or too late. With respect to obesity, it is quite possible that some overweight boys and girls are not given the opportunity for heterosexual contact that their normal-weight peers receive in early adolescence. Thus, they are not given the support of their peers, do not receive equal preparation for a new role, and might not be able to take pride and satisfaction in these experiences. Early-maturing girls weigh more than their less physically mature counterparts, a potentially stressful situation. Changes in their bodies might be associated more with weight than maturity in these girls' minds. Furthermore, they might be pressured to assume more mature roles interpersonally, roles for which they are probably not well prepared.

Dieters or successful weight losers might also become a source of stress to those around them and be punished for it. For example, if a woman who used food to regulate her emotions quits and becomes more assertive, aggressive, or passive-aggressive, there will be others who will be pressured to cope with this woman's new style of relating. For every woman who quits eating as a way of socializing, there is another person who has lost an eating partner. Furthermore, people might assume that weight losers, by their actions, are implying that others should do similarly and they might feel judged or condemned. Not only must these newly thin people or conscientious dieters learn to manage their emotions and eating behaviors, but they must also learn to cope with the new reactions of their environment. They might react by becoming angry. It might not seem fair that thin people can eat and stay thin, when they can't. Some dieters feel that thin people do not understand and certainly do not have to work so hard, feel so weak, and deprive themselves so much. Some dieters might feel that they are being taught to distrust their own bodies, to ignore basic survival messages regarding hunger, and to say no to themselves, and that what they want is "bad." The eventual outcome of the effort will probably be determined by the balance of the stresses, whether it is more stressful to change or not to change.

Stress management and anorexia and bulimia.

Most of the issues raised with respect to obesity also apply to the treatment of the anorexic and the bulimic. We will highlight here those additional areas of concern.

Person factors.

Descriptors such as extreme compliancy, emotional reservedness, compulsivity, and lack of independence have been used to describe anorexic and bulimic patients (Bruch, 1973; Kay & Leigh, 1954; King, 1963; Halmi, 1974; Morgan & Russell, 1975). Recent psychometric studies by Strober (1980; 1981) comparing anorexic patients with age-matched depressive and personality disordered controls have supported these observations. The anorexics were found to be relatively obsessional, introverted, emotionally reserved and socially insecure, self-denying, deferential to others, overcompliant, and self-abasing and less autonomous, as well as overly rigid and stereotyped in their thinking. These characteristics did not disappear after weight recovery and thus were not due to the effects of near-starvation body weights. Compared with extremely weight preoccupied women, anorexics are significantly different in terms of feelings of ineffectiveness, interoceptive unawareness, and interpersonal distrust, but they are not different in terms of dieting, perfectionism, and attitudes about shape (Garner, Olmsted, Polivy & Garfinkel, 1984). Further studies have shown that anorexics can be meaningfully separated into two

groups: those who lose weight by not eating, restricting anorexics, and those who binge eat and purge, usually by vomiting (Casper, Eckert, Halmi, Goldberg, & Davis, 1980; Garfinkel, Moldofsky & Garner, 1980; Russell, 1979; Strober, Salkin, Burroughs, & Morrell, 1982). Bulimic anorexics are described as unable to identify and articulate internal states, impulsive (e.g., shoplift, abuse multiple substances, self-mutilate), extroverted, sexually active, and labile in mood. Bulimic patients have been identified as having difficulties with affective stability and control involving impulsivity, guilt, depression, and anxiety (Katzman & Wolchik, 1984; Norman & Herzog, 1983; Pyle et al., 1981). Loro (1984) has suggested that bulimics not only are perfectionists, but also think in dichotomous, all-or-none polarities. Restricting anorexics have been found to be more socially withdrawn, more introverted, and more independent than normal controls and a vomiters-and-purgers group (Beumont, 1977).

A distorted body image and fear of weight gain are salient features of anorexia and bulimia (Bruch, 1962, 1973, 1977; Garfinkel & Garner, 1982; Garner & Garfinkel, 1981; Garner, Garfinkel, & Moldofsky, 1978; Hawkins, Fremouw, & Clement, 1984; Schlesier-Stropp, 1984; Slade & Russell, 1973; Wooley & Kearney-Cooke, 1986). Subjective distress and visceral arousal to weight-gain images have been found to be related to severity of bulimia (Cutts & Barrios, 1985). Body image disturbance is greater in bulimic than restrictive anorexics (Button, Fransella, & Slade, 1977; Freeman, Thomas, Solyom, & Miles, 1983), and it is a negative treatment prognosticator (Garfinkel, Moldofsky, & Garner, 1977). Freeman et al. (1983) have suggested that body image disturbance is related to adherence to a "thin is competent" stereotype, suggesting that competence and effectiveness is the underlying value.

In highlighting these cognitive and "personality" factors, we do not wish to imply that anorexia and bulimia are the results of immutable, causally prepotent, intrapsychic variables. It is our view that anorexia and bulimia are multidetermined, multidimensional disorders. Such descriptions merely point out probable areas of difficulty. Whether such factors actually play a role is something that requires investigation on an individual basis. The behavioral parameters to explore in such an investigation include weight-regulation behaviors (dieting, eating habits, exercising, scale behavior, reactions to weight loss and gain, and knowledge about nutrition), purge behaviors, and binge behaviors. In all cases, incidents and activities around the times these behaviors were initiated, times these behaviors increased, and times these behaviors decreased offer clues to the functions of the symptoms. Interpersonal and heterosexual relationships are frequently significant.

Commitments and values.

The relentless dietary restraint displayed by restrictive anorexics might be connected to appraisals that are similar to those made by persons who binge and purge. For them, however, resisting food and losing weight become a way to gain a sense of mastery, virtue, self-control, and accomplishment (Garner & Bemis, 1982, 1985; Garner, Garfinkel, & Bemis, 1982). These feelings are particularly strong when there is extreme dissatisfaction in other areas of life (Slade, 1982). Anorexics tend to evaluate themselves exclusively in terms of their weight (Ben-Tovim, Hunter, & Crisp, 1977; Fransella & Button, 1983; Fransella & Crisp, 1979). For Bruch (1986), the therapeutic task is to help the anorexic develop a sense of competence in other areas of life. Because self-initiation and self-direction become a primary goal, the therapist is placed in an ambivalent role. The primary difficulty in treating anorexics is their denial of a need for treatment. Weight gain, in particular, is highly threatening and to be avoided at all costs. Professionals are engaged to bring about weight gain and stabilization. The therapist is caught in the position of encouraging the client to feel effective, competent, and powerful and, at the same time, he or she cannot support the pathway (starvation) by which the client seeks to develop these capacities. The therapist must be mindful of the need to bolster feelings of adequacy and competence.

Bulimics tend to experience interpersonal relationships, maturity demands, emotional regulation, and transitions as stressful. It has been suggested (Bruch, 1973; Coffman, 1984; Johnson, 1985) that bulimic behavior is a desperate attempt to assert personal authority, effectiveness, and power. This attempt could be particularly significant if, as some have argued, bulimics are overly dependent upon the opinions of others for their self-esteem and try excessively to please (Coffman, 1984; Loro, 1984). Loro argued that bulimics assume that others are constantly evaluating them, scan others' behavior continuously to receive such messages, selectively attend to evaluations that are negative, and interpret the messages as wholly good or more often wholly bad. It might seem paradoxical or contradictory,

then, that these same people are also described as being counterdependent and rebellious (Coffman, 1984; Loro, 1984). If one accepts that bulimics are both overly compliant and rebellious, the paradox can be explained by assuming that bulimics alternate between these two modes of interacting and move from one extreme to the other. This implies that both values and resources or skills might be important.

Dichotomous thinking has a profound impact on many areas of life. If, for example, bulimics think in dichotomous patterns, then the normal distribution of events and happenings that are positive and negative changes. Not only are events more negative or more positive, there are also more value-laden events. If events are dichotomized, there are no gray areas. Events otherwise located in those gray areas become charged with evaluative connotations. Similarly, actions judged as appropriate and necessary tend to be "all" or "none." To manage stress, the dichotomous thinking must be changed, the interpretation of others' behavior as indicating negative evaluations must be altered, the reliance on others' opinions and its associated "constant scanning" must be reduced, *and* more moderate courses of action need to be developed. How one goes about provoking such change and stimulating such development is a difficult matter. The most obvious intervention is to challenge beliefs and teach ways of acting directly. In our experience, this sometimes works. When it doesn't, it can be helpful to encourage the patient to use a diary to record activities and others' evaluations. Teaching bulimics to discriminate between various degrees of negativity might be more productive than trying to convince them that the evaluation was or should have been more positive or that such opinions simply should not be *that* important. When progress has not been made using traditional techniques, the therapist might choose to voice agreement with the client regarding the hopelessness of the situation. This is a risky technique and requires considerable skill of the therapist, but it sometimes produces dramatic reversals or good-humored acknowledgement that the problem is not so extreme.

Symptomatic food-related behavior might also be related to the regulation of affect and consequently to affect-regulation skills and values. Johnson, Lewis, and Hagman (1984) have argued that binging and purging can serve to express erotic, aggressive, oppositional, and self-punishing impulses. If binging and purging serve to express erotic or aggressive impulses, then it can be deduced that eroticism and aggression, or actions directly associated with them, are negatively valued and threatening, more threatening, in fact, than binging and purging behaviors. By having a binging problem, bulimics might be able to shift condemnation of themselves to a condemnation of their binging behavior. They can then escape the responsibility by experiencing the symptomatic behavior as beyond their control. Defiance and oppositionality might also be expressed through food-related behavior, and the expression of these impulses in this way might be less threatening than other alternatives for both the person with the eating disorder and the environment that she or he lives in. Following the binge, purging behaviors serve as self-punishment and a way to escape from the natural consequences of overeating. Purging might also help the binger regain a sense of adequacy and control. In the binge–purge cycle, feelings progress from irritability, weakness, lack of control, and increased appetite just prior to a binge to feelings of guilt, shame, anger, and decreased control and adequacy during the binge, followed by increased feelings of control and adequacy with decreased anger and guilt (Johnson & Larson, 1982). Eventually, however, those who seek treatment do so because the binging and purging behavior has become disruptive and destabilizing both affectively and socially.

Once the core values and commitments and associated thoughts, feelings, actions, and environments of an individual that contribute to the symptomatic behavior are identified, targets and modes of intervention can be designed or chosen. It is assumed that thoughts, feelings, actions, and environments are interactively and reciprocally influential. The degree to which emphasis is placed on each of these areas varies across treatment orientations and packages (several reviews are available: see Gandour, 1984; Schlesier-Stropp, 1984; Wilson, 1986). Coffman's (1984) clinically derived treatment model aims at modifying the bulimic's appraisal of the binge itself as adaptive and functional; the therapist is encouraged to communicate that the binging and purging is a statement of strength and determination, integrity and power against an "old" master. The client is given the control, becomes the "master," and can choose to eat or not eat, to binge or not binge. Exposure plus response prevention treatments (Leitenberg, Gross, Peterson, & Rosen, 1984; Rosen & Leitenberg, 1982) attempt to change the actions directly. If binging is only tolerable when there is an escape, namely, purging, then, by preventing the purge, one can stop the binging. The paradoxical technique of programmed binging (Loro & Orleans, 1981; Moley, 1983) is another intervention and is recommended particularly for "rebellious" binge eating. Clients are instructed to have a premeditated binge. They are generally told that the purpose of the voluntary binge is to gather assessment data, but the value of the technique is primarily therapeutic, in that the client generally experiences the symptomatic behavior in a new, different way.

Environmental Factors.

Cultural influences and familial relationships are two broad categories that have been implicated as influential in the development and maintenance of eating disorders. What might be stressful for families and cultures (with what values, under what circumstances, with what resources, and at what point in time) is beyond the scope of this chapter. Given our clinical observations, we suspect that adolescence and the entrance into adulthood might be one of the most salient stressors. It would be interesting to apply the formal characteristics of environments as outlined by Lazarus and Folkman (1984) to adolescence, a reputedly threatening time (particularly for parents). Because the focus of this chapter is on eating disorders rather than on adolescence, however, we will instead review how systems theorists have conceptualized the role of the environment in anorexia and bulimia.

Dym (1985), along with Bronfenbrenner (1979) has argued that there are many levels of systems that are hierarchically organized. The family represents one level; the broader culture, another. Dym stated that living systems tend simultaneously toward equilibrium and disequilibrium, and if the balance is in the direction of disequilibrium, due to natural causes such as aging or random events like a car accident, a system can be pushed beyond its capacity to return to its previously stable state, requiring adaptation, reorganization, and a new balance. This theoretical position is not unlike that applied to the individual by Lazarus and Folkman (1984). "Stress" would be something akin to a threatening imbalance. This likely happens in both families and today's culture, particularly with respect to the changing roles of women. It is argued that, within the culture, women are being given contradictory and conflicting messages regarding achievement, autonomy, and self-control. Wooley and Wooley (1982) pointed out that weight is one of the few areas in which competition between women has been encouraged and permitted wholeheartedly. Similarly, Bennett and Gurin (1982) suggested that the thinner-shape standard began as an expression of female liberation from a solely maternal, reproductive role. Within the family, anorexia and bulimia are thought to be responses to the restructuring of the family, which is generally precipitated by entrance into adolescence. Anorexic and bulimic behavior serves to keep "children" from leaving home, it adds to the blurring of boundaries (e.g., justifies the invasion of privacy, forces others to take control of and regulate the intake of another person), provides a way for parents to express conflict, and, at the same time, gives the child considerable power and influence (Minuchin, Rosman, & Baker, 1978; Selvini-Palazzoli, 1978).

Schwartz, Barrett, and Saba (1985) have discussed how patterns of relating that were developed (and adaptive) in previous generations might be responsible for the development of bulimia when they are carried over to later generations in which the patterns, and their underlying values, are no longer adaptive and appropriate. They argue that, if one traces the lineage of bulimics and their families, one will find a stable kin network, a network in which a close, intimate relationship between parents was not adaptive because of close and high levels of involvement with relatives. In such a context, everyone is involved in everyone else's conflicts and "children" never leave the network. Network loyalty is of greatest importance, children are raised to be obedient, not personally ambitious, and to distrust strangers. Additionally, food is the center of most of the family rituals and interactions. If these values and styles of interacting are transplanted outside of such a network, parents might become overinvolved with children and ambivalent about the values of the new culture. Clearly, this would be stressful.

CONCLUSIONS

The role of stress in obesity and the eating disorders is as complex as the disorders themselves. What is stressful, to whom, and in what way varies considerably across individuals. In today's society, great pressure is placed on people, women particularly, who are not of a desirable weight and who do not exercise and "eat right." Fitness has become a fad that sometimes seems to have the righteousness and fanaticism of a religious cult, as well as the backing of much of the scientific community and many in the health professions. It is not clear that this pressure has helped people to become healthier, happier, or, certainly, any less stressed. It is our hope that this chapter represents a beginning effort to understand individuals who are obese and have eating disorders such that they will be better helped to lead more effective lives. It is our belief that this cannot be done without a thorough understanding of the meaning, role, and complexities of eating and dietary behaviors.

REFERENCES

Abramson, E. E. & Stinson, S. G. (1977). Boredom and eating in obese and non-obese individuals. *Addictive Behaviors, 2,* 181–185.

Abramson, E. E., & Wunderlich, R. A. (1972). Anxiety, fear and eating: A test of the psychosomatic concept of obesity. *Journal of Abnormal Psychology, 77,* 317–321.

Antelman, S. M., & Szechtman, H. (1975). Tail pinch induces eating in sated rats which appears to depend upon striatal dopamine. *Science, 189,* 731–733.

Atkinson, R. M., & Ringuette, E. L. (1967). A survey of biographical and psychological features in extraordinary fatness. *Psychosomatic Medicine, 29,* 121–133.

Ben-Tovim, D. I., Hunter, M., & Crisp, A. H. (1977). Discrimination and evaluation of shape and size in anorexia nervosa: An exploratory study. *Research Communications in Psychology, Psychiatry and Behavior, 2,* 241–257.

Bennett, W. G., & Gurin, J. (1982). *The dieter's dilemma: Eating less and weighing more.* New York: Basic Books.

Beumont, P. J. V. (1977). Further categorization of patients with anorexia nervosa. *Australian and New Zealand Journal of Psychiatry, 11,* 223–226.

Bronfenbrenner, U. (1979). *The ecology of human development.* Cambridge, MA: Harvard University Press.

Bruch, H. (1962). Perceptual and conceptual disturbances in anorexia nervosa. *Psychosomatic Medicine, 24,* 187–194.

Bruch, H. (1973). *Eating disorders: Obesity, anorexia and the person within.* New York: Basic Books.

Bruch, H. (1977). Psychological considerations of anorexia nervosa. In R. A. Vigeisky (Ed.), *Anorexia nervosa.* New York: Raven Press.

Bruch, H. (1980). The importance of overweight. In P. J. Collipp (Ed.), *Childhood obesity* (2nd ed.). Littleton, MA: PSG Publishing.

Bruch, H. (1981). Developmental considerations of anorexia nervosa and obesity. *Canadian Journal of Psychiatry, 26,* 212–216.

Bruch, H. (1986). Anorexia nervosa: The therapeutic task. In K. D. Brownell & J. P. Foreyt (Eds.), *Handbook of eating disorders: Physiology, psychology and treatment of obesity, anorexia and bulimia.* New York: Basic Books.

Button, E., Fransella, F., & Slade, P. (1977). A reappraisal of body perception distortion in anorexia nervosa. *Psychological Medicine, 7,* 235–243.

Casper, R. C., Eckert, E. D., Halmi, K. A., Goldberg, S. C., & Davis, J. M. (1980). Bulimia: Its incidence and clinical importance in patients with anorexia nervosa. *Archives of General Psychiatry, 37,* 1030–1034.

Castelnuovo-Tedesco, P., & Schiebel, D. (1975). Studies of superobesity: I. Psychological characteristics of superobese patients. *International Journal of Psychiatry in Medicine, 6*, 465–480.

Chambliss, C. A., & Murray, E. J. (1979). Efficacy attribution, locus of control, and weight loss. *Cognitive Therapy and Research, 3*, 349–353.

Coddington, R. D. (1972). The significance of life events as etiologic factors in the diseases of children. I. A survey of professional workers. *Journal of Psychosomatic Research, 16*, 7–18.

Cofer, C. N., & Appleby, M. H. (1964). *Motivation: Theory and research.* New York: John Wiley & Sons.

Coffman, D. A. (1984). A clinically derived treatment model for the binge–purge syndrome. In R. C. Hawkins, W. J. Fremouw, & P. F. Clement (Eds.). *The binge-purge syndrome: Diagnosis, treatment, and research.* New York: Springer.

Cousins, J. H. (1985). Personal communication.

Cutts, T., & Barrios, B. A. (1985, March). Fear of weight gain as a diagnostic indicator of bulimia. Paper presented at the meeting of the Southeastern Psychological Association, Atlanta.

Doell, S. R., & Hawkins, R. C. II (1982). Pleasures and pounds: An exploratory study. *Addictive Behaviors, 1*, 65–69.

Dym, B. (1985). Eating disorders and the family: A model for intervention. In S. W. Emmett (Ed.). *Theory and treatment of anorexia nervosa and bulimia: Biomedical, sociocultural, and psychological perspectives.* New York: Brunner/Mazel.

Edelman, B. (1981). Binge eating in normal weight and overweight individuals. *Psychological Reports, 49*(3), 739–746.

Folkman, S., & Lazarus, R. S. (1980). An analysis of coping in a middle-aged community sample. *Journal of Health and Social Behavior, 21*, 219–239.

Fransella, F., & Button, E. J. (1983). The "construing" of self and body size in relation to maintenance of weight gain in anorexia nervosa. In P. L. Darby, P. E. Garfinkel, D. M. Garner, & D. V. Coscina (Eds.), *Anorexia nervosa: Recent developments.* New York: Alan R. Liss.

Fransella, F., & Crisp, A. H. (1979). Comparisons of weight concepts in groups of neurotic, normal and anorexic females. *British Journal of Psychiatry, 134*, 79–86.

Freed, S. C. (1947). Psychic factors in development and treatment of obesity. *Journal of the American Medical Association, 133*, 369–373.

Freeman, R. C., Thomas, C. D., Solyom, L., & Miles, J. E. (1983). Body image disturbances in anorexia nervosa: A reexamination and a new technique. In P. L. Darby, P. E. Garfinkel, D. M. Garner, & D. V. Coscina (Eds.), *Anorexia nervosa: Recent developments in research.* New York: Alan R. Liss.

Gandour, M. J. (1984). Bulimia: Clinical description, assessment, etiology and treatment. *International Journal of Eating Disorders, 3*(3), 3–38.

Garfinkel, P. E., & Garner, D. M. (1982) *Anorexia nervosa: A multidimensional perspective.* New York: Brunner/Mazel.

Garfinkel, P. E., Moldofsky, H., & Garner, D. M. (1977). Prognosis in anorexia nervosa as influenced by clinical features, treatment and self-perception. *Canadian Medical Journal, 177*, 1041–1045.

Garfinkel, P. E., Moldofsky, H., & Garner, D. M. (1980). The heterogeneity of anorexia nervosa. *Archives of General Psychiatry, 37*, 1036–1040.

Garner, D. M. (1986). Cognitive therapy for anorexia nervosa. In K. D. Brownell & J. P. Foreyt (Eds.), *Handbook of eating disorders: Physiology, psychology and treatment of obesity, anorexia, and bulimia.* New York: Basic Books.

Garner, D. M., & Bemis, K. M. (1982). A cognitive–behavioral approach to anorexia nervosa. *Cognitive Therapy and Research, 6*, 123–150.

Garner, D. M., & Bemis, K. M. (1985). Cognitive therapy for anorexia nervosa. In D. M. Garner & P. E. Garfinkel (Eds.), *A handbook of psychotherapy for anorexia nervosa and bulimia.* New York: Guilford Press.

Garner, D. M., & Garfinkel, P. E. (1981). Body image in anorexia nervosa: Measurement, theory and clinical implications. *International Journal of Psychiatry in Medicine, 11*, 263–284.

Garner, D. M., Garfinkel, P. E., & Bemis, K. M. (1982). A multidimensional psychotherapy for anorexia nervosa. *International Journal of Eating Disorders, 1*, 3–46.

Garner, D. M., Garfinkel, P. E., & Moldofsky, H. (1978). Perceptual experiences in anorexia nervosa and obesity. *Canadian Psychiatric Association Journal, 23*, 249–263.

Garner, D. M., Olmsted, M. P., Polivy, J., & Garfinkel, P. E. (1984). Comparison between weight-preoccupied women and anorexia nervosa. *Psychosomatic Medicine, 46*(3), 255–266.

Gormally, J., Rardin, D., & Black, S. (1980). Correlates of successful response to a behavioral weight control clinic. *Journal of Counseling Psychology, 27*, 179–191.

Gross, L. (1968). The effects of early feeding experience on external responsiveness. Unpublished doctoral dissertation, Columbia University.

Halmi, K. A. (1974). Anorexia nervosa: Demographic and clinical features in 94 cases. *Psychosomatic Medicine, 36*, 18–25.

Hamburger, W. W. (1951). Emotional aspects of obesity. *Medical Clinics of North America, 35*, 483–499.

Hawkins, R. C., Fremouw, W. J., & Clement, P. F. (Eds.). (1984). *The binge–purge syndrome: Diagnosis, treatment, and research.* New York: Springer.

Herman, C. P., & Mack, D. (1975). Restrained and unrestrained eating. *Journal of Personality, 43*, 647–660.

Herman, C. P., & Polivy, J. (1975). Anxiety, restraint and eating behavior. *Journal of Abnormal Psychology, 84*, 666–672.

Hibscher, J. A., & Herman, C. P. (1977). Obesity, dieting, and the expression of "obese" characteristics. *Journal of Comparative Physiology and Psychology, 91*, 374–380.

Holland, J., Masling, J., & Copley, D. (1970). Mental illness in lower class normal, obese, and hyperobese women. *Psychosomatic Medicine, 32*, 351–357.

Holmes, T. H., & Rahe, R. H. (1967). The social readjustment rating scale. *Journal of Psychosomatic Research, 11*, 213–218.

Jacobs, S. B., & Wagner, M. K. (1984). Obese and nonobese individuals: Behavioral and personality characteristics. *Addictive Behaviors*, 9(2), 223–226.

Janis, I. L. (1983). The role of social support in adherence to stressful decisions. *American Psychologist*, 38, 143–160.

Johnson, C. (1985). Initial consultation for patients with bulimia and anorexia nervosa. In D. M. Garner & P. E. Garfinkel (Eds.), *Handbook of psychotherapy for anorexia nervosa and bulimia*. New York: Guilford Press.

Johnson, C., & Larson, R. (1982). Bulimia: An analysis of moods and behavior. *Psychosomatic Medicine*, 44, 341–353.

Johnson, C., Lewis, C., & Hagman, J. (1984). The syndrome of bulimia. Review and synthesis. *Psychiatric Clinics of North America*, 7(2), 247–273.

Jones, E. (1953). *The life and work of Sigmund Freud*. New York: Basic Books.

Kagan, D. M., & Squires, R. L. (1983). Dieting, compulsive eating, and feelings of failure among adolescents. *International Journal of Eating Disorders*, 3(1), 15–26.

Kalucy, R. S., & Crisp, A. H. (1974). Some psychological and sociological implications of massive obesity: A study of some psychosocial accompaniments of major fat loss occuring without dietary restrictions in massively obese patients. *Journal of Psychosomatic Research*, 18, 465–473.

Katzman, M. A., & Wolchik, S. A. (1984). Bulimia and binge eating in college women: A comparison of personality and behavioral correlates. *Journal of Consulting and Clinical Psychology*, 52(3), 423–428.

Kay, D. W. K., & Leigh, D. (1954). The natural history, treatment, and prognosis of anorexia nervosa, based on a study of 38 patients. *Journal of Mental Sciences*, 100, 411–439.

King, A. (1963). Primary and secondary anorexia nervosa syndromes. *British Journal of Psychiatry*, 109, 470–479.

Klesges, R. C., Beatty, W. W., & Berry, S. L. (1985). Some behavioral, attitudinal, and perceptual correlates of obesity in a university population. *International Journal of Eating Disorders*, 4(2), 237–245.

Larson, R., & Johnson, C. (1985). Bulimia: Disturbed patterns of solitude. *Addictive Behaviors*, 10(3), 281–290.

Lazarus, R. S., & Folkman, S. (1984). *Stress, appraisal, and coping*. New York: Springer.

Leitenberg, H., Gross, J., Peterson, J., & Rosen, J. C. (1984). Analysis of an anxiety model and the process of change during exposure plus response prevention treatment of bulimia nervosa. *Behavior Therapy*, 15, 3–20.

Leon, G. R., Carroll, K., Chernyk, B., & Finn, S. (1985). Binge eating and associated habit patterns within college student and identified bulimic populations. *International Journal of Eating Disorders*, 4(1), 43–57.

Leon, G. R., & Chamberlain, K. (1973a). Comparison of daily eating habits and emotional states of overweight persons successful or unsuccessful in maintaining a weight loss. *Journal of Consulting and Clinical Psychology*, 41, 108–115.

Leon, G., & Chamberlain, K. (1973b). Emotional arousal, eating patterns, and body image as differential factors associated with varying success in maintaining a weight loss. *Journal of Consulting and Clinical Psychology*, 40, 474–480.

Leon, G. R., & Rosenthal, B. S. (1984). Prognostic indicators of success or relapse in weight reduction. *International Journal of Eating Disorders*, 3(4), 15–24.

Leon, G. R., & Roth, L. (1977). Obesity: Psychological causes, correlations, and speculations. *Psychological Bulletin*, 84(1), 117–139.

Loro, A. D., Jr. (1984). Binge-eating: A cognitive-behavioral treatment approach. In R. C. Hawkins, W. J. Fremouw, & P. F. Clement (Eds.), *The binge-purge syndrome: Diagnosis, treatment, and research*. New York: Springer.

Loro, A. D., Jr., & Orleans, C. S. (1981). Binge-eating in obesity: Preliminary findings and guidelines for behavioral analysis and treatment. *Addictive Behaviors*, 6, 155–166.

Lowe, M. R., & Fisher, E. B. (1983). Emotional reactivity, emotional eating, and obesity: A naturalistic study. *Journal of Behavioral Medicine*, 6(2), 135–149.

Marlatt, G. A., & Gordon, J. R. (1980). Determinants of relapse: Implications for the maintenance of behavior change. In P. Davidson & S. Davidson (Eds.), *Behavioral medicine: Changing health lifestyles*. New York: Brunner/Mazel.

McKenna, R. J. (1972). Some effects of anxiety and food cues on the eating behavior of obese and normal subjects: A comparison of the Schachterian and psychosomatic conceptions. *Journal of Personality and Social Psychology*, 22, 311–319.

Meyer, J. E., & Pudel, V. (1972). Experimental studies on food-intake in obese and normal weight subjects. *Journal of Psychosomatic Research*, 16, 305–308.

Minuchin, S., Rosman, B. L., & Baker, L. (1978). *Psychosomatic families: Anorexia nervosa in context*. Cambridge, MA: Harvard University Press.

Moley, V. A. (1983). Interactional treatment of eating disorders. *Journal of Strategic and Systemic Therapies*, 2(4), 10–29.

Morgan, H. G., & Russell, G. F. M. (1975). Value of family background and clinical features as predictors of long-term outcome in anorexia nervosa: Four year follow-up study of 42 patients. *Psychological Medicine*, 5, 355–371.

Norman, D. K., & Herzog, D. B. (1983). Bulimia, anorexia nervosa and anorexia nervosa with bulimia: A comparative analysis of MMPI profiles. *International Journal of Eating Disorders*, 2, 43–52.

O'Leary, A. (1985). Self-efficacy and health. *Behaviour Research and Therapy*, 23(4), 437–451.

Peele, S. (1985). Out of the habit trap. In A. Monat & R. S. Lazarus (Eds.), *Stress and coping: An anthology* (2nd ed.). New York: Columbia University Press.

Perri, M. G., Shapiro, R. M., Ludwig, W. W., Twentyman, C. T., & McAdoo, W. G. (1984). Maintenance strategies for the treatment of obesity: An evaluation of relapse prevention training and posttreatment contact by mail and telephone. *Journal of Consulting and Clinical Psychology*, 52(3), 404–413.

Pliner, P., Meyer, P., & Blankstein, K. (1974). Responsiveness to affective stimuli by obese and normal subjects. *Journal of Abnormal Psychology*, 83, 74–80.

Plutchik, R. (1976). Emotions and attitudes related to being overweight. *Journal of Clinical Psychology, 32*, 21-23.

Polivy, J. (1976). Perception of calories and regulation of intake in restrained and unrestrained subjects. *Addictive Behaviors, 1*, 237-243.

Pyle, R. L., Mitchell, J. E., & Eckert, E. (1981). Bulimia: A report of 34 cases. *Journal of Clinical Psychiatry, 42*, 60-64.

Reznick, H., & Balch, P. (1977). The effects of anxiety and response cost manipulations on the eating behavior of obese and normal weight subjects. *Addictive Behaviors, 2*, 219-225.

Robbins, T. W., & Fray, P. J. (1980). Stress-induced eating: Fact, fiction, or misunderstanding? *Appetite, 1*, 103-133.

Rodin, J. (1977). Research on eating behavior and obesity: Where does it fit in personality and social psychology? *Personality and Social Psychology Bulletin, 3*(3), 333-335.

Rodin, J. (1982). Obesity: Why the losing battle? In B. B. Wolman (Ed.), *Psychological aspects of obesity: A handbook.* New York: Van Nostrand Reinhold.

Rodin, J., Elman, D., & Schachter, S. (1974). Emotionality and obesity. In S. Schachter & J. Rodin (Eds.), *Obese humans and rats.* Hillsdale, NJ: Lawrence Erlbaum.

Rosen, J. D. & Leitenberg, H. (1982). Bulimia nervosa: Treatment with exposure and response prevention. *Behavior Therapy, 13*, 117-124.

Rowland, N. E., & Antelman, S. M. (1976). Stress-induced hyperphagia and obesity in rats: A possible model for understanding human obesity. *Science, 191*, 310-312.

Rozensky, R. H., & Bellack, A. S. (1976). Individual differences in self-reinforcement style and performance in self- and therapist-controlled weight reduction programs. *Behaviour Research and Therapy, 14*, 357-364.

Ruderman, A. J. (1983). Obesity, anxiety, and food consumption. *Addictive Behaviors, 8*(3), 225-242.

Russell, G. F. M. (1979). Bulimia nervosa: An ominous variant of anorexia nervosa. *Psychological Medicine 9*, 429-448.

Sarason, I. G., Sarason, B. R., Potter, E. H. III, & Antoni, M. H. (1985). Life events, social support, and illness. *Psychosomatic Medicine, 47*(2), 156-163.

Schachter, S., Goldman, R., & Gordon, A. (1968). Effects of fear, food deprivation, and obesity on eating. *Journal of Personality and Social Psychology, 10*, 91-97.

Schlesier-Stropp, B. (1984). Bulimia: A review of the literature. *Psychological Bulletin, 95*(2), 247-257.

Schwartz, R. C., Barrett, M. J., & Saba, G. (1985). Family therapy for bulimia. In D. M. Garner & P. E. Garfinkel (Eds.), *Handbook of psychotherapy for anorexia nervosa and bulimia.* New York: Guilford Press.

Selvini-Palazzoli, M. (1978). *Self-starvation.* New York: Jason Aronson.

Selye, H. (1956). *The stress of life.* New York: McGraw-Hill.

Slade, P. D. (1982). Towards a functional analysis of anorexia nervosa and bulimia. *British Journal of Clinical Psychology, 21*, 167-179.

Slade, P. D., & Russell, G. F. M. (1973). Awareness of body dimensions in anorexia nervosa: Cross-sectional and longitudinal studies. *Psychological Medicine, 3*, 188-199.

Slochower, J. (1976). Emotional labeling and overeating in obese and normal weight individuals. *Psychosomatic Medicine, 38*, 131-139.

Slochower, J. A. (1983). *Excessive eating: The role of emotions and the environment.* New York: Human Sciences Press.

Slochower, J., & Kaplan, S. P. (1980). Anxiety, perceived control, and eating in obese and normal weight persons. *Appetite, 1*, 75-83.

Slochower, J., Kaplan, S. P., & Mann, L. (1981). The effects of life stress and weight on mood and eating. *Appetite, 2*, 115-125.

Spencer, J. A., & Fremouw, W. J. (1979). Binge eating as a function of restraint and weight classification. *Journal of Abnormal Psychology, 88*(3), 262-267.

Strober, M. (1980). Personality and symptomatological features in young, nonchronic anorexia nervosa patients. *Journal of Psychosomatic Research, 24*, 353-359.

Strober, M. (1981). A comparative analysis of personality organization in juvenile anorexia nervosa. *Journal of Youth and Adolescence, 10*, 285-295.

Strober, M. (1984). Stressful life events associated with bulimia in anorexia nervosa: Empirical findings and theoretical speculations. *International Journal of Eating Disorders, 3*(2), 3-16.

Strober, M., Salkin, B., Burroughs, J., & Morrell, W. (1982). Validity of the bulimia-restrictor distinction in anorexia nervosa: Parental personality characteristics and family psychiatric morbidity. *Journal of Nervous and Mental Diseases, 170*, 345-351.

Weinberg, R. S., Hughes, H. H., Critelli, J., W., England, R., & Jackson, A. (1984). Effects of preexisting and manipulated self-efficacy on weight loss in a self-control program. *Journal of Research on Personality, 18*, 352-358.

White, C. (1973). The effects of viewing film of different arousal content on the eating behavior of obese and normal weight subjects. *Dissertation Abstracts International, 34*(5) 2324B.

Wilson, G. T. (1986). Cognitive-behavioral and pharmacological therapies for bulimia. In K. D. Brownell & J. P. Foreyt (Eds.), *Handbook of eating disorders: Physiology, psychology, and treatment of obesity, anorexia, and bulimia.* New York: Basic Books.

Wold, P. N. (1983). Anorexic syndromes and affective disorder. *Psychiatric Journal of the University of Ottawa, 8*(3), 116-119.

Wolf, E. M., & Crowther, J. H. (1983). Personality and eating habit variables as predictors of severity of binge eating and weight. *Addictive Behaviors, 8*(4), 335-344.

Wooley. S. C., & Kearney-Cooke, A. (1986). Intensive treatment of bulimia and body-image disturbance. In K. D. Brownell and J. P. Foreyt (Eds.), *Handbook of eating disorders: Physiology, psychology, and treatment of obesity, anorexia, and bulimia.* New York: Basic Books.

Wooley, O. W., & Wooley, S. C. (1982). The Beverley Hills eating disorder: The mass marketing of anorexia nervosa. *International Journal of Eating Disorders, 1*, 57-69.

Chapter 15

Psychological and Pathophysiological Factors in Respiratory Disorders[1]

Victor S. Alpher
Martin J. Tobin

HISTORICAL OVERVIEW

Background of the Psychology of Breathing

Most psychologists and behavior therapists who deal directly with patients who have emotional and medical problems would agree that respiration seems easily modifiable by factors such as emotions, verbal expression, and exercise. Yet, the regulation of respiration is considered to be a metabolic process, out of the psychological domain. Thus study of the control of breathing is largely left to the techniques and methods of pulmonary physiologists. Another area of difficulty, noted by Blanton and Alpher (in press), results from the fact that the psychologist is under an implicit, though overly positivistic, obligation at times to rule out the "lower level" and more "fundamental" physiological explanations of respiratory data. The physiological explanation is assumed to be the most parsimonious. However, the findings of respiratory physiologists typically result in the identification of a so-called *neurogenic factor* in the determination of even the most basic respiration data (see, e.g., Alpher, Nelson, & Blanton 1986; Bartlett, 1977). Higher cortical influences on the response to respiratory distress are acknowledged, but psychologists to date have produced little experimental data to suggest the basic mechanisms involved in the effects of these descending cortical modifications of the "metabolic" process.

Early approaches to the psychology of breathing have guided the experimental work on which behavioral treatments are grounded. Beckmann (1915) demonstrated that respiratory activity increased subsequent to the induction of emotional states; this produced decreased carbon dioxide tension of alveolar air. Von Heyer (1925) showed that, if subjects were directed to hyperventilate voluntarily, they consistently reported subjective excitement and emotionality and showed increased

Contributions of authors were equal. We thank Thelma Canessa and Debbie Peace for their assistance in preparation of the manuscript.

CO_2 output. These were important early demonstrations, but the relative crudeness of measurement techniques available through most of the early period of this country impaired advances beyond observations such as these. This can be contrasted with advances in the basic research base for understanding the epigenesis of pain perception (see Chapter 8).

Stress and Breathing: Empirical Foundations

Respiratory phenomena are commonly observed in clinical practice. Among the alternative behaviors available to an individual under stress, voluntary modification of breathing behavior could be an important short-term coping strategy because of its physiological and psychological effects. For example, it has been repeatedly observed that breathing behaviors produce changes in psychophysiological measures of arousal (Katkin, 1965; Stern & Anschel, 1986). Cappo and Holmes (1984) have demonstrated a reliable somatic and cognitive arousal-reducing effect by voluntary manipulation of the inspiration – expiration ratio in the manner of certain yogic practices.

Wolpe (1969) reported that breathing high concentrations of carbon dioxide had an ameliorative effect on pervasive anxiety that outlasted its effect on blood gas concentrations; he attributed this effect to a ''powerful anxiety-inhibiting excitation'' (Wolpe, 1969, p. 177), but the mechanism is still not clear. Orwin and his colleagues (Orwin, 1971, 1973; Orwin, Le Boeuf, Dovey, & James, 1975) have used the state following maximum voluntary respiratory arrest, *respiratory relief*, to countercondition phobias in a desensitization paradigm. This research suggests that there might be significant aspects of the breathing cycle that, when altered by pathophysiological processes, contribute to the distress of breathing disorders.

Hyperventilation (that is, ventilation in excess of what is required to maintain the normal range of blood balance of oxygen and carbon dioxide pressure in the blood) has long-term detrimental consequences. These include respiratory alkalosis (Lum, 1975, 1976, 1981; Missri & Alexander, 1978) and potential neuropsychological impairments. It could be considered an adaptive response in the short run because of its initial activating effects for behavior responding to stress. These effects might be due to afferent input to the ascending reticular activating system, because, in the short run,

hyperventilation actually decreases the chemically based drive to breathe (Mines, 1981). The observation that so many patients diagnosed with syndromes ranging from hysteria to psychosis also manifest the symptoms of the hyperventilation syndrome (Compernolle, Hoogduin, & Joele, 1979) is perhaps testimony to the human's ability to overlearn and overgeneralize once-adaptive behavior patterns. After this pattern is established, however, corrective measures, such as relearning abdominal ventilation patterns, can ameliorate pathological physiological, and psychological effects of hyperventilation (Lum, 1975, 1976).

Across numerous investigations, it has been demonstrated repeatedly that stress facilitates changes in many significant respiratory parameters, several of which occur in the hyperventilation syndrome described by Lum (1975, 1976, 1981) and others (e.g. Brown, 1953; Compernolle et al., 1979; McKell & Sullivan, 1947; Missri & Alexander, 1978; Rice, 1950). These changes include increased rate of respiration, irregular breathing, increased minute ventilation, changes in tidal volume, and changes in partial pressure of carbon dioxide in the blood $[P_a CO_2]$ (Ax, 1953: Bechbache, Chow, Duffin, & Orsini, 1979; Beckmann, 1915; Clark & Hemsley, 1982; Dudley, 1969; Dudley, Holmes, Martin, & Ripley, 1964; Dudley, Martin, & Holmes, 1964; Fenz & Epstein, 1967; Fenz & Jones, 1972; Finesinger & Mazick, 1940a, 1940b; Garssen, 1980; Goldstein, 1964; Heim, Knapp, Vachon, Globus, & Nemetz, 1968; Jong, Berg, & Jong, 1975; Liberson & Liberson, 1975; Mathews & Gelder, 1969; Oken et al. 1962; Salter, Meunier, & Triplett, 1976; Schnore, 1959; Skarbek, 1970; Stevenson & Ripley, 1952; Suess, Alexander, Smith, Sweeney, & Marion, 1980; Van Egeren, Feather, & Hein, 1971; Willer, 1975).

Sensations related to respiratory drive (e.g., *dyspnea*: the awareness of a need for increased ventilation) are common and consistent correlates of stress manipulations. Small changes in PCO_2 can dramatically influence respiratory drive and breathing behavior; an increase of as little as 2 torr (2 mm Hg) can under certain circumstances, increase resting ventilation by a factor of two (Mines, 1981). Even when the metabolic set point for PCO_2 has changed, as appears to occur with chronic hyperventilators, a small increase in PCO_2 causes significant dyspnea. This occurs even though the absolute gas tension in the absence of pathology, is associated with reduced respiratory drive.

Respiratory changes occur in not only the so-called

hyperventilation syndrome, but also many of the affective and anxiety disorders in which panic attacks and generalized anxiety are observed (American Psychiatric Association, 1980). Although peripheral psychophysiological measures do not differentiate the anxiety components across diagnostic categories, there is increasing evidence that important central processes associated with respiratory chemoreceptor activity are involved in phobic and free-floating anxiety (Freedman, Ianni, Ettedgui, Pohl, & Rainey, 1984; Uhde et al. 1984).

We continue an investigation of the factors associated with successful treatment of pulmonary disease with behaviorally, and psychologically, informed methods with the following challenge. As one researcher summarized the state of the art fairly recently, "it must now be accepted that the evidence points *securely* toward the conclusion that no relaxation method of any kind has a *clinically* significant effect on pulmonary physiology in either childhood or adult asthmatics" (Alexander, 1981, p. 386). Unfortunately, it must be admitted that the early promise of many approaches to managing stress, such as systematic desensitization and biofeedback, likewise produce no reliable changes in the actual pathophysiology or pulmonary dynamics associated with respiratory disorders.

Asthma was a disorder of obvious attraction to psychological researchers because of the presumed importance of emotional factors, such as anxiety and stress, in the manifestation of the clinical features of the disorder. Anxiety, or panic-induced, asthma attacks are well documentated clinically. With chronic bronchitis and emphysema (chronic obstructive pulmonary disease), the direct association between emotional factors and the generation of the clinical syndrome is more obscure. For example, the emotional and psychological predisposing factors to cigarette smoking are certainly causally related to chronic airway obstruction, but by the time the clinical disorder is manifested , the relationship might be formal but not material.

In general, psychological approaches to the breathing disorders have been focused on antecedent and consequent factors. This is consistent with a behavioral formulation of response to a stressor. The stress to be reduced is the *response* to the chronic disease, which has cognitive, affective, and behavioral aspects that can be addressed through treatments involving, for example, cognitive – behavioral modification, relaxation training, biofeedback, social skills training, and so forth. It is assumed that a modification of the

clinical response to the pathophysiological state occurs through either the modification or elimination of dysfunctional stimulus conditions or behavioral responses. Thus, a behavioral formulation proceeds along the lines of psychological principles in which the commonalities of response to distressing stimuli are emphasized. In this sense, many types of chronic diseases are presumed to be conceptually equivalent. It makes sense, therefore, that accepted behavioral treatments would be attempted with asthmatic and chronic obstructive pulmonary disease (COPD) populations, just as with populations of cancer patients, end-stage renal disease patients, and burn patients.

MANAGEMENT APPROACH TO BREATHING DISORDERS

Management versus Treatment as Paradigms

We will now selectively survey the current literature on psychological and behavioral approaches to breathing disorders. Clearly, much of this work focuses on using psychological knowledge and principles to inform *management* of the clinical course. Demonstrated *treatment* effects on the underlying pathophysiology or respiratory distress are equivocal. We note such attempts at documenting treatment effects where relevant. In later sections treatment issues will be further explored.

Biofeedback

Biofeedback can be used to address both management issues and treatment issues. The management approach with biofeedback is exemplified by Chai and colleagues. They employed the Wright Peak Flow Meter in attempting to teach asthmatics to detect the onset of bronchial obstruction more accurately and reliably (Chai, Purcell, Brady, & Falliers, 1968). Chai et al. were able to increase the correlation between the patient's subjective perceptions of asthmatic state and the index of pulmonary function, the maximal airflow. The main goal of such an approach (a form of biofeedback) is to attempt to enhance the patient's compliance with appropriate treatment regimens by responding more consistently to the underlying pathophysiology. However, it is not a treatment *per se*; its goal is not a modification of the disease state.

Using the biofeedback approach to breathing disorders involves the consideration of potential underlying mechanisms. Harding and Maher (1982) reasoned that biofeedback learning of cardiac acceleration would result in reduced bronchomotor tone, due to increased parasympathetic efferent activity. These researchers found a significant effect of learned cardiac acceleration on peak expiratory flow measures for asthmatics. Although asthmatic subjects were not instructed to use the procedure outside the experimental situation, there was a drop in reported frequency of attacks and amount of bronchodilator medicine used. Harding and Maher posed the hypothesis that the cardiac biofeedback procedure "classically conditioned" the vagal efferent tone, but this is best regarded as speculative. Other cognitive variables (control, efficacy) could be implicated in the results. Any treatment effect on a heterogeneous group of asthmatics, given this known effect of anxiety on the cause, could be due to the medication of changes in anxiety level. The problem associated with peak expiratory flow rates will be discussed below.

In an interesting clinical investigation, Janson-Bjerklie and Clarke (1982) provided two groups of asthmatics with visual feedback indicating a measure they termed *thoracic respiratory resistance* (TRR). After five training sessions, they found subjects were able to decease TRR. However, the change in TRR, although statistically significant within and across subjects, was small, and its clinical significance is doubtful. The findings of Janson-Bjerkle and Clarke comprise an interesting demonstration of the biofeedback paradigm as applied to breathing, but Steptoe, Phillips, and Harling (1981) also attempted to use TRR as a biofeedback approach with asthmatics. The significance and meaningfulness of their approach is likewise questionable, because no reliable results within and across subjects were attained.

Mussell (1986) has reported on a biofeedback device that provides the subject with trachea noise feedback. Presumably, this would enable patients with asthma to learn to reduce their wheezing, a major correlate of bronchoconstriction. Mussell suggested that, if wheezing is reduced, this would indicate bronchodilation. However, the utility, effectiveness, and practicality of this device are at present speculative. Tiep and his colleagues have also experimented with a variety of biofeedback devices, but most are still in the development stage (B. Tiep, personal communication). A recent interesting area of research relevant to treatment involves feedback of CO_2 levels in expired air. This area has application to asthma because asthmatic patients often hyperventilate prior to an asthmatic attack. Hyperventilation is associated with decreasing levels of arterial carbon dioxide (PCO_2). The hypocapnic state caused by decreased PCO_2 produces bronchoconstriction, which can aggravate the asthmatic attack. The goals of biofeedback differ, depending on the nature of the pathophysiological disturbance. Asthmatic patients would benefit from a method that reliably increased PCO_2 levels. COPD patients, on the other hand, would benefit from a reliable behavioral method for decreasing PCO_2.

Folgering, Lenders, and Rosier (1980) used this logic to attempt to intervene psychologically (through biofeedback) with the physiological "vicious circle" (lowered PCO_2 increases anxiety, which, through more hyperventilation, lowers PCO_2). Using both visual and auditory feedback, they demonstrated that normal subjects reliably increase PCO_2 at a clinically significant level (1.5 torr). Subjects learned, therefore, to alter their breathing pattern to increase PCO_2, although, in this case, the increase above normal resting level was experienced as distressing (as could be predicted). Folgering et al. suggested that biofeedback that returns a hypercapnic (COPD) or hypocapnic (hyper-ventilating asthmatic) patient to more normal PCO_2 levels should produce a reduction in distress and, therefore create a positive feedback loop. However, supporting evidence for this hypothesis has not been forthcoming, to our knowledge. One reason could be the fact that an internally valid experimental trial, uncomplicated by pharamacological and disease-pathophysiological factors, is difficult to obtain in these populations.

Renne and Creer (1976) equipped asthmatic children with peak flow meters and asked them to predict the peak flow (maximum airflow that can be generated and maintained for 10 seconds) they thought they would produce at different times of the day. Using a positive-reinforcement procedure, children were able to improve their ability to correlate self-reported perceptions of asthma and more objective peak flow indexes. Taplin and Creer (1978) reported that children could use peak flow information, produced by the more portable Mini-Wright Peak Flow Meter, to predict asthmatic attacks. Presumably, such enhanced prediction through feedback could lessen the deleterious effects of unanticipated attacks, if routinely used.

Biofeedback from facial skeletal muscles (actually a form of relaxation training) and biofeedback of airway resistance both have some demonstrated short-term effects (Kotses & Glaus, 1981). However, not only are long-term effects unknown, but also the mechanism of short-term effects is open to a number of alternative interpretations. Wide variation in study design further aggravates the possibility of sorting out specific testable hypotheses based on previously conducted, well-controlled experiments.

It can be seen from studies such as these that biofeedback approaches are potentially useful in ameliorating sequelae of pathologic respiratory states. However, a variety of methodological issues makes it difficult to infer the mechanism of these effects. As noted by Creer (1983), several cognitive factors affect the interpretation of sensory information related to the physical changes of airway obstruction. The patient might simply fail to detect the information, delaying effective treatment. Context of the attack might influence detection of the information. Alternatively, the signals might be misinterpreted as signals of other events, rather than as asthmatic attacks. Clearly, biofeedback of a respiratory function related to obstruction can have a beneficial effect, if patients learn to predict attacks and initiate treatment.

Relaxation and Desensitization

Relaxation training and systematic desensitization must be considered together because they are often compared in relevant studies, particularly with asthmatics for whom a densitization hierarchy is easily constructed. (The term *systematic desensitization* here refers to the behavioral procedure, rather than to the amelioration of hypersensitivity reactions through administration of graded doses of an allergen).

Lehrer, Hochron, McCann, Swartzman, and Reba (1986) provided 11 asthmatics a 16-session combined relaxation-therapy treatment consisting of relaxation, systematic desensitization, and trapezius and frontalis EMG biofeedback. Nine subjects received a "complex" placebo across 15 sessions including music-attention, body awareness training, placebo desensitization, a vigilance task with covert anti-anxiety rehearsal, and false EMG biofeedback. Experimental subjects improved in their reactivity to the methacholine challenge test, a measure of airway reactivity associated with asthma. Subjects in both groups improved on self-report measures of asthma symptoms and psychopathology, however. Medication use was lower in the experimental group. These findings must be viewed cautiously, however. First, many subjects dropped out of the study, and desensitization was particularly aversive for subjects

(see also Shenkman, 1985, concerning dropouts in pulmonary rehabilitation). Also, the reduction in frequency of asthma attacks appeared to be associated with the frequency of *emotional precursors* to the attacks. Thus, consistent with previous findings, any effects on the underlying pathophysiological mechanism must be considered speculative. The findings of Lehrer et al. do seem to indicate a positive effect of cognitive-relaxation-technique effects on *reported* symptoms and distress.

In an early study with children, Alexander, Miklich, and Hershkoff (1972) tested the hypothesis that progressive relaxation would improve peak expiratory airflow, compared with a quiet resting control. Asthmatic children in this study showed an improvement in airflow as predicted. Alexander (1972) also found that progressive relaxation was superior to resting, especially if highly anxious subjects comprised a subset of emotional-onset asthmatics. Alexander suggested, then, that the mechanism of the effect of relaxation training was on the emotional mediating component, rather than on the asthma itself.

Hook, Rodgers, Reddi, and Kennard (1978) compared relaxation training to assertiveness training and a combined treatment in children. Relaxation training and the combined manipulation improved frequency of attacks and airflow after 2 months of treatment. The assertive-training group worsened. This suggested an effect of relaxation, but, at a 1-month follow-up, all subjects had returned to baseline on all measures. Overall, these findings suggest the temporary effects on gross measures (frequency, airflow) but an impact of little clinical significance. However, no attempt at long-term maintenance was made.

In a review of research on relaxation training and behavioral therapy with adult bronchial asthma, Richter and Dahme (1982) reached disappointing conclusions. In fact, their reanalysis of a classic study showing positive results (Moore, 1965) shows that unreliable measurement (Wright Peak Flow Meter) and other design and statistical flaws led to the conclusion that subjects who received relaxation training actually worsened in peak expiratory flow efficiency, whereas desensitization (reciprocal inhibition) could not be interpreted as positively affecting wheezing frequency or peak expiratory flow. Likewise, a reanalysis of the study by Yorkston, Eckert, McHugh, Philander, and Blumenthal (1979) revealed that *post hoc* comparisons were improperly conducted, and the results were inconclusive for relaxation, as compared with desensitization procedures. However, they employed the Wright Peak Flow Meter, which is neither accurate nor reliable for research purposes. Erskine and Schonell (1979) also failed to show an affect of relaxation therapy on symptoms and signs of asthma when cognitive relaxation was combined with progressive muscle relaxation or used alone. In controlled studies of relaxation and systematic desensitization in asthma, more precisely controlled work and reliable measurement are clearly needed.

Hypnosis and Meditation

Because of the presumption that emotional states can influence the occurrence of asthma with some patients, it would seem reasonable to investigate the effects of hypnosis on asthma in susceptible subjects. M. M. Smith, Colebatch, and Clarke (1970) used hypnotic induction of emotional states (fear, anger, and suggestion of an attack of asthma) to study this phenomenon. These suggestions did increase pulmonary resistance in two chronic asthmatic subjects, and the suggestion of relaxation decreased resistance (cm H_2O/liter/sec). They argued that changes in bronchial diameter only could account for these effects and that the effects were "consistent with a mental mechanism" and suggested that "airway size can be rapidly altered under the influence of higher cerebral centers" (p. 240). Interestingly, the induction of the hypnotic trance (thought to be a sign of a highly relaxed state) had no effect on pulmonary resistance or transpulmonary pressure, whereas the suggestion of relaxation did. Clearly this study could be replicated more precisely with noninvasive measurement to clarify further the mechanism of beneficial effects, whether due to relaxation or to activation of bronchodilation processes.

Spector and his associates studied the effect of hypnosis on 9 asthmatic subjects (Spector, Luparello, Kopetzky, Souhrada, & Kinsman, 1976). They found hypnotic suggestion of bronchoconstriction substantially affected plethysmographic measures (of airway conductance and resistance) but not spirometric measures. Airway resistance and 1-second forced expiratory volume showed statistically significant but relatively small changes to the bronchodilation suggestion, which followed the bronchoconstriction suggestion. The greater effect on plethysmographic measure than on spirometric measures suggests further

investigation is needed before conclusions may be drawn concerning the nature of effects of hypnosis or bronchial dynamics in asthmatics.

An important study by Wilson, Honsberger, Chiu, and Novey (1975) compared the effects of the transcendental meditation procedure (TM) with reading a book by the founder of TM, but they did not describe the technique. They employed actual airways resistance (not peak flow) as the dependent measure. In a crossover design, TM resulted in improved airways resistance. Wilson et al. suggested three possible mechanisms of effect for TM: (a) reduction of psychological stress, (b) reduction of bronchomotor tone via reflex or chemical factors, and (c) reduction in minute ventilation through decreased oxygen consumption and need for CO_2 elimination. Richter and Dahme (1982) called for a replication of this important finding, but it apparently has not been done. We would add the caution that not only replication, but also careful dismantling-type investigations, are needed to determine the mechanism of effect. Even reduction of psychological stress could have complex underlying components (e.g. distraction, as discussed later).

Behavior Modification and Behavior Management

It can be seen that asthma has generated much interest from psychologists in the breathing disorders, and a variety of methods has been explored. On the other hand, emphysema and chronic bronchitis have been more often the subjects of behavior modification and management interventions than the other approaches just discussed. An example of the management approach, in this case with COPD patients, comes from Atkins, Kaplan, Timms, Reinsch, and Lofback (1984). In this study, COPD patients were assigned to one of five experimental groups: behavior modification, cognitive–behavioral modification, cognitive modification, attention control, and no-treatment control (attention control involved contact with the experimenters only). The purpose of the treatment comparison was to determine effects of the manipulations on compliance with an exercise regimen, as it is generally accepted that regular exercise improves the clinical status of COPD patients. Although they concluded that the three treatment groups exercised more than the control groups, in fact there was an increase in time spent walking for *all* groups, with the attained significant comparison being perhaps an artifact of the a priori hypotheses (for example, behavior modification and attention-control groups showed almost the same increases across the 11-week program). Other measures assessed the status of patients in other domains (e.g. Index of Well-Being scores). This study clearly exhibits the paradigmatic approach to the study of the psychological treatment of breathing disorders. It represents a management approach, rather than a clarification of the underlying mechanisms of the effect.

Other approaches to behavioral management of the clinical course of breathing disorders have shown a range of effects. Such programs typically do not presume to reflect directly on modified pulmonary function but, rather, on enhanced adjustment to disease or improved health status throughout other means, such as in smoking-cessation programs (e.g. Turner, Daniels, & Hollandsworth, 1985). One focus has been on enhancing compliance with various aspects of medical treatment (e.g. Weinstein, 1985; Weinstein & Cuskey, 1985). As with Atkins et al. (1984), increasing exercise is seen as a goal that will improve clinical status (e.g. J. T. King, Bye, & Demopoulos, 1984). Studies such as these suffer from a variety of uncontrolled variables. Much further work needs to be done to specify subpopulations of patients with particular types of disorders and the numerous behavioral approaches on aspects of complex psychosocial–pharmacological interventions before conclusions can be drawn about long-range effects of such programs on breathing disorders (see e.g. Cluss, 1986; Dudley, Glaser, Jorgenson, & Logan, 1980; N. J. King, 1980; LeBaron & Zeltzer, 1983).

Review

It has been seen that results with populations of patients with respiratory disease, compared with other disorders, leave us in need of new conceptual and methodological tools. Alexander (1981) concluded that the behavioral-medicine specialist would continue to have a role in the treatment of asthma, but the areas of functioning suggested are clearly not central to the disorder. He mainly saw such personnel as involved in the overall clinical management of the psychosocial sequelae of asthma, such as enhancing adjustment to impairment, treatment compliance, and general anxieties and fears associated with asthma. He stated, "The fundamental role of behavioral intervention in asthma should be rehabilitation" (p. 392).

On the other hand, Creer has seen the future of behavioral methodology more optimistically in relation to asthma and COPD (Creer, 1983). Creer's focus was also on behavioral management rather than behavioral treatment. Behavioral management has as its goal the amelioration of sequelae of a medical condition. These can include a variety of changes in the psychosocial domain. Behavioral treatment, on the other hand, includes a systematic effort to utilize psychologically informed methods to mediate changes in the pathophysiology of the disorder. We consider this distinction to be manifestly important, for it guides the conceptualization of variables to be investigated and could limit the understanding produced by any single investigation.

Recent studies such as those cited here and in the extensive reviews of Alexander (1981) and Creer (1982) do little, we think, to unpack the relevant psychological variables in breathing disorders, although the association between psychological factors and a variety of breathing parameters can now be considered well established. There is an analogous process occurring in the area of psychotherapy research, where there is a consensus that what is needed is no longer a series of "horseraces" to determine the most effective treatment; all treatments are about equally, but nonetheless substantially, effective (Lambert, Shapiro, & Bergin, 1986; Smith, Glass, & Miller, 1980). We would expect that a metanalysis of studies assessing behavioral approaches to breathing disorders would yield statistically reliable effects and that they would hover somewhere around or below the "clinically significant" threshold referred to by Alexander. Such a metanalysis would, as in the case of the vast body of research in psychotherapy, be limited to conclusions about general adjustment, not about the process of the effects on disorders. The psychological nature of respiratory disease does not yield to this kind of experimental paradigm. What is needed are conceptual tools for unpacking the psychological and physiological components of the system and combining these variables into a useful model that can be applied to the treatment of the disorders themselves. If this effort fails, then the main contributions of psychology will continue to be in the management of the clinical course of the disorder.

The present audience might be familiar with the basic parameters of the treatment-outcome paradigm specified earlier, as it can be applied to various chronic diseases. What is unfamiliar, however, to most psychologists who enter the field of breathing disorders is the complex nature of respiratory distress, or dyspnea, and the major pathophysiological aspects of the diseased respiratory system. It is to these issues that we now turn.

FOUNDATIONS OF A TREATMENT APPROACH FOR BREATHING DISORDERS

The Significance of Dyspnea

Surprisingly, dyspnea is one of the least understood aspects of respiratory disease from the psychologist's perspective. Yet, for the pulmonary physician seeking noninvasive components of a treatment program, amelioration of dyspnea would be a primary benefit. It is the single clinical feature of greatest concern to the practitioner of pulmonary medicine. What contributions from psychology are relevant to the endeavor of addressing this problem?

There is modern experimental evidence to support the contention that psychological factors play a vital role in the epigenesis and response to dyspnea. For example, Campbell, Sanderson, and Laverty (1964) administered curare to subjects without the subjects' awareness or informed consent. Subjects reported intense panic and terror in response to the loss of breathing capacity.

E. J. M. Campbell, Freedman, Clark, Robson, and Norman (1967) administered curare to subjects who were informed about the immediate availability of mechanical ventilation on request. These subjects reported no panic and experienced no generation of dyspnea whatsoever. In fact, mechanical ventilation had to be introduced lest subjects allow a toxic respiratory acidosis to develop. In both cases, the peripheral afferent information that could contribute to generating dyspnea was eliminated. These findings strongly suggest that cognitive and affective factors are important in mediating the response to pathophysiological variables known to affect breath-holding control.

Studies such as these provide the foundation for an appreciation of the substantial impact of psychological factors on dyspnea. What is presently lacking, given such impressive demonstrations, is a research strategy for investigating the relationships among affective and cognitive factors, on the one hand, and dyspnea, on the other. A psychological approach to dyspnea would seem to be predicted on the interpretation of such relevant data.

An Experimental Approach to Dyspnea

Alpher and his colleagues have recently addressed the need for experimental exemplars for investigations in this area (cf. Blanton & Alpher, 1983, in press). Two recently completed studies have tested the usefulness of a within-subjects, repeated measures design for testing hypotheses about the effects of psychological factors on dyspnea.

In the initial investigation, Alpher et al. (1986) tested the hypothesis that breath-holding span at functional residual capacity (FRC) could be extended by cognitive and psychomotor manipulations. (FRC denotes the lung volume obtained at the end point of a normal passive exhalation.) Although previous investigators had shown that breath-holding span could be extended simply by the act of breathing (with gas content in rebreathed air held constant) or other mechanical effects (such as vibration of the thorax by external manipulation), such studies tended to confound mechanical or chemical factors with psychological ones (Fowler, 1954; Sempik & Patrick, 1980). Alpher et al. compared the effects on voluntary FRC in subjects who completed three blocks of four trials each. During the four trials, which were completed in a randomized order within each block, subjects performed a hand dynamometer bulb squeeze (BS), a mental arithmetic task (MA), and a combined bulb squeeze–mental arithmetic task (BSMA). It was found that BS, MA, and BSMA tasks significantly extended the FRC breath holding beyond baseline. These results showed an increase in FRC breath-holding span of 15%–20% at a point when dyspnea would be predicted to be intolerable; yet, subjects did not break their breath holds at the point that would be theoretically predicted on the basis of mechanical and chemical factors alone.

Alpher and Blanton (1986) further studied the utility of the single-subject repeated measures design for investigating effects of psychological factors on dyspnea. The previous study had established the effectiveness of BS and MA tasks on breath-holding span. Several questions were raised by this study, however. In particular, tasks involved a performance challenge to subjects, adding psychological stress to experimental manipulations. Both MA and BS tasks include such potential stress components. It was hypothesized that attentional factors in the perception and appraisal of dyspneigenic sensations might account for the effects of MA and BS tasks but that such factors were confounded by performance stress. The

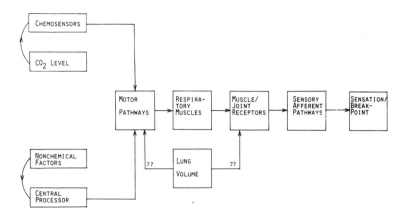

FIGURE 15.1. Adapted schematic depiction of Godfrey and Campbell's model of breath-holding control and epigenesis of dyspnea.

contribution of attentional factors to the genesis and response to dyspnea is an important one, for it adds a potential psychological component to a model of dyspnea on which relevant clinical treatments could be based.

Godfrey and Campbell (1968, 1969) first presented the model of breath-holding control and dyspnea in which attentional factors, or the appraisal of sensory inputs, was specified (see Figure 15.1). In this model, the cognitive appraisal of and response to chemical and mechanical factors is clearly acknowledged in the epigenesis of dyspnea. Another explanation for previous findings that FRC breath holding could be extended includes, as implied by this model, a manipulation of central processes as an explanatory construct.

Following this line of reasoning, Alpher and Blanton (1986) compared the effects of mantra meditation with two types of performance stress during FRC breath holding. Two memory tasks, one involving performance for monetary reward and the other performance for avoiding an electric shock, completed the three tasks to be compared in the randomized, blocked-trial design successfully employed by Alpher et al. (1986). The mantra meditation manipulation showed reduction of breath-holding performance, compared to baseline. Although the positive-incentive condition had no effect on FRC breath holding, the negative-incentive (shock avoidance) condition actually extended breath holding. During mantra meditation, subjects were less aroused than during baseline FRC breath holding. Arousal during FRC breath holding did not differ from arousal during the memory task with positive incentive. However, during negative incentive, subjects were significantly more aroused than during baseline.

These findings suggest several hypotheses directly relevant to understanding psychological–attentional factors in the epigenesis of dyspnea and potential avenues for empirically exploring this common feature in breathing disorders. First, because psychophysiological arousal is associated with stress and coping responses, the detrimental effect of mantra meditation on FRC breath-holding points to a possible explanation for the generally poor results of relaxation and desensitization treatments for dyspnea in asthma, emphysema, and chronic bronchitis. Such treatments are based on the a priori assumption that stress aggravates these conditions, that psychological stress and physiological dysfunction are basically summative in producing a maladaptive stress response state. However, the findings of Alpher and his colleagues point to the potential importance of stress in *facilitating* adaptive responses to dyspnea. Thus, to suggest that relaxation facilitates coping in breathing disorders might be not only misleading but also simply incorrect. These findings are not definitive, but they do suggest an experimental approach that minimizes the untoward effects of individual differences in breathing on experimental manipulations and statistical power, by the use of single-subject designs.

Pathophysiological Aspects of Dyspnea

These experimental findings are certainly heuristic, and they suggest that psychological factors

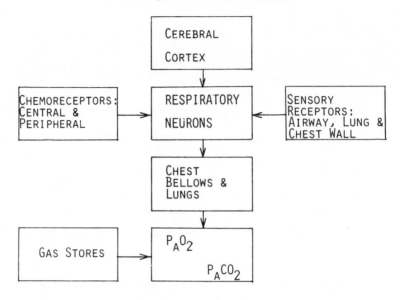

FIGURE 15.2. Schematic representation of the respiratory control system. The respiratory neurons in the brainstem receive information from the chemoreceptors, the peripheral sensory receptors, and the cerebral cortex. This information is integrated, and the resulting neural output to the chest bellows and lungs, in association with the gas stores in the body, determines the arterial tensions of oxygen (P_aO_2) and carbon dioxide (P_aCO_2). In addition, the cerebral cortex can act directly on the chest bellows through a neural pathway that bypasses the brainstem respiratory neurons.

can be specified in not only the clinical cause of breathing disorders but also in the primary clinical problem associated with them, that is, dyspnea itself. To assess more fully the prospects for a complete model of dyspnea that provides a theoretical understanding of the mechanisms involved in psychological interventions, it is imperative even for the psychologist to be familiar with the fundamentals of current pathophysiological knowledge of dyspnea. Here the current state of knowledge on dyspnea in the breathing disorders will be presented. Our ultimate goal is to begin the process of integrating pathophysiological and psychological perspectives.

CONTROL OF BREATHING

General Overview

The remarkable stability of arterial oxygen and carbon dioxide tensions (P_aO_2 and P_aCO_2, respectively) despite up to twentyfold increases in oxygen consumption and carbon dioxide production, emphasizes the precision with which the body regulates ventilation. This automatic homeostasis is dependent on the integrative function of the three components of the respiratory control system: the

respiratory control centers, the respiratory sensors, and the respiratory effectors (Figure 15.2).

The neurons controlling ventilation are located at several levels of the brainstem. The most important network resides in the medulla oblongata, where respiratory rhythm originates. These brainstem centers are responsible for the automatic control of breathing, but they can be overridden by the cerebral cortex, as occurs during speech and other actions requiring the voluntary control of ventilation. For example, Phillipson, McClean, Sullivan, and Zamel (1978) have demonstrated that the ventilatory response to hypercapnia is markedly depressed during speech, with alleviation of the associated distress. The additional observation that minute ventilation drops significantly during sleep (10%–25% reduction) indicates that mechanisms involving conscious behavior are important in the control of resting breathing (Douglas, 1985; Krieger, 1985; Tobin et al. 1983a).

The respiratory sensors consist of the chemoreceptors and the peripheral sensory receptors. The chemoreceptors consist of two types, central and peripheral. The central chemoreceptors located in the brainstem respond primarily to P_aCO_2; hypercapnia causes an increase in ventilation. The peripheral chemoreceptors, located at the bifurcation of the carotid arteries, respond primarily to P_aO_2; hypoxia causes an increase in ventilation. The peripheral sensory receptors consist of those in the chest wall and in the lower airways and lungs. Mechanoreceptors in the respiratory muscles, such as muscle spindles and tendon organs, respond to stretch. The intrapulmonary receptors consist of (a) airway irritant receptors, which respond to physical or chemical stimulation; (b) pulmonary stretch receptors, which respond to marked increases in lung volume; and (c) J-receptors, found in the alveolo–capillary junctions, which respond to vascular engorgement and congestion.

The effectors of respiratory-center output are the respiratory muscles. Contraction of the respiratory muscles during normal inspiration causes expansion of the thoracic cavity. The associated fall in intrathoracic pressure facilitates the flow of air from the atmosphere to the alveoli, so permitting gas exchange. The resulting changes in thoracic displacement, P_aO_2 and P_aCO_2 are fed back to the central nervous system by afferent nerves arising in the lungs, the chest wall, and the chemoreceptors.

Innervation of the Respiratory System

Some knowledge of the innervation of the respiratory muscles and lungs is essential to an understanding of the neuroanatomical basis of respiratory sensation (Figure 15.3). The major muscles of respiration are the diaphragm and the intercostal, abdominal, and accessory muscles. The phrenic nerves are the only motor nerves of the diaphragm. They arise from the third, fourth, and fifth cervical segments and descend through the neck to reach the diaphragm. In addition to their motor function, they are the main source of diaphragmatic sensory innervation. Likewise, the intercostal nerves provide both motor and sensory innervation of the intercostal muscles. They arise from the 1st to the 12th thoracic segments (T_1–T_{12}). The abdominable muscles, the most powerful muscles of expiration, are innervated by the lower six intercostal nerves (T_7–T_{12}) and the first lumbar nerve. Two major accessory muscles of respiration, the sternomastoid and scalene muscles, are found in the neck. The sternomastoid muscles are innervated by the spinal accessory nerve and the second cervical nerve, whereas the scaleni are supplied by the lower five cervical nerves (C_4–C_8).

Two main types of sensory receptors are found in the respiratory muscles: muscles spindles and tendon organs. The muscle spindles are abundant in the intercostal muscles but relatively scarce in the diaphragm. Muscle spindles are found within the special intrafusal fibers that are arranged in parallel with the main extrafusal muscle fibers. The contractile extrafusal fibers of a muscle receive the integrated output of the respiratory centers through alpha motoneurons, whereas the gamma motoneurons, also present in peripheral nerves, innervate the intrafusal fibers within the muscle spindles (fusiform system). A disturbance in the equilibrium between the two fiber systems might be important in the generation of respiratory sensation during loaded breathing. Tendon organs are found in both the intercostal muscles and the diaphragm. Unlike its scarcity of muscle spindles, the diaphragm is richly innervated with tendon organs. These receptors are arranged in series within the muscle fibers and provide a restricted but accurate estimate of the forces generated by muscle contraction (Altose, 1986).

The lung and airways are innervated by the sympathetic and parasympathetic nervous systems. The sympathetic nerves cause bronchodilation, bronchial vessel constriction, and inhibition of glandular secretion, whereas the vagus (parasympathetic) nerves have opposing actions. Practically all of the afferent information from the sensory receptors in the lower airways and lungs travels in the vagus nerves.

Afferent information from the sensory chemoreceptor cells of the carotid body travels in a branch of the carotid sinus nerve and reaches the brainstem in the glossopharyngeal (ninth cranial) nerve.

Assessment

Investigation of respiratory-center control in humans has traditionally been limited to assessment of the ventilatory response to progressive hypercapnia or hypoxia. The respiratory control center is exquisitely sensitive to small changes in P_aCO_2. During resting breathing, healthy subjects have a minute ventilation of about 6 1/minute and maintain P_aCO_2 between 35 and 45 torr. In a given individual P_aCO_2 varies by less than 3 torr during normal daily activities. If P_aCO_2 is increased by 1 torr, minute ventilation increases by about 2 1/minute, on average. In contrast, the hypoxic ventilatory response is minimal until PO_2 falls to about 60 torr.

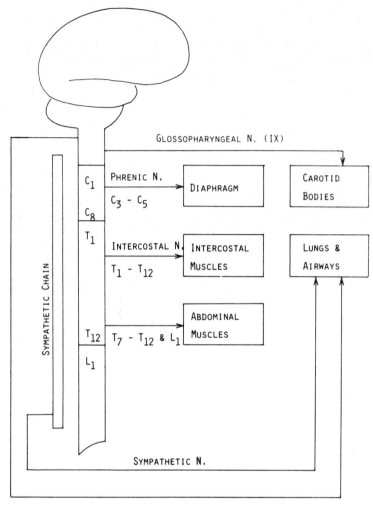

FIGURE 15.3. Schematic representation of the innervation of the respiratory system. See text for details.

Studies of chemosensitivity are based on the assumption that the respiratory response reflects the action of an automatic metabolic control system. However, unlike other automatically controlled systems in the body, breathing is achieved through the action of skeletal muscles and, thus, is under direct voluntary control. Indeed, the forebrain can transmit signals to the respiratory system along an independent neural pathway, bypassing the automatic metabolic control center in the brainstem (Aminoff & Sears, 1971; Newsom-Davis & Plum, 1972; Rikard-Bell, Bystrazycka, & Nail, 1985). This suggests that voluntary and reflexly mediated ventilation might have different neural pathways. Investigations that ignore these consciously controlled behavioral mechanisms could result in considerable confusion regarding the overall regulation of respiration. Measuring the ventilatory response to hypoxia and hypercapnia requires the use of instrumentation that is known to cause major changes in respiratory-center output. For example, the simple use of a mouthpiece and nose clips is known to cause significant changes in the pattern of breathing (Gilbert, Auchincloss, Brodsky, & Broden, 1972, Perez & Tobin, 1985). This leaves us in the difficult situation in which the instrumentation being used causes changes in the very phenomena that it is being employed to measure. The additional discomfort engendered by chemical stimulation is also likely to affect the modulating influence of the

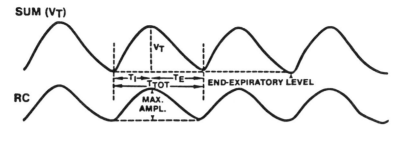

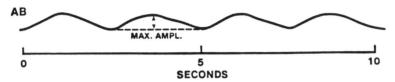

FIGURE 15.4. Schematic recording of the respiratory cycle depicting the points of reference for computation of various breathing pattern parameters. The signals have been obtained with a respiratory-inductive plethysmograph, thus SUM (V_T) indicates tidal volume, which has been calibrated to spirometry and represents the algebraic sum of the rib-cage (RC) and abdominal (AB) excursions. T_I represents inspiratory time, T_E expiratory time, T_{TOT} time of a total breath, V_T/T_I mean inspiratory flow rate, and V_T/T_E mean expiratory flow rate. Alterations in the end expiratory level represent changes in functional residual capacity, provided movement artifact is absent. Maximum amplitude is the trough-to-peak amplitude of the rib cage and abdominal excursions, irrespective of their phase relationship to the SUM signal; their arithmetic sum, designated maximum compartmental amplitude, is equivalent to the algebraic SUM signal (tidal volume) when the rib-cage and abdomen move-in phase. *Note.* From "Effect of Positive and Expiratory Pressure on Breathing Patterns of Normal Subjects and Intubated Patients with Respiratory Failure". by M. J. Tobin, G. Jenouri, S. Birch, et al. 1983, *Critical Care Medicine, 11,* p. 859, Copyright 1983 by Williams & Wilkins Co.. Reprinted by permission.

cerebral cortex on the respiratory centers, as even cognitive activity has a major effect on respiratory-center output (Tobin, Perez, Auenther, D'Alonzo, & Dantzker, 1986). In fact, there is evidence that even short-term chemical stimulation might have a direct effect on higher brain centers independent of its action on the chemoreceptors (Neubauer, Santiago, & Edelman, 1981).

In recent years, an alternative approach to respiratory-center assessment has been developed. By measurement of rib-cage and abdominal motion using a respiratory-inductive plethysmograph, ventilation can be measured indirectly without requiring any connection to the airway (Tobin, 1986a, 1986b). Over the same period that technology for noninvasive measurement of ventilation improved, significant advances occurred in our analytical approach to the pattern of breathing (Milic-Emili, 1983; Tobin, 1983a, 1983b) (see Figure 15.4). This approach provides an assessment of not only respiratory drive but also respiratory-center timing. Minute ventilation ($\dot{V}_I$) is traditionally examined in terms of tidal volume (V_T) and respiratory frequency (f),

$$\dot{V}_I = V_T \text{ x f.}$$

This equation can be rearranged, as f is equal to 60 divided by the time of a total respiratory cycle, (T_{TOT}) or single breath,

$$\dot{V}_I = V_T \text{ x } 60/T_{TOT}.$$

Conceptually, 60 can be deleted and the equation reduced to

$$\dot{V}_I = V_T \text{ x } 1/T_{TOT}.$$

This equation can be further modified by dividing V_T by inspiratory time (T_I), and multiplying $1/T_{TOT}$ by T_I, to give

$$\dot{V}_I = V_T/T_I \text{ x } T_I/T_{TOT}.$$

The first parameter, V_T/T_I, is termed mean inspiratory flow, and the second parameter, T_I/T_{TOT}, has been called the fractional inspiratory time. This form of analysis is appealing because V_T/T_I reflects central respiratory drive (Clark & von Euler 1972; Lind, Truve, & Lindborg, 1984; Milic-Emili, 1983), whereas T_I/T_{TOT} reflects phase switching (inspiration, expiration) of the respiratory center. Using this analytical approach, it is possible to examine respiratory-center drive and timing on a breath-to-breath basis in different experimental situations.

PHYSIOLOGIC ASPECTS OF DYSPNEA

Definition

There is no universally accepted definition of dyspnea, but everybody has experienced the sensation and thus has an intuitive understanding of the phenomenon. At an international symposium on breathlessness in 1965, the noted physiologist, Julius Comroe, outlined his concept of dyspnea: "It is *not* tachypnea, which is rapid breathing; it is *not* hyperpnea, which is increased ventilation in proportion to increased metabolism; it is *not* hyperventilation, which is ventilation in excess of metabolic requirements. Instead, dyspnea is difficult, labored, uncomfortable breathing; it is an unpleasant type of breathing, though it is not painful in the usual sense of the word. It is subjective and, like pain, it involves both perception of the sensation by the patient and his reaction to the sensation (Comroe, 1966a p. 1)" In his closing remarks at the end of the symposium, he returned to this issue: "We have learned here that there are five or six different grades or types of this sensation. One is an awareness that there is a little increase in ventilation. Another is a little shortness of breath ('harder to get one's breath'), and this may be slightly unpleasant. Another is an almost pleasant or satisfying sensation such as the deep breathing of an individual who has just run a race. Others are the sensation of hindered breathing, the sensation of suffocation with acute need for a deeper inspiration, and the sensation at the breaking point of breath-holding. Unfortunately, we do not have different, precise terms for each of these (Comroe, 1966b, p. 235). This imprecision in terminology becomes a problem when reviewing investigations that have addressed the basis, clinical presentation, and management of dyspnea. Given this situation, one has to be careful to avoid repeating the error of Alice in Wonderland (Carroll, 1970 p. 95).

"Then you should say what you mean" the March Hare went on.

"I do," Alice hastily replied; "at least — at least I mean what I say — that's the same thing, you know."

"Not the same thing a bit!" said the Hatter.

Pathophysiologic Basis of Dyspnea

The considerable advances in or understanding of the pathophysiologic basis of dyspnea have recently been reviewed in detail by Altose (1986) and Killian and Campbell (1985). Readers requiring more

detailed information are referred to these sources.

In attempting to understand the basis of dyspnea, it is important to keep in mind that it is a conscious sensation and thus needs to be investigated not only in neuroanatomical terms but also in terms of psychophysics (Killian & Campbell, 1985). The neuroanatomical approach focuses on the individual role of the various neural processes and pathways involved in sensation. A sensory stimulus excites a receptor, and the resulting signal is transmitted along afferent neural pathways to the central nervous system. The information is centrally processed and integrated, and the resulting sensory impression is the reconstruction of the receptor stimulation. This model, however, ignores the essential fact that conscious perception is interpreted in the light of previous experience. Thus, investigations into the mechanism of dyspnea need to take into account not only the neuroanatomical aspects but also the role of psychophysics, which deals with the relationship between physical stimuli and the evoked conscious sensation.

A variety of experimental methods have been employed in investigating the pathophysiologic mechanisms responsible for dyspnea. A number of investigators have employed the experimental model of breath holding, which is similar to a severe form of dyspnea. When a healthy subject holds his or her breath at resting lung volume, there is no unpleasant sensation for about the first 30 seconds. Then, the respiratory muscles begin to contract, and the subject becomes increasingly uncomfortable. Factors that determine the duration of the breath-holding period and the associated discomfort have been intensively investigated. Although these studies have provided important information on respiratory sensation, their application to our understanding of dyspnea in patients with respiratory disease should be made with caution.

A second experimental approach has consisted of employing a number of psychophysical techniques in the investigation of changes in evoked conscious sensation produced by breathing through external resistive (breathing through narrow tubing) or elastic loads (breathing from a small box or drum of air) (Altose, 1986; Killian & Campbell, 1985). The major psychophysical techniques that have been employed include (a) threshold discrimination, which determines the amount of change in the intensity of a stimulus that is required for the subject to detect a just noticeable difference in sensation; (b) magnitude scaling, which assesses the subject's response to a variety of sensory stimuli of differing intensity; (c) interval scales used to quantitate dyspnea, such as the visual analogue scale (Aitken, Zealley, & Rosenthal, 1970) and the Borg category scale (Borg, 1982). Again, one potential limitation of studies using this approach is the assumption that the sensation produced by loaded breathing is similar to the sensation of dyspnea occurring in patients with respiratory disease. A third method involves examining the sensation of insufficient ventilation that occurs while rebreathing CO_2. The fourth experimental approach studies a number of experiments of nature (patients with a variety of neurologic lesions) and the effect of different nerve blocks, in an attempt to define the neuroanatomical basis of respiratory sensation (Table 15.1).

Mechanism of Dyspnea

The potential mechanisms responsible for the development of dyspnea can be separated into four major categories: disturbance of chemosensitivity, pulmonary receptors, respiratory muscle receptors, and outgoing respiratory motor command (Altose, 1986).

Sensation of Chemoreceptor Stimulation

Although it is well recognized that both hypoxia and hypercapnia cause severe dyspnea, it has not been clear whether the altered chemoreceptor stimulation can be directly perceived or whether the distress is due to the accompanying increase in respiratory motor output activity and the resulting increase in minute ventilation. Two early investigations conducted in patients with severe paralytic poliomyelitis suggested that an increase in P_aCO_2 to about 40–50 torr was associated with the development of dyspnea (Opie, Smith & Spalding, 1959; Patterson, Mullinay, Bain, Krueger, & Richardson, 1962). However, respiratory efferent activity was not measured in these studies. This question was recently readdressed by Castele, Connors, and Altose (1985), who studied a group of healthy volunteers during mechanical ventilation at a fixed tidal volume and respiratory frequency. They initially induced hypocapnia (P_aCO_2 of 30 torr) and then gradually increased the inspired concentration of CO_2, while keeping the ventilator settings constant. A dyspneic sensation was noted when P_aCO_2 rose to 42 torr, but only *after* respiratory efferent activity had increased and the subjects were actively assisting the ventilator. These results suggest that the alteration in respiratory sensation

was primarily dependent on the respiratory efferent activity, rather than being due directly to changes in P_aCO_2. The studies of total neuromuscular blockade by E. J. M. Campbell, Godfrey, Clark, Freedman, and Norman (1969) also suggest that chemoreceptor stimulation does not play a primary role in the pathogenesis of dyspnea, because respiratory distress was not noted during a prolonged breath hold despite an increase in P_aCO_2 to 72 torr.

Pulmonary Receptor Stimulation

Various pulmonary diseases cause stimulation of pulmonary stretch, irritant, and J sensory receptors. The importance of these receptors in the airways has been examined through the use of inhaled local anesthesia. The ability to detect resistive and elastic loads remains unchanged (Chaudhary & Burki, 1978, 1987; Burki, 1983), as does the ability to hold one's breath (Cross et al., 1976) This suggests that upper airway receptors are probably not important in these respiratory sensations. Almost all of the afferent impulses arising from airway and intrapulmonary receptors are carried in the vagus nerve. Consequently, a number of investigators have examined the part played by the vagi in the pathogenesis of dyspnea, using a variety of experimental approaches.

Guz, Noble, Widdicombe, Trenchard & Mushin (1966a) examined the effect of bilateral vagal block in two healthy volunteers and one patient with sarcoidosis. In the healthy subjects, lignocaine was injected around the vagus nerve at the base of the skull. This procedure is inevitably complicated by simultaneous block of the glossopharyngeal nerves. Because afferent stimuli from the peripheral chemoreceptors are transmitted via the glossopharyngeal nerves, the investigators produced a functional denervation of these nerves by having the subjects inspire 100% oxygen. Vagal block caused prolongation of the breath-holding time despite an increase in P_aCO_2 to 66 torr, and the associated distress was alleviated. The sensation of inability to get enough air while rebreathing CO_2 was also abolished (Guz, Noble, Widdicombe, Trenchard, Mushin, 1966b). In contrast, the resting breathing pattern and the ability to detect added loads were unaffected. The results of this study do not indicate whether afferent vagal information is directly perceived, but they do suggest that the drive to breathe during breath holding and the unpleasant sensation during breath holding and CO_2 rebreathing is dependent on vagal afferent information. The

TABLE 15.1. Investigations of the Neuroanatomical Basis of Respiratory Sensation

NATURE OF LESION OR BLOCK	NEUROLOGIC EFFECTS	PHYSIOLOGIC CONSEQUENCES	COMMENTS AND IMPLICATIONS	AUTHOR
Curare	Blocks respiratory muscle activity; lung and respiratory center output	Increase BHT, despite PCO_2 of 72 torr; no distress	Respiratory muscle contraction is necessary to cause distress. Pulmonary afferents and outgoing motor command are insufficient, in themselves, to cause distress.	E. J. M. Campbell, Freedman, Clark, Robson, & Norman, 1967; E. J. M. Campbell, Godfrey, Clark, Freedman, & Norman, 1969
Spinal anesthesia to T_1	Blocks afferents & efferents from intercostals, & sympathetic n; phrenic & vagi remain intact	BHT and load detection are unaffected	Intercostal receptors are not essential for sensing volume and distress	Eisele, Trenchard, Burki, & Guz, 1968
Low cervical quadriplegia (below C_5)	Same as above	Respiratory volume reproduction and volume scaling are unaffected	Intercostal receptors are not essential for sensing respiratory displacement (i,e., inspired volume).	DiMarco, Wolfson, Gottfried, & Altose, 1982
Bilateral phrenic nerve block	Diaphragmatic paralysis	Increased BHT with decreased distress; load detection unaffected	Diaphragm is involved in sensations of breath-holding but does not alone mediate load detection	Noble, Trenchard, & Guz, 1970; Noble, Eisele, Frankel, Else, & Guz, 1971
Vagal nerve block	Blocks vagal afferents; intercostals & diaphragm remain intact	Increased BHT, despite PCO_2, of 66 torr; distress during CO_2 rebreathing abolished; load detection unaffected	Unpleasant sensation of breathholding is dependent on vagi	Guz, Noble, Widdicombe, Trennchard, & Mushin, 1966; Widdicombe, Trenchard, Mushin, & Makey, 1926
High cervical quadriplegia (C_1–C_3)	near total respiratory muscle paralysis; loss of all somatic sensation below neck; vagi intact	Normal respiratory volume perception	Vagal afferents can be consciously perceived	Lansing, Bunzett, Brown, & Kimball, 1985
Local anesthesia to upper and lower airways	Blocks airway receptors	Load detection unaffected	Upper airways are not essential for load detection	Chaudhary & Burki, 1978, 1980

BHT = Breath-holding time.

question of whether vagal afferent information can be perceived was recently addressed by Lansing, Banzett, Brown, and Kimball (1985). They studied five patients with high-level quadriplegia, C_1-C_3 level. These patients have total respiratory muscle paralysis, with the exception of the sternomastoid muscles, and loss of all somatic sensation below the neck, but the vagi remain intact. In their preliminary communication, Lansing et al. (1985) reported that changes in lung volume were normally perceived in these patients. They interpreted this to suggest that vagal afferent signals from the lung can in fact be consciously perceived.

The effect of vagotomy on breathing pattern and exercise performance has been studied in 5 patients with severe emphysema, although only one of the patients had a bilateral vagotomy (Bradley, Hale, Pimble, Rowlandson, & Noble, 1982). Symptomatic improvement was reported in two patients, and another two patients were reported to show minor improvement. The study is difficult to interpret, but it is unlikely that vagotomy will become a popular procedure in the management of dyspnea.

Respiratory Muscle Receptors

There is a considerable body of evidence implicating the respiratory muscles as a major source of dyspnea. As early as 1908, Hill and Flack showed that breath-holding time could be prolonged by a rebreathing maneuver, despite the associated increase in P_aCO_2 and the fall in P_aO_2. This finding was verified in an elegant study by Fowler (1954), who showed that by rebreathing a gas mixture whose composition had been chosen to increase P_aCO_2 and lower P_aO_2 at the breaking point of a breath hold, the discomfort was immediately relieved and further breath holding became possible. These studies show that movement of the chest wall and lungs alleviates the distressing sensation of breath holding. In addition, they indicated that alteration in arterial blood gases does not directly cause the distress, although the gases might partly contribute to it.

These findings and subsequent studies performed during loaded breathing led E. J. M. Campbell and Howell (1963) to formulate a general hypothesis for the mechanism of dyspnea, which they termed the *length–tension inappropriateness* theory. They proposed that, during normal breathing, there is an appropriate relationship between the tension developed by the respiratory muscles and the resulting displacement in muscle length. They suggested that subjects are able to detect added

mechanical loads because the displacement achieved in terms of volume or flow is less than the displacement that was expected. They considered that breath holding was the ultimate form of length–tension inappropriateness and suggested that the relief achieved by a rebreathing maneuver at the break point of a breath hold was due to shortening of the respiratory muscles, leading to reduction in the extent of length–tension inappropriateness. This theory formed the framework for much of the subsequent experimental work that has been conducted on the possible mechanisms of respiratory sensation.

Strong evidence for a primary role by the respiratory muscles in the pathogenesis of dyspnea was provided by studies using the neuromuscular blocking agent, curare. This agent paralyzes all of the respiratory muscles while leaving the pulmonary afferent and respiratory-center activity intact. Campbell et al. (1967, 1969) showed that curare caused marked prolongation of breath-holding time, despite an increase in P_aCO_2 to 72 torr and abolition of the distress usually associated with breath holding. From these studies they concluded that the distress of breath holding is a result of respiratory muscle contraction and not of stimuli arising in the lung.

Subsequent studies have been performed to separate the contribution of the diaphragm and rib-cage muscles in the development of dyspnea (Table 15.1). Eisele, Trenchard, Burki, and Guz (1968) studied 4 patients undergoing spinal anesthesia up to the level of the first thoracic segment (T_1). This blocks both afferent and efferent nervous activity from the intercostal muscles, while innervation of the diaphragm (phrenic nerve, C_3-C_5) and pulmonary sensory activity (vagus nerves) remain intact (see Figure 15.3). In addition, the sympathetic afferents are blocked, because the sympathetic nervous system enters the cords at segments T_1-T_{12}. They found that chest wall block caused no changes in breath holding time, the distress associated with rebreathing CO_2, or the ability to detect respiratory loads. Similarly, DiMarco, Wolfson, Gottfried, and Altrose (1982) noted that patients with low cervical quadriplegia (below C_5, which causes similar neurologic consequences to spinal anesthesia) have normal respiratory volume reproduction and scaling. These studies suggest that the intercostal muscles are not essential for sensing respiratory volumes or the distress of breath holding. In contrast, Gottfried, Leech, DiMarco, Zacardelli, and Altose (1984) observed a partial impairment of load sensation in a similar group of patients with low cervical quadriplegia, suggesting that intercostal muscle receptors are important in sensing respiratory muscle force.

The role of the diaphragm was studied by Noble, Eisele, Frankel, Else, and Guz (1971), who induced bilateral phrenic nerve block in 3 healthy subjects. Breath-holding time was prolonged, and the associated distress was alleviated. In contrast, the ability to detect resistive loads was unaffected by bilateral phrenic nerve block (Noble, Eisele, Trenchard, & Guz 1970).

These studies suggest that the diaphragm, but not the intercostal muscles, is involved in respiratory distress breath holding. Although it has long been recognized that afferent discharges from muscle receptors are transmitted to subconscious levels of the central nervous system, there is now electrophysiological evidence suggesting that information from the muscle receptors can be directly transmitted to the cerebral cortex (Altose, 1986).

Sensation of Respiratory Motor Command

Recent interest has been expressed in the role of *sense of effort* in the development of dyspnea. This term refers to a conscious feeling of innervation that accompanies the departure of voluntary motor impulses from the cerebral cortex (Merton, 1970). This concept is based on von Helmholtz's demonstration in 1867 that vision required a mechanism that relied on an outgoing motor discharge, rather than being solely dependent on afferent information. The neurophysiology of this sense of effort remains obscure, but it is likely that it is at least partly related to the outgoing motor command, although evidence for this remains largely circumstantial (Killian & Campbell, 1985). For instance, McCloskey, Ebeling, and Goodwin (1974) have shown that the perceived heaviness of a weight is greater in a fatigued muscle.

Merton (1970) suggested the possibility that the ability to detect respiratory loads might be related to a mismatch between effort and the inspiratory volume achieved. Similarly, there is a disturbance in the relationship between the sense of respiratory effort and the ventilation being achieved in a number of disease states associated with dyspnea, such as obstructive and restrictive lung disease, chest bellows disease, and neuromuscular disease (Killian & Campbell, 1985). This raises the possibility that

TABLE 15.2. Clinical Causes of Dyspnea.

Respiratory disease	Obstructive airways disease
	Restrictive lung disease
	Pulmonary vascular disease
	Pleural disease
Chest Wall Disease	Respiratory muscle weakness
	Kyphoscoliosis
	Obesity
Other	Cardiac disease
	Acidosis
	Anemia
	Psychogenic causes

the sensation of dyspnea might simply represent the conscious awareness of the outgoing respiratory motor command (Altose, 1986). If this were the sole source of conscious respiratory sensation, however, one would expect intolerable dyspnea during the prolonged breath hold in subjects undergoing total neuromuscular blockade with curare. The absence of distress in these subjects suggests that the outgoing motor command needs to be coupled to achieved muscular force before a sense of effort is generated or that some feedback from the respiratory muscles is necessary to produce the sensation.

From this discussion of investigations into the mechanism of dyspnea it is apparent that several different sensations produced by different mechanisms are likely to be involved and that the warning of E. J. M. Campbell and Howell (1963) should still be heeded: 'A respiratory physiologist offering a unitary explanation for breathlessness should arouse the same suspicion as a tattooed archbishop offering a free ticket to heaven' (p. 237).

DYSPNEA IN THE CLINICAL SETTING

Dyspnea in Patients with Respiratory Diseases

Dyspnea is a cardinal manifestation of respiratory and cardiac disease. Practically all forms of respiratory disease can cause dyspnea (Table 15.2). From a clinical standpoint, dyspnea in these patients results from (a) an increase in the respiratory drive or effort necessary to overcome the imposed load, for example, obstructive or resistive lung disease; (b) an increase in the proportion of respiratory muscle force required for breathing, that is, neuromuscular weakness or hyperinflation; and (c) an increase in ventilatory requirements, that is, hypoxemia or pulmonary vascular disease.

The fact that some patients are more aware of dyspnea than others, despite similar levels of functional impairment, is a perplexing problem. For example, Rubinfeld and Pain (1976) demonstrated that asthmatics show enormous variability in the degree of change in lung function before the perceptive threshold is reached. About 15% of their asthmatics were unaware of marked airflow obstruction (forced expiratory volume in 1 second (FEV_1) of less than 50% of the predicted normal value). Studies in healthy volunteers have shown that, when background resistance is increased, the threshold of load detection is increased proportionately, so that the Weber fraction remains relatively constant. Similarly, Burki (1984) has shown that perception of added resistive loads is similar in asthmatic and healthy subjects, although the perceived sensory magnitude for any given load is greater in the asthmatics. In another study of load detection in asthma, Hudgel, Cooperson, and Kinsman (1982) found that the threshold values were greater in subjects who were anxious or dependent, compared with those who were adaptive or rigidly independent. In contrast with the asthmatic patients, Gottfried, Altose, Kelsen, and Cherniack (1981) found that load perception was blunted in patients with chronic obstructive pulmonary disease. They questioned whether this might be due to attenuation of respiratory mechanoreceptor activity as a result of adaptation or whether it might reflect changes in the central processing of the sensory information. The second explanation was shown to be more important in a subsequent study by these investigators (Gottfried, Redline, & Altose, 1985).

The question as to why some patients with lung disease have dyspnea that is disproportionate to the severity of their disease was examined by Burns and Howell (1969). They studied two groups, each consisting of 31 patients with chronic bronchitis. The severity of dyspnea was considered the same in the two groups, but the degree of abnormality in lung function differed. The control patients had evidence of severe airway obstruction (all had an FEV_1 of less than *1* liter (*1*), mean 0.67 *1*) and thus were considered to have "appropriate" dyspnea, whereas all of the patients with disproportionate dyspnea had less severe abnormalities in pulmonary function (FEV_1 was greater than 1 liter in all patients, mean 1.88 *1*). All of the patients with disproportionate dyspnea were considered psychiatrically ill: depression (52%), anxiety (22%), and hysterical reactions (26%). None of the controls were considered to suffer from formal psychiatric illness. The group with disproportionate dyspnea was different from the controls in that its members' dyspnea was of shorter duration, and the patients were younger, more socially isolated, and subject to more recent stress and had had more psychiatric illness in the past. Characteristics of the dyspnea differed in the two groups. Features found more commonly in the patients with disproportionate dyspnea included poor relationship of dyspnea to exercise, increased dyspnea at rest, acute hyperventilation attacks with fear of sudden death, rapid fluctuations in the severity of dyspnea, aggravation by social stress, waking at night because of dyspnea, difficulty on inspiration rather than expiration, and relief by sedatives or alcohol. All of the patients with disproportionate dyspnea received psychiatric treatment including benzodiazepine tranquilizers for 26 of the patients. On follow-up over 2 to 3 years, successful treatment of the psychiatric disorder was associated with complete or partial resolution of the dyspnea.

The implications of this study are important and, thus, it is unfortunate that subsequent investigations have not (to our knowledge) been published addressing the issue. In a review paper, Rosser and Guz (1981) took issue with this concept of disproportionate dyspnea. Based on their clinical experience, they felt that the cluster of symptoms considered to be characteristic of disproportion was found in patients who had severe dyspnea, irrespective of whether or not they had severe pulmonary disease. Although they provided no details, Rosser and Guz reported that relief of psychiatric symptoms was not accompanied by diminution in dyspnea, suggesting that the psychiatric disorder is a consequence, rather than a cause, of the dyspnea.

In contrast with the large body of data pertaining to the neuroanatomical and psychophysiological basis of respiratory sensation, we are still very ignorant as to what causes dyspnea in patients with cardiopulmonary disorders and why some patients display more distress than others. A nihilistic evaluation of our current status was recently enunciated by Altschule: "Measurements made at rest or in different respiratory maneuvers have been used in attempts to produce evaluatable changes in dyspnea in healthy and sick persons. They have not added much to our knowledge, although they have provided some physicians who cannot tolerate uncertainty with what appears to be answers to questions about mechanisms" (1987, p. 267).

Hyperventilation Syndrome

The hyperventilation syndrome consists of a characteristic constellation of symptoms and signs associated with hyperventilation and anxiety. It is a common condition, affecting 6%–11% of the general patient population (Brashear, 1983; Lum, 1981), but it is frequently missed in clinical practice. The facts that emotional factors aggravate dyspnea and that anxiety in itself can cause hyperventilation are well recognized. It is also known that hyperventilation, in turn, can produce apprehension and anxiety. It is not clear whether the hyperventilation syndrome is an extreme form of this association between emotion and breathing or whether it represents a discrete syndrome.

Historical background.

The term *hyperventilation syndrome* was coined by Kerr in 1937 to describe a cluster of clinical features associated with hyperventilation and anxiety (Kerr, Dalton, & Gliebe 1937). An earlier, detailed account of the clinical features had been published by Da Costa in 1871, although he did not appreciate their association with hyperventilation. He described a curious malady consisting of dyspnea, dizziness, palpitations, chest pain, and fatigue in soldiers fighting the American Civil War. This syndrome still bears his name, although a number of other epithets have also been attached to it (Brashear, 1983; Magarian, 1982). The development of giddiness, tingling, and numbness with hyperventilation was demonstrated by Haldane and Poulton (1908), and Goldman (1922) noted that involuntary hyperventilation can produce the manifestations of muscular hypertonicity known as *tetany*. Dudley-White and Hahn (1920) published detailed documentation of the association between frequent sighing and "nervous instability." This association had been recognized 75 years earlier by William Stokes (1854): "I lately saw a case of long-continuous sighing, in which it had apparently arisen from depression and anxiety of the mind, but had, as it were, become a habit. The patient was a lady of nervous disposition" (p. 325).

Etiology.

Hyperventilation might be produced by organic or psychogenic causes. The organic disorders include encephalitis, salicylate intoxication, hepatic failure, and severe pain, and it is occasionally observed in patients with interstitial lung disease or pulmonary embolism. Some years ago, Plum and Swanson (1959) described a syndrome of central neurogenic hyperventilation in patients with brainstem lesions. However, all of these patients had P_aO_2 values below normal, and autopsies revealed pulmonary congestion (Plum & Posner, 1980). Thus, the central neurogenic basis of this syndrome is in some doubt. Respiratory dyskinesia causing hyperventilation has been reported in a small number of patients (Greenberg & Murray, 1981). This choreatic-movement disorder occurs in patients with neuroleptic-induced tardive dyskinesia or other extrapyramidal disorders. The breathing pattern is described as being irregular and awkward, and it is associated with grunting. Like other choreiform movements, it usually disappears during sleep. Psychogenic hyperventilation is almost invariably attributed to anxiety. However, in a recent study of 21 patients with good documentation of the hyperventilation syndrome, Bass and Gardner (1985a) found that only 10 of the patients were neurotic (suffering from chronic anxiety, panic, and phobic symptoms), and 11 had no detectable psychiatric disorder. After use of the most exhaustive physical and psychiatric investigative techniques, there were at least 6 patients who failed to show any conspicuous organic or psychiatric disturbance, apart from profound hypocapnia and the presence of mild long-standing phobic traits in 3 of the patients. Contrary to common wisdom, this study indicates that some patients might not complain of anxiety.

The basic mechanisms responsible for initiating and sustaining the hyperventilation syndrome are unknown (Bass & Gardner, 1985b). It is well recognized that stressful situations cause a disturbance in the pattern of breathing in normal subjects (Dudley & Pitts-Poarch, 1980; Suess et al., 1980; Tobin et al., 1986), but it is unclear whether the response of patients with the hyperventilation syndrome is qualitatively or only quantitatively different from that occurring in normal subjects. In other words, afflicted patients might simply represent one end of a continuum of susceptibility to hyperventilate in stressful situations rather than a specific over responsivity of the respiratory system (Bass & Gardner 1985b). The role of psychologic stress in causing hyperventilation is complex and likely to be modified by compensating physiologic mechanisms. For example, Tobin et al. (1986) have shown that the stress associated with the anticipation of exercise causes a marked increase in minute ventilation (Figure 15.5). However, this increase in ventilation was not associated with a comparable fall in PCO_2, indicating that it cannot be

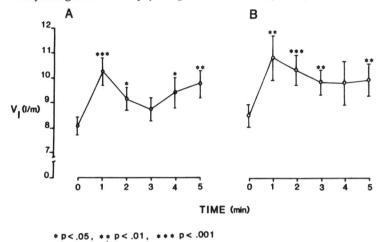

$*$ p < .05, $**$ p < .01, $***$ p < .001

FIGURE 15.5. A. Sequential change in minute ventilation (V_I) from baseline to period of exercise anticipation. After the baseline measurements were obtained over 10 minutes, the subject was informed that he or she would be requested to exercise in 5 minutes. The greatest increase in V_I was observed in the 1st minute, falling to nonsignificant levels by the 3rd minute and rising again during the 4th and 5th minutes of anticipation . B. To obtain control measurements of cortical activity without exercise anticipation, the subjects performed mental arithmetic over a 5 minute period following baseline measurements. Bars, $\pm$ SE. * Statistical difference from baseline, P < 0.05. **Statistical difference from baseline, P < 0.01 ***Statistical difference from baseline, P < 0.001.

Note. "Breathing Pattern and Metabolic Behavior during Anticipation of Exercise" by M. J. Tobin, W. Perez, S. M. Guenther, G. D'Alonzo, and D. R. Dantzker, 1986, *Journal of Applied Physiology*, 60, pp. 1306 to 1312. Copyright 1986 by American Physiological Society. Reprinted by permission.

simply due to cortical excitation of the respiratory centers.

In a complementary study, the constant PCO_2 in the face of the increased minute ventilation was shown due to increased CO_2 production. These changes could have been due to cortical stimulation of the autonomic nervous system causing the release of catecholamines, because administration of adrenergic agents is known to cause similar increases in CO_2 production and minute ventilation (Eisenhofer, Lambie, & Johnson 1985; Stone, Keltz, Sarkar, & Singzon, 1973). Similarly, the finding of Bass and Gardner (1985a) that only about half of their patients with well-documented hyperventilation syndrome showed evidence of a psychiatric disorder suggests that noncortical factors could be important, at least in some patients. Likewise, Lum (1981) has suggested that only a minority of patients have a primary psychogenic cause, and he believes that the primary cause is the bad habit of exaggerated thoracic breathing. This habit is considered to be responsible for the hyperventilation, and the anxiety is considered to be a consequence of the hyperventilation, rather than the reverse. However, in a quantitive study of rib cage–abdominal contribution to tidal volume, (Tobin et al. 1983a; 1983b) noted no differences between healthy subjects and patients with chronic anxiety states;

although these patients were not hyperventilating at the time of the study. In contrast to these studies, the finding that PCO_2 gradually increases toward normal during sleep (Gardner & Meah, 1986) suggests that cortical factors are involved in the development of hypocapnia.

Garssen (1980) proposed that the hyperventilation syndrome reflects an over responsivity of the respiratory system to stress and that patients who have an increased respiratory-center sensitivity could be the ones who develop symptoms. Support for this hypothesis is provided by the findings of Tobin et al. (1983a, 1983b) which indicate that mean inspiratory flow (V_T/T_I), a measure of respiratory-center drive, is significantly higher in patients with a chronic anxiety state, compared with healthy controls, 310 and 250 ml/sec, respectively. It also appears that the respiratory centers in these patients have a hypocapnic setpoint. Gardner and Meah (1986) have shown that, despite increasing PCO_2 to normal by inhaling CO_2-enriched gas mixtures for periods of up to 40 minutes, the PCO_2 returns to the previous hypocapnic setpoint within 5 minutes of breathing room air. Further evidence supporting the concept of an abnormal setpoint is suggested by their measurements of end-tidal pCO_2 in 5 patients during sleep. End-tidal pCO_2 rose from a value of 26 torr during wakefulness to 33 within 1 hour of sleep and

38 torr after 6 hours of sleep. Within 1 hour of awakening the following morning, it returned to 26 torr. These findings suggest that the hypocapnia in these patients is very resistant to change. It is well known from studies in healthy volunteers that, once hypocapnia has been achieved, the markedly decreased levels of P_aCO_2 can be easily maintained with very little effort such as occasional deep sigh superimposed on a normal breathing pattern (Okel & Hurst, 1961; Saltzman, Heyman, & Sieker, 1963). For example, a single deep inspiration and expiration can lower P_aCO_2 by 7–16 torr (Ferris, Engel, Stevens, & Webb 1946).

Most attention has been focused on the effect of psychological factors on the ventilatory pattern, but this relationship has also been studied from the opposite direction. There is now a growing body of evidence to suggest that the ventilatory pattern can modify psychological distress (Bass & Gardner, 1985b). This concept was first suggested by Rice (1950) and is strongly supported by Lum (1981), who believes that anxiety is the result, and not the cause, of hyperventilation. Experimental support for this concept has been provided by McCaul, Solomon and Holmes (1979), who showed that voluntary slowing of the respiratory rate in subjects waiting to receive electric shocks caused a reduction in physiological arousal, as measured by skin resistance, finger pulse volume, and reduced self-reported anxiety. These results suggest that paced respiration might be a useful coping strategy in stressful situations. Additional evidence emphasizing the role of voluntary regulation of ventilation in alleviating distress has been recently reported by Adams, Lane, Shea, Cockcroft, and Guz (1985). Subjects were requested to voluntarily copy a displayed oscilloscope tracing of their breathing pattern during a previous hypercapnic stimulation test. During the voluntarily induced increases in ventilation, the inspired concentration of CO_2 was titrated to maintain end-tidal PCO_2 at a normal resting level. Despite a similar level of minute ventilation in the two settings, there was a marked reduction in the scores of dyspnea during the voluntary isocapnic–hyperventilation run. This suggests that the feeling of distress and helplessness can be diminished when individuals are able to take control and issue commands to their respiratory center, rather than simply be its servant.

Clinical features.

The protean manifestations of the hyperventilation syndrome might mimic disorders of almost any organ

TABLE 15.3. Clinical Features of the Hyperventilation Syndrome.

General	Easy fatigability
	Weakness
	Exhausation
Respiratory	Dyspenea
	Sighing
	Nonproductive cough
Cardiovascular	Chest pain
	Palpitations
	Tachycardia
Neurologic	Numbness and tingling
	Dizziness
	Giddiness
	Lightheadedness
	Visual disturbance
	Impaired thinking
Musculoskeletal	Myalgia
	Stiffness
	Carpopedal spasm
	Generalized tetany (rare)
Psychiatric	Anxiety
	Panic attacks
	Phobias
	Tension
Gastrointestinal	Aerophagia
	Bloating
	Belching
	Flatulence
	Globus hystericus
	Dry mouth

or system (Table 15.3). An early clue to the diagnosis is afforded by the fact that such patients have frequently seen a variety of subspecialists and undergone extensive evaluations without a satisfactory diagnosis being established.

Dyspnea is observed in 50%–90% of patients with this syndrome (Brashear, 1983). Characteristically, they communicate this as "a sense of being unable to take a deep enough breath" (air hunger) or a sense of suffocation or oppression in the chest. Unlike the dyspnea of patients with cardiovascular or pulmonary disease, this form of dyspnea has a less clear-cut relationship to exercise and is less likely to improve with rest. Indeed, it might actually develop shortly after activity has ceased, rather than during it (Magarian 1982). Although many of the physiologic consequences of hyperventilation disappear during sleep (Gardner & Meah, 1986), it is important to realize that these patients might awaken with dyspnea, thus mimicking the paroxysmal nocturnal dyspnea that occurs with heart failure (Magarian, 1982).

When interviewing and examining the patient, particular attention should be paid to the presence of

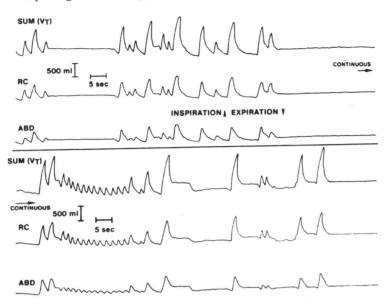

FIGURE 15.6. Chaotic breathing pattern in a patient with chronic anxiety. Deep sighing respirations alternate with periods of rapid, shallow breathing and prolonged apneic episodes occurring at different lung volumes *Note*. From "Breathing Patterns 2, Diseased Subjects" by M. J. Tobin, T. S. Chadha, G. Jenouri, S. J. Birch, H. B. Gazeroglu, and M. A. Sackner, 1983, *Chest*, *84*, p. 286. Copyright 1983 by American College of Chest Physicians. Reprinted by permission.

frequent sighing. The importance of this sign was first indicated by Stokes (1854), and it has since been emphasized by a number of investigators. A satisfactory definition of a sigh does not exist, and, for physiological purposes, it is currently characterized in arbitrary terms as a threefold or greater increase in tidal volume (Tobin et al., 1983a). During resting breathing, young healthy subjects take zero to four sighs per hour, or less than 0.4% of all breaths (Tobin et al., 1983a). Using a less stringent criterion for sighing (50% increase in the tidal volume of at least 10 breaths over a 10-minute period), Dudley-White and Hahn (1929) noted excessive sighing in 80% of 100 patients with the effort syndrome (Da Costa's syndrome), and they concluded that sighing is solely a nervous phenomenon associated with fatigue or habit. Subsequent investigators have confirmed this association between frequent sighing and anxiety or the hyperventilation syndrome (Christie, 1935; Finesinger, 1944; Lewis, 1953; Tobin et al., 1983b). In a recent investigation employing nonobtrusive, quantitative methods to study the breathing pattern, Tobin et al. (1983b) noted that patients with a chronic anxiety state sighed at a rate of 16 to 100 per hour. These sighs frequently alternated with prolonged apneas and periods of rapid shallow breathing (see

Figure 15.6). This chaotic breathing pattern was frequently masked when the subjects breathed through a mouthpiece.

Chest pain is frequently a presenting symptom and can mimic angina pectoris (Bass et al., 1983). The lack of a constant relationship to exercise is helpful in differentiating it from angina. However, confusion can result from the fact that hyperventilation can in itself cause ST- and T-wave changes on the electrocardiogram (Brashear, 1983; Magarian, 1982). The reader interested in further details of the relationship between hyperventilation and cardiovascular disturbances is referred to an excellent review of this topic by Margarian (1982).

Tetany is commonly considered to be a characteristic feature of the syndrome, but it is in fact quite uncommon. When tetany is present in its full-blown form, Chvostek's and Trousseau's signs can usually be detected. Chvostek's sign consists of a rapid contraction of the ipsilateral facial muscles in response to tapping over the facial nerve at the angle of the jaw. Trousseau's sign refers to muscle spasm causing flexion of the wrist and thumb with extension of the fingers. If this sign is not clinically present, it can sometimes be induced by using a sphygmomanometer cuff to occlude the circulation to the limb for a few minutes.

Diagnosis.

None of the multiple symptoms are pathognomonic, and most are nonspecific (Table 15.3). A variety of investigative procedures has been proposed to aid in making a diagnosis, but none are specific (Folgering & Colla, 1978), and the diagnosis usually depends on the physician or therapist having a high index of suspicion. The importance of excluding organic disease was recently highlighted in a study of 21 patients with the classic features of the hyperventilation syndrome, including documentation of hypocarbia (Bass & Gardner, 1985a). Previously unrecognized respiratory disorders were discovered in five of the patients, although it is not clear whether treatment of the underlying respiratory disorder caused resolution of the hyperventilation and dyspnea.

In the strict physiological sense, hypocapnia should be present, because the term *hyperventilation* indicates an increase in ventilation in excess of metabolic requirements. However, Lum (1981) found a P_aCO_2 that was either equivocal or in the low-normal range in more than one-third of the patients who otherwise fitted the diagnosis of hyperventilation syndrome. Measurement of arterial blood gases could be confusing, as the apprehension associated with an arterial needle puncture can in itself cause hyperventilation and hypocapnia. In addition, a spot measurement could miss the diagnosis in patients with intermittent symptoms. Recording end-tidal CO_2 at the nose or mouth provides much the same information (although without pH) in a noninvasive manner. Bass and Gardner (1985b) advocated inserting a small, narrow catheter inside the nasal vestibule. After an adaptation period of 5 minutes, measurements are obtained over a further 5 minute period. Many of these patients have chronic hyperventilation and hypocapnia as indicated by end-tidal PCO_2 plateaux of less than 30 torr. In a study of 21 patients partly selected on the basis of having a PCO_2 of less than 30 torr while resting in a seated position, the mean end-tidal PCO_2 was 24 torr, with some patients having values as low as 13 torr (Bass & Gardner 1985a). Their finding that end-tidal PCO_2 rises during sleep suggests that this might be an additional, although expensive, method of assisting with the diagnosis.

A hyperventilation provocation test is generally recommended to confirm the diagnosis (Lum, 1981; Magarian, 1982). The patient is instructed to breathe deeply at a rate of about 30–40 breaths per minute and encouraged to describe the sensations that develop. It is preferable not to indicate the purpose of the test to the patient, so that she or he can spontaneously recognize the association between hyperventilation and her or his symptoms. Most patients generally replicate their symptoms within 2 or 3 minutes; if not, the test should be discontinued after another 1 or 2 minutes. After the symptoms are recognized, the patient is requested to rebreathe from a bag, to increase P_aCO_2 and to demonstrate the ability to control the symptoms voluntarily. This test has a number of limitations (Bass & Gardner, 1985b): interpretation of the result is subject to overseer bias, the patients might feel that the symptoms are similar but not identical to a spontaneous attack, and the reassurance of a controlled laboratory or clinical setting might attenuate the apprehension that usually accompanies a spontaneous attack.

Management.

A general therapeutic approach to dyspnea is discussed later, and only a brief overview of specific items pertaining to the hyperventilation syndrome is provided here. Four major therapeutic approaches are employed: psychotherapy, behavior therapy, psychotropic drugs, and adrenergic-blocking drugs (Brasher, 1983). Psychological management includes hypnosis, symptom reframing, and other techniques noted here. Behavior therapy includes modification of the breathing habit. This approach has been especially advocated by Lum (1981). Reviewing his 1,735 cases of documented hyperventilation, he claims that breathing retraining and relaxation usually abolish the symptoms with 1–6 months, and only 5% of patients have intractable symptoms. Unfortunately this technique has not been subjected to a controlled trial. Psychotropic drugs are occasionally employed, but their value is not well defined. A number of clinical trials suggest that adrenergic blocking agents might be helpful. If a therapeutic trial is considered, a beta$_2$-selective agent, such as metaprolol, is probably preferable because of its cardioselectivity.

MANAGEMENT OF DYSPNEA

Pharmacotherapy of Dyspnea

Treatment of the underlying disease is the cardinal principle in the therapy of any symptom. Bronchodilators achieve considerable or complete relief of dyspnea in patients with asthma, but relief is usually incomplete in patients with chronic obstructive pulmonary disease. Consequently, other therapeutic approaches to the relief of dyspnea have been examined.

Respiratory-center drive is usually increased in patients with chronic lung disease (Tobin et al., 1983b). Because an elevation in drive can contribute to the development of dyspnea, it appears reasonable to wonder whether a reduction in respiratory drive might alleviate respiratory distress. Ideally, such an agent should blunt the intensity of respiratory sensation without decreasing the level of alveolar ventilation.

This question was first examined by Mitchell-Heggs et al. (1980). In a single-blind crossover study, they administered 25 mg of diazepam per day to 4 patients with the pink-puffing variety of emphysema. Although there was a 30%–50% decrease in the ventilatory response to hypercapnia, an increase in P_aCO_2 was only transiently observed in one patient. These patients reported a striking reduction in dyspnea and improvement in exercise tolerance. However, assessment of the relief of dyspnea and exercise tolerance were based on the patients' description, rather than on rigorous testing. A more systematic evaluation of the use of diazepam (25 mg daily for 2 weeks) in patients with emphysema was conducted by Woodcock et al. (1981a). They enrolled 18 patients, but 3 were unable to complete the trial because of intolerable side effects or death. Diazepam had no significant effect on dyspnea or arterial blood gases and, in fact, caused a *reduction* in exercise tolerance. In subsequent studies of dyspnea during exercise, Stark, Gambles and Lewis (1981) found that diazepam produced no relief in healthy subjects, and Man, Hsu, and Sproule (1986) noted no benefit with alprazolam in patients with chronic obstructive pulmonary disease.

Opiates are the second major category of agents that have been examined. These agents are known to cause respiratory depression through a direct effect on the brainstem respiratory centers and also by decreasing carotid body discharge (Weil, McCullough, Kline, & Sodal, 1975). In addition, they cause a reduction in metabolic rate and oxygen consumption and a decrease in the ventilatory response at any given level of exercise (Santiago, Johnson, Riley & Edelman, 1979). In a study of 12 patients with chronic obstructive pulmonary disease, Woodcock et al. (1981) found that a moderate dose of dihydrocodeine (1 mg/Kg) caused a reduction in O_2 consumption during rest and in ventilation and O_2 consumption during exercise. Exercise tolerance and dyspnea were improved by about 20%. A brief follow-up study indicated concern regarding the

development of side effects with prolonged use (Woodcock, Johnson, & Geddes, 1982). Long-term administration of opiates has been examined by Sackner (1984). He measured respiratory drive and other breathing pattern indexes following the adminstration of a 5-mg dose of hydrocodone (Hycodan) to 25 patients with severe obstructive and restrictive lung disease. There was a 12% fall in mean inspiratory flow (V_T/T_I), an index of respiratory drive, but, unfortunately, measurements of dyspnea were not made. On follow-up of these patients for a period of up to 2 years, 17 of the 25 patients noted subjective relief of dyspnea while taking an average of one Hycodan tablet four times a day. Although these results are promising, further studies are clearly needed, because these agents pose a considerable risk of addiction and side effects.

TOWARD INTEGRATION OF MANAGEMENT AND TREATMENT OF BREATHING DISORDERS

Attentional Control and Amelioration of Dyspnea

We have seen that numerous attempts have been made to apply relaxation, systematic desensitization, medication, and other methods to the management of asthma. Behavioral-management methods have more often been employed in the psychological approach to emphysema and chronic bronchitis, whereas anxiety-reduction methods have typically focused on asthma. It cannot be concluded that any approach has garnered much evidence for clinical potency. We suggest that a fruitful paradigm with potential clinical utility could be developed on a clearer understanding of dyspnea, across all types of breathing disorders. This, it is suggested here, would constitute a treatment approach with a psychological foundation.

We suggest one avenue along which to formulate an appreciation for dyspnea, in addition to the physiological, pharmacological, and clinical aspects we have discussed. Models of breath-holding control (Godfrey & Campbell, 1968, 1969) include the appraisal of sensory inputs as an important process in determining the breaking point of voluntary breath holding (see Figure 15.1). This implies that dyspnea is in part cognitively determined. Psychological treatment of dyspnea, it would seem, must focus at least in part on this cognitive component. There is an important parallel in current understanding of pain and means for coping with pain.

Pain and Attention in the Epigenesis of Dyspnea

In a recent review, McCaul and Malott (1984) assessed the empirical literature on methods of coping with pain through distraction. Distraction does not always have an ameliorating effect, but the belief that it is generally effective is persistent. McCaul and Malott attempted to develop a theoretical rationale for the application of distraction techniques to pain. They noted that many so-called behavioral methods (e.g., relaxation, meditation, hypnosis) contain the potential for achieving an effect, at least partially, through distraction.

To develop a cognitive model of pain, several assumptions are made: (a) The experience of pain requires information processing, that is, sense data are not isomorphic or identical with the experience of pain; (b) attentional capacity is limited; (c) for sensory information to be subjected to information processing, it must be attended to; (d) controlled (nonautomatic) processing is constrained by a specific limit on capacity. These assumptions are consistent with the empirical literature on attentional limitations on information processing.

If pain perception were automatic (not requiring focused attention for "task performance," that is, for the detection of information specifying pain), then distraction would never be effective. Pain experience would be a parallel process to other attention-demanding processes. Because pain is modifiable for the same physical stimulus within the same individual, the controlled (nonautomatic) processing of relevant stimulus information is reasonably assumed. If the pain experience is a controlled process, then, for a distracting task to be effective, it too must require attentional capacity for the *controlled* processing of the components of pain (McCaul & Malott, 1984, p. 518).

Extension to Dyspnea.

The structure of the argument is homologous for dyspnea. It seems reasonable, as in the research on pain in the laboratory, that distracting tasks could reduce dyspnea in a manner analogous to the effects of attention-demanding tasks on pain. Any given task, however, might demonstrate some vicissitudes in its demands on controlled processing, both within and across subjects. These vicissitudes depend on the reduction of attentional capacity demands across time for learned tasks.

For example, consider a relaxation task, such as progressive muscle relaxation. Initially, the learning of the unfamiliar task involves performance demands, self-evaluation, and focused attention on technique and a novel stimulus (cf. Berlyne, 1960). This would reduce dyspnea if the epigenesis of dyspnea involved a constraint on attentional capacity in processing. However, as task performance becomes an automatized skill (cf. LaBerge & Samuels, 1974; Norman & Bobrow, 1975; Sedlacek, 1979), its effectiveness is reduced over time. Thus, for any given test of a particular technique, such as desensitization, meditation, or hypnosis exercise, the effect of the manipulation would tend to wash out over time, unless further demands were placed on attentional capacity as the skill became automatized. This could explain in large part the abysmal failure, overall, of various management techniques to impact on breathing disorders as noted. Although Tobin noted the dramatic effects of mouthpieces on breathing parameters, (as described), their effect on dyspnea could be substantial — by increasing distraction. This possibility could be further investigated experimentally utilizing respiratory-inductive plethysmography (Tobin, 1986b).

Research considerations.

The series of studies by Alpher and his colleagues on breath-holding tolerance is one example of the use of an experimental design that controls for the reduction of attention demands for effortful tasks across time. This design is a within-subjects design in which treatments are rotated randomly within several blocks of trials. In one of those studies, it was demonstrated that a mantra-meditation task actually impaired subjects' performance on breath holds (even though by self-report subjects were more relaxed; cf. Holmes, 1984, on cognitive versus somatic relaxation). The meditation task used by Alpher et al. could have been particularly ineffective in reducing dyspnea and enhancing performance of breath holding. This is because there was no implicit task demand, such as a performance check, to insure allocation of effort to the meditation (cf. Kahneman, 1973).

An even more interesting aspect of these particular findings, in light of the discussion of pain, dyspnea, and attention, was for the comparison of two memory tasks performed during breath holding. Subjects were to memorize a list of 12 words; they expected to receive a monetary reward for each recalled word. For another list of 12 words, equated for difficulty and familiarity, subjects expected to receive an electric shock for failing to recall words. In free recall at the conclusion of the experiment, subjects did not differ in the number of words recalled from each list ($N = 52$). However, subjects' breath holds under the shock-avoidance memory conditions were significantly longer, indicating a greater tolerance for dyspnea while attempting to learn words, even though actual memory performance did not differ. Subjects did report, however, greater levels of activation with shock-avoidance trials, perhaps indicating greater attentional focusing despite no enhancement of performance.

This experimental approach would seem at first glance to have traded off too much external validity (generalizability) for internal validity (internal experimental control). Such research is, however, the basis on which clear tests of the attentional-capacity hypothesis for dyspnea can be accomplished (cf. Mook, 1983).

Other experimental paradigms could yet be developed. Advantages of the present approach include (a) elimination of practice effects (automatizing and decreased attentional demands) to enhance discovery of lawful relationships between tasks and tolerance of respiratory distress; (b) use of a performance measure (tolerance) that is theoretically related to the phenomenon of interest, in this case, dyspnea; (c) ability to compare tasks varying in attentional requirements, essential for testing hypotheses about the relationship of attention to dyspnea; (d) ability ultimately to introduce combined pharmacological–psychological interventions to test their effectiveness. Among the weaknesses of the approach are the facts that (a) The relationship of duration of exposure to dyspnea and the intensity of dyspnea is unknown (and, given findings of D. Campbell, Sanderson, & Laverty, 1964, and E. J. M. Campbell et al., 1967, this could be irrelevant); (b) the psychophysical relationship between dyspnea generated by voluntary breath holding and by involuntary bronchoconstriction (as in COPD) has not been investigated. Obviously, many avenues for future research are open.

Implications for Coping with Dyspnea

Ultimately, any psychological technique that is effective must become a self-control or self-treatment technique that can be maintained and self-monitored. "Simple" distraction techniques tend to diminish in effectiveness over time because of automatization of the task performance. When this occurs, either a novel or a more complex task must

be instituted to maintain effectiveness. If the *intensity* of the dyspnea has increased by this point, a shift in strategy might be needed. McCaul and Malott (1984) suggested four principles that apply to the matrix of this task involvement continuum (attention capacity utilization) and stressor intensity.

Principle 1: Distraction will reduce distress, as compared with uninstructed or placebo control conditions.

Principle 2: Distraction techniques that require more attentional capacity will be more effective.

Principle 3: Distraction will have stronger impact on distressing stimuli of low intensity.

Principle 4: Distraction will be more effective than "sensation redefinition" (which necessitates attending to the stressor) for relatively low intensity; "sensation redefinition" will be more effective at higher levels of intensity.

The appropriateness of the analogy of dyspnea and pain could be systematically tested in accord with these principles. Of particular interest would be the applicability of *sensation redefinition* to dyspnea. Redefinition might be defined as any strategy that facilitates a nonemotional interpretation of sensory input. Redefinition requires, then, first *attending* to the sensations, rather than attending to another task. McCaul and Malott reviewed several supportive studies in the pain literature (1984, pp. 527–528). Whether these strategies apply to dyspnea in breathing disorders in analogous fashion is an important area for further study.

Integrating Psychological and Pathophysiological Knowledge: Prospects for Clinical Research

Once the psychological basis for epigenesis of dyspnea has been experimentally dismantled into effective components, systematic testing of combined psychological, pharmacological, and behavioral treatments can ensue. The challenge of both ameliorating dyspnea and improving adjustment to breathing disorders could bring to the forefront treatments and management approaches that are both psychologically and pathophysiologically informed. The integration of these factors into treatment programs affords the possibility of extending the contribution of psychology from management approaches to legitimate treatments of breathing disorders.

REFERENCES

Adams, L., Lane, R., Shea, S. A., Cockcroft, A., & Guz, A. (1985). Breathlessness during different forms of ventilatory stimulation: A study of mechanisms in normal subjects and respiratory patients. *Clinical Science, 69*, 663–672.

Aitken, R. C. B., Zealley, A. K., & Rosenthal, S. V. (1970). Some psychological and physiological considerations of breathlessness. In R. Porter (Ed.), *Breathing: Hering-Breuer Centenary Symposium (pp. 253–273)*. London: Churchill.

Alexander, A. (1972). Systematic relaxation and flow rates in asthmatic children. Relationship to emotional precipitants and anxiety. *Journal of Psychosomatic Research, 16*, 405–410.

Alexander, A. B. (1981). Behavioral approaches in the treatment of bronchial asthma. In C. K. Prukop & L. A. Bradley (Eds.), *Medical psychology: Contributions to behavioral medicine (pp. 373–394)*. New York: Academic Press.

Alexander, A., Miklich, D., & Hershkoff, H. (1972). The immediate effects of systematic relaxation training on peak expiratory flow rates in asthmatic children. *Psychosomatic Medicine, 34*, 388–394.

Alpher, V. S., & Blanton, R. L. (1986). *Respiratory drive and the inhibition of behavior: An approach to the psychology of breathing*. Unpublished manuscript, Department of Psychology, Vanderbilt University.

Alpher, V. S., Nelson, R. B. III, & Blanton, R. L. (1986). Effects of cognitive and psychomotor tasks on breath-holding span. *Journal of Applied Physiology, 61*, 1149–1152.

Altose, M. A. (1986). Dyspnea. In D. H. Simmons (Ed.), *Current pulmonology (pp. 199–226)*. Chicago: Year Book Medical.

Altschule, M. D. (1987). Dyspnea in cardiorespiratory disease. *Chest, 91*, 267.

American Psychiatric Association (1980). *Diagnostic and statistical manual of mental disorders* (DSM-III). Washington, DC: American Psychiatric Association.

Aminoff, M. J., & Sears, T. A. (1971). Spinal integration of segmental, cortical and breathing inputs to thoracic respiratory motoneurons. *Journal of Physiology, 215*, 557–575.

Atkins, C. J., Kaplan, R. M., Timms, R. M., Reinsch, S., & Lofback, K. (1984). Behavioral exercise programs in the management of chronic obstructive pulmonary disease. *Journal of Consulting and Clinical Psychology, 52*, 591–603.

Ax, A. F. (1953). The physiological differentiation between fear and anger in humans. *Psychosomatic Medicine, 15*, 433–442.

Bartlett, D., Jr. (1977). Effects of Valsalva and Mueller maneuvers on breath-holding time. *Journal of Applied Physiology, 42*, 717–721.

Bass, C., & Gardner, W. N. (1985a). Respiratory and psychiatric abnormalities in chronic symptomatic hyperventilation. *British Medical Journal, 290*, 1387–1390.

Bass, C., & Gardner, W. (1985b). Emotional influences on breathing and breathlessness. *Journal of Psychosomatic Research, 29*, 599–609.

Bass, C., Wade, C., Gardner, W. N., Cawley, R., Ryan, K. C., & Hutchison, D. C. S. (1983). Unexplained breathlessness and psychiatric morbidity in patients with normal and abnormal coronary arteries. *Lancet, i*, 605–609.

Bechbache, R. R., Chow, H. H. K., Duffin, J., & Orsini, E. C. (1979). The effects of hypercapnia, hypoxia, exercise, and anxiety on the breathing pattern in man. *Journal of Physiology (London), 293*, 285–300.

Beckmann, K. (1915). Ueber Aenderungen in der Atmungsregulation durch psychische und pharmakologische Einfluesse. *Deutsches Archiv fuer Klinische Medizin, 117*, 419–437.

Berlyne, D. (1960). *Conflict, arousal, and curiosity*. New York: McGraw-Hill.

Blanton, R. L., & Alpher, V. S. (1983). Experimental models for psychophysiological studies of breathing. *Biological Psychology, 16*, 285–286.

Blanton, R. L., & Alpher, V. S. (in press). Psychological factors in respiration. In B. Timmons (Ed.), *Behavioral approaches to breathing disorders*. London: Plenum.

Borg, G. A. V. (1982). Psychophysical bases of perceived exertion. *Medicine and Science in Sports and Exercise, 14*, 377–381.

Bradley, G. W., Hale, T., Pimble, J., Rowlandson, R., & Noble, M. I. M. (1982). Effect of vagotomy on the breathing pattern and exercise ability in emphysematous patients. *Clinical Science, 62*, 311–319.

Brashear, R. E. (1983). Hyperventilation syndrome. *Lung, 161*, 257–273.

Brown, E. B., Jr. (1953). Physiological effects of hyperventilation. *Physiological Review, 33*, 445–471.

Burns, B. H., & Howell, J. B. L. (1969). Disproportionately severe breathlessness in chronic bronchitis. *Quarterly Journal of Medicine, 38*, 277–294.

Burki, N. K. (1984). Effects of bronchodilation on magnitude estimation of added resistive loads in asthmatic subjects. *American Review of Respiratory Disease, 129*, 225–229.

Burki, N. K., Davenport, P. W., Safdar, F., & Zechman, F. W. (1983). The effects of airway anesthesia on magnitude estimation of added inspiratory resistive and elastic loads. *American Review of Respiratory Disease, 127*, 2–4.

Campbell, D., Sanderson, R. E., & Laverty, S. G. (1964). Characteristics of a conditioned response in human subjects during extinction trials following a single traumatic conditioning trial. *Journal of Abnormal and Social Psychology, 59*, 627–639.

Campbell, E. J. M., & Howell, J. B. L. (1963). The sensation of dyspnea. *British Medical Journal* (letter), 36–40.

Campbell, E. J. M., Freedman, S., Clark, T. J. H., Robson, J. G., & Norman, J. (1967). The effect of muscular paralysis produced by tubocurarine on the duration and sensation of breath-holding. *Clinical Science, 32*, 425–432.

Campbell, E. J. M., Godfrey, S., Clark, T. J. H., Freedman, S., & Norman, J. (1969). The effect of muscular paralysis induced by tubocurarine on the duration and sensation of breath-holding during hypercapnia. *Clinical Science, 36*, 323–328.

Cappo, B. M., & Holmes, D. S. (1984). The utility of prolonged respiratory exhalation for reducing physiological and psychological arousal in nonthreatening situations. *Journal of Psychosomatic Research, 28*, 265–273.

Carroll, L. (1970). *The annotated Alice in Wonderland* (2nd Ed.). Middlesex: Penguin.

Castele, R. J., Connors, A. F., & Altose, M. D. (1985). Effects of changes in CO_2 partial pressure on the sensation of respiratory drive. *Journal of Applied Physiology, 59*, 1747–1751.

Chai, H., Purcell, K., Brady, K., & Falliers, C. J., (1968). Therapeutic and investigational evaluation of asthmatic children. *Journal of Allergy, 41*, 23–36.

Chaudhary, B. A., & Burki, N. K. (1978). Effects of airway anaesthesia on the ability to detect added inspiratory resistive loads. *Clinical Science and Molecular Medicine, 44*, 621–626.

Chaudhary, B. A. & Burki, N. K. (1980). The effects of airway anesthesia on detection of added inspiratory elastic loads. *American Review of Respiratory Disease, 122*, 635–639.

Christie, R. V. (1935). Some types of respiration in the neuroses. *Quarterly Journal of Medicine New Series, 4*, 428–432.

Clark, D. M., & Hemsley, R. R. (1982). The effects of hyperventilation in normals: Individual variability and its relation to personality. *Journal of Behavior Therapy and Experimental Psychiatry, 13*, 41–47.

Clark, F. J. & von Euler, C. (1972). On the regulation of depth and rate of breathing. *Journal of Physiology (London), 22*, 267–295.

Cluss, P. A. (1986). Behavioral interventions as adjunctive treatments for chronic asthma. *Progress in Behavior Modification, 20*, 123–60.

Compernolle, T., Hoogduin, K., & Joele, L. (1979). Diagnosis and treatment of the hyperventilation syndrome. *Psychosomatics, 20*, 612–625.

Comroe, J. H. (1966a). Some theories of the mechanism of dyspnea. In J. B. Howell and E. J. M. Campbell (Eds.), *Breathlessness* (pp. 1–7). Oxford: Blackwell.

Comroe, J. H. (1966b). Summing up. In J. B. Howell & E. J. M. Campbell (Eds.), *Breathlessness* (pp. 233–238). Oxford: Blackwell.

Creer, T. L. (1983). Respiratory disorders. In L. Brantley (Ed.)., *Coping with chronic disease* (pp. 313–336). New York: Academic Press.

Cross, B. A., Guz, A., Jain. S. K., Archer, S., Stevens, J. & Reynolds, F. (1976). The effect of anaesthesia of the airway in dog and man: A study of respiratory reflexes, sensations and lung mechanics. *Clinical Science and Molecular Medicine 50*, 439–454.

DaCosta, J. M. (1871). On irritable heart: A clinical study of a form of functional cardiac disorder and its consequences. *American Journal of Medical Science, 61*, 17–52.

DiMarco, A. F., Wolfson, D. A., Gottfried, S. B., & Altose, M. D. (1982). Sensation of inspired volume in normal subjects and quadriplegic patients. *Journal of Applied Physiology, 53*, 1481–1486.

Douglas, N. J. (1985). Control of ventilation during sleep. *Clinics in Chest Medicine, 6*, 563–575.

Dudley, D. L. (1969). *Psychophysiology of respiration in health and disease.* New York: Appleton-Century-Crofts.

Dudley, D. L., Glaser, E. M., Jorgenson, B. N., & Logan, D. L. (1980). Psychosocial concomitants to rehabilitation in chronic obstructive pulmonary disease. Part 2. Psychosocial treatment. *Chest, 77*, 544–551.

Dudley, D. L., Holmes, T. H., Martin, C. J., & Ripley, H. W. (1964). Changes in respiration associated with hypnotically induced emotion, pain, and exercise. *Psychosomatic Medicine, 26*, 46–53.

Dudley, D. L., Martin, C. J., & Holmes, T. H. (1964). Psychophysiological studies of pulmonary ventilation. *Psychosomatic Medicine, 26*, 645–660.

Dudley, D. L., & Pitts-Poarch, A. R. (1980). Psychophysiologic aspects of respiratory control. *Clinics in Chest Medicine, 1*, 131–143.

Dudley-White, P. & Hahn, R. G., (1929). The symptom of sighing in cardiovascular diagnosis with spirographic observations. *American Journal of Medical Science, 177*, 179–188.

Eisele, J., Trenchard, D., Burki, N., & Guz, A. (1968). The effect of chest wall block on respiratory sensation and control in man. *Clinical Science, 35*, 23–33.

Eisenhofer, G., Lambie, D. G., & Johnson, R. H. (1985). β-adrenoceptor responsiveness and plasma catecholamines as determinants of cardiovascular reactivity to mental stress. *Clinical Science, 69*, 483–492.

Erskine, J., & Schonell, M. (1979). Relaxation therapy in bronchial asthma. *Journal of Psychosomatic Research, 23*, 131–139.

Fenz, W. D., & Epstein, S. (1967). Gradients of physiological arousal in parachutists as a function of an approaching jump. *Psychosomatic Medicine, 29*, 33–51.

Fenz, W. D., & Jones, G. B. (1972). Individual differences in physiological arousal and performances of sport parachutists. *Psychosomatic Medicine, 34*, 1–8.

Ferris, E. B., Engel, G. L., Stevens, C. D., & Webb, J. (1946). Voluntary breathholding. III. The relation of the maximum time of breathholding to the oxygen and carbon dioxide tensions of arterial blood, with a note on its clinical and physiological significance. *Journal of Clinical Investigation, 25*, 734–743.

Finesinger, J. E. (1944). The effect of pleasant and unpleasant ideas on the respiratory pattern (spirogram) in psychoneurotic patients. *American Journal of Psychiatry, 100*, 659–667.

Finesinger, J. E., & Mazick, S. G. (1940a). Effects of a painful stimulus and its recall upon respiration in psychoneurotic patients. *Psychosomatic Medicine, 2*, 333–370.

Finesinger, J. E., & Mazick, S. G. (1940b). Respiratory response of psychoneurotic patients to ideational and to sensory stimuli. *American Journal of Psychiatry, 97*, 27–48.

Folgering, H., & Colla, P. (1978). Some anomalies in the control of P_aCo_2 in patients with a hyperventilation syndrome. *Bulletin of European Physiopathology and Respiration, 14*, 503–512.

Folgering, H., Lenders, J., & Rosier, I. (1980). Biofeedback control of $PaCO_2$: A prospective therapy for hyperventilation. *Progress in Respiration Research, 14*, 26–30.

Fowler, W. S. (1954). Breaking point of breath-holding. *Journal of Applied Physiology, 6*, 539–545.

Freedman, R. R., Ianni, P., Ettedgui, E., Pohl, R., & Rainey, J. M. (1984). Psychophysiological factors in panic disorder. *Psychopathology, 17*, (suppl. 1). 66–73.

Gardner, W. N., & Meah, M. S., (1986). Controlled study of respiratory response during prolonged measurement in patients with chronic hyperventilation. *Lancet, ii*, 826–830.

Garssen, B. (1980). The role of stress in the development of the hyperventilation syndrome. *Psychotherapy and Psychosomatics, 33*, 214–225.

Gilbert, R., Auchincloss, J. H., Brodsky, J., & Broden, W. (1972). Changes in tidal volume, frequency, and ventilation induced by their measurement. *Journal of Applied Physiology, 33*, 252–254.

Godfrey, S., & Campbell, E. J. M. (1968). The control of breath-holding. *Respiration Physiology, 5*, 385–400.

Godfrey, S., & Campbell E. J. M. (1969). Mechanical and chemical control of breath-holding. *Quarterly Journal of Physiological Cognitive Medical Science, 54*, 117–128.

Goldman, A., (1922). Clinical tetany by forced respiration. *Journal of American Medical Association, 22*, 1193–1195.

Goldstein, I. B. (1964). Physiological responses in anxious women patients. *Archives of General Psychiatry, 10*, 382–388.

Gottfried, S. B., Altose, M. D., Kelsen, S. G., & Cherniack, N. S. (1981). Perception of changes in airflow resistance in obstructive pulmonary disorders. *American Review of Respiratory Disease, 124*, 566–570.

Gottfried, S. B., Leech, I., DiMarco, A, F., Zacardelli, W., & Altose, M. D. (1984). Sensation of respiratory force following low cervical spinal transection. *Journal of Applied Physiology, 57*, 989–994.

Gottfried, S. B., Redline, S., & Altose, M. D. (1985). Respiratory sensation in chronic obstructive pulmonary disease. *American Review of Respiratory Disease, 132*, 954–959.

Greenberg, D. B., & Murray, G. B. (1981). Hyperventilation as a variant of tardive dyskinesia. *Journal of Clinical Psychiatry, 42*, 401–403.

Grossman, P. (1983). Respiration, stress, and cardiovascular function. *Psychophysiology, 20*, 284–300.

Guz, A., Noble, M. I. M., Widdicombe, J. G., Trenchard, D., & Mushin, W. W. (1966b). The effect of bilateral block of vagus and glossopharyngeal nerves on the ventilatory response to CO_2 of conscious man. *Respiration Physiology, 1*, 206–210.

Guz, A., Noble, M. I. M., Widdicombe, J. G., Trenchard, D., Mushin, W. W., & Makey, A. R. (1966a). The role of vagal and glossopharyngeal afferent nerves in respiratory sensation, control of breathing and arterial pressure regulation in conscious man. *Clinical Science, 30*, 161–170.

Haldane, J. S., & Poulton, E. P. (1908). The effects of want of oxygen on respiration. *Journal of Physiology (London), 37*, 390.

Harding, A. V., & Maher, K. R. (1982). Biofeedback training of cardiac acceleration: Effects on airway resistance in bronchial asthma. *Journal of Psychosomatic Research, 26*, 447–454.

Heim, E., Knapp, P. H., Vachon, L., Globus, G. G., & Nemetz, S. J. (1968). Emotion, breathing, and speech. *Journal of Psychosomatic Research, 12*, 261–274.

Hill, L., & Flack, M. (1908). The effect of excess of carbon dioxide and of want of oxygen upon the respiration and the circulation. *Journal of Physiology (London), 37*, 77–111.

Holmes, D. S. (1984). Meditation and somatic arousal reduction: A review of the experimental evidence. *American Psychologist, 39*, 1–10.

Hook, R. A., Rodgers, C. H., Reddi, C., & Kennard, D. W., (1978). Medicopsychological interventions in male asthmatic children: An evaluation of physiological change. *Psychosomatic Medicine, 40*, 210–215.

Hudgel, D. W., Cooperson, D. M., & Kinsman, R. A. (1982). Recognition of added resistive loads in asthma. *American Review of Respiratory Disease, 126*, 121–125.

Janson-Bjerklie, S., & Clarke, E. (1982). The effects of biofeedback training on bronchial diameter in asthma. *Heart and Lung, 11*, 200–207.

Jong, M. A. d., Berg, A. N. v. d., & Jong, A. J. d. (1975). Hypnosis, stimulus preference and autonomic response. *Psychotherapy and Psychosomatics, 26*, 78–85.

Kahneman, D. (1973). *Attention and effort*. Englewood Cliffs, NJ: Prentice-Hall.

Katkin, E. S. (1965). Relationship between manifest anxiety and two indices of automatic response to stress. *Journal of Personality and Social Psychology, 2*, 324–333.

Kerr, W. J., Dalton, J. W., & Gliebe, P. A. (1937). Some physical phenomena associated with the anxiety states and their relation to hyperventilation. *Annals of Internal Medicine, 11*, 961–992.

Killian, K. J., & Campbell, E. J. M., (1985). Dyspnea. In C. Roussos & P. T. Macklem (Eds.), *The thorax* (pp. 787-828). New York: Marcel Dekker.

King, J. T., Bye, M. R., & Demopoulos, J. T. (1984). Exercise programs for asthmatic children. *Comprehensive Therapy, 10*, 67–71.

King, N. J. (1980). The behavioral management of asthma and asthma-related problems in children: A critical review of the literature. *Journal of Behavioral Medicine, 3*, 169–189.

Kotses, H., & Glaus, K. D. (1981). Applications of biofeedback to the treatment of asthma: A critical review. *Biofeedback and Self-Regulation, 6*, 573–593.

Krieger, J. (1985). Breathing during sleep in normal subjects. *Clinics in Chest Medicine, 6*, 577–594.

Lambert, M. S., Shapiro, D. A., & Bergin, A. E. (1986). The effectiveness of psychotherapy. In S. L. Garfield & A. E. Bergin (Eds.), *Handbook of psychotherapy and behavior change* (3rd ed.) (pp. 157–212). New York: John Wiley & Sons.

Lansing, R., Banzett, R., Brown, R., & Kimball, W. (1985). High-level quadraplegics perceive lung volume change. *Federation Proceedings, 44*, 429.

LeBaron, S., & Zeltzer, L. (1983). The treatment of asthma with behavioral intervention: Does it work?

Texas Medicine, 79, 40–42.

LeBerge, D., & Samuels, S. J. (1974). Toward a theory of automatic information processing in reading. *Cognitive Psychology, 6,* 293–323.

Lehrer, P. M., Hochron, S. M., McCann, B., Swartzman, L., & Reba, P. (1986). Relaxation decreased large-airway but not small-airway asthma. *Journal of Psychosomatic Research, 30,* 13–25.

Lewis, B. I., (1953). The hyperventilation syndrome. *Annuals of Internal Medicine, 38,* 918–927.

Liberson, C. W., & Liberson, W. T. (1975). Sex differences in autonomic response to shock. *Psychophysiology, 12,* 182–186.

Lind, F. G., Truve, A. B., & Lindborg, B. P. O. (1984). Microcomputer-assisted on-line measurement of breathing pattern and occlusion pressure. *Journal of Applied Physiology, 56,* 235–239.

Lum, L. C. (1975). Hyperventilation: The tip and the iceberg. *Journal of Psychosomatic Research, 19,* 375–383.

Lum, L. C. (1976). The syndrome of habitual chronic hyperventilation. In O. Hill (Ed.) *Modern trends in psychosomatic medicine,* Vol. 3 (pp. 196–230). London: Butterworth.

Lum, L. C. (1981). Hyperventilation and anxiety state. *Journal of the Royal Society of Medicine, 74,* 1–4.

Magarian, G. J. (1982). Hyperventilation syndromes: Infrequently recognized common expressions of anxiety and stress. *Medicine, 61,* 219–236.

Man, G. C. W., Hsu, K., & Sproule, B. J. (1986). Effect of alprozolam on exercise and dyspnea in patients with chronic obstructive pulmonary disease. *Chest, 90,* 832–836.

Mathews, A. M., & Gelder, M. G. (1969). Psychophysiological investigations of brief relaxation training. *Journal of Psychosomatic Research, 13,* 1–12.

McCaul, K. D., & Malott, J. M. (1984). Distraction and coping with pain. *Psychological Bulletin, 95,* 516-533.

McCaul, K. D., Solomon, S., & Holmes, D. S., (1979). Effects of paced respiration and expectations on physiological and psychological responses to threat. *Journal of Personality and Social Psychology, 37,* 564–571.

McCloskey, D. I., Ebeling, P., & Goodwin, G. M. (1974). Estimation of weights and tensions and apparent involvement of a "sense of effort." *Experimental Neurology, 42,* 220–232.

McKell, T. E., & Sullivan, A. J. (1947). The hyperventilation syndrome in gastroenterology. *Gastroenterology, 9,* 6–16.

Merton, P. A. (1970). The sense of effort. In R. Porter (Ed.), *Breathing: Hering-Breuer Centenary Symposium* (pp. 207–217). London: Churchill.

Milic-Emili, J. (1983). Recent advances in clinical assessment of control of breathing. *Lung, 160,* 1–17.

Mines, A. H. (1981). *Respiratory physiology.* New York: Raven Press.

Missri, J. C., & Alexander, S. (1978). Hyperventilation syndrome: A brief review. *Journal of the American Medical Association, 240,* 2093–2096.

Mitchell-Heggs, P., Murphy, K., Minty, K., Guz, A., Patterson, S. C., Minty, P. S. B., & Rosser, R. M. (1980). Diazepam in the treatment of dyspnea in the pink puffer syndrome. *Quarterly Journal of Medicine,*

New Series, 49, 9–20.

Mook, D. G. (1983). In defense of external invalidity. *American Psychologist, 38,* 379-387.

Moore, N. (1965). Behavior therapy in bronchial asthma: A controlled study. *Journal of Psychosomatic Research, 9,* 257-276.

Mussell, M. J. (1986). Trachea noise biofeedback device to help reduce bronchospasm in asthmatics. *Journal of Biomedical Engineering, 8,* 341–344.

Neubauer, J. A., Santiago, T. C., Edelman, N. C. (1981). Hypoxic arousal in intact and carotid denervated sleeping cats. *Journal of Applied Physiology, 51,* 1294–1299.

Newsom-Davis, J., & Plum, F. (1972). Separation of descending spinal pathways to respiratory motoneurons. *Experimental Neurology, 34,* 78–94.

Noble, M. I. M., Eisele, J. H., Frankel, H. L., Else, W., & Guz, A. (1971). The role of the diaphragm in the sensation of holding the breath. *Clinical Science, 41,* 275–283.

Noble, M. I. M., Eisele, J. H., Trenchard, D., & Guz, A. (1970). Effect of selective peripheral nerve blocks on respiratory sensations. In R. Porter (Ed.), *Breathing: Hering-Breuer Centenary Symposium* (pp. 233–246). London: Churchill.

Norman, D. A., & Bobrow, D. G. (1975). On data-limited and resource-limited processes. *Cognitive Psychology, 7,* 44–64.

Okel, B. B., & Hurst, J. W. (1961). Prolonged hyperventilation in man. *Archives of Internal Medicine, 108,* 757–762.

Oken, D., Grinker, R. R., Heath, H. A., Korchin, S., Sabshin, M., & Schwartz, N. B. (1962). Relation of physiological response to affect expression. *Archives of General Psychiatry, 6,* 336–351.

Opie, L. H., Smith, A. C. & Spalding, J. M. K. (1959). Conscious appreciation of the effects produced by independent changes of ventilation volume and of end-tidal pCO_2 in paralysed patients. *Journal of Physiology, 149,* 494–499.

Orwin, A. (1971). Respiratory relief: A new and rapid method for the treatment of phobic states. *British Journal of Psychiatry, 119,* 635–637.

Orwin, A. (1973). Augmented respiratory relief: A new use for CO_2 therapy in the treatment of phobic conditions: A preliminary report on two cases. *British Journal of Psychiatry, 122,* 171–173.

Orwin, A., LeBoeuf, A., Dovey, J., & James S. (1975). A comparative trial of exposure and respiratory relief therapies. *Behavior Research and Therapy, 13,* 205–214.

Patterson, J. L., Mullinax, P. F., Bain, T., Krueger, J. J., & Richardson, D. W. (1962). Carbon-dioxide induced dyspnea in a patient with respiratory muscle paralysis. *American Journal of Medicine, 32,* 811–816.

Perez, W., & Tobin, M. J. (1985). Separation of factors responsible for change in breathing pattern induced by instrumentation. *Journal of Applied Physiology, 59,* 1515–1520.

Phillipson, E. A., McClean, P. A., Sullivan, C. E., & Zamel, N. (1978). Interaction of metabolic and behavioral respiratory control during hypercapnia and speech. *American Review of Respiratory Disease, 117,* 903–909.

Plum, F., & Posner, J. B., (1980). *The diagnosis of stupor and coma* (3rd ed.) Philadelphia: F. A. Davis.

Plum, F., & Swanson, A. G., (1959). Central neurogenic hyperventilation in man. *A. M. A. Archives of Neurology and Psychiatry, 81*, 535–549.

Renne, C., & Creer, T. L. (1976). The effects of training on the use of inhalation therapy equipment by children with asthma. *Journal of Applied Behavior Analysis, 9*, 1–11.

Rice, R. L. (1950). Symptom patterns of the hyperventilation syndrome. *American Journal of Medicine, 202*, 691–700.

Richter, R., & Dahme, B. (1982). Bronchial asthma in adults: There is little evidence for the effectiveness of behavioral therapy and relaxation. *Journal of Psychosomatic Research, 26*, 533–540.

Rikard-Bell, G. C., Bystrazycka, E. K. & Nail, B. S. (1985). Cells of origin of corticospinal projections to phrenic and thoracic respiratory mononeurons in the cat as shown by retrograde transport of HRP. *Brain Research Bulletin, 14*, 39–47.

Rosser, R. & Guz, A. (1981). Psychological approaches to breathlessness and its treatment. *Journal of Psychosomatic Research, 25*, 439–447.

Rubinfield, A. R., & Pain, M. C. F. (1976). Perception of asthma. *Lancet, i*, 882–884.

Sackner, M. A. (1984). Effects of hydrocodone bitartrate on breathing pattern of patients with chronic obstructive pulmonary disease and restrictive lung disease. *Mount Sinai Journal of Medicine, 51*, 222–226.

Salter, C. A., Meunier, J. C., & Triplett, N. M. (1976). Multiple measurement of anxiety and its effects on complex learning. *Psychological Reports, 38*, 691–694.

Saltzman, H. A., Heyman, A., & Sieker, H. O. (1963). Correlation of clinical and physiologic manifestations of sustained hyperventilation. *New England Journal of Medicine, 268*, 1431–1436.

Santiago, T. V., Johnson, J., Riley, D. J., & Edelman, N. H. (1979). Effects of morphine on ventilatory response to exercise. *Journal of Applied Physiology: Respiratory, Environmental and Exercise Physiology, 47*, 112–118.

Schnore, M. M. (1959). Individual patterns of physiological activity as a function of task differences and degree of arousal. *Journal of Experimental Psychology, 58*, 117–128.

Sedlacek, K. (1979). Biofeedback for Raynaud's disease. *Psychosomatics, 20*, 535–541.

Sempik, A., & Patrick, J. M. (1980). The effect of thoracic vibration on ventilation and breathholding in man. *Respiratory Physiology, 44*, 381–391.

Shenkman, B. (1985). Factors contributing to attrition rates in a pulmonary rehabilitation program. *Heart and Lung, 14*, 53–58.

Skarbek, A. (1970). A psychophysiological study of breathing behavior. *British Journal of Psychiatry, 116*, 637–641.

Smith, M. L., Glass, G. V., & Miller, T. I. (1980). *The benefits of psychotherapy*. Baltimore, Johns Hopkins University Press.

Smith, M. M., Colebatch, H. S. H., & Clarke, P. S. (1970). Increase and decrease in pulmonary resistance with hypnotic suggestion in asthma. *American Review of Respiratory Disease, 102*, 236–242.

Spector, S., Luparello, T. J., Kopetzky, M. T., Souhrada, J., & Kinsman, R. A. (1976). Response of asthmatics to methacholine and suggestion. *Respiratory Disease, 112*, 43–49.

Stark, R. D., Gambles, S. A., & Lewis, J. A. (1981). Methods to assess breathlessness in healthy subjects: A critical evaluation and application to analyse the acute effects of diazepam and promethazine on breathlessness induced by exercise or by exposure to raised levels of carbon dioxide. *Clinical Science, 61*, 429–439.

Steptoe, A., Phillips, J., & Harling, J. (1981). Biofeedback and instructions in the modification of total respiratory resistance: An experimental study of asthmatic and non-asthmatic volunteers. *Journal of Psychosomatic Research, 25*, 541–551.

Stern, R. M., & Anschel, C. (1968). Deep inspirations as stimuli for responses of the autonomic nervous system. *Psychophysiology, 5*, 132–141.

Stevenson, I., & Ripley, N. (1952). Variations in respiration and respiratory systems during changes in emotions. *Psychosomatic Medicine, 14*, 476–490.

Stokes, W. (1854). *The diseases of the heart and aorta*. Dublin: Hodges & Smith.

Stone, D. J., Keltz, H., Sarkar, T. K., & Singzon, J. (1973). Ventilatory response to alpha-adrenergic stimulation and inhibition. *Journal of Applied Physiology, 34*, 619–623.

Suess, W. M., Alexander, A. B., Smith, D. D., Sweeney, H. W., & Marion, R. J. (1980). The effects of psychological stress on respiration: A preliminary study of anxiety and hyperventilation. *Psychophysiology, 17*, 535–540.

Taplin, P. S. & Creer, T. L. (1978). A procedure for using peak expiratory flow rate data to increase the prediction of asthma episodes. *Journal of Asthma Research, 16*, 15–19.

Tobin, M. J. (1986b). *Development and application of inductive plethysmography for non-invasive respiratory monitoring*. Unpublished M. D. thesis, National University of Ireland.

Tobin, M. J. (1986a). Noninvasive evaluation of respiratory movement. In M. L. Nochomovitz & N. S. Cherniack (Eds.), *Nonivasive respiratory monitoring* (pp. 29-57). New York: Churchill Livingstone.

Tobin, M. J., Chadha, T. S., Jenouri, G., Birch, S. J., Haik Gazeroglu, H. B., & Sackner, M. A. (1983a). Breathing patterns 1. Normal subjects. *Chest, 84*, 202–205.

Tobin, M. J., Chadha, T. S., Jenouri, G., Birch, S. J., Gazeroglu, H. B., & Sackner, M. A. (1983b). Breathing patterns 2. Diseased subjects. *Chest, 84*, 286–294.

Tobin, M. J., Perez, W., Guenther, S. M., D'Alonzo, G., & Dantzker, D. R. (1986). Breathing pattern and metabolic behavior during anticipation of exercise. *Journal of Applied Physiology, 60*, 1306–1312.

Turner, S. A., Daniels, J. L., & Hollandsworth, J. G. (1985). The effects of a multicomponent smoking cessation program with chronic obstructive pulmonary disease outpatients. *Addictive Behavior, 10*, 87–90.

Uhde, T. W., Boulenger, J. P., Post, R. M., Siever, L. J., Vittone, B. J., Jimerson, D. C., & Roy-Byrne, P. P. (1984). Fear and anxiety: Relationship to noradrenergic function. *Psychopathology, 17* (suppl. 3), 8–23.

Van Egeren, L. F., Feather, B. W., & Hein, P. L. (1971). Desensitization of phobias: Some psychophysiological propositions. *Psychophysiology, 8*, 213–228.

von Heyer, G. R. (1925). *Das koerperlich-seelische zusammenwerken in den lebensvorgaengen. An hand klinischer und experimenteller tatsachen darestellt.* Munich: Bergmann.

Weil, J. V., McCullough, R. E., Kline, J. S., & Sodal, I. E., (1975). Diminished ventilatory response to hypoxia and hypercapnia after morphine in normal man. *New England Journal of Medicine, 292,* 1103–1106.

Weinstein, A. G. (1985). Behavioral strategies and theophylline compliance in asthmatic children. *Annals of Allergy, 55,* 16–21.

Weinstein, A. G., & Cuskey, W. (1985). Theophylline compliance in asthmatic children. *Annals of Allergy, 54,* 19–24.

Willer, J. C. (1975). Effects of pain on the nociceptive component of the flexor reflex. *Physiology and Behavior, 15,* 411–415.

Wilson, A. F., Honsberger, R., Chiu, J. T., & Novey, H. S. (1975). Transcendental meditation and asthma. *Respiration, 32,* 74–80.

Wolpe, J. (1969). *The practice of behavior therapy.* Elmsford, New York: Pergamon Press.

Woodcock, A. A., Gross, E. R., Gellert, A., Shah, S., Johnson, M., & Geddes, D. M. (1981). Effects of dihydrocodeine, alcohol, and caffeine on breathlessness and exercise tolerance in patients with chronic obstructive lung disease and normal blood gases. *New England Journal of Medicine, 305,* 1611–1616.

Woodcock, A. A., Johnson, M. A., & Geddes, D. M. (1982). Breathlessness, alcohol and opiates. *New England Journal of Medicine, 306,* 1363–1364.

Yorkston, N. J., Eckert, E., McHugh, R. B., Philander, D. A., & Blumenthal, M. N. (1979). Bronchial asthma: Improved lung function after behavior modification. *Psychosomatics, 20,* 325–331.

Chapter 16

Stress Management In Diabetes Mellitus

Danita Czyzewski

OVERVIEW OF DIABETES AND DIABETES MANAGEMENT

Diabetes mellitus is a complex medical condition that is a leading cause of morbidity and mortality. Taking into account the various complications of diabetes mellitus, the disease is directly or indirectly responsible for 300,000 deaths per year in the United States. The complications of the disease are responsible for much human suffering. Compared to the general population, people with diabetes are twice as likely to suffer stroke or heart disease, 17 times more likely to develop renal failure, and 20 times more likely to go blind (Davidson, 1981).

Diabetes mellitus subsumes a number of heterogeneous conditions, the etiologies of which are not precisely known. In general, the condition is characterized by chronic high blood glucose (hyperglycemia). Glucose is an essential fuel for the cells, and an accumulation of glucose in the bloodstream indicates that the glucose is not being properly used by the cells. An essential element in allowing glucose to be used by the cells is the hormone insulin. The action of the insulin, which is secreted by the pancreas, makes the cell membranes permeable to glucose. The two types of diabetes mellitus are basically differentiated by the way in which insulin fails to properly support glucose metabolism. In Type I diabetes mellitus or insulin-dependent diabetes mellitus (IDDM), formerly known as juvenile-onset diabetes mellitus, the beta cells of the pancreatic islets of Langerhans secrete little or no insulin. In Type II diabetes, or non-insulin-dependent diabetes mellitus (NIDDM), formerly known as adult-onset diabetes mellitus, insulin is secreted, but the body is unable to fully use, or is resistant to, the insulin. When the body cannot use glucose as a fuel, fat is metabolized as an alternate fuel. The accumulation of the by-products of the fat metabolism, ketones, results in diabetic ketoacidosis (in Type I only), which, when untreated, progresses from severe dehydration to coma, to death (Karam, 1981).

Type I diabetes mellitus (IDDM) is typically diagnosed in children and is always diagnosed before age 40. Type II diabetes mellitus (NIDDM) is most commonly diagnosed in those over 40, more frequently in females. Sixty percent to 90% of NIDDM patients are obese, which is thought to induce insulin resistance. It is believed that as many as 5 million Americans have undiagnosed NIDDM, making NIDDM 7 to 10 times more prevalent than IDDM (Surwit, Feinglos, & Scovern, 1983).

The primary management goal for diabetes mellitus is to achieve and maintain levels of blood glucose that are normal or near normal. To achieve this goal, persons with IDDM take one or more injections of insulin per day. The action of this

I would like to thank Douglas G. Rogers for his suggestions and critique of the medical aspects and Marco J. Mariotto and Lynnda M. Dahlquist for their comments on an earlier draft of this chapter.

exogenous insulin peaks several times per day, and, in general, meals must be timed to coincide with the action of the insulin. Further, the amount of carbohydrates consumed at meals must coincide with the amount of insulin injected to metabolize the carbohydrates. If insulin and meal timing and amount are not well matched, high or low blood glucose results.

To monitor the adequacy of blood glucose control, patients are asked to monitor their blood glucose several times per day. Self-monitoring of blood glucose (SMBG) has largely replaced urine glucose testing as a much more accurate method of assessment. Urine glucose can only be measured after blood glucose rises high enough to surpass the renal threshold and "spill" into the urine. Urine glucose is less adequate than blood glucose because, not only do renal thresholds vary among individuals, but also blood glucose values near normal and below normal cannot be differentiated (Sonksen, Judd, & Lowy, 1980). SMBG requires that one obtain a drop of blood from the fingertip, place in on a reagent strip, time the reaction, and read the results either visually or with a reflectance meter. If blood glucose readings are high (240 mg/dl or greater), the urine must be tested for the presence of ketones. Further, if hyperglycemia (with or without ketones) is discovered, additional insulin is given, to lower the blood glucose.

Persons with NIDDM generally do not receive insulin injections but must make other adjustments to lower their blood glucose. For many patients, weight loss alone greatly decreases insulin resistance, and for obese NIDDM patients a reduced calorie diet is the first step in treatment. Many patients also need to take oral hypoglycemic agents one to three times per day to facilitate the action of insulin. The strict timing of meals is less crucial in NIDDM, but carbohydrate loads spread evenly throughout the day can facilitate glucose tolerance.

Both types of diabetic patients are subject to hypoglycemia (low blood sugar, insulin reactions) at times when they have too little food, too much insulin, or both. These reactions range from uncomfortable to disorienting to life threatening (in IDDM only) and must be treated promptly with glucose.

Regular physical exercise is frequently recommended for patients with diabetes (Zinman, 1984). There are several potential benefits of exercise. Exercise appears to have a short-term effect on facilitation of insulin action, and, for obese patients, the important goal of weight reduction is supported with exercise. Especially for older, obese NIDDM patients and for patients with retinopathy, physical restrictions and cautions are placed on the type, intensity, and duration of exercise. In all patients with diabetes who receive insulin or oral medication, efforts to prevent hypoglycemia, such as ingesting extra carbohydrates, need to be undertaken prior to exercise.

Physical illness and trauma produce hormonal reactions that increase hyperglycemia. During periods of physical illness, patients with diabetes must monitor blood glucose more frequently, and make adjustments in their regimen to treat hyperglycemia. For NIDDM patients, this type of physical stress can prompt a need for exogenous insulin until the stress is resolved.

Although SMBG assesses diabetic control at the moment, a rather recently developed measure, glycosolated hemoglobin (GHb or HbA1), provides assessment of longer term diabetic control. HbA1 reflects the percentage of hemoglobin bound with glucose. Although brief elevations in blood glucose do not significantly effect HbA1 levels, longer term elevations are reflected. The half-life of hemoglobin is approximately 8 weeks; therefore, HbA1 reflects control over several months (Gonen, Rachman, Rubenstein, Tanega, & Horwitz, 1977; Nathan, Singer, Hurxthal, & Goodson, 1984). Glycosylated hemoglobin values vary slightly from lab to lab. An example of one lab's values is nondiabetic normals, 4% to 8%; good diabetic control, 8% to 10%; and poor diabetic control, greater than 14% (Fisher, Delamater, Bertelson & Kirkley, 1982).

STRESS AND DIABETES

Emotional factors have long been known to influence diabetic instability, and patients themselves are likely to mention emotional factors as a precipitant for diabetic decompensation (Cohen, Vance, Runyan, & Hurwitz, 1960; Nabarro, 1965). This relationship appears to hold up over diverse populations and types of investigations. For example, hospitalizations for diabetic ketoacidosis occur more frequently in children with unstable families (White, Kolman, Wexler, Polin, & Winter, 1984), and diabetic children in poor control, as opposed to those in good control, are more likely to come from families with more reported conflict (Simonds, 1976–1977). In adults, anxiety levels and glycosylated hemoglobin levels are significantly correlated (Turkat, 1982).

Unlike previous explanations based upon enduring

personal characteristics such as "diabetic personality," diabetic instability related to emotional factors is currently better understood as a response or series of responses to more transient external or internal events. For example, negative life events have been related to negative diabetic control in studies with diabetic adults and children. (Barglow et al., 1983; Chase and Jackson, 1981; Grant, Kyle, Teichman, & Mendels, 1974; Rand, & Hauser, 1985). In a recent study, patients with recent-onset diabetic retinopathy (Jacobsen et al., 1985), were more likely to be adversely effected, as measured by HbA1 levels, by additional negative life events than those patients with either no retinopathy or long-standing retinopathy. The authors suggested that this vulnerability to negative life events occurs because the patients are temporarily emotionally distressed by their decreasing vision. Mazze, Lucido, and Shamoon (1984) demonstrated no relationship between personality factors and diabetes control but an inverse relationship between diabetic control and state psychosocial factors (depression, anxiety, and low quality of life). Further, they demonstrated that this relationship remained constant while the patients changed both physiological and psychological states. Briefly, 84 IDDM subjects were recruited and monitored on their diabetic control (under one of two treatment regimens) and psychosocial functioning. Sixty percent of the patients changed in diabetic control status over the 36 weeks of the study, but at each measurement point those in poor control were those displaying more anxiety and depression and a lower quality of life.

The preceding studies illustrate the concept that has become known as the negative effect of stress on diabetes. Stress is a very broad concept around which much ambiguity exists. The term *stress* has been used to refer to the external events that disrupt the normal activity of the person, the psychological and physiological responses of the organism to disruption, and the field of study that examines the process through which organisms adapt to disruption (Leventhal & Nerenz, 1983). In the preceding nonexperimental studies, various levels of inference were required to conclude that stress has had a negative impact on diabetes. These vary from studies that describe likely external stressors (negative life events, family conflict) to studies that describe psychological responses to stress (anxiety) as they relate to diabetic control. Later in the chapter, physiological and behavioral responses to stress will also be discussed. In this chapter,

stressor will be used to describe the environmental or other pressure on the person and *stress* to describe the psychological, physiological, or behavioral response to the stressor.

Two mechanisms are generally considered to explain the connection between stress and poor diabetic control: lack of adherence to the diabetic regimen as an indirect effect of stress and diabetic decompensation based on the body's direct physiological response to stress.

STRESS-ADHERENCE-CONTROL HYPOTHESIS

The general issue of adherence to the diabetic regimen has been well studied, and the results are not encouraging. Despite the fact that diabetes is a condition that places much responsibility on the patient for self-management, fewer than 7% of patients have been judged to adhere completely to the regimen (Bloom-Cerkoney & Hart, 1980). Estimates of nonadherence to various parts of the regimen range from 75% for the dietary regimen, 80% for the insulin administration regimen (including measuring and timing), and 40% for the urine-testing regimen (Watkins, Williams, Martin, Hogan, & Anderson, 1967). Clinically, patients report that, when they are distressed, they are more likely to ignore their diets and not monitor blood sugars, and some even report failure to give themselves insulin.

Stress is a well-known factor in disrupting adherence to many types of life-style regimens including weight control, alcohol, smoking, and drug cessation (Marlatt & Gordon, 1980; Rosenthal and Marx, 1981), but studies of adherence to the diabetic regimen or treatment studies to increase adherence to the diabetic regimen do not usually address the impact of psychosocial stressors. For example, Schafer, Glasgow, and McCaul (1982) attempted to increase adherence to the diabetic regimen in 3 adolescents with diabetes, using a variety of behavioral techniques. The intervention was successful with two of the patients, but the authors explained that the third patient could not participate reliably in the intervention because of psychosocial stressors (family problems). Schafer, Glasgow, McCaul, and Dreher, 1983 evaluated environmental situational barriers to adherence and family conflict and support for adherence, as they related to various aspects of compliance to the regimen. As evidenced in their treatment study, psychosocial factors did impact on adherence. Clearly intervention studies need to address the treatment of these psychosocial deterents to adherence.

There are two features inherent in the diabetic regimen that increase the likelihood of nonadherence, given less than optimal patient motivation. First of all, the regimen impacts on a basic physiologic and usually pleasurable need, eating, and prescribes the amount and types of food and the timing of meals and snacks. In addition, other basic physiologic patterns might be altered. For example, for those who test urine glucose, voiding must be done several times daily in an inconvenient manner, specifically, by emptying the bladder once and then again within 30 minutes. Surwit, Feinglos, and Scovern (1983) summarized the second feature that can compromise adherence to the regimen: lack of response-maintaining contingencies. "The benefits that accrue from following such regimens are often not obvious to the patient. The diabetic is precariously poised between hypoglycemia (too little blood glucose) and hyperglycemia (too much blood glucose). Although hyperglycemia may be responsible for the numerous sequelae of the disease, its symptoms are often difficult to recognize unless blood glucose is markedly elevated. Hypoglycemia, on the other hand, triggers an autonomic reaction that is extremely aversive to the patient. The diabetic is severely punished for erring on the side of low blood sugar, while hyperglycemia deviations often go unnoticed" (p. 258).

Another example of the lack of response-maintaining contingencies is in the area of glucose monitoring. Glucose monitoring, whether by urine or blood (with its mildly uncomfortable fingersticks), assumes a patient who is motivated to receive feedback about her or his glycemic control and willing to act to alter her or his blood sugar level if necessary. Obviously patients under stress might not have the motivation to perform a procedure that gives them information that either tells them to maintain the status quo (therefore making the test a waste of time) or to treat hyperglycemia (therefore giving them more work or something to worry or feel guilty about). In summary, many aspects of the diabetic regimen either impact strongly on life-style patterns or are not obviously supported by short-term contingencies and are, therefore, likely to present adherence problems.

Evidence to support the relationship among stress, adherence, and diabetic control assumes first a positive relationship between adherence and control and then a negative impact of emotional factors on adherence, which effects control. Anecdotal, correlational, and experimental evidence support the first assumption. For example, in a study of adolescents with IDDM (Simonds, Goldstein, Walker, et al., 1980) glycohemoglobin levels were positively correlated with active parental supervision of diabetic care and negatively correlated with self-care. Increased adherence to the regimen, through educational or behavioral interventions, typically results in better diabetic control (e.g., Carey, Schechter, & Davis, 1983). The assumption that emotional factors have a negative impact on adherence is also supported in the literature. Rosen and Lidz (1949) reported that repeated incidents of ketoacidosis in diabetic adolescents with emotional distress were related to nonadherence to the regimen rather than to the direct metabolic impact of stress. Cohen et al., (1960) reviewed 72 cases of ketoacidosis. Twenty-seven percent of these were due to omission of insulin, and one half of these omissions were attributed to psychological stress. Kirkley (1982) reported that diabetics attributed incidents of dietary nonadherence to negative emotions (19%) and conflict (7%).

STRESS-HORMONE-CONTROL HYPOTHESIS

A long-described component of the fight-or-flight response in normal animals is hyperglycemia (Cannon, 1941), and the autonomic nervous system is generally cited as the pathway through which stress affects diabetic control. Complex mechanisms, by which blood glucose and ketones increase, have been proposed to describe the effects of stress on metabolic derangement. In normals, these physiologic responses play a major role in preventing hypoglycemia. Because the brain requires a continuous supply of glucose to function, severe hypoglycemia is extremely detrimental to the survival of the organism. Therefore, the body has many systems through which to maintain blood glucose levels. Two hormones, stimulated under conditions of stress, epinephrine and glucagon, are thought to play a major role in this process. Blood glucose is increased by epinephrine through several mechanisms: (a) decreasing the peripheral effects of insulin, (b) stimulating the release of glucose from the liver, and (c) in nondiabetic and NIDDM persons, decreasing the release of insulin from the pancreas. Glucagon stimulates the release of glucose from the liver and the production of ketones, though it does not have the effect of peripheral insulin antagonism.

Epinephrine increases ketone production in two ways: *First*, there is a direct action by epinephrine on fat cells to increase lipolyses and mobilize free fatty acids, which are subsequently converted to ketones in the liver. *Second*, because of the antagonism of insulin, fat metabolism is further promoted (resulting in fatty acids and subsequently ketones). Figure 16.1 illustrates simplified mechanisms of stress-induced diabetic decompensation.

Some of the earliest purported support for the metabolically destabilizing effect of stress on diabetes is found in the case studies of Hinkle and Wolf in the 1950s (Hinkle & Wolf, 1952). Sixty-four patients, heterogeneous for type and severity of diabetes were deprived of insulin for 24 hours and interviewed in a fasting state in the morning. During stressful interviews, patients were noted to have increases in urine volume, excretion of glucose and ketones, and increases and decreases in blood glucose. These physiological changes reversed when the stressful interviews ended. These physiologic changes under stress were also noted in the nondiabetic control subjects, though the diabetic patients with high ketones prior to stress exhibited more pronounced increases in ketones when stressed.

The results of the Hinkle and Wolf studies might be challenged on the grounds of clinical utility, because the patients were interviewed under very poor conditions of diabetic management-no insulin for 24 hours. Although the finding that diabetics in poor metabolic control react even more poorly to psychological stressors is interesting, it cannot be generalized to the usual treated diabetic state with exogenous insulin. In attempting to decide whether stress management is a useful adjunctive treatment for diabetes, the effect of stress under usual conditions of management (following the prescribed insulin and dietary regimen) must be investigated.

Vandenbergh, Sussman, and Titus (1966) performed a series of studies similiar to Hinkle and Wolf's, with the important difference of studying diabetic patients who were neither fasted nor insulin-deprived. Vanderbergh et al. induced stress via hypnotic interview and through exposure to 1 hour of unpredictable shock. Again, both diabetic and control subjects showed increases in urine volume and ketones, but only the diabetic subjects showed decreased blood glucose levels. Baker's case studies of two adolescent "superlabile juvenile diabetic" girls (Baker, Barcai, Kay, & Haque, 1969) are also generally viewed as part of the early evidence supporting the metabolic link between stress and diabetic decompensation. During stressful interviews, increase in cortisol, growth hormone,

and epinephrine were noted with an associated 100% increase in free fatty acids. In subsequent stressful interviews, when patients were given a beta adrenergic blocking agent, these metabolic changes were not noted. The authors argued that this supports the idea that stress hormones mediated the previously seen metabolic changes.

The previously described studies provide suggestive evidence to support the hypothesis that psychological stressors negatively impact on diabetic control. However, there are multiple methodological criticisms of this series of studies (Lustman & Carney, 1981). Among these are the inclusion of IDDM and NIDDM patients in the same study, the investigation of very select patients, poorly controlled or poorly defined initial diabetic control conditions, and failure to standardize stress conditions or ascertain that stress occurred.

Several studies (Kemmer et al., 1986; Naliboff, Cohen, & Sowers, 1985) have attempted to address these criticisms by using standarized laboratory acute stress-inducing procedures and ascertaining by both self-report and physiological measures of arousal (e.g., blood pressure, heart rate, plasma cortisol, epinephrine, etc) that the subjects were stressed. Further, patients were homogeneous for type of diabetes, and current metabolic state was controlled. Appropriate nondiabetic control groups were used in each case. Naliboff et al. (1985) studied 8 NIDDM subjects and 8 controls, who fasted overnight, under two kinds of stressors, physical (standing and exerting 50% maximal grip on a dynamometer for 10 minutes) and psychological (serial sevens and mental calculations with an authoritarian examiner for 15 minutes). Higher levels of catecholamines and heart rate were seen for all subjects under stress. However, except for the overall higher glucose levels in diabetic subjects, no differences in glucose response to stress were noted. The authors concluded that this type of "milder, more real-life stressor," in contrast with analogous stress situations induced by epinephrine infusion or pyrogen fever, did not result in an abnormal metabolic response in persons with diabetes. Epinephrine elevations in this study were approximately one half of those measured or induced by the latter methods. The authors speculated that the fasting state (lack of glucose load) in their subjects might have curbed a stronger metabolic response. Other studies have suggested that epinephrine has its more powerful effect as an insulin agonist (rather than an insulin or glucose elicitor), but, without a glucose load, this is difficult to observe.

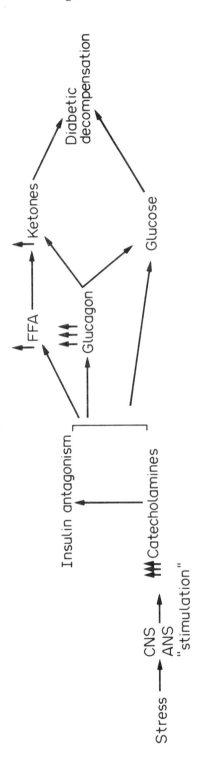

FIGURE 16.1. Mechanism of stress-induced diabetic decompensation

Note: From "Stress in Juvenile Diabetes Mellitus" by J. D. Tarnow and S. W. Silverman, 1981–82. *International Journal of Psychiatry in Medicine, 11*(1), p. 32. Copyright 1981 by Baywood Publishing Co., Inc. Reprinted by permission

Standardized caloric intake prior to stress was an additional modification in a study by Kemmer et al. (1986). Two groups of IDDM patients, one group on usual insulin therapy, one group insulin deprived, were compared to each other and a normal control group under two conditions of psychological stress: serial sevens from 4,500 (45 minutes) and public speaking to a television camera (15 minutes). In the stress conditions, patients in all groups showed physiological signs of arousal, increased heart rate, blood pressure, epinephrine and norepinephrine, and self-reported emotional arousal. Epinephrine increase was greater for diabetic subjects in good control under conditions of stress, and there was a group effect for cortisol levels (higher cortisol in insulin-deficient patients). However, although mean plasma glucose levels differed among groups, as expected, there was no effect of stress on blood glucose. Further, there was no change in ketones or free fatty acids in any group. The authors pointed out that the plasma catecholamine concentrations were similiar to those found in everyday stressors such as driving a car but less than those found in actual public speaking and more stressful events. They reported that the somewhat higher levels of catecholamines are required to cause a metabolic effect, specifically through hepatic glucose production. The fact that increases in ketones and fatty acids were not observed, as they had been in previous studies, also suggests a less potent stressor. The authors concluded that "metabolic control in insulin treated diabetes patients is not jeopardized by sudden, short lived emotional arousal that may be produced by the common stressful events of daily life". (p, 1083).

The appropriate measure of diabetic control or dyscontrol is a question throughout the various research efforts. Laboratory research frequently uses blood glucose levels, but naturalistic studies report incidents of ketoacidosis, hospitalizations, or HbA1 levels. Bradley (1979) factor analyzed a number of variables relating to diabetic control in a 12-month period. These variables included a number of life events, incidences of glycosuria, changes in insulin or tablet regimen, clinic visits, and measures of blood glucose. Life events and incidents of glucosuria loaded on one factor, and blood glucose measures loaded on another factor. Bradley concluded that glycosuria, reflecting levels of blood glucose above the renal threshhold, was a diabetic control measure more closely related to life stress in this poorly controlled population than was blood glucose alone.

The finding that short-term mild stressors do not disrupt metabolic control in people with diabetes is useful, but it will not stop the argument that more chronic stress is disruptive, through endrocine pathways, to diabetic control. Barglow, Hatcher, Edidin, & Sloan-Rossiter (1984) argued that cortisol, as a "crucial agent in the chronic stress adaptation syndrome" could be more relevant to control than the acute stress effects of epinephrine or glucagon (though this was not found in Kemmer et al., 1986). Shamoon, Hendler, and Sherwin (1980) showed that epinephrine, glucagon, and cortisol were interactive in their effect on stress-related hyperglycemia. Investigation of the interactive effects of these hormones on chronic stress has not been done at this time.

Obviously, the effects of chronic stressors are more difficult to follow empirically than are the effects of acute stressors. The following studies of naturalistic stressors are frequently cited to support the case that chronic stress does effect control through metabolic pathways. McLesky, Lewis, and Woodruff (1978) found a hyperglycemia response of IDDM and NIDDM patients during surgical stress, though it could be argued that the physical effects of this stressor are sufficient to effect diabetic control without the additional explanation of a psychological stressor.

Kaplan, Mass, Oixleg, and Ross (1960) treated 5 depressed diabetic patients with imipramine, which blocks uptake of norepinephrine. With diet and activity level controlled, they found decreases in glycosuria, presumably attributable to the metabolic intervention. This result illustrates a complicating factor in evaluating the interactions of stress and diabetes; specifically, the fact that diabetic decompensation is a physical stressor, and the body responds to this stressor with an increase in stress hormones including catecholamines and cortisol. Therefore, the fact that imipramine improved control on a metabolic basis is not surprising, given the physiological condition of diabetic instability.

Vandenbergh and Sussman (1967) reported decreases in blood glucose, along with increases in anxiety level, prior to and during examination week in 5 of 6 diabetic university students studied. This study provides a strong naturalistic experiment in psychological stress, but it is flawed by the heterogeneity of the patients, the inability to monitor the actual conditions of the reportedly "unchanged" dietary and insulin regimen, and the possible presence of a physiological stressor (sleep deprivation).

ADHERENCE-VERSUS-HORMONES INVESTIGATIONS

Recently, efforts have been made to more directly address the issue of metabolic effects, versus adherence effects, on stress-mediated diabetic control problems. Cox et al. (1984) designed a study to evaluate the effect of stress (daily hassles) on HbA1 levels and asked whether this relationship is influenced by factors thought to mediate the psychological and physiological effects of stress, such as Type-A behavior and social supports. Further, they evaluated the extent to which this stress-control relationship was related to adherence or nonadherence to the diabetic regimen. All 60 patients in the study used insulin, and 32% performed home blood glucose monitoring. Subjects volunteered to participate in a study investigating "whether emotions play a role in diabetes." Because glycosylated hemoglobin levels estimate control over a 6- to 8-week period, subjects were asked to complete the psychosocial measures on the basis of previous 2-month period. The psychosocial measures were the Hassles Scale (Kanner, Coyne, Schaefer, & Lazarus, 1981), the Jenkins Type A Scale (Jenkins, Zyzanski, & Rosenman, 1971), a social support scale to measure amount and quality of support, and a compliance scale, asking patients to rate their degree of compliance to physicians' recommendations in four areas: insulin usage, diet, exercise, and urine or blood glucose testing.

Because diet, exercise, and glucose-monitoring compliance were highly correlated with each other and not correlated with insulin compliance, these three factors were combined and analyzed as "other compliance." Simple correlations among the variables revealed only one significant correlation (r = .25), between daily hassles and HbA1. To test the unique contribution of each independent variable to HbA1 variance, an additional set of analyses was performed. Each variable was entered last into a stepwise multiple regression. Daily hassles was the only variable that significantly added to the variance after the other variables were entered. Further, no interactions between hassles and compliance (or any of the other variables) accounted for a significant portion of the HbA1 variance. The authors concluded that this study supported the idea that stress impacts directly on diabetic control (presumably through metabolic pathways) rather than indirectly through lapses in adherence. However, the authors noted a very restricted range in insulin compliance (63%-100%), which could account for a lack of correlation

with this variable and control. This lack of statistical power is interesting and problematic, given the anecdotal and case study findings that omission of insulin is frequently an important factor in ketoacidosis and suggests a lack of utility with correlational research to understand the fairly infrequent event of diabetic decompensation. A second potential criticism of this study is the usual problem with the measurement of compliance of any kind.

Schafer et al. (1983) also looked at adherence and psychosocial factors as they relate to control in 34 adolescents (average HbA1 level = 10.7) with IDDM and found the opposite results. A questionnaire on diabetic adherence in the last week in 4 areas (diet, insulin injections, glucose testing, and exercise) and questionnaires on family behavior in relation to diabetes, as well as more general measures of family functioning, were related to control as measured by HbA1. A difference from the Cox study was the fact that the 4 areas of adherence were not related. Glycosylated hemoglobin levels were predicted (R = .68) from a combination of three adherence measures (following of the diet, care in measuring insulin doses, and number of daily glucose tests), but the psychosocial factors did not predict control (correlations ranged from .01 to .28). The diabetic psychosocial variables, though not the general psychosocial measures, did show a slight, though significant, relationship (6 of 15 correlations greater than .25) to adherence to various regimens, however.

These two studies designed to investigate the relationship of the same concepts produced opposite results. These might be accounted for by the different age cohorts; more, versus less, direct measures of stress (hassles versus family functioning); and the length of time the questionnaires covered (1 week versus 8 weeks).

Summary

In summary, the oft-cited clinical position that psychological stressors disturb diabetes control through the adverse effect of insulin-regulating stress hormones is much more complicated than previously thought. The evidence for physical stress effecting diabetic control is strong, and, at times, the circularity of psychological stressor, decompensation, and resultant physical stress clouds the issue of precipitating psychological stress. Improved laboratory techniques and research design in several studies suggest that short-term mild psychological stressors do *not* result in problems in diabetic control. However, increasingly sophisticated correlational studies persist in finding relationships between psychological stressors and poor control. These relationships can be mediated by the endrocine effects of chronic stress hormones as yet unstudied or by lapses in adherences to the diabetic regimen. An interaction of factors is the most likely, though least studied, explanation. For example, psychological stressors might negatively effect diabetic control when the person is already experiencing metabolic decompensation. Barglow et al. (1984) stated that "stress reduction would facilitate diabetic control if high levels of stress could be proven to change compliance behavior or to produce large, rapid, or prolonged changes in carbohydrate and fat metabolism", (p. 132). The evidence presented in the previously reviewed studies suggests that, to date, there is more evidence to support the former than the latter position.

REVIEW OF RELAXATION-TREATMENT STUDIES

Despite the fact that adherence is very frequently a mediating factor in the relationship between emotional distress and diabetic control, the interventions to counter the negative effects of stress have largely ignored this factor. Generally the interventions focus on stress-mediated physiological changes and prescribe some form of progressive muscle relaxation.

One of the earliest and most frequently cited case studies of behavioral intervention into stress-mediated diabetic control problems is a study by Fowler, Budzynski, and Vanderbergh (1976). The patient was a 20-year-old female college student with an 11-year history of IDDM and a 5-year history of poor control. By her history, the patient appeared to be very reactive to physical and psychological stressors; positive and negative emotions disrupted her diabetic control. "Insulin doses of several hundred units a day were common, as were massive swings in blood sugar. Episodes of ketoacidosis were often followed by hypoglycemic reactions" (p. 106). Some improvement in control had been obtained through her participation in family therapy and through the use of beta blockers to blunt her physiological reactions to stress. After the end of these interventions, continued improvement in control was sought via electromyographu (EMG) biofeedback and relaxation training, to decrease

overall emotional lability. During an extended baseline period (2½ months), the patient recorded daily insulin levels and rated herself on two scales. The Diabetes scale (D-Scale) was a subjective measure of diabetic control from severe hyperglycemia to severe hypoglycemia, with optimal functioning at the midpoint. The Emotional Scale (E-Scale) (*relaxed* [1], *average amount of tension* [2], *tense* [3]) was a measure of subject feeling state, "reflecting general tension and psychological conflict (or lack thereof)." During the training period, the same variables were recorded, and the patient practiced deep-muscle relaxation while attached to an EMG feedback unit, listening to relaxation tapes. Also, she was asked to use the skill in stressful situations. The patient discontinued practice with the EMG unit and tapes after the training period, but the authors reported that she "continued to use her relaxation ability in stressful situations", (p. 109). A follow-up of 1½ months was carried out approximately 1 year after the baseline.

The authors used weekly mean-insulin units as the primary outcome variable and reported that these dropped from a baseline mean of 85 units to a training mean of 59 units, to a follow-up mean of 44 units. E-Scale ratings dropped from baseline (mean = 2.11) to the training phase (mean = 1.74) and were positively correlated ($r = .35$) with insulin dose. The D-Scale was also positively correlated ($r = .77$) with insulin dose. D-Scale ratings changed from primarily hyperglycemic during baseline to euglycemic and hypoglycemic during the training phase. Severe insulin reactions were noted during the training phase, indicating to the authors that the patient's need for insulin was decreasing more quickly than the dose was being adjusted. The authors concluded that training in "cultivated relaxation" is effective for helping "certain" patients with diabetes improve their control. They cautioned that a rapid decrease in insulin requirement in the treatment phase could result in frequent episodes of hypoglycemia.

If insulin dose is taken as a good measure of diabetic control, and this is very doubtful, this single case presents, at first impression, a compelling argument for the use of relaxation techniques as an adjunctive therapy for poorly controlled diabetes. However, aside from the fact that this very strong physiological effect of relaxation was seen in a person who described herself as only very mildly tense at baseline, a very strong competing hypothesis exists to explain the results in insulin dosage and on the subjective Diabetic scale. In the management of diabetes, very high doses of insulin, near 2 units per kilogram of body weight daily, frequently produce the effect of very rapid fluctuations in blood glucose levels — hypoglycemia very quickly followed by hyperglycemia (Bolli et al., 1984; Somogyi, 1959). The treatment of this condition is to decrease insulin. The data presented provide no reason to reject the hypothesis that improved control was obtained because of the decrease in insulin alone. In this case, expectancy of improved control (as measured by insulin dosage) might have prompted initial decreases in dosage. The decrease in massive amounts of exogenous insulin surpressed the previous very rapid response to hypoglycemia that had resulted in rebound hyperglycemia. Thus, in the treatment phase, the patient experienced hypoglycemia with the still too large dosage of insulin.

A second published case study on the effects of EMG-assisted relaxation on diabetes also lacks some important data upon which to evaluate or generalize the results. In this case (Seeburg & DeBoer, 1980), the patient was a 24-year-old female with a 6-year history of IDDM. The goal of the EMG-assisted relaxation was to stabilize the patient's diabetes at a lower insulin dosage. Several factors are unusual in the patient's presentation. The first is the management of the condition using only 1 dose (22 – 24 units) of regular insulin per day. This single dose of short-acting insulin is very unusual in the patient who has virtually no insulin-secreting capacity of her own (as would be typical for a patient with IDDM for 6 years). Even more remarkable, the patient, managed in this manner, had not had measurable urine glucose or ketones for 6 years. Thus, not only is this a very atypical patient with juvenile-onset diabetes, but also an improved control, at least as measured by urine glucose and ketones, was not possible.

Again the idea of improved control as measured solely by insulin dosage is very questionable. During the intervention, the patient decreased her already low level of frontalis muscle tension. She reported low levels of subjective tension as well, but she began to experience episodes of hypoglycemia and subsequently decreased her insulin dosage. The patient then discontinued biofeedback, but fluctuating glucose levels necessitated the commencement of a more usual insulin regimen with split doses of long- and short-acting insulin. When she began biofeedback again, fluctuating episodes of hypoglycemia and hyperglycemia occurred, and the intervention was permanently discontinued. The authors warn that this type of intervention should be attempted with caution with insulin-requiring diabetes. Others (Fotopoulos & Sunderland, 1978)

used this case to warn against using decreased insulin dose as the sole sign of success, with the fear that patients might lower their doses without appropriate attention to their blood glucose levels. In many ways, this case is an excellent example of the old adage "If it ain't broke, don't fix it."

The following control-group studies investigated the effects of relaxation procedures on short-term control in IDDM and NIDDM patients. Bradley (1982) provided limited support for the idea that 20 minutes of progressive muscle relaxation, as compared with 20 minutes of reading or watching TV, decreases blood glucose levels as measured after relaxation. One of the three treatment subjects responded consistently in the hypothesized direction for the 14 days of the study. Another treatment subject had difficulty relaxing, and the blood glucose changes in the third were not reported. In this pilot study, the level of overall control in these IDDM subjects was not presented, nor were the effects on blood glucose at other times of the day, nor were the subjective stress levels of the patients.

Surwit and Feinglos (1983) investigated the effect of relaxation training on glucose tolerance in 12 patients with NIDDM. The study took place in a hospital research unit in which conditions were standardized. During the hospitalization, diets were served to maintain weight (though 11 of the 12 patients lost weight, ranging from ½ to over 8lb). For 5 days, half the patients practiced progressive muscle relaxation twice daily using a recorded cassette and once daily using EMG feedback. During the hospitalization, all patients improved in fasting glucose levels, though only the treatment subjects improved in glucose levels 2 hours after a 100 gm glucose challenge. Though the improvement is reported to be statistically significant, the posttreatment differences between treatment and control groups are enhanced by the *decrement* in glucose tolerance by the control group, perhaps due to the sedentary life-style in the hospital. Further assessment of the patients (Surwit & Feinglos, 1984) revealed a significant decrease in plasma cortisol levels in the treatment patients, which would in fact impact on glucose metabolism in the aforementioned manner. This result is especially interesting, given the previous speculations that cortisol, which is effected by long-term stress, might be more responsible for consistently poor diabetic control than epinephrine, which fluctuates under acute stressors. (No posttreatment differences in epinephrine levels were found in these subjects). Unfortunately, the pretreatment cortisol levels were much higher in the treatment group, and it is, therefore, possible that the decrease in cortisol levels can be attributed to regression toward the mean rather than the treatment effect of relaxation. The authors have planned further investigation of this effect in NIDDM patients.

The final two studies are the long, multiple-baseline studies of IDDM patients with more complete treatment programs than those previously presented. The studies differ in their outcome variables and in the fact that in one case, poorly controlled subjects were selected and, in the other, well-controlled subjects were selected.

Rose, Firestone, Heick, and Faught (1983) carried out a study of the impact of stress reduction on 5 poorly controlled (mean fractionated glucose values ranged from 80–159 g/24 hours) adolescent females who were followed over a 6-month period using a single-subject multiple-baseline design. To obtain 5 subjects the investigators recruited 36 patients, 30 of whom declined. One patient who initially agreed to be in the study produced unusable data because she was repeatedly hospitalized. In an effort to control for expectancy effects and changes in adherence to the regimen, all patients went through an attention-control (AC) phase lasting from 14 to 29 days. During this phase, patients received 7 hours of psychological testing and feedback and were given the rationale that knowledge of one's psychological nature should improve one's ability to manage daily life experiences and result in better diabetic control. (A manipulative check found this explanation was plausible in 4 of 5 patients).

The treatment was Anxiety Management Training (AMT) (Suinn, 1975), which was taught over a 2-week period. AMT teaches the patients to use autonomic and muscular cues as a discriminative stimulus for relaxation. After the 7 hours of training, the patients were given a relaxation tape and told to practice three times a week and in response to stress. This treatment phase lasted from 71 to 115 days. No compliance data were collected on this behavior, however. Insulin dosages were not changed throughout the 6 months of the study. Caloric intake was prescribed initially to maintain or lose small amounts of weight, though compliance to the diet was known to be poor in 3 of the 5 patients.

Outcome of the intervention was measured in several ways. No patients reported any changes on a multifactorial scale of anxiety. However, all patients reported decreases in main urine glucose values as measured three times daily via the Diastix method. Nonsignificant decreases were noted from baseline

to the attention-control phase in 4 subjects, and all 5 decreased significantly from the AC to the treatment phase.

The second measure of diabetic control was weekly 24-hour urine glucose tests. On this variable, the results were much less clear and much more varied. The data were presented as phase means, but, because of the differing phase lengths, the number of data points in each mean ranged from 2 to 16. In four of the five cases, the mean fractionated urine glucose values were lower in the AMT phase than in the baseline phase. However, in three cases the AC-phase levels were inexplicably higher than the baseline levels. And overall, the standard deviations were very large (sometimes greater than half of the mean value), suggesting large fluctuations in this value from week to week.

It would have been much more informative to have this single-subject data presented in graphic form to see if it conformed to the expected trend of a high baseline, lowered with AC-phase expectancy effects, further lowered with progressively more skill in AMT. Assuming that the decreasing means of 24-hour urine glucose collections and daily urine glucose readings represented genuine improvement in diabetic management, the authors presented two hypotheses to account for this improvement. The first mode of change is through the positive effects of increased self-monitoring and increased adherence to the diabetic regimen. This explanation appears likely, especially given the very small number of patients who agreed to participate in the study. The investigators could very well have identified people who were motivated to change their control because they were doing poorly. The alternative explanation is that "muscular relaxation caused somatic-autonomic connections to reduce sympathethic activity levels leading to decreased levels of urine glucose" p, 392. This explanation would be much more persuasive if the patients had reported initially high levels of stress or tension, and if there had been a drop in this perceived level of tension. Early levels of stress were not reported, and no changes in anxiety levels were found. The authors believe that the most likely cause of the improved diabetic control was through direct and indirect effects of anxiety management. They concluded that a reasonable approach to improved diabetic management includes the improvement of self-care and "reducing the destabilizing effects of stress and anxiety," (p. 392) though it is unclear whether the effects are believed to be destabilizing physiologically or behaviorally.

Landis et al. (1985) reported on a multiple-baseline

biofeedback-assisted relaxation project with 5 IDDM patients. They selected subjects in good diabetic control (HbA1 range 7.1 to 8.9) to avoid the unknown variable introduced by poor metabolic control. The goal of the study was to further improve control, as measured by daily range of glucose, average daily glucose level, and daily insulin dose. Patients kept daily journals of factors related to diabetes management, blood glucose levels, insulin dosage, and so on, and completed a daily psychophysiologic stress questionnaire. Prior to the study, the patients received 40 hours of diabetic education. Normal average daily blood glucose levels were obtained by all by the end of the course.

The intervention consisted of 15 weekly biofeedback-assisted relaxation sessions with three modes of feedback- EMG, galvanic skin response (GSR), and skin temperature. After the initial training, three monthly training sessions were held, patients were taught to integrate relaxation into their daily routines, and daily relaxation practice sessions were held. Because of the variability among patients on the length of baseline observations, 2 weeks to 2 months, comparisons were made between the early relaxation training period (period II) and the 13-week posttraining period (period IV).

The results indicated no change in mean daily blood glucose level, insulin dosage, or HbA1. However, in 4 of the 5 patients there was a decrease in the range of daily glucose readings of 17% to 38%. The authors asserted that "if 'tight control' of glucose excursions can be shown to prevent long-term microvascular complications, the effects of stress should be counteracted whenever possible" (p, 626). In this study, the daily stress ratings were unrelated to any measure of glycemic control, though the authors believed this might not be true in persons in poorer metabolic control than this group of subjects. The authors further concluded that relaxation training might play a part in improving metabolic stability in *some* patients with diabetes mellitus. The idea that some patients might be helped is important in this study, because it seems this could represent a very select, highly motivated group. In this subset of patients, it would be difficult to argue that increased adherence accounted for the decreased range of daily blood glucose levels. Not only was there a baseline period after extensive educational effects were made to maximize adherence, but also the excellent diabetic control, as measured by HbA1 levels, suggests that these patients possessed and used exemplary diabetic self-management skills. For example, the patients recorded an average of 4.2,

out of a requested 7, blood glucose monitoring per day. Most diabetic specialists would agree that this adherence to SMBG suggests a motivational level and involvement far greater than for the average diabetic patient.

Summary and Critique

Similiar to the results of assessment studies, the results of the treatment studies do not present a strong case for the widespread use of relaxation methods as an adjunctive treatment in diabetes mellitus. In the two long-term studies (Landis et al., 1985; Rose et al., 1983) various issues have been raised about the reliability and generalizability of the outcome, as well as about the mode through which success was obtained. Especially in the Rose et al. study, increased adherence is a likely competing hypothesis. In both studies, very select samples of patients participated. In the Rose study less than 20% of the poorly controlled patients who were approached agreed to participate, and in the Landis study, the sample appeared to adhere to the regimen and achieve levels of diabetic control far better than those of the average patient.

In fact a major criticism of the stress-management studies in diabetes conducted to date is that not only have they studied a select group of patients but also a selection criterion for inclusion has *not* been high self-reported or observed levels of stress. Patients have either not been evaluated on this dimension or have not changed due to the intervention, even if metabolic control was improved postintervention. Unlike dietary management or glucose measurement, stress management via relaxation is probably not necessary for all patients with diabetes. The across-the-board application of a technique such as relaxation training might cause problems in itself, as could have occurred in the case study by (Seeburg and DeBoer, 1980), or complicate the accurate assessment of metabolic control problems. Further, in an illness such as diabetes, which is so patient-management intensive, adding another behavior to the regimen, especially one that has not been assessed to improve the patient's quality of life, only increases the probability that some parts of the regimen will be neglected.

NONRELAXATION TREATMENT MODES

Other avenues of psychological intervention have been employed to treat patients with presumed stress-mediated, diabetic-control problems. Baker and his colleagues (Minuchin et al. 1975) presented several classic case examples of "superlabile" adolescents from psychosomatic families, who were treated with success via family therapy. Several examples of group treatment are also evident in the literature. Lower glycohemoglobin levels were achieved with a group of adolescents who met together for 18 months (Warren-Boulton, Anderson, Schwartz, & Drexler, 1981). Therapeutic modes were likely to have been not only peer modeling and nonjudgmental staff encouragement but also active problem solving and peer support. Group training in SMBG produced improved blood glucose and glycosylated hemoglobin levels and lower levels of depression in a group of initially depressed young adults and adolescents (Dupuis, 1980). Repeated feedback on blood glucose levels and a problem-solving orientation helped the patients change from denial of hyperglycemia to a sense of mastery in achieving more adequate control. In a study with younger patients, 6 children who were in poor diabetic control and were assessed to be shy and embarrassed about their diabetes participated in 5 weeks of social skills training. Improvement in social skills and comfort with peers were noted in the posttest and in naturalistic settings, but there was no improvement in glycosylated hemoglobin levels in the 5-week treatment or the 6-week follow-up. Failure of this intervention to improve control can be explained in several ways. The 11-week period of monitoring might not have been long enough to reveal differences in HbA1 levels. Alternatively, because these children were preadolescent (ages 9–12 years), still largely supervised by their parents and not likely to make the majority of self-management decisions apart from the supervision of their parents, it could be that poor control was not caused by peer-influenced poor self-management decisions.

MODELS OF ASSESSMENT AND MANAGEMENT OF STRESS-MEDIATED DIABETIC-CONTROL PROBLEMS

The varying success rates for psychological interventions with diabetes in poor control reinforce the fundamental need for accurate assessment *prior* to treatment. A few interesting assessment studies have paid heed to individual differences as they affect diabetic control. Cox et al. (1984) found that patients varied widely in their perception of how strongly stress affected their blood glucose, from *"not at all"*

(16.3% to *"extremely,"* (19.5%) (though the distribution was skewed to indicate that the majority believed there was an effect of stressors on blood sugars). Factor analyses of the subjects' responses indicated that the patients' reported that emotional stressors affected blood glucose reactions in three ways: (a) passive depression and frustration; (b) active fear or anger resulting in blood glucose increases; and (c) positive feelings resulting in blood glucose decreases. The authors discussed the outcome of their study as it counters both the homogeneity of stressor myth and the homogeneity of respondent myth; specifically, that there is not reason to believe that different stressors have similiar physiological effects or that all persons perceive the same stressfulness in similiar events.

A second study that addressed the individualistic relationship of diabetic control and psychosocial variables was pilot study by Peyrot and McMurry (1985). Application of a multifactorial biopsychosocial model to the problem of diabetic control revealed a complex set of factors facilitating control. Several of these factors were curvilinear in their relationship with control. For example, extremes of anxiety were related to poor control. It was speculated that persons with low anxiety were not motivated to act, and persons with high anxiety were paralyzed with fear or their behavior was disrupted by the affect. Further, very internal or very external health locus of control, as well as very optimistic and very pessimistic views of the illness, were related to poor control. The model presented by these authors offers a potentially useful assessment tool that considers the predisposing (orientational), enabling (resource and barrier), and conditioning (inhibiting and motivating) factors that influence diabetic management and control.

In the following section several models of assessment or treatment will be examined as they apply to the evaluation and remediation of diabetes control problems.

RELAPSE-PREVENTION TRAINING

The first model addresses the problem of relapse in self-management or behavioral change programs. The preceding reviews of the relevant research support the idea that the most likely pathway through which stress effects diabetic control is through adherence to the regimen. Therefore in the vast majority of cases, when there is evidence of external stresses and poor diabetic control, the avenue of remediation is through adherence.

Although adherence per se is not a focus of this chapter, a short discussion of the factors affecting adherence or nonadherence to a medical regimen is appropriate here. These factors include those inherent in the regimen (e.g., pain, knowledge and skills to perform the tasks, complexity and intrusiveness of the regimen), characteristics in the individual (e.g., anxiety level, belief in vulnerability to complications, belief in efficacy of treatment to prevent complications), changeable factors (e.g., arm versus leg injections, time of SMBG), and unchangeable factors (e.g., patient gender, patient socioeconomic status). A myriad of educational and behavioral programs have been designed and carried out with varying success, to address the factors which influence adherence (Haynes, Taylor, & Sackett, 1979).

As is typical in many other regimens that require life-style change (e.g., weight-control), diabetes-management behaviors can begin to decay over time. Recently, behavioral life-style management programs have begun to incorporate *relapse-prevention training* into the treatment, and this element might also prove useful in enhancing adherence to the diabetes regimen (Rosenstock, 1985). Initially described in the addiction-treatment literature, relapse-prevention training attempts to incorporate strategies to help patients manage the inevitable events that will threaten their adherence to a regimen. The process of relapse is described in four steps (Marlatt & Gordon, 1980), illustrated here with several examples from the diabetes regimen.

1) The person finds himself in a high risk situation where deviance from the regimen is likely.
   Example A: The patient feels rushed and is tempted to skip blood or urine glucose monitoring.
   Example B: The patient is in a bad mood in a restaurant and is tempted to order chocolate cake.
2) The person does not have a planned strategy to counter the temptation and furthermore foresees that positive and/or anxiety reducing consequences may result from the deviance from the regimen.
   Example A: The person will not be late if he or she skips the monitoring.
   Example B: The chocolate cake tastes good and she or he will feel soothed after a bad day.

3) The person deviates from the regimen and feels guilt and loss of self-control.
   Example A: The person skips the glucose monitoring.
   Example B: The person orders and eats the chocolate cake.
4) These feelings of guilt and loss of self-control in themselves make it easier to deviate (relapse) again, and result in other behaviors or situations which also promote relapse.
   Example A: Neglect of glucose monitoring results in the inability to make necessary insulin adjustments, and, therefore increases the likelihood of high glucose levels later in the day. The patient might skip the next monitoring to avoid seeing the results of the first deviance.
   Example B: Eating chocolate cake will probably result in high blood sugar. The patient might monitor glucose and feel more guilty or avoid monitoring, again to avoid feedback on the results of his or her deviation from the regimen.

Relapse-prevention training helps the person recognize and plan for potential high-risk situations. These situations are quite individually determined, but high-risk situations are generally situations associated with negative emotions, interpersonal conflicts, or social pressures. Prior to being confronted with the situation, the relapse-prevention-trained patient has planned how to handle this situation. For example, the patient might institute some self-talk. "Managing my diabetes correctly is very important to my overall well-being, and I cannot forget that. Even if I am a few minutes late this morning, I will feel better, physically and emotionally, all day if I know I have made the proper insulin adjustment." She or he must plan a substitute behavior: "Instead of eating chocolate cake, I'll buy myself some flowers to cheer myself up after this bad day!" Any number of skills such as seeking social support, practicing progressive muscle relaxation, and refuting negative self-statements could be used to effectively manage high-risk situations, but the crucial variable is that the high-risk situations have been foreseen, and the coping strategies have been well planned and rehearsed. The second crucial aspect of relapse-prevention training is to teach the patient to avoid the cycle of guilt and perceived loss of self-control over an incident of deviation from the regimen. Patients are taught to view such incidents as temporary lapses and to return quickly to adherence to the regimen.

Case Study

This case presents an example of relapse and the attempts made to prevent further episodes of relapse. Mrs. L. was a 45-year-old woman who had been diagnosed with NIDDM 8 months earlier. She was married, the mother of a teenage son, and a loan officer in a bank. In the first 6 months of treatment, she had been the ideal patient. She had followed her diet faithfully, and, despite a history of no organized physical exercise, she had joined a low-impact aerobics course after it was suggested by her physician. These efforts had resulted in a 20-lb weight loss and had allowed her to manage her diabetes with diet and without oral hypoglycemic agents. Further, Mrs. L. had been diligent in obtaining blood glucose measurements before breakfast four times per week and three pre- and postprandial measures 1 day each week. She was pleased that 90% of her readings were within normal limits and was eager to discuss reasons or suggestions for the slightly elevated levels.

Approximately 8 months after diagnosis, after canceling and rescheduling her appointment, Mrs. L. presented to the physician complaining of fatigue and having gained 13 pounds. Her typically excellent records were sketchy, and the SMBG readings recorded were generally between 200 and 250 mg/dl. Her glycosylated hemoglobin level had increased for the first time since her diagnosis.

In an interview with Mrs. L. about the sudden decrement in her diabetic control, she stated that she believed the problem had started when her husband lost his job. Although the family was not experiencing financial difficulties, Mr. L. was somewhat depressed about his situation. To be supportive of her husband, Mrs. L. had begun coming directly home from work and had stopped attending her low-impact aerobics class. Another change in Mrs. L.'s life-style was her baking behavior. Much of Mr. and Mrs. L.'s extended family lived in close proximity, and Sundays were usually spent with various members of the family. Much of this camaraderie centered around food, and Mrs. L. was a prime supplier of homemade pastries. After her diagnosis, Mrs. L. had been careful to bake only for this gathering, to not have pastries at home on a regular basis, and to not eat them at the gathering. However, after her husband lost his job, she began to bake for him to cheer him up, and she eventually

started to snack more and more. When she began to see the blood increases induced by these changes in her habits, Mrs. L. became quite distressed. Because she did not see any way out of this dilemma, given the circumstances of her husband's job loss, she took fewer blood glucose measures, to avoid the negative feedback.

From Mrs. L.'s presentation, it was apparent that, although she had done well with the structured regimen, she had no skills to alter the regimen to cope with stress-induced changes in her life-style. She received a refresher course in diabetic management with heavy emphasis on problem solving and relapse-prevention training. Using the concepts she had learned, Mrs. L. made several alterations in her behavior. She decided that social support was very important in maintaining her weight-loss objectives, and she realized that she had been receiving this support in her exercise class. To fill this need, Mrs. L. joined a weight-control support group offered weekly through employee assistance in her bank. These meetings were held during work hours, so she could continue to go home to her husband directly after work. However, realizing the importance of exercise to her glucose tolerance, weight-loss objectives, and sense of well-being, she negotiated with her husband to walk briskly together each night after she got home (starting with 30 minutes). This plan had the extra benefits of providing Mr. L. with exercise, as well as giving the couple time together doing something positive. Mrs. L. resolved once again not to bake except for family gatherings and instead started experimenting with low-cholesterol meals to serve her husband and son. Most important, Mrs. L. was encouraged by her ability to adapt to changing circumstances, and she was able to use feedback, such as increasing weight or increased blood glucose levels, to signal a need for modification somewhere in the regimen, rather than as a sign of failure.

TRANSACTIONAL MODEL

Turk and Speers (1983) presented a transactional model for understanding diabetic control. An important feature of the model is the assumption that the stressfulness of external events, situations, and circumstances is not based upon a priori assumptions but upon the person's own appraisal of the situations, events, and circumstances. A further assumption is that the focus of intervention is more likely to be on the maladaptive beliefs, expectancies, or evaluations that mediate the effect of the stressor on the

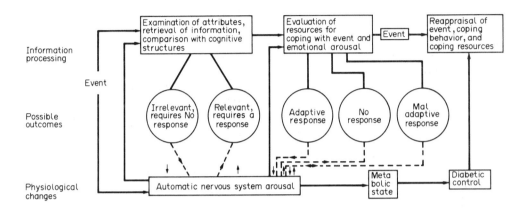

FIGURE 16.2. Transactional model of the effects of psychological factors on diabetic control.
- - - - - = Interaction between Information Processing and Physiological Activity
From "Diabetes Mellitus: A Cognitive-Functional Analysis of Stress" by D. C. Turk and M. A. Speers, 1983, in L. A. Bradley and T. C. Burish (Eds.), *Coping with Chronic Disease* (p. 205). Copyright 1983 by Academic Press, Inc. Adapted by permission.

symptom. The symptom in this case is nonadherence or, less likely, anxiety. The model suggests that application of treatment directly to symptoms such as nonadherence or anxiety results in a lower likelihood of success. Figure 16.2 more fully illustrates the transactional process of information processing on event-diabetes control mediation.

A daily event in the life of many diabetics, blood glucose monitoring, can be used to illustrate the transactional model. The need to do daily SMBG may be viewed as one of the daily stressors of the diabetic, whereas the performance of SMBG is one of the tasks of the regimen. Assuming there are no physiological symptoms to signal the need for blood glucose monitoring, the clock or proximity to meals should cue the patient that it is time for blood glucose monitoring. The patient can appraise this situation as a task that needs or does not need to be performed. Prior diabetes education will have supported the

need to monitor, but the patient might appraise it on the basis of his or her own idiosyncratic experience with SMBG. If the patient appraises it as "no need," there will be no arousal to initiate further steps. If the patient decides there is a need, she or he will then appraise her or his ability to carry out this behavior. This appraisal is again based upon many factors in the patient's background that support or detract from his or her appraisal that SMBG can be carried out. These include beliefs about skill ("I know how to measure blood glucose"), appropriateness of setting ("I cannot stick my finger out in public"), and efficacy of procedure ("I never find high blood sugars anyway"). The patient continues through a series of appraisals of the stimuli and her or his ability to appropriately act on these stimuli, along with a series of behaviors for responding to the appraised circumstances, until the situation is resolved (e.g., SMBG complete, appropriate action taken; SMBG ignored, no action aroused; SMBG complete, action ignored).

Case Study

The next case illustrates use of the transactional model in practice and the fairly unusual case of stress-mediated poor diabetic control through metabolic pathways. Jay, a 10-year-old boy with a 6-year history of IDDM, and his family were referred with the symptom of "flagrant disregard for the diabetic regimen" after two similiar episodes with severe hyperglycemia. During both episodes, Jay's mother called his physicians repeatedly every few hours to report high blood glucose levels and to request help with the appropriate dose of insulin to treat the hyperglycemia. Jay's mother continued to call back, saying the hyperglycemia was not relieved, until, after many attempts to treat him via insulin at home, the physicians asked the parents to bring Jay to the emergency room. On both occasions, after administration of the same dose of insulin that had been prescribed over the telephone, Jay's blood glucose level returned to normal in the emergency room. The assumption by the physicians was that Jay's mother was not giving insulin as prescribed.

Assessment of the child and family revealed a more complex situation. Jay had had difficult-to-control diabetes for years and had had many trips to the emergency room. Typically, he was very ill when brought in, but he felt much better after emergency treatment. These repeated experiences with being rescued in the emergency room instilled in Jay the firm belief that it was the only place where he could recover from severe hyperglycemia and ketosis. When the family moved farther from the medical center, the physicians attempted to treat him by telephone before requesting that he come to the emergency room. This was when the two incidents occurred. It is hypothesized that, when he was ill and being treated at home, Jay was not only physiologically stressed from the diabetic decompensation but also further psychologically stressed from his belief that he was not being taken to the only place that could help him. This psychological arousal diminished when he was brought to the emergency room, and the same dose of insulin, with diminished circulating counter-regulatory hormones, was effective to counter the hyperglycemia.

The treatment in this case was to help change the child's belief about the efficacy of treatment at home, to decrease the anxiety interfering with the insulin action. This intervention required education of the child, as well as support for his mother, so she would also be confident that Jay's hyperglycemia could respond to treatment outside of the emergency room. In this case, it was not necessary to teach relaxation methods, because the child was able to relax as soon as he understood that he could be safe at home with management through his mother and his physicians.

SUMMARY

Diabetes mellitus is a serious chronic condition that is effectively controlled only through patients' administration of a daily multitask treatment regimen. Because diabetes is a metabolic condition, external and internal stressors, which impact upon the autonomic nervous system, can promote problems in diabetic control. Therefore, there are theoretically two pathways through which psychological stressors can mediate poor control, - through disruption of adherence to the treatment regimen and counter-regulatory hormones. To date the weight of the research evidence supports the idea that psychological stressors, certainly everyday stressors, impact on control through lack of adherence, rather than on metabolic pathways. The adherence-versus-hormone dilemma is complicated by the fact that poor diabetic control, and certainly diabetic decompensation, are accompanied by subjective feelings of distress and are experienced by the body as physiological stressors with attendant autonomic nervous system arousal. However, it cannot be assumed that, because psychological stress accompanies poor control or because interventions on the autonomic nervous system improve control, that psychological stressors cause poor control through metabolic pathways.

In terms of clinical utility, the first consideration with stress-mediated control problems should be along the lines of adherence to the regimen. There is no possibility of adequate glycemic control without following the regimen. After psychological interventions have been made to either reduce or eliminate the stressor, to allow the person to cope with the stressor and adhere to the diabetic regimen, or both, an assessment can be made to see if further diminution of autonomic nervous system arousal might further facilitate glycemic control. At that point, it is reasonable to consider relaxation procedures.

In general, the widespread prescription of relaxation techniques to the diabetic regimen is not supported. In selected cases, in which patients are assessed as experiencing high levels of generalized tension that decrease their capacity to follow the regimen, relaxation procedures might be useful. An alternative procedure, and one that incorporates a moderately important aspect of the diabetic regimen, is the use of daily exercise for the reduction of generalized tension and the enhancement of a sense of well-being. On the other hand, further research along the lines of Landis et al. (1985) might support the idea that relaxation procedures provide optimal control by reducing daily blood glucose fluctuations in well-controlled, highly motivated, and adherent patients.

Several models were presented to identify treatment targets when stress-induced diabetic-control problems are an issue. These targets can be behavioral, cognitive, or affective, and the usual psychological interventions to address these targets are applicable.

Often health professionals erroneously believe they are motivating patients with information they themselves find motivating (e.g., "you must maintain good glycemic control or you will lose kidney function in 20 years"). Awareness of the individual nature of appraisal of stressors might aid these professionals in understanding and treating their patients. Turk and Speers' (1983) model could be very useful for these professionals in eliciting new avenues of assessment. It should be remembered that the diabetes regimen itself is appraised by many to be a stressor. Helping the patient obtain an optimal level of arousal to effectively manage this stressor is an important part of the health professional's role in maintaining adherence to the regimen, and it requires an approach tailored to the individual. For example, some patients might be motivated to maintain good control to avoid longer term complications. Others, less future oriented, might not be at all motivated by the potential of problems in 20 years, but they might be motivated by the prospect of feeling more energy in the present. Some patients might work for praise from their physicians and be fearful or disappointed if they receive disapproval for their adherence behavior.

The second treatment model presented was relapse-prevention training. The addition of relapse-prevention training could be very useful as part of the total educational and behavioral training for patients with diabetes mellitus. Not only would this treatment component introduce the problem of stress-induced adherence problems as a very typical and expectable event, but it would also reinforce the idea of patient as expert in self-management. For many, if not most,

patients, diabetes management is the first occasion where their input has been critical to the outcome of the management. In summary, any manner in which professionals can facilitate optimal self-management, including helping the patient combat stress, can only facilitate a better outcome.

REFERENCES

Baker, L., Barcai, A., Kaye, R., & Haque, N. (1969). Beta adrenergic blockade and juvenile diabetes: Acute studies and long-term therapeutic trial. *Pediatrics, 75,* 19–29.

Barglow, P., Edidin, D. V., Budlong-Springer, A. S., Berndt, D., et al., (1983). Diabetic control in children and adolescents: Psychosocial factors and therapeutic efficacy. *Journal of Youth and Adolescence, 12*(3), 77–94.

Barglow, P., Hatcher, R., Edidin, D. V., Sloan-Rossiter, D. (1984). Stress and metabolic control in diabetes: Psychosomatic evidence and evaluation of methods, *Psychosomatic Medicine, 46*(2), 127–144.

Bloom-Cerkoney, K. A., & Hart, L. K. (1980). The relationship between the health beliefs model and compliance of persons with diabetes mellitus. *Diabetes Care, 3,* 594–598.

Bolli, G. B., Gottlesman, I. S., Campbell, P. J., Haymond, M. W., Cryer, P. E., & Gerich, J. E. (1984). Glucose counter regulation and warning of insulin in the Somoghi phenomenon (post hypoglycemic hyperglycemic) *New England Journal of Medicine, 311,* 1214–1219.

Bradley, C. (1979). Life events and the control of diabetes mellitus. *Journal of Psychosomatic Research, 23,* 159.

Bradley C. (1982). Psychophysiological aspects of the mangement of diabetes mellitus. *International Journal of Mental Health, 11,* 117–132.

Cannon, W. B. (1941). Bodily changes in pain, hunger, fear and rage (2nd ed.). *Behavioral Medicine Update,* New York: Macmillan.

Carey, R. M., Schechter, K., & Davis, T. (1983). Improving adherence to blood glucose testing in insulin dependent diabetic children. *Behavior Therpay, 14*(2), 247–254.

Chase, H. P., & Jackson, G. G. (1981). Stress and sugar control in children with insulin-dependent diabetes mellitus. *Journal of Pediatrics, 98*(6), 1011–1013.

Cohen, A. S., Vance, V. K., Runyan, J. W., & Hurwitz, D. (1960). Diabetes acidosis: An evaluation of the cause, course, and therapy of 73 Cases, *Annals of Internal Medicine, 52,* 55–86.

Cox, D. J., Taylor, A. G., Nowacek, G., Holley-Wilcox, P., Pohl, S. L., & Guthrow, E. (1984). The relationship between psychological stress and insulin-dependent diabetic blood glucose control: Preliminary investigations. *Health Psychology 3,* 63–75.

Davidson, M. D. (1981). *Diabetes mellitus: Diagnosis and treatment.* New York: John Wiley & Sons.

Dupuis, A. (1980). Assessment of the Psychological factors and responses in self-managed patients. *Diabetes Care, 3*(T), 117–120. *January/February.*

Fisher, E. B., Delamater, A. M., Bertelson, A. D., Kirkley, B. G. (1982). Psychological factors in diabetes and its treatment. *Journal of Consulting and Clinical Psychology, 50,* 993–1003.

Fotopoulos, S. S., & Sunderland, W. P. (1978). Biofeedback in the treatment of psychophysiologic Disorders. *Biofeedback and Self-Regulation, 3*(4), 331–360.

Fowler, J. E., Budzynski, T. H., & Vanderbergh, R. L. (1976). Effects of an EMG biofeedback relaxation program on the control of diabetes. *Biofeedback and Self-Regulation, 1*(1), 105–112.

Gonen, B., Rachman, H., Rubenstein, A. H., Tanega, S. P., & Horwitz, D. L. (1977). Hemoglobin A: An indicator of the metabolic control of diabetic patients. *Lancet, ii,* 734–737.

Grant, I., Kyle, G. C., Teichman, A., & Mendels, J. (1974). Recent life events and diabetes in adults. *Psychosomatic Medicine, 36,* 121–128.

Gross, A. M., Heimann, L., Shapiro, R., & Schultz, R. M. (1983). Children with diabetes. *Behavior Modification, 7*(2), 151–164.

Haynes, R. B., Taylor, D. W., & Sackett, D. C. (Eds.) (1979). *Compliance in health care,* Baltimore: John Hopkins Press.

Hinkle, L. E., & Wolf, S. (1952). The effects of stressful life situations on the concentration of blood glucose in diabetic and nondiabetic Humans. *Diabetes, 1*(5), 383–392.

Jacobson, A. M., Rand, L. I., & Hauser, S. T. (1985). Psychological Stress and glycemic control: A comparison of patients with and without proliferative diabetic retinopathy. *Psychosomatic Medicine, 47,* 372–381.

Jenkins, C. D., Zyzanski, S. J., & Rosenman, R. H. (1971). Progress toward validation of a computer-scored test for the Type A coronary-prone behavior pattern. *Psychosomatic Medicine, 33,* 193–202.

Kanner, A. D., Coyne, J. C., Schaefer, C. A., & Lazarus, R. S. (1981). Comparison of two modes of stress measurements: Daily hassles and uplifts versus major life events. *Journal of Behavioral Medicine, 4*(1), 1–39.

Kaplan, S. M., Mass, J. W., Oixleg, J. M., & Ross, D. (1960). Use of imipramine in diabetes. *Journal of the American Medical Association, 174*(5), 119.

Karam, J. H. (1981). Diabetes mellitus, hypoglycemia and lipoprotein disorders. In M. A. Krepp & M. J. Chatton (Eds.), *Current medical diagnosis and treatment.* Los Altos, CA: Lange Medical.

Kemmer, F. W., Bisping, R., Steingruber, H. J., Baar, H., Hardtmann, F., Schlaghecke, R., & Berger, M. (1986). Psychological stress and metabolic control in patients with type I diabetes mellitus. *New England Journal of Medicine, 314*(17), 1028–1084.

Kirkley, B. G. (1982). Behavioral and social antecedents of noncompliance with nutritional management of diabetes. Unpublished doctoral dissertation, Washington University.

Landis, B., Jovanovic, L., Landis, E., Peterson, C. M., Groshen, S., Johnson, K., Miller, N. E. (1985). Effect of stress reduction on daily glucose range in previously stabilized insulin-dependent diabetic patients. *Diabetes Care, 8*(6), 624–626.

Leventhal, H., & Nerenz, D. R. (1983). Representation of threat and the control of stress. In D. Meichenbaum & M. E. Jaremlco (Eds.), *Stress Reduction and*

Prevention, (pp. 5–38). New York: Plenum.

Lustman, P., & Carney, R. (1981). Amadott acute stress and metabolism in diabetes. *Diabetes Care, 4,* 659–659.

Marlatt, G. A., & Gordon, J. R. (1980). Determinants of relapse: Implications for the maintenance of behavior change. In. P. O. Davidson & S. M. Davidson (Eds.), *Medicine: Changing Health Lifestyles.* (pp. 410–452). New York: Brunner/Mazel.

Mazze, R. S., Lucido, D., & Shamoon, H. (1984). Psychological and social correlates of glycemic control. *Diabetes Care, 7,* 360–366.

McLesky, C. H., Lewis, S. B., & Woodruff, R. E. (1978). Glucagon levels during anesthesia and surgery in normal and diabetic patients. *Diabetes, 27S2,* 492.

Minuchin, S., Baker, L., Rosman, B. L., Liebman, R., Milman, L., & Todd, T. C. (1975). A conceptual model of psychosomatic illness in children. *Archives of General Psychiatry, 32,* 1031–1038.

Nabarro, J. B. (1965). Diabetic acidosis: Clinical aspects. *Excerpta Medica International Congress Series, 84,* 545.

Naliboff, B. D., Cohen, M. J., & Sowers, J. D. (1985). Physiological and metabolic responses to brief stress in non-insulin dependent diabetic and control subjects. *Journal of Psychosomatic Research, 29*(4), 367–374.

Nathan, D. M., Singer, D. E., Hurxthal, K., & Goodson, J. D. (1984). The clinical information value of glycosolated hemoglobin assay. *New England Journal of Medicine, 310,* 341–383.

Peyrot, M., & McMurry, J. F. (1985). Psychological factors in diabetes control: Adjustment of insulin treated adults. *Psychosomatic Medicine, 47,* 542–557.

Rose, M. I., Firestone, P., Heick, H. M. C., & Faught, A. K. (1983). The effects of anxiety management training on the control of juvenile diabetes mellitus. *Journal of Behavioral Medicine, 6*(4), 381–395.

Rosen, H., & Lidz, R. (1949). Emotional factors in the precipitation of recurrent diabetic acidosis. *Psychosomatic Medicine, 2,* 211.

Rosenthal, B. S., & Marx, R. D. (1981). Determinants of initial relapse episodes among dieters. *Obesity/Bariatric Medicine, 10,* 94–97.

Rosenstock, M. (1985). Understanding and enhancing patient compliance with diabetic regimens. *Diabetes Care, 8*(6), 610–616.

Schafer, L. C., Glasgow, R. E., McCaul, K. D., & Dreher, M. (1983). Adherence to IDDM regimens: Relationship to psychosocial variables and metabolic control. *Diabetes Care, 6*(5), 493–498.

Schafer, L. C., Glasgow, R. E., McCaul, K. D. (1982). Increasing the adherence of diabetic adolescents. *Journal of Behavioral Medicine, 5,* 353–362.

Seeburg, K. N., & DeBoer, K. F. (1980). Effects of EMG biofeedback on diabetes. *Biofeedback and Self-Regulation, 5*(2), 289–293.

Shamoon, J., Hendler, R., & Sherwin, R. S. (1980). Altered responsiveness to cortisol, epinephrine, and glucagon in insulin-fused juvenile-onset diabetes. *Diabetes, 29,* 284.

Simonds, J. F. (1976–1977). Psychiatric status of diabetic youth in good and poor control. *International Journal of Psychiatry in Medicine, 7,* 133–151.

Simonds, J., Goldstein, D., Walker, B., et al. (1980). Diabetes mellitus in adolescents: The relationship between behavioral, psychological variables and glucose control. *Diabetes, 29,* 42A.

Somogyi, M. (1959). Exacerbation of diabetes by excess insulin action. *American Journal of Medicine, 26,* 169–191.

Sonksen, P. H., Judd, S., & Lowy, C. (1980). Home monitoring of blood glucose: New approach to management of insulin-dependent diabetic patients in Great Britain. *Diabetes Care, 3,* 100–107.

Suinn, R. (1975). Anxiety management training for general anxiety. In Suinn, R., & Weigel, R. (Eds.), *The Innovative Psychological Therapies.* New York: Harper & Row.

Surwit, R. S., Feinglos, M. N. (1983). The effects of relaxation on glucose tolerance in non-insulin-dependent diabetes. *Diabetes Care, 6*(2), 176–179.

Surwit, R. S., & Feinglos, M. N. (1984). Relaxation-induce Improvement in Glucose Tolerance is Associated with Decreased Plasma Cortisol. *Diabetes Care, 7*(2), March/April, 203.

Surwit, R. S., Feinglos, M. N., & Scovern, A. W. (1983). Diabetes and behavior. *American Psychologist, 38,* 255–262.

Tarnow, J. D., & Silverman, S. W. (1981–1982). The psychophysiologic aspects of stress in juvenile diabetes mellitus. *International Journal of Psychiatry in Medicine, 11*(1), 25–44.

Turk, D. C., & Speers, M. A. (1983). Diabetes mellitus: A cognitive-functional analysis of stress. In L. A. Bradley & T. C. Burish (Eds.), *Coping with chronic disease.*

(pp. 191–217). New York: Academic Press.

Turkat, I. D. (1982). Glycosylated hemoglobin levels in anxious and nonanxious diabetic patients. *Psychosomatics, 23*(10), 1056–1058.

Vanderbergh, R. L., & Sussman, K. E. (1967). Alterations of blood glucose levels with emotional stress: The effect of final examinations in university students with insulin requiring diabetes mellitus. 27th Annual Meeting of the American Diabetic Association. Abstract in *Diabetes, 14,* (p. 487).

Vandenbergh, R. L., Sussman, K. E., & Titus, C. C. (1966). Effects of Hypnotically induced acute emotional stress on carbohydrate and lipid metabolism in patients with diabetes mellitus. *Psychosomatic Medicine, 28,* 382–390.

Warren-Boulton, E., Anderson, B. J., Schwartz, N. L., & Drexler, A. J. (1981). A group approach to the management of diabetes in adolescents and young adults. *Diabetes Care, 4,* 620–623.

Watkins, J. D., Williams, F., Martin, D. A., Hogan, M. D., & Anderson, E. (1967). A study of diabetic patients at home. *American Journal of Public Health, 57,* 452–459.

White, K., Kolman, M. L., Wexler, P., Polin, G., & Winter, R. J. (1984). Unstable diabetes and unstable families: A psychosocial evaluation of diabetic children with recurrent ketoacidosis. *Pediatrics, 73*(6), 749–755.

Zinman, B. (1984). Diabetes mellitus and exercise. *Behavioral Medicine Update, 6*(1), 22–25.

Author Index

Subject Index

About the Editor
and Contributors

EDITOR

Michael L. Russell received his Ph.D. in Counseling Psychology in 1974 from Stanford University. He was Assistant Professor in the Departments of Medicine, Community Medicine, and Psychiatry, Baylor College of Medicine from 1976 to 1986. Prior to that, he served as Director of Education Research and Evaluation, Department of Psychology, Pacific Medical Center. Dr. Russell's primary research area was medical psychology, especially adherence and compliance to medical and behavioral regimens. Dr. Russell passed away in 1986.

CONTRIBUTORS

Victor S. Alpher (Assistant Professor of Psychiatry and Behavioral Sciences, University of Texas Medical School at Houston). Dr. Alpher earned his Ph.D. in clinical psychology in the Graduate School of Arts and Sciences at Vanderbilt University. His current research interests include the application of psychoanalytic and interpersonal models to the understanding of change processes in psychotherapy. He is also involved in predoctoral clinical psychology internship training, postgraduate psychiatric and undergraduate medical education at the University of Texas Medical School at Houston.

Merrill P. Anderson (Private Practice, Houston). Dr. Anderson received his doctorate in counseling psychology from the University of Texas at Austin in

1975. Between 1975 and 1980 he held teaching and research positions at Boston University, Pennsylvania State University, and the University of Minnesota. Since 1980 he has been working in several behavioral medicine areas including cardiac rehabilitation, chronic pain, obesity and weight loss, and preventive medicine. He is presently engaged in the private practice of psychology and works with behavioral medicine programs at The Methodist Hospital in Houston, Texas.

Paul E. Baer (Professor and Head, Psychology Division, Baylor College of Medicine). Paul Baer received the doctorate from the University of Chicago. His interests span clinical and research areas. In addition to research on cardiovascular disease and cancer, current research includes the role of stress and the family in adolescent substance use, and the development and evaluation of prevention programs in adolescent substance use.

Gleb G. Bourianoff (Clinical Assistant Professor of Internal Medicine and Psychiatry, Baylor College of Medicine). He is a practicing internist with an interest in stress related illnesses. He completed a residency in internal medicine at the University of Michigan and postgraduate fellowship in psychosomatic medicine at the University of Virginia.

Christine T. Bradshaw (Assistant Professor of Psychiatry, Baylor College of Medicine, Houston, Texas). Dr. Bradshaw received her doctorate in clinical psychology from Virginia Commonwealth University. Her research interests have focused on psychological issues relating to pregnancy and childbirth, particularly the grief reaction to perinatal loss.

Edward A. Charlesworth (licensed Psychologist, Director of Willowbrook Psychological Associates, P.C., and President of Psychological Associates of Texas, P.C.). Dr. Charlesworth completed his graduate work in clinical psychology at the University of Houston, and his internship at Baylor College of Medicine. Dr. Charlesworth is the co-author of *Stress Management: A Comprehensive Guide to Wellness* (1984), *Stress Management: A Conceptual and Procedural Guide* (1981), and the audiotherapeutic cassette program *The Relaxation and Stress Management Program* (1981).

Sidney F. Cleveland (Clinical Professor of Psychology, Department of Psychiatry, Baylor College of Medicine; Chief, Psychology Service, Veterans Administration Medical Center, Houston, Texas (Retired)). He received his doctorate in clinical psychology from the University of Michigan. Dr. Cleveland's research interests include the relation between personality and body image as well as attitudes toward tissue donation and organ transplant.

Gerard J. Connors (Research Scientist with the Research Institute on Alcoholism, Buffalo, New York). He received his doctoral degree in clinical psychology from Vanderbilt University. Prior to joining the staff of the Research Institute, he was on the faculty of the Department of Psychiatry and Behavioral Sciences at the University of Texas Medical School at Houston. While there he was actively involved in the assessment and treatment of inpatients and outpatients experiencing acute and chronic pain. Dr. Connors maintains his interests in the areas of behavior therapy and the maintenance of treatment gains.

Donna R. Copeland (Associate Professor of Psychology in the Department of Pediatrics, University of Texas M.D. Anderson Hospital and Tumor Institute where she is Director of the Mental Health Section). She received her doctorate in clinical psychology from the University of Houston. Her current research interests are in the psychosocial and neuropsychological effects of cancer and its treatment of children and families.

Danita Czyzewski (Assistant Professor of Psychiatry (Psychology) and Pediatrics, Baylor College of Medicine). Dr. Czyzewski received her doctorate in clinical psychology from Purdue University and works as a pediatric psychologist at Texas Children's Hospital with an emphasis on chronic medical conditions requiring long-term self-management.

Roberta M. Diddel (Associate Clinical Director, Texas Pain and Stress Center, Houston, Texas). Roberta Diddel has worked in the field of pain management since 1979 and currently specializes in self-hypnosis training with chronic pain sufferers. She studied clinical psychology at Boston University and did her doctoral research on TMJ.

John P. Foreyt (Associate Professor, Department of Medicine, Baylor College of Medicine). He received his Ph.D. in clinical psychology in 1969 from the Florida State University. He served on the faculty there until 1974 when he moved to Baylor College of Medicine, Houston, Texas. He is currently Associate Professor in the Departments of Medicine and Psychiatry and is the Director of the Diet Modification Clinic. Dr. Foreyt has published extensively in the areas of diet modification, cardiovascular risk reduction, and obesity, and has published nine books and more than 100 articles in these areas.

Blair Justice (Professor, Behavioral Science, University of Texas School of Public Health). He received his Ph.D. from Rice University, and now teaches graduate courses on the biopsychosocial bases of mental and physical health and on stress, coping and illness at the University of Texas Health Science Center. He is the author of *Who Gets Sick: Thinking and Health.*

Jill K. McGavin (Doctoral Candidate, University of Houston). Ms. McGavin holds a Masters Degree in psychology from University of Houston. Her current research interest is the role of interpersonal relationships in medical disorders.

Ronald G. Nathan (Director of Educational Development, Coordinator of Behavioral Science, and Associate Professor in the Departments of Family Practice and Psychiatry, Albany Medical College). A Phi Beta Kappa from Cornell University, Dr. Nathan took his graduate work in clinical psychology at the University of Houston and interned in the Texas Medical Center. Dr. Nathan developed and evaluated the country's first required stress management course for medical students at Louisiana State University School of Medicine in Shreveport.

Rebecca S. Reeves (Instructor, Department of Medicine, Baylor College of Medicine). She is a registered dietitian who received her Master of Public Health from the University of Texas School of

Public Health. She is currently employed as the chief dietitian in the Diet Modification Clinic at Baylor College of Medicine. Mrs. Reeves' research interests are nutrition-related behavioral studies involving changes in dietary habits. She is listed in *Outstanding Young Women of America* and *Who's Who in Texas Today*.

Keith T. Revel (Director, Canyon Creek Psychological Associates, San Antonio, Texas). Dr. Revel has served as a therapist and consultant to a number of cardiac rehabilitation programs. He received his doctorate degree from the University of Houston.

Michele J. Rusin (Assistant Professor of Rehabilitation Medicine, Emory University School of Medicine, Atlanta, Ga.). Dr. Rusin received her Master's Degree and doctorate in clinical psychology from the Florida State University. Prior to joining the Emory faculty, she was a clinical Assistant Professor in the Department of Physical Medicine at the Baylor College of Medicine. Her current interests include gerontology, adjustment to chronic illness, and family adjustments to disability.

Gene L. Stainbrook (Associate Professor, Oregon Graduate School of Professional Psychology). He received an MPH from University of California at Berkeley and a Ph.D. in Medical Psychology from University of Oregon Medical School. In addition he completed a post-doctoral fellowship in behavioral medicine at the Harvard Medical School. His teaching and research interests are in the areas of health psychology and behavioral medicine.

Eva Stubits (Director, Houston Psychological Associates). Dr. Stubits received her doctorate in clinical psychology from the University of Miami. She is on clinical faculty with the Baylor College of Medicine and the University of Texas Medical School. Engaged in full-time private practice, her clinical interests include treatment of stress-related physical and psychological disorders.

Arthur R. Tarbox (Clinical Associate Professor, Department of Psychiatry, University of Texas Medical School). Dr. Tarbox received his doctorate in clinical psychology from Emory University and then served as a Fellow at Southwestern Medical School, University of Texas Health Science Center in Dallas prior to joining the faculty at the University of Texas Medical School in 1979. Prior to entering private practice one year ago, he served as the Associate Director for Outpatient Psychiatry Services at the University of Texas Medical School in Houston.

Martin J. Tobin (Assistant Professor, Department of Internal Medicine, University of Texas Health Science Center). He received a doctorate in medicine from University College, Dublin. He has undertaken postgraduate training in Dublin, London, Miami and Pittsburgh. His primary research interest is in the neuromuscular control of breathing.

Anita M. Woods (Assistant Professor, Department of Family Practice and Community Medicine, University of Texas Medical School). She received her doctorate in psychology (emphasis in aging) from The University of Southern California. Her current research interests are in health promotion in mid to late life and in the delivery of mental health services to the aged in primary care settings. Dr. Woods' teaching involves the training of physicians and other health care professionals in gerontology/geriatrics.

Pergamon General Psychology Series

* Out of print in original format. Available in custom reprint edition.